Fearon's Introduction to Biochemistry

Fearon's Introduction to Biochemistry

by William John Edward Jessop MSc MD DPH

Fellow of Trinity College, Dublin, and Professor of Social Medicine and Consultant in Chemical Pathology, University of Dublin. Fellow of the Royal College of Physicians of Ireland. Fellow of the Royal Institute of Chemistry.
Formerly Professor of Physiology and Biochemistry, Royal College of Surgeons in Ireland

Fourth Edition

1961

Academic Press, New York

First Edition, 1934.
Spanish Edition, 1936.
Second Edition, February 1940.
Reprinted, with revisions, August 1940.
Third Edition, April 1946.
Reprinted, with revisions, May 1947.
Reprinted, with revisions, July 1948.
Reprinted, with revisions, October 1949.
Fourth Edition, March 1961.

*Distributed in the
Western Hemisphere,
excluding Canada, by*

ACADEMIC PRESS INC.
111 Fifth Avenue
New York 3, New York

*Printed in Great Britain by
The Whitefriars Press Ltd.
London and Tonbridge*

Preface to the Fourth Edition

William Robert Fearon died on December 27th 1959. He had been ill for most of the autumn, but very few even of his close friends realised the serious nature of his complaint. When he died there was a general impression that the preparation of the fourth edition of his "Introduction to Biochemistry" was well advanced, but none of his colleagues knew either the precise stage it had reached or his intentions regarding it, for his work on it, as on previous editions, had been entirely single-handed. It transpired that he had wished me to complete the book and to see it through the press. I was very glad to undertake this task, both because of his friendship, which I had enjoyed for over thirty years, and because of the book itself, which I have always felt to be unique in biochemical literature.

The third edition appeared in 1946 and Fearon often expressed his concern that the present edition had been so long delayed. He was only able to make a serious start on it about a year before the commencement of his illness, and the advances of the previous twelve years then made it necessary to rewrite the book almost entirely.

Fearon was interested in many things besides Biochemistry—literature, music, art, the drama. Evidence of these interests was clear in the number and variety of the papers that were found in his house. When the twenty-five chapters of the book were identified they were partly in typescript and partly in manuscript. There were large gaps, and even those portions which appeared to be complete had obviously not been read by him since he had taken them from his typewriter.

In dealing with this material I have tried to follow Fearon's manner of presentation. This was often difficult, for he was not just an author with an extensive knowledge of his subject, nor is his book merely a storehouse of information. Like a good architect, he thought deeply about the design and fabric of his work and his fertile imagination ranged widely over it. His narrative, enriched by his accomplishments in so many other spheres, was not restrained by formal biochemical conventions.

This edition follows the plan of its predecessors in approaching the more extensive territory of organic biochemistry by way of the elements that occur in biological material and the biological properties of water and aqueous solutions. The sequence has been improved by placing the chapter on Nutrients before that on Catalysis and the chapter on the Internal Environment before that on Hormones. This enables the text to be divided into two almost equal sections dealing respectively with " Constitutive " and " Dynamic " aspects of Biochemistry.

Except in the earlier part of the book there was so much new material to be incorporated that each chapter had to be virtually re-written. Judicious rearrangement enabled some space to be saved, as did also the drastic reduction in the amount of space given to certain practical procedures, the directions for which could more properly be obtained from practical class sheets or from books on practical Biochemistry. This allowed the book to be confined to about the same size as the third edition. There are, in fact, fewer pages but the pages are somewhat bigger than those of the first three editions.

The most important reconstructions and additions have been in the sections and chapters dealing with protein structure and metabolism, Vitamin B_{12}, enzymes and enzyme kinetics, glycolysis, tissue respiration, hormones, and the chemistry of tissues. Fearon had incorporated a short section on the rH scale into the chapter on Tissue Respiration. In deference to what I felt would have been his wish I decided that it should be allowed to remain. This edition contains several new diagrams, some of which were found with Fearon's typescript and some of which were prepared by me. Those that were with the typescript appeared to have been prepared by Fearon, and I have not been able to trace any prior source. If, through lack of information, I have failed to acknowledge my indebtedness to another author for anything in this book, I can only express my regret.

It is a pleasure to offer my best thanks to the publishers for the trouble they have taken. I feel sure that the book, in its pleasant contemporary style, would have had Fearon's warm approval.

I would also like to thank Dr W. A. Boggust, Department of Biochemistry, Trinity College, and Professor John Pryde and Dr Brian Spencer, Department of Biochemistry, University College, Cardiff, for helping me to read the proofs. Dr Boggust also helped in the preparation of the index, as did Mr J. Carson, Department of Social Medicine, Trinity College, and my secretary, Miss M. Hanna, and I am very grateful to them for this welcome assistance.

W. J. E. J.

January 1961

Table of Contents

Part I   Constitutive Biochemistry

Part II   Dynamic Biochemistry

Part I

Constitutive Biochemistry

Chapter 1 The Subject-matter
of Biochemistry

" Definitions, formulæ (some would add, creeds) have their use in any society in that they restrain the ordinary unintellectual man from making himself a public nuisance with his private opinions."

Arthur Quiller-Couch.

Biochemistry is molecular biology, the study and the interpretation of the chemical changes associated with life. Life is indefinable, but is recognised by its manifestation in material organisms assembled from a limited number of relatively common chemical elements, temporarily associated as compounds and systems. *An organism is an entity that maintains its individual structure by means of self-controlled transformation of energy.* It is characterised by a group of properties: Growth, Self-maintenance in varying circumstances, Self-repair, Self-perpetuation, and Self-conditioned response to stimuli.

Molecular Biology. The phenomena of life can be studied at various levels. Constitutive or descriptive biochemistry is concerned with the composition of organisms and their products, and seeks to identify the reactants involved in the *metabolic*, or chemical operations taking place within and around the cells. Dynamic or kinetic biochemistry is concerned with the chemical mechanisms of life and their biological control. Medicine, or molecular surgery, is the application of biochemistry to the treatment of abnormal conditions in the higher animal.

Development of Biochemistry. A distinction between the chemistry of living and non-living substances is implicit in the writings of the alchemists, one of whom, as Dr. Needham has pointed out, gave biochemistry its charter:—

" The Body is a conglomeration of chemical matters; when these are deranged, illness results, and nought but chemical medicines may cure the same."

Theophrastus Paracelsus, 1527.

In 1675, Nicholas Lemery, the author of the first rational textbook on chemistry, classified the science as *animal, vegetable*, and *mineral*. Lavoisier, about 1770, observed that animal and vegetable material differed from minerals in being very rich in carbon, hydrogen, and oxygen. Subsequently, he detected nitrogen and phosphorus in animal matter, and concluded that in this respect it differed from vegetable matter. Later work showed that

1

this conclusion was false; all plants contain nitrogen and phosphorus, although these elements may be absent from some vegetable products. As a result, animal and plant chemistry were grouped together under the name of *organic chemistry*, in distinction from *inorganic* or *mineral chemistry*.

Early in the nineteenth century it was assumed that a fundamental difference existed between these two classes, organic compounds being the exclusive products of vital activity. Then, in 1828, Wöhler accidentally obtained urea from ammonium cyanate, by the action of heat. Urea, the chief nitrogenous solute of mammalian urine, is a typical organic compound; indeed, from the point of view of a vegetable it would be regarded as the chief useful product of the animal kingdom. Wöhler's startling discovery altered the outlook of chemistry. The synthesis of other vital products gradually followed, and by the end of the century the term *organic chemistry* had lost its original vitalistic implications, and was applied to all the combustible compounds of carbon, irrespective of their natural or artificial origin. In the meantime, the chemistry of animal and plant materials had been pursued under such titles as: medical chemistry, agricultural chemistry, chemical physiology and chemical pathology, until the term *biological chemistry* (abbreviated to the hybrid, *biochemistry*) was introduced to include all applications of chemistry to the study of life and its products.

Vitalism, Mechanism, and Organicism. To a vitalist, the changes in a living organism are not completely explicable in terms of physics and chemistry. To the mechanist, life is a manifestation of higher material properties, which, given suitable conditions, appear along with the other products of chemical reactions, and are equally devoid of purpose. To the organicist, there is neither life-substance nor life-force, but, instead, there is a specific life-structure within which various changes take place according to the laws of physics and chemistry. These metaphysical considerations are outside the scope of most workers, who well may agree with Whitehead that:—

" The mode of approach to the problem, so far as science is concerned, is merely to ask if molecules exhibit in living bodies properties which are not to be observed amid inorganic surroundings."

To a disembodied observer, a living organism is only a form in which hydrogen and carbon are collected, stored and oxidised. Why this should occur under these restricted conditions, or whether the organism has any cosmic function other than to delay the dissipation of solar energy, is a problem beyond the horizon of the biochemist, whose task is to find what changes occur and how they are brought about. The existence of life is accepted as a self-evident fact in the hope that man's experience of it will eventually enable him to understand its meaning.

The Four-Dimensional Organism. In the early period of organic chemistry it was possible to represent compounds by two-dimensional formulæ on paper, but the discovery of optical isomerism made it necessary to employ three-dimensional perspective formulæ to show the distinction between related compounds. The living organism is more complex than a three-dimensional solid; it is a structure undergoing changes in time as well as in space, and its composition and pattern at a given moment must be considered in relation to its previous and future history. Knowledge of the earlier states of an organism enables an observer to predict the immediate future states, and for this reason serial observations are widely used.

Forms of Life. The *biosphere*, or inhabited surface of the world, is colonised by representatives of two great kingdoms: the animals and the plants; and also by the vast republic of micro-organisms, most of which have their home and factory in the soil. All forms of life investigated are assembled chiefly from water, proteins, carbohydrates and lipides; and all are engaged in a continuous chemical traffic with their environment.

In unicellular organisms the affairs of life are carried out by single microscopic units; higher organisms are characterised by progressive differentiation of structures and functions, as shown by the presence of specialised tissues, organs and systems, designed to serve the general purpose of life, which is survival.

While both animals and plants are constructed of identifiable compounds undergoing transformations in measurable and predictable ways, the highest animals display increasing capacity for selecting and modifying their environments. Bacteria are unicellular organisms of microscopic dimensions, usually 1 to 2 microns (μ) in diameter. The cell membrane is strong, and enables some varieties to withstand extremes of temperature from $0°$ C. up to $70°$ C., while others can survive an acidity equivalent to N.HCl. Owing to their wide distribution, rapidity of growth and chemical versatility, bacteria and other micro-organisms profoundly affect the geographical pattern of life. By fixing nitrogen in the soil, they divert it from the atmosphere to the plant, and thence to the animal. By breaking down organic compounds returned to the soil, they maintain the circulation of biological elements. As inhabitants of the alimentary tracts of all animals, they aid in the digestion of cellulose and the synthesis of certain vitamins; as pathological agents, they are responsible for many of the infectious diseases; while, when exploited industrially, they provide man with the instruments for making many of his characteristic foods, and other useful products.

The Fabric of Life. Unaided vision can recognise objects down to about 200 μ (0·2 mm.) in diameter. Visible-light microscopy can reveal particles down to 150 millimicrons (0·15 μ). Ultra-violet micrography can reach 70 millimicrons. Electron-micrography can disclose particles down to one millimicron (1 mμ), or 10 Ångström units (10Å). But the world of molecular and atomic structures explored by the chemist and physicist is not reached until the scale of significant distances has decreased to the order of a few Ångström units, " and in this almost uncharted region lies the structural framework behind almost all cytological problems, including fundamental issues such the physical basis of life " (Manton, 1942).

Cytoplasm, the substance of the cell, is non-homogeneous, being function-ally organised for respiration, energy storage and transfer, and the various chemical changes involved in growth, maintenance, secretion and decay.

Subdivisions. Biochemistry may be classified according to the material examined and according to the purpose of the examination. The first sub-division includes plant biochemistry, animal biochemistry, human bio-chemistry, cytological chemistry, tissue chemistry, embryological chemistry,

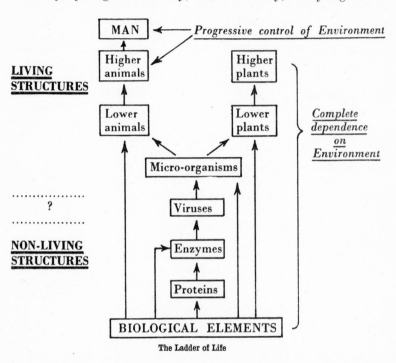

The Ladder of Life

bacterial chemistry, enzyme chemistry, and the like. The second subdivision includes physiological, pathological, clinical, medical, industrial, analytical and theoretical biochemistry. A more or less practical form of the science is now part of medical education, and is pursued partly for the information it gives about the normal working of the human machine, partly for the means it affords of detecting and measuring pathological conditions, and partly for the weapons it offers in the chemical warfare against disease and death.

Course of Study. The plan most usually adopted in studying animal bio-chemistry is to start with the general composition of the organism, and the chemical characteristics of the chief organic and inorganic compounds that enter into its structure. Then, the chemical composition of the tissues and physiological systems is examined, and tissue properties are explained in terms of tissue chemistry. Finally, the composition of the diet is investigated, along with the significance of each constituent, its changes during digestion, and its intermediate metabolism and forms of excretion. Thus, starting with static, analytical biochemistry, the student proceeds to explore the innumerable and interlinked reactions that determine, in part, at least, the behaviour of " the thing called Man."

Synopsis

I. **CONSTITUTIVE BIOCHEMISTRY:** The Ingredients of Life.

Classification, distribution, properties and significance of the constituents of organisms.

  1. **Biological Elements:** Elements invariably or variably present in animals, plants, and micro-organisms.

  2. **Inorganic Compounds and Systems** derived from the biological elements.

  3. **Organic Compounds** present in organisms, and classified by structure and by significance.

  4. **Nutrition:** Intake of matter from the environment.

II. **DYNAMIC BIOCHEMISTRY:** The Drama of Life.

  5. **Catalysts.**

  6. **Intermediate Metabolism:** Chemical changes within the cell.

  7. **Cellular Respiration:** Energy transformations within the cell.

  8. **Excretion:** Return of matter to the environment.

  9. **Chemical Co-ordination.**

10. **The Departments of Life:** The internal environment. The cells and tissues.

General References

Bayliss, W. M. (1924), " Principles of General Physiology." 4th Ed. London.

Bernal, J. D. (1953), " Physical Basis of Life." London.

Chittenden, R. H. (1930), " Development of Physiological Chemistry in the United States." New York.

Engström, A., and J. B. Finean (1958), " Biological Ultrastructure." New York; London.

" Handbook of Biological Data." Ed. by W. S. Spector (1956). Philadelphia; London.

" Hopkins and Biochemistry." Ed. by J. Needham and E. Baldwin (1949). Cambridge.

International Union for Pure and Applied Chemistry, *Proc. Chem. Soc.*, Oct., 1959.

Lieben, F. (1935), " Geschichte der physiologischen Chemie." Leipsic.

Manton, I. (1942), *Nature*, **150**, 362.

" New currents in biochemistry." *British Med. Bull.*, 1948, **5**, No. 4.

" Origin of Life." Symposium by J. B. S. Haldane, J. D. Bernal, N. W. Pirie, and J. W. S. Pringle (1954). *New Biology*, No.16.

Oparin, A. I. (1957), " The Origin of Life." New York; London.

Peters, R. A. (1957), " Forty-five years of biochemistry." *Ann. Rev. Biochem.*, **26,** 1.

ATOMIC WEIGHTS *

Atomic number.	Name.	Symbol.	Atomic weight.	Atomic number.	Name.	Symbol.	Atomic weight.
1	Hydrogen	H	1·0081	47	Silver	Ag	107·880
2	Helium	He	4·003	48	Cadmium	Cd	112·41
3	Lithium	Li	6·940	49	Indium	In	114·76
4	Beryllium	Be	9·02	50	Tin	Sn	118·70
5	Boron	B	10·82	51	Antimony	Sb	121·76
6	Carbon	C	12·01	52	Tellurium	Te	127·61
7	Nitrogen	N	14·008	53	Iodine	I	126·92
8	Oxygen	O	16·0000	54	Xenon	Xe	131·3
9	Fluorine	F	19·00	55	Cæsium	Cs	132·91
10	Neon	Ne	20·183	56	Barium	Ba	137·36
11	Sodium	Na	22·997	57	Lanthanum	La	138·92
12	Magnesium	Mg	24·32	58	Cerium	Ce	140·13
13	Aluminium	Al	26·97	59	Praseodymium	Pr	140·92
14	Silicon	Si	28·06	60	Neodymium	Nd	144·27
15	Phosphorus	P	31·02	61	Promethium	Pm	145
16	Sulphur	S	32·06	62	Samarium	Sm	150·43
17	Chlorine	Cl	35·457	63	Europium	Eu	152·0
18	Argon	A	39·944	64	Gadolinium	Gd	156·9
19	Potassium	K	39·096	65	Terbium	Tb	159·2
20	Calcium	Ca	40·08	66	Dysprosium	Dy	162·46
21	Scandium	Sc	45·10	67	Holmium	Ho	163·5
22	Titanium	Ti	47·90	68	Erbium	Er	167·2
23	Vanadium	V	50·95	69	Thulium	Tm	169·4
24	Chromium	Cr	52·01	70	Ytterbium	Yb	173·04
25	Manganese	Mn	54·93	71	Lutecium	Lu	175·0
26	Iron	Fe	55·84	72	Hafnium	Hf	178·6
27	Cobalt	Co	58·94	73	Tantalum	Ta	180·88
28	Nickel	Ni	58·69	74	Tungsten	W	183·92
29	Copper	Cu	63·57	75	Rhenium	Re	186·31
30	Zinc	Zn	65·38	76	Osmium	Os	190·2
31	Gallium	Ga	69·72	77	Iridium	Ir	193·1
32	Germanium	Ge	72·60	78	Platinum	Pt	195·23
33	Arsenic	As	74·91	79	Gold	Au	197·2
34	Selenium	Se	78·96	80	Mercury	Hg	200·61
35	Bromine	Br	79·916	81	Thallium	Tl	204·39
36	Krypton	Kr	83·7	82	Lead	Pb	207·21
37	Rubidium	Rb	85·48	83	Bismuth	Bi	209·00
38	Strontium	Sr	87·63	84	Polonium	Po	210
39	Yttrium	Y	88·92	85	Astatine	At	211
40	Zirconium	Zr	91·22	86	Radon	Rn	222
41	Niobium	Nb	92·91		(Emanation)		
	(Columbium)	(Cb)		87	Francium	Fr	223
42	Molybdenum	Mo	95·95	88	Radium	Ra	226·05
43	Technetium	Tc	99·4	89	Actinium	Ac	227
44	Ruthenium	Ru	101·7	90	Thorium	Th	232·12
45	Rhodium	Rh	102·91	91	Protoactinium	Pa	231
46	Palladium	Pd	106·7	92	Uranium	U	238·07

Transuranide Elements: (93) Neptunium, Np, 237; (94) Plutonium, Pu, 239; (95) Americium, Am, 241; (96) Curium, Cm, 242; (97) Berkelium, Bk, 247; (98) Californium, Cf, 249; (99) Einsteinium, E, 254; (100) Fermium, Fm, 252; (101) Mendelevium, Mv, 256; (102) Nobelium, Nm, 253.

*It has recently been recommended (International Union for Pure and Applied Chemistry, 1959) that the reference standard for atomic weights should be the carbon isotope $^{12}_{6}C$. This will mean that the atomic weight of hydrogen will be 1·0079 and of oxygen 15·9993. Weights given to the third decimal place will remain unchanged.

Chapter 2 Biological Elements

" This was the heavenly hiding-place
Wherein the spirit laughed a day.
All its proud ivories and fires
Shrunk to a shovelful of clay."

George Russell.

Whether the living organism is regarded as an episode in the history of matter or of spirit, its behaviour is conditioned by the chemical properties of its constituents, all of which are derived ultimately from the biological elements, about forty of which are of established significance, and at least twenty more are known to occur either as contaminants or as micro-constituents of unknown function.

Classification. Biological elements may be classified (*a*) *Quantitatively*, according to the amount present; and (*b*) *Qualitatively*, as *Invariable Elements*, which are present in all organisms, and *Variable Elements*, which are restricted to particular types of organism.

(1) **Invariable Primary Elements.** *Hydrogen, Carbon, Nitrogen, Oxygen, Phosphorus*. These make up the greater part of the organism, their percentage contribution to the total weight being of the order of: H, 10; C, 20; N, 2·5; O, 63; P, 1.

(2) **Invariable Secondary Elements.** *Sodium, Magnesium, Sulphur, Chlorine, Potassium, Calcium, Iron*. These are equally necessary for life, but occur in much smaller individual amounts, usually from 0·05 to 1 per cent. of the total weight of the organism. Among the vertebrates, calcium contributes about 2·5 per cent. to the body-weight, and is included among the Primary Elements. In plants, sodium, calcium, and iron are micro-constituents.

(3) **Invariable Micro-constituents.** *Silicon, Manganese, Copper, Cobalt, Zinc, Molybdenum, Iodine*. The individual concentrations are minute, usually less than 0·005 per cent.

(4) **Variable Secondary Elements.** *Titanium, Vanadium, Bromine*. These elements occur in relatively high concentrations in a few species only.

(5) **Variable Micro-constituents.** *Lithium, Cæsium, Beryllium, Fluorine, Boron, Aluminium, Chromium, Nickel, Gallium, Germanium, Arsenic, Selenium, Rubidium, Strontium, Silver, Cadmium, Tin, Barium, Lead*. Some of these elements are very restricted in distribution; their significance is obscure.

(6) **Contaminants.** Non-biological elements, when relatively abundant in an

8

environment may tend to accumulate in plants and animals, notably: *Indium, Gold, Mercury, Thallium, Uranium.*

Periodic Classification of the Biological Elements. Chemical elements may be arranged and tabulated in order of increasing atomic weight, a.w., and atomic number, a.n., or number of protons in the nucleus, which is equivalent to the number of satellite electrons carried by the atom. The atomic number increases with increase in atomic weight, and is indicated by the numerical position of the element in the periodic table. The fundamental properties of an element are determined by its atomic weight and atomic number and these are indicated by prefixes to the symbol for the element, the upper prefix representing the atomic weight and the lower representing the atomic number; thus $^{14}_{7}N$ denotes nitrogen of a.w. 14 and a.n. 7. This convention is not adopted uniformly; sometimes a.w. values are indicated as an upper suffix. Many forms of periodic classification are available; some lend themselves readily to the segregation of the biological elements (Fearon, 1951).

Isotopes. Many elements exist naturally as mixtures of two or more closely related forms having the same atomic number and chemical properties, but differing slightly in atomic weight. Thus, hydrogen, a.w. 1·0081, is chiefly ^{1}H, with about 0·02 per cent. ^{2}H (deuterium, or hydrogen-2). Such related forms are termed *isotopes*, and are defined as elements of the same atomic number but of different atomic weight. Isotopes are of two classes: *stable*, and *unstable*, or *radioactive*. Stable isotopes occur naturally and are permanent. Unstable isotopes, most of which are artificial, are undergoing spontaneous nuclear decomposition, accompanied by one or more types of discharge: (1) *alpha-particles* (helium nuclei), (2) *beta-particles* (electrons or positrons), (3) *gamma-rays* (electro-magnetic radiation of very high frequency). By measuring the discharge it is possible to classify an unstable isotope in terms of its *half-life*, the time required for its radioactivity to be reduced to half of its initial value. Atomic disintegration is an uncontrollable process, and half-life values depend only on the nature of the particular isotope, and range from less than a second to more than a million years.

Functions of the Biological Elements

(1) *Tissue Structure.* Carbon, the chain-forming element, makes up the hydrogen-carrying framework of carbohydrates and lipids, and with nitrogen, the peptide-linking element, provides the axis of the protein molecules.

(2) *Energy Provision.* Hydrogen, which in atomic form is the ultimate fuel of life.

(3) *Energy Accumulation.* Phosphorus, in the form of condensed phosphates, captures and stores in easily accessible form the energy made available by cell metabolism.

(4) *Electrolytes and Osmotic Regulators.* Cations of sodium, potassium, calcium, and magnesium. Anions of chloride, phosphate, and carbonate.

(5) *Catalysts.* Metals that confer catalytic properties on special proteins: iron,

9

copper, zinc, manganese, magnesium, cobalt. Non-metals that operate in oxidation-reduction systems: sulphur, iodine.

(6) *Skeleton Formation.* Calcium, magnesium, phosphorus, silicon.

(7) *Micro-constituents of Special Significance.* Molybdenum, in nitrogen-fixation; boron, in plant growth.

Detection and Estimation of the Elements. Micro-constituents or primary constituents in micro-samples can be identified and estimated spectrographically by the characteristic emission spectra obtained when the ash is heated to incandescence (flame-photometry). Ions in solution can be estimated in microgram quantities by polarography (Stiles, 1946), or colorimetry.

THE BIOLOGICAL ELEMENTS IN GROUP ORDER

Although every element associated with life is of interest to some organism, only the invariable elements of the higher animal will be considered in detail. They are indicated by heavy type in the Groupings.

Group I: $\begin{cases}\textbf{Hydrogen.}\\ \textit{Alkali metals:} \text{ Lithium, } \textbf{Sodium, Potassium,} \text{ Rubidium, } \textbf{Copper,}\\ \text{Silver.}\end{cases}$

Hydrogen. H, a.n. 1; a.w. 1·0081. Although because of its low density hydrogen accounts for only 9 to 10 per cent. of the weight of higher organisms, it represents some 60 per cent. of the total number of atoms present, and hence it is the most abundant element in living organisms.

Occurrence. Molecular, or gaseous hydrogen, H_2, or H..H, is an end-product in the fermentation of carbohydrates and fatty acids by some bacteria, and thus can arise in the alimentary tract of herbivora. Otherwise, H_2 is rare in the biosphere, though a few organisms, including photosynthetic bacteria and *Escherichia coli* can use it as a source of energy.

Atomic hydrogen, (.H), a highly reactive free-radicle, is the form in which hydrogen is trapped when water vapour is decomposed during photosynthesis. It is a probable intermediate in many metabolic processes.

Ionic hydrogen, H^+, the most electro-positive and mobile of the ions, is liberated by all acids and acid salts, and is present, potentially, in all aqueous solutions.

Combined hydrogen occurs chiefly as water, $(H_2O)_n$, which forms 60 to 85 per cent. of most tissues, and 90 to 99 per cent. of body fluids and secretions. Other important examples of combined hydrogen are fats (12 to 14 per cent.), proteins and carbohydrates (6 to 7 per cent.).

Significance. Hydrogen has the greatest heat of combustion of all the elements (62·8 kilocalories per gram-molecule); and the energy that maintains life is obtained ultimately by the oxidation of hydrogen derived from organic food materials.

Isotopes. Hydrogen-2, or deuterium, D, a stable isotope, accompanies ordinary hydrogen, and accumulates in natural waters as HDO and D_2O, the overall ratio D/H being about 1/6,000 in rain water. By evaporation, a *heavy-water* fraction can be concentrated, from which H_2O and HDO are removed by fractional electrolysis. Heavy-water is used as a tracer compound in estimating the water-content of living organisms. Hydrogen-3, or tritium, an artificially-prepared radioactive isotope of half-life 31 years, is used to label compounds for metabolic research. It is of note in that its disintegration releases positrons, or " positively-charged electrons ", which can act as " anti-matter " particles by destroying negatively-charged ordinary electrons.

Sodium. Na, a.n. 11; a.w. 22·99. The earth's crust contains about 2·8 per cent of Na. Sea water has an average content of 10·72 gm. Na^+ per litre. In animals, sodium values represent 0·1 to 0·5 per cent. of the total body weight, the concentration being higher in the extracellular liquids than in the cells. Among plants sodium is a micro-constituent, values range from 0·007 to 0·15 per cent. of fresh tissue, marine species being the richer.

Occurrence. The body of a new-born child contains about 4·7 gm. Na; that of a 70-kg. adult contains about 65 to 105 gm., depending on the amount of fat present. About a quarter of the total sodium of the mammalian body is held, non-ionised, in the skeleton, the Na/Ca ratio of which is almost constant. In general, apart from a few marine species, there is no evidence that sodium is necessary for the growth of plants, which suggests that the vegetable kingdom had an evolutionary origin other than the salty pastures of the sea, and that " the earth brought forth grass ".

Average values for fresh human tissues or secretions, in mg. Na per 100 gm., are: fistula bile, 320; blood, entire, 175; plasma or serum, 325; red corpuscles, 20; brain, 110; fat-free bone, 170; cartilage, up to 550; cerebro-spinal fluid, 325; liver, 170; lung, 250; muscle, cardiac, 117, skeletal, 67; skin, 147; sweat, 120. Similar values for food materials are: meat, 65 to 80; milk, 43; eggs, 185; fish, 125; cereals, 5 to 30; potato, 3; green vegetables, 3 to 15, root vegetables, 10 to 60; fruits, 0 to 3; nuts, 2 to 10.

Significance. Sodium is the chief extra-cellular cation in the animal body. The solubility of sodium salts favours uptake, but restricts storage, and the metal must be supplied continually in the diet. The minimum requirement for adult man is provided by 0·2 gm. NaCl per 24 hours, an amount greatly exceeded in the ordinary diet. Forced loss of sodium and chloride evoked in the human subject by salt-deficient diets, aggravated by sweating, results in cramp and cardio-respiratory distress.

Special Functions of Sodium. (1) *Ionic-balance.* Sodium provides most of the cations required to balance the anions present in the blood and tissue fluids (Cl, HCO_3, HPO_4), and thus maintains ionic neutrality.

(2) *Osmotic regulation.* Because of its unequal distribution between cells and tissue fluids, sodium takes part in the osmotic equilibrium regulation in the organism.

11

(3) *Physiological response.* Na^+ is a member of a group of cations, which includes K^+, Ca^{2+}, Mg^{2+}, and H^+, concerned in the maintenance of excitability in muscle and other tissues. The sodium and potassium contents of the blood plasma are controlled by the pituitary gland, which operates indirectly through the hormones of the adrenal cortex so as to regulate the excretion of electrolytes by the kidney. Cortical dysfunction, as seen in Addison's disease, is characterised by increased renal excretion of Na^+, with consequent fall in the level of plasma Na^+, and migration of K^+ from the tissue cells.

Isotopes. Sodium-24, radiosodium, obtained from sodium-23 by the cyclotron, has a half-life of 14·8 hours, and is used for estimations of sodium balance and extracellular fluid volume.

Potassium. K, a.n. 19; a.w. 39·10. The earth's crust contains about 2·6 per cent. of K. Sea water has an average content of 0·38 gm. K^+ per litre. Potassium is a primary constituent of plants, the values ranging from 0·1 to more than 1 per cent. The potassium content of land animals is 0·1 to 0·25 per cent. of the total body weight, which is usually somewhat greater than the corresponding sodium content. However, the internal distribution of the elements is different: potassium, maintaining a vegetable tradition, accumulates in the tissue cells; sodium, true to its marine ancestry, circulates in the fluids.

Occurrence. The body of a 70-kg. human adult contains about 100 to 160 gm. of potassium, depending on the amount of fat present. In general, fat-free human tissues contain about 0·28 per cent.

Average values for fresh human tissues or secretions, in mg. K per 100 gm., are: fistula bile, 19; blood, entire, 195; plasma or serum, 21; red corpuscles, 424; fat-free bone, 58; brain, 310; cartilage, 235; cerebro-spinal fluid, 20; liver, 192; pancreas, 213; lung, 150; muscle, cardiac, 240, skeletal, 310; skin, 95.

Species differences in distribution occur. The chief cation in the red corpuscles of man, monkey, and rabbit is K^+; in the corpuscles of the dog and the cat it is Na^+. In the human red corpuscle, the concentration of K^+ is about twenty times that in the plasma, while the plasma concentration of Na^+ is about seventeen times that in the corpuscle. Tracer isotope studies show that while the corpuscle is permeable both to K^+ and to Na^+, some intracellular mechanism, or " sodium pump " is at work to concentrate the one while excluding the other. When blood is stored under sterile conditions, the pump fails from lack of fuel, and potassium gradually diffuses out of the corpuscles. This process is greatly accelerated at low temperatures, suggesting that the normal state depends on enzyme activity.

Significance. (1) *Plant Growth.* Potassium is necessary for cell-division, nitrate reduction, protein synthesis, and the operation of the chloroplasts in photosynthesis of carbohydrates.

12

(2) *Animal Growth* and Maintenance. Young animals fail to grow when the potassium intake falls below a critical value. In adults potassium deficiency can arise from deprivation, gastro-intestinal disturbance, or renal disease, leading to cellular potassium depletion, not necessarily accompanied by a low plasma level, or *hypokalœmia*. Potassium deficiency is characterised by mental apathy, atony of skeletal and intestinal muscle, and cardiac disturbance. The human adult requirement is assumed to be one gram per 24 hours, which is about one-third of the amount provided by the ordinary mixed diet.

Special Functions of Potassium. Potassium is the chief metal cation of plant and animal cells, and its chief function appears to be the activation of enzyme-controlled energy transfer reactions involving the phosphate esters. Hence, potassium is necessary both for the general maintenance of cell activity, and for the functions exerted by specialised tissues, such as skeletal muscle and secreting glands. In nerve, the passage of the impulse is accompanied by escape of K^+ and local depolarisation of the nerve fibre. Simultaneously, Na^+ diffuses into the fibre, replacing K^+. The condition is reversed during the resting state of the nerve.

Potassium, unlike sodium, is potentially toxic. Doses equivalent to 25 ml. of M/1 K^+ per kg. body weight are fatal, and evoke a rise in the plasma potassium level, or *hyperkalœmia*, which results in cardiac arrest when the concentration has exceeded 8 to 10 m.equiv. K^+ per litre.

Isotopes. Potassium-40, radiopotassium of half-life 1,270 million years, represents about 0·01 per cent. of the total potassium of the earth's crust, and occurs as an ultra-micro-constituent of all organisms. Artificially-prepared radioactive potassium-42 (half-life, 12·4 hours) is used as a tracer element in research.

Copper. Cu, a.n. 29; a.w. 63·57. An invariable micro-constituent of plants and animals. Plant values range from 0·5 to about 10 mg. Cu per kg. fresh material, depending on species and soil. The element is concentrated in regions of active growth. Leguminous plants and their seeds are relatively rich. Higher animals display copper-rich tissues (liver, kidney, heart, brain, hair) and copper-poor tissues (skin, lung, pancreas, spleen, skeletal muscle). The 70-kg. human adult body contains 100 to 150 mg. Cu. Large stores of the metal accumulate in the fœtal liver.

Values for fresh material, in mg. Cu per kg., are: almond, 12; apple, 0·8; bean, 6·5; cabbage, 0·5; carrot, 0·8; pea, 2·4; potato, 1·7. Corresponding values for human tissues are: adult liver, 3 to 13; infant liver, 15 to 80; brain, 3 to 6; blood, 1·8 to 2·3; red corpuscles, 2; milk, 0·05 to 0·5. Among animals, oysters are exceptionally rich, the range being 24 to 60 mg. Cu per kg.

Copper is a primary element in the blood and body-fluids of marine and some other invertebrates, notably lobster (*Palinurus vulgaris*), king crab (*Limulus polyphemus*), octopus, snail, scorpion, where it occurs constitutes 0·15 to 0·4 per cent. of the respiratory pigment *hœmocyanin*, an analogue of the iron-

13

containing hæmoglobin present in the blood of higher animals. Hæmocyanin is blue in the oxidised state, and colourless when reduced. Its existence shows the ability of the organism to accumulate micro-constituents from the environment. Sea water contains only about one part of copper per 100 million.

Occurrence. (1) *Hæmocuprein*, a blue chromoprotein containing 0·34 per cent. Cu, present in red blood corpuscles.

(2) *Hæmocuprin*, a porphyrin derivative containing 0·15 to 0·4 per cent. Cu, present in hæmocyanin.

(3) *Turacin*, a purple uroporphyrin derivative found in the feathers of the *Touracous* and some other birds.

(4) *Copper-proteins*, represented by the enzymes *cytochrome oxidase, polyphenol oxidases, ascorbic oxidase*, and by *hepatocuprein*, a storage pigment in liver.

Significance. (1) *A Respiratory Catalyst.* Like iron, copper may be an essential factor in the respiration of cells. Its multivalency enables it to accept and release electrons, $Cu^{2+} + e' \to Cu^+$, and thus effect electron-transport in oxidation-reduction systems. As hæmocyanin, it is responsible for the transport of molecular oxygen in the blood of many arachnids, crustaceans, and molluscs. Copper is necessary for the synthesis of hæm, and its important derivatives, the cytochromes and hæmoglobins.

(2) *Plant Growth.* In optimal minima, copper is necessary for the growth and germination of plants. In higher concentration, it is toxic to all forms of plant life, especially algæ.

(3) *Animal Growth.* Copper is a micro-essential nutrient for animals, and when deficient in soil and pasture, characteristic diseases occur among grazing animals, such as " sway-back " in young lambs. These may be caused by shortage of cytochrome oxidase, a necessary enzyme in the last stages in cellular respiration.

The minimum copper requirement of the human adult is assessed at 0·1 mg. per 24 hours; the ordinary mixed diet provides 0·2 to 5 mg. daily. Sources range from 0·1 mg. Cu per kg., fresh vegetables, to 40 mg. Cu per mg., fresh calf liver. Milk usually is deficient, and the diet of pre-school children should be adjusted so as to ensure an intake of about 0·1 mg. per kg. body weight. The distribution of copper, both as a constituent and a contaminant of food materials, is discussed by Monier-Williams (1949).

Group II: $\begin{cases} Alkaline\text{-}earth \ metals: \textbf{Magnesium, Calcium,} \ \text{Strontium, Barium.} \\ \text{Zinc, Cadmium.} \end{cases}$

Magnesium. Mg, a.n. 12; a.w. 24·32. The earth's crust contains about 2 per cent. of Mg. Sea water has an average content of 1·36 gm. Mg^{2+} per litre, the metal ranking next to Na^+ in quantitative importance.

Magnesium is the essential metal in chlorophyll, and, therefore, is present in all green plants. It is a universal micro-constituent of lower plants.

Values for fresh material, in mg. Mg per 100 gm., are: wheat grain, 129; spinach leaf, 76; carrot root, 19; potato tuber, 32; lentil, 45; cherry fruit, 20; chlorophyll, dry, 2,700.

Some marine animals are rich in magnesium, and the skeletons of echinoderms may contain 10 per cent. of $MgCO_3$, the metal being concentrated in preference to calcium because of its greater abundance in the environment. The body of the new-born child contains about 0·7 gm.; that of the 65- to 70-kg. adult contains about 20 gm. of magnesium. The distribution is very uneven.

Average values for human body fluids and fresh tissues, in mg. Mg per 100 gm., are: fistula bile, 0·5; blood, entire, 4·5; plasma or serum, 2·4; red corpuscles, 6·6; fat-free bone, 100; brain, 15; cartilage, 11; kidney, liver, pancreas, 19; lung, 7·5; muscle, cardiac, 50, skeletal, 22; skin, 13; testicle, thyroid, adrenal gland, 10; milk, 60.

Occurrence. (1) Basic phosphate and carbonate of magnesium supplement calcium in skeletal tissues of animals.
(2) Inositol hexaphosphates, or phytates, of magnesium and calcium occur in the outer covering of cereal and other seeds.
(3) Magnesium porphyrans are represented by the chlorophylls.

Significance. (1) *Structural.* Magnesium, like calcium, contributes to the inorganic matrix of the animal skeleton.
(2) *Enzyme activation.* Magnesium ions are necessary for the working of several enzymes, notably: phosphatases, aminopeptidases, dipeptidases, pyruvic decarboxylase, and enolase, which is a magnesium-containing enzyme.
(3) *Plant Growth.* Magnesium is necessary both for the production of chlorophyll and for the operation of various enzymes.
(4) *Animal Growth.* Higher animals on deficient diets display a magnesium-deficiency syndrome resembling avitaminosis B_1, or thiamine deficiency, and leading to epileptiform convulsions and death. The effect is attributed to the inability of the organism to manipulate thiamine diphosphate, in the absence of Mg^{2+}.
(5) *Ionic Balance.* Mg^{2+} and Ca^{2+} are the divalent ions concerned in tissue excitability. The effect is complex. In muscle, they are complementary to a limited extent, and can antagonise K^+. In nerve, Mg^{2+} and Ca^{2+} are antagonistic; Mg^{2+} has a specific depressant action, partly neutralised by Ca^{2+}. Intravenous injection of sufficient Mg^{2+} to raise the blood level above 20 mg. per 100 ml. results in deep anæsthesia and paralysis of voluntary muscles; the effect is rapidly abolished by injection of an equivalent amount of Ca^{2+}. The human requirement of magnesium, 0·2 to 0·5 gm. per 24 hours, is adequately provided by a mixed diet rich in green vegetables.

15

Calcium. Ca, a.n. 20; a.w. 40·07. The earth's crust contains about 3·63 per cent. of calcium. Sea water contains about 0·4 gm. Ca^{2+} per litre.
The calcium content of plants ranges from about 10 to 100 mg. per 100 gm. fresh tissue, depending on soil conditions.

Values for fresh, edible material, in mg. Ca per 100 gm., are: asparagus, 28; beetroot, 21; cabbage leaf, 119; lettuce leaf, 35; onion bulb, 42; potato tuber, 11; oat grain, 117; barley and wheat grain, 88.

Among animals, calcium occurs in all tissues; it is the chief metal in the vertebrates. The adult human body contains 0·9 to 1·7 kg., or $2 \pm 0·5$ per cent. Ca, 97 per cent. of which is located in the skeleton. Fresh bone contains about 10 per cent. Ca, chiefly present as the double salt $(Ca_3(PO_4)_2)_3 . CaCO_3$. Fresh, soft vertebrate tissue values range from 6 mg. Ca per 100 gm. in muscle, up to 20 mg. in kidney, and 34 mg. in thyroid. Milk is rich in calcium; values in mg. per 100 ml. are: human milk, 30 to 80; cow's milk, 100 to 120.

Occurrence. (1) *Insoluble Salts.* Tricalcium phosphate, calcium carbonate, calcium fluoride occur in bone and in teeth. Calcium inositol hexaphosphate, or calcium phytate, forms part of the protective covering of seeds. Calcium soaps are the chief form in which calcium is excreted by the intestine, especially when the diet is rich in fats. Calcium oxalate appears as a urinary deposit.
(2) *Soluble Calcium.* In addition to Ca^{2+}, calcium can exist as soluble complexes with proteins and some organic acids (citric and glucuronic acids, amino acids) and can occur in tissue fluids in the non-diffusible (colloidal) and diffusible (non-colloidal) state. A varying proportion of the diffusible fraction is ionised, the remainder being non-ionised.
Human blood serum has a calcium value of 9 to 11 mg. per 100 ml., about 6 mg. of which are non-colloidal and diffusible. The red corpuscles are almost free from calcium in any form.

Significance. (1) *Plant Growth.* Calcium carbonate is one of the natural factors concerned in reducing the acidity of soil, and is used for this purpose in agriculture.
(2) *Structure.* Because of the natural abundance of calcium, and its property of forming salts and compounds of low solubility, it has been employed extensively in the biosphere as a skeletal metal. It is necessary for tissue repair in marine plants and invertebrates. As an alginate in seaweeds and a pectate in higher plants, it imparts rigidity to cell walls and fruits. It is the characteristic metal of the animal skeleton, although it may be replaced in part by magnesium, or entirely by silicon, in some lower forms of life.
In addition to its mechanical functions, bone provides a good but somewhat inaccessible reserve of calcium.

(3) *Ionic Balance.* In plants Ca^{2+} can neutralise the toxic effects of excess of K^+, Mg^{2+}, and Na^+. In higher animals Ca^{2+} and Mg^{2+} supplement and antagonise, partly by mutual competition for phosphate, with which they form insoluble salts. Consequently, a high dietary intake of Ca or of Mg can aggravate the effects, respectively, of Mg or Ca deficiency, and a fall in either the Ca or the Mg level in the blood tends to evoke a tetany that can be relieved by lowering the blood level of the counterpart ion. Ca^{2+} is necessary for heart muscle contraction; excess causes increase in tone, leading to a state of " calcium rigor ". The effect is antagonised by K^+. Ca^{2+} is required for the conversion of prothrombin into thrombin, a necessary stage in the coagulation of blood; it can be replaced, less effectively, by the related metals Mg, Sr, and Ba. When casein (caseinogen), the characteristic protein of milk, is acted on by the enzyme chymase, or rennin, it is converted into paracasein, which forms an insoluble complex with the Ca^{2+} present in the milk, and separates as a curd. Hence, cheeses are richer in calcium than the original milk, and form an important dietary source of the metal.

The calcium level of the blood and tissue fluids in higher animals is regulated by three factors: (1) the parathyroid hormone; (2) the calciferols, or D vitamins, notably cholecalciferol; and (3) solar or ultra-violet irradiation. Parathyroid hormone promotes phosphate excretion, and by releasing calcium phosphate from the bones raises the Ca level in the blood plasma. The calciferols promote the absorption of calcium and phosphate from the alimentary tract. Ultra-violet irradiation enables the animal to produce cholecalciferol in its surface tissues from a provitamin, 7-dehydrocholesterol.

Zinc. Zn, a.n. 30; a.w. 65·38. The earth's crust contains about 65 mg. Zn per kg. Values for sea water are up to 14 mg. per 1,000 litres.

Zinc appears to be an essential micro-constituent of all forms of life. Plant values, in mg. Zn per kg. fresh tissue range from 1 in fruit pulp, 10 in green leaves, 20 to 80 in cereal grain, and up to 150 in bran and wheat germ. Values for marine animals range from 3 in elasmobranchs, to more than 300 in oysters. Higher animals have range of 20 to 50 mg. Zn per kg., the metal being concentrated in hair, fur, bone, and the melanoid pigments of the eye. The yolk of the hen's egg contains 0·2 to 0·9 mg. per egg. Some snake venoms are notably rich in zinc. The adult human body contains about 2·2 gm. of zinc.

Average values for fresh, human tissue, in mg. per kg., are: blood, entire, 8·8, plasma, 3·0; brain, 8·3; bone, 100; hair, 163; kidney, muscle, 32; pancreas, spleen, 12; testis, 300; milk, 3 to 5.

Occurrence. At least half the zinc in tissues is protein-bound, and non-dialysable. Zinc is a necessary constituent of the enzyme carbonic anhydrase (0·16 to 0·3 per cent.), and is closely associated with other enzymes: aldolase, carboxypeptidases, enolase, phosphatases, uricase, and with the hormone insulin.

17

Significance. As an activator of enzymes employed in carbohydrate metabolism, zinc is required by all cells and tissues, and is probably necessary for plant and animal growth and maintenance.

Zinc deficiency in higher animals is associated with retarded development, alopecia, and dermatitis. The exact human requirement is unknown, but is met by the ordinary mixed diet, which provides 10 to 15 mg. Zn per 24 hours.

Group III: { **Boron, Aluminium.** Gallium.

Boron. B, a.n. 5; a.w. 10·82. The earth's crust contains about 3 mg. B per kg. Sea water contains about 4·5 mg. per litre. Borate forms an important part of the buffer mechanism of the ocean, being second only to bicarbonate, and exceeding the combined effects of phosphate, arsenate, and silicate.

Borate has been found in all plants examined. Values, in mg. B per kg. dry material, range from 1 to 5, in cereals and hay, up to 50, in leguminous plants. Beetroot, date fruit, grape vines, and wine are relatively rich in the non-metal. Animal tissues have low values, 0·01 mg. B per kg. fresh material, or less.

Significance. Boron is an essential micro-constituent in plant growth, and appears to be associated with carbohydrate transport. Concentrations above 100 mg. per kg. boric acid, H_3BO_3, in the environment retard plant growth. Fungi and some green algæ are relatively inert to borate, and its toxic effect may be used to differentiate them from the susceptible bacteria.

Boron does not appear to be necessary for animal life. Large doses are toxic, and cause gastro-intestinal disturbance, inhibition of dermal secretion, and loss of hair. Some of these effects may depend on changes in the micro-flora of the intestine.

Aluminium. Al, a.n. 13, a.w. 26·97. After oxygen and silicon, aluminium is the most abundant element in the earth's crust (8 per cent.), occurring chiefly as silicate. No function has yet been found for the metal in plants or animals. In view of its natural abundance, the low concentration found in fresh plant (1 to 20 mg. per kg.) and animal tissues (0·5 to 1 mg. per kg.) is remarkable, and supports the belief that the metal is not necessary for growth or function.

Group IV: { **Carbon, Silicon,** Titanium. Germanium, Tin, Lead.

Carbon. C, a.n. 6; a.w. 12·01. The twelfth element in order of abundance in the crust of the earth (0·15 per cent.). It occurs chiefly in oxidised form, as CO_2 in the atmosphere, H_2CO_3 and HCO_3^- in the ocean and other waters, and as insoluble carbonates in rocks and soil.

Carbon is the characterising element of organic material, and accounts for 12 to 20 per cent. of the total weight of higher organisms. About one-thousandth part of the carbon of the earth's crust is in biological use, and the world-total of organic carbon immobilised in plant products, cellulose, wood,

18

peat, and coal, is at least 7×10^{11} kg., and represents one-third of the carbon dioxide believed to have been the primitive atmosphere of the earth.

Carbon comes midway in the periodic table, and, having four electrons in its outer shell, can combine by sharing electrons with electro-positive donors, such as hydrogen, or with electro-negative attractors, such as chlorine atoms.

$$
\overset{..}{:}\overset{\cdot\cdot}{Cl}: \qquad\qquad\qquad\qquad\qquad H
$$
$$
:\overset{..}{Cl}:\overset{..}{C}:\overset{\cdot\cdot}{Cl}:\leftarrow 4:\overset{..}{Cl}.+.\overset{\cdot}{C}.+4.H\rightarrow H:\overset{..}{C}:H
$$
$$
:\overset{..}{Cl}: \qquad\qquad\qquad \cdot \qquad\qquad\qquad H
$$

The stability of these and similar co-ordination compounds enables them to function as groups or *radicals*, such as $..CH_3$. Carbon is chief among the chain-forming elements, and can link up with itself by sharing one, two, or three pairs of electrons, as in *ethane*, $H_3C..CH_3$, *ethylene*, $H_2C::CH_2$, and *acetylene*, $HC \vdots CH$. Carbon in organic combination is detected and estimated by combustion, since every organic carbon-containing substance can be burned in oxygen, with liberation of carbon dioxide.

Isotopes. Naturally-occurring carbon, free or combined, is a mixture containing about 70 atoms of the stable isotope, heavy carbon, or carbon-13, per 9,929 atoms of the common carbon-12, and a minute amount of the radioactive isotope, carbon-14, depending on the age of the material.

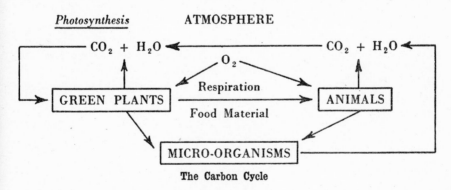

The Carbon Cycle

The Carbon Cycle. Carbon occurs fully oxidised as CO_2 in the atmosphere as a micro-constituent, 460 mg. per kg., or 0 03 to 0·04 per cent. by volume. The atmosphere regulates the carbon dioxide content of the ocean and surface waters, in which it dissolves forming H_2CO_3, HCO_3^- and CO_3^{2-}. From these sources it is taken up by living organisms, and subsequently elaborated into organic compounds by the photo-synthetic mechanisms present in all green plants and in some pigmented bacteria. This provides, structural, storage, and nutritive material for the plant, and, indirectly, for animals and micro-organisms that feed on plants or plant products. By the respiratory processes necessary for the maintenance of all forms of life, organic compounds are degraded with release of carbon dioxide, which is restored to the environment.

Silicon. Si, a.n. 14; a.w. 28·06. The most abundant element in Nature, next to oxygen. Aluminium silicate is the chief constituent of clay, and silicates as a class constitute 55 per cent. of the earth's crust. Silica, SiO_2, is universal in plants, and is a structural element in the stems of cereals, bamboo, and coarser grasses, where it forms 20 to 40 per cent. of the total ash. It is also the characteristic structural component of the skeleton of silicious sponges and unicellular marine organisms, where its high transparency may be of service in photosynthetic activities. The value for sea water varies from 0·1 to 4 mg. Si per litre in shallow water containing suspended silicate. Organic forms of silicate occur in plants and in some feathers.

In higher animals, silica is a common micro-constituent of no known function. Representative values for fresh tissues range from 10 to about 350 mg. SiO_2 per 100 gm., the highest being in connective tissue. In *silicosis*, a fibrosis of the lung caused by inhalation of silica dust values up to 600 mg. per 100 gm. have been reported.

Group V: $\begin{cases} \text{Vanadium.} \\ \textbf{Nitrogen, Phosphorus,} \text{ Arsenic.} \end{cases}$

Nitrogen. N, a.n. 7; a.w. 14·01. Nitrogen has a low affinity for other elements, and most of the nitrogen of the environment occurs free in the atmosphere. As nitrate, inorganic nitrogen is widely distributed in the earth's crust (46 mg. N per kg.), and is concentrated in vast deposits in arid regions, such as parts of Chile. Nitrogen is a major element in all forms of life, percentage values ranging from about 1·5 to 9, depending chiefly on the amount of protein present.

Occurrence. (1) *Inorganic:* NH_3, $NH_2.OH$ (hydroxylamine), $NH_2.COOH$ (carbamic acid), HNO_2, HNO_3.
(2) *Simple Organic:* HCN, HSCN, CON_2H_4 (urea), $R.NH_2$ (amines), $R.CO.NH_2$ (amides), $R(NH_2).COOH$ (amino acids), $R.NH.CO.NH_2$ (carbamides), $R.NH.C(NH).NH_2$ (guanidines).
(3) *Cyclic:* pyrimidines, purines, pteridines, flavins, pyridines, porphyrins.
(4) *Macromolecular:* proteins, nucleic acids.
Important biological properties reside in the amino function, $-NH_2$. Nitrogen has five electrons in its outer shell, and therefore can accept and share three additional electrons to complete its electron octet. Thus it functions as a typical trivalent element; but when its three valencies are satisfied, it still possesses a " lone pair " of unshared electrons, which are able to trap a hydrogen ion, and form a positively-charged " onium " ion.

$$\text{Ammonia} \quad \overset{\text{H}}{\underset{\text{H}}{\text{H}:\overset{..}{\text{N}}:}} + \text{H}^+ \longleftrightarrow \overset{\text{H}}{\underset{\text{H}}{\text{H}:\overset{..}{\text{N}}{}^+:\text{H}}} \text{ Ammonium ion}$$

$$\text{Amino base } R.NH_2 + H^+ \longleftrightarrow R.N^+H_3 \text{ Onium ion}$$

By this means, ammonia and other amino compounds act as bases, or hydrogen-ion acceptors, forming onium compounds, which can act as acids, or hydrogen-ion donors. Using isotopic hydrogen as a tracer, it can be shown that all the hydrogen atoms in such an onium ion are equally labile, and any one of them can be released, or exchanged with a hydrogen ion in the environment. Stable onium ions of the type R_4N^+ occur, in which R is a radical other than hydrogen. For example, tetramethyl-ammonium, $(CH_3)_4N^+$, and the important cation choline, or hydroxyethyl - trimethyl - ammonium, $HO.C_2H_5.(CH_3)_3N^+$.

The imino function, $>NH$, reacts similarly with hydrogen ions, and can occur in linear compounds, such as dimethylamine, $CH_3—NH—CH_3$, and in cyclic compounds, such as proline and pyrrole.

Isotopes. Naturally occurring nitrogen contains about 0·14 per cent. of the stable, heavy isotope, nitrogen-15, which is used as a tracer element in research.

The Nitrogen Cycle. Nitrogen leaves the atmosphere both directly and as oxides of nitrogen. The oxides are formed in the upper reaches of the atmosphere by photo-oxidation, and, dissolved in rain, reach the sea and soil as nitrous and nitric acids. Atmospheric nitrogen is assimilated by soil organisms, and by root-nodules of leguminous plants (peas, beans and clover). Thus are made available for life several highly reactive forms of nitrogen, ranging from the strong acid, HNO_3, to the base, NH_3. From these, the plant synthesises proteins and other nitrogen compounds which may be transmitted to the animal, or back again to the soil. The higher animal excretes its waste nitrogen as urea, which is rapidly attacked by micro-organisms, and converted into ammonia, thus enabling the nitrogen to continue in circulation. Among birds and reptiles, waste nitrogen is excreted as purines, principally uric acid, which is a much more stable and less soluble compound than urea. By this process, nitrogen has been temporarily diverted to form the great guano deposits of the Pacific Islands.

Absorption of atmospheric nitrogen by leguminous plants, with consequent enrichment of the soil, was demonstrated, in 1838, by Boussingault, and shown to be located in the root-nodules, by Hellriegel, in 1886. From these nodules, Beijerinck, in 1888, isolated a nitrogen-fixing organism, *B. radicicola*, now termed *Rhizobium*, which, however, seems incapable of operating when apart from the host plant. Nitrogen-fixing nodules occur in a few higher plants, such as the roots of alder trees and the leaves of *Rubiacea*. Atmospheric nitrogen is also assimilated by soil organisms, notably by the anaerobe *Clostridium pastorianum* (Vinogradsky, 1893), and the aerobe *Azotobacter*

21

(Beijerinck, 1894), which occurs in all fertile soils down to a depth of about 50 cm. *Clostridium* occurs at a lower depth, and also is found in fresh and salt waters. *Radiobacter*, which accompanies *azotobacter*, has the power of oxidising N_2 into HNO_2 and HNO_3, which, in turn, can be reduced to NH_3.

The elements Ca (or Sr), Mg, Fe and Mo (or Va) are necessary soil constituents for the biological fixation of nitrogen. Ammonia, derived from the decomposition of nitrogenous compounds such as proteins and urea, is oxidised to HNO_2 by the soil organism *Nitrosomonas*, and subsequently oxidised to HNO_3 by *Nitrobacter*.

The Nitrogen Cycle

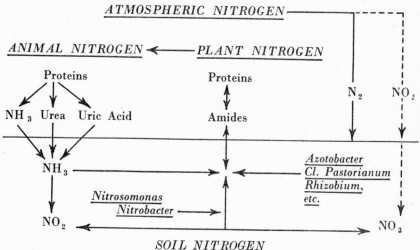

SOIL NITROGEN

Phosphorus. P, a.n. 15; a.w. 31·02. The earth's crust contains about 1·3 gm. P per kg. Phosphate in sea water ranges from less than 0·1 mg., at the surface, to about 20 mg. P (or 60 mg. PO_4) per litre. Phosphorus is noteworthy in that it is the only element that was originally discovered in biological material, and was first obtained by the destructive distillation of urinary residues, by Brand, about 1674. Since then, it has been found in all organisms examined, and in all fertile soils.

Phosphorus does not occur as the free element in the environment or the organism, but exists almost entirely as the fully-oxidised phosphate radical, PO_4, in various types of combination. Analytical data, however, often are expressed in terms of P, from which the corresponding PO_4 values can be obtained by multiplying by 3·06.

Plant values range from 0·1 to 0·8 per cent. P, in dry material, and tend to increase with progress up the evolutionary scale. Animal phosphorus values rise sharply with the acquisition of a bony skeleton by the vertebrates.

A new-born child contains about 13·8 gm. P, and a 65-kg. adult has about

620 gm., of which 555 gm. are in the skeleton, 52 gm. in the muscles, 4·6 gm. in brain and nerves, and 1·8 gm. in the blood. Percentage phosphorus values for fresh human tissue range from 0·6 for skin, up to 5 for fat-free bone; the average value is about one.

Occurrence. (1) *Phosphoric acid*, orthophosphoric acid, H_3PO_4, is represented by the ions $H_2PO_4^-$ and HPO_4^{-2} of tissues and tissue fluids, by the soluble phosphate esters of sugars and other compounds, and by the insoluble phosphates of skeletal material.

(2) *Condensed phosphates*, assembled from PO_4 units held by oxygen linkage, are represented by the polyphosphates and metaphosphates of the energy-accumulating systems in the cell.

The formulation of these acids is arbitrary. Phosphorus, like nitrogen, has a " lone pair " of electrons in its outer shell, and when its trivalency is satisfied by union with three hydroxyl radicals, the lone pair of electrons is able to bind an uncharged oxygen atom, so as to form the phosphate system, H_3PO_4. This may be written as $(HO)_3P \rightarrow O$, the arrow denoting that the phosphorus atom has contributed its two unpaired electrons to complete the octet of the fourth oxygen atom. However, as tracer isotopes show, all the oxygen atoms in the phosphate radical are equivalent, and the acid may be more accurately represented as $H_3^+(PO_4)^{3-}$.

The condensed phosphates: diphosphoric, or pyrophosphoric, and triphosphoric acids usually are formulated as:

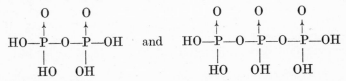

The unstable metaphosphoric acid, HPO_3, tends to occur in comparable chains of 3 or 4 units.

Isotopes. The radioactive isotope, phosphorus-32 (half-life, 14·3 days), is produced from sulphur-32 in the cyclotron or the atomic reactor. It was introduced into biology by Hevesy as a tracer in studies on phosphate

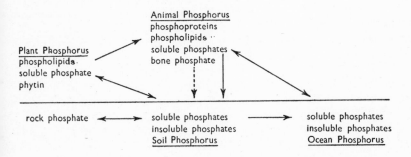

metabolism, and is employed therapeutically to provide an intracellular source of radiation in treatment of some malignant diseases.

The Phosphate Cycle. Phosphorus circulates in the kingdoms of life in the oxidised form of phosphate. Plants elaborate soil phosphate into phospho-lipids and other phospho-compounds, which are transformed by the animal into phosphoproteins and tissue phosphates, the residue being returned to the soil or the sea as free phosphate. Soil phosphate is one of the important limiting factors in plant growth, and its provision is one of the tasks of applied agriculture.

Arsenic. As, a.n. 33; a.w. 74·91. A universal micro-contaminant of plants and animals. Soil values range from 0·1 to 2 mg. As per kg ; sea water contains 0·003 to 0·02 mg. As per litre. From the trioxide, As_2O_3 are derived the highly poisónous acids $HAsO_2$ and H_3AsO_3. From the pentoxide, As_2O_5, is derived the relatively non-poisonous arsenic acid, H_3AsO_4.

Marine crustacea and fish that feed upon them are comparatively rich in As Values, in mg. As_2O_3 per kg. soft tissue, are: plaice, 3; oyster, 3 to 10; lobster, 36 to 110; prawn, 40 to 174; shrimp, 12 to 40; mussel, 40 to 119. The urine of fish-eaters has been found to contain up to 0·58 mg. As_2O_3 per litre, a value previously associated with chronic arsenical poisoning. The absence of harmful effects may be because most of the metal has been ingested as organic arsenate, though it is possible that some cases of poisoning by shell-fish, attributed to bacterial contamination, are caused by arsenic. Among mammals, the distribution is so minute and variable that the metal can have little biological significance. It tends to accumulate in skin, hair, and nails. Apart from shell-fish, preservatives and impure table salt are the chief sources of arsenic in the human diet.

The minimum fatal dose for man is 0·8 to 2·4 gm. As_2O_3 per kg. body weight.

Group VI: $\begin{cases} \text{Chromium, } \textbf{Molybdenum.} \\ \textbf{Oxygen, Sulphur,} \text{ Selenium.} \end{cases}$

Molybdenum. Mo, a.n. 42; a.w. 95·95. An essential micro-constituent for soil fertility, the usual range being 0·1 to 0·3 mg. per kg. Excess in soil can indirectly cause disorders in grazing animals, the effect being antagonised by copper.

Molybdenum forms part of the prosthetic group of the flavoprotein enzymes, nitrate reductase and xanthine oxidase, and, therefore, is necessary for Azotobacter and related nitrogen-fixing organisms, for plants and for animals. Representative values, in mg. Mo per kg. dry material, are: plants, 0·5; invertebrates, 2; vertebrates, 0·8.

Cereal seed germ and some molluscs are relatively rich in the metal.

Oxygen. O, a.n. 8, a.w. 16·0. The most abundant and widely distributed of the elements. It constitutes about 46·6 per cent. of the earth's crust, and about 60 to 80 per cent. by weight of fresh plant and animal tissue.

Oxygen is unique in being the only element assimilated in free, molecular form by animals and higher plants. By combining with transferred hydrogen atoms to produce water, oxygen provides the last link in the respiratory chain in the aerobic organisms, so-called because they require a continual supply of free oxygen, although some, when compelled, can go into a temporary state of " oxygen debt ". Some lower organisms, chiefly bacteria and fungi, are anaerobic, and do not employ free oxygen; for a sub-group, the obligatory anaerobes, it is actually toxic.

Oxygen Poisoning. At or below atmospheric pressure, exposure of animals to pure oxygen has no harmful effects over short periods. Prolonged exposure, or high pressure, results in convulsions, coma, and death. This is attributed to the oxidative destruction of the thiol, or —SH groups in enzyme systems, such as succinic dehydrogenase, that are continuously working in the maintenance of life.

Prolonged exposure of premature infants to high concentrations of oxygen tends to produce changes in the eye posterior to the lens, with gross impairment of vision—*retrolental fibroplasia.*

Isotopes. The stable, heavy isotope, oxygen-18, represents about 0·2 per cent. of the total number of oxygen atoms in Nature. It is used as a tracer element in work on photosynthesis, oxidations, and other metabolic processes.

The oxygen of the earth's atmosphere (23·15 per cent. by weight; 20·95 per cent. by volume) is believed to have arisen from the incessant photoactivity of plants. This is a possible explanation of the absence of detectable oxygen from the atmosphere of the vegetation-free neighbouring planets, Venus and Mars.

Sulphur. S, a.n. 16; a.w. 32·06. The sulphur content of the earth's crust is about 0·52 gm. S per kg. The element is irregularly distributed; it occurs free in volcanic districts, as sulphide in iron pyrites (FeS_2), and as sulphate in gypsum ($CaSO_4 . 2H_2O$).

Because of natural variations in isotope content, the atomic weight of sulphur has a range of 32·06 $\pm$ 0·003; the average percentage composition of the mixture being: ^{31}S, 16; ^{32}S, 72; ^{33}S, 4; ^{34}S, 8.

In plants, sulphur is distributed as protein, organic sulphide, and sulphate. Values for fresh material, in percentage S, range from 0·01 to 0·2. In higher animals, the sulphur content depends largely on the amount of scleroprotein present. Thus, fresh muscle has about 0·2 per cent. S; skin, hair, feathers, and other epidermal structures may have up to 2 per cent., or more.

Occurrence. Sulphate ions from soil and sea are the form in which sulphur is assimilated by plants and bacteria. Higher animals accept it only in form of sulphur-containing amino acids, cysteine, cystine, methionine, and thio-lipids. Sulphate esters occur as taurine, in bile, as chondroitin sulphate and mucoitin sulphate, in mucopolysaccharides, and as detoxication solutes, in urine. Sulphur in cyclic form is represented by some vitamins (thiamine, thioctic acid) and antibiotics (the penicillins).

Significance. Sulphur in the form of the thiol function, —SH, is a link-forming element, because of its ability to undergo reversible dehydrogenation to disulphide.

$$\text{Thiol R—SH} + \text{HS—R} \rightleftharpoons \text{R—S—S—R} + 2\text{H}$$

Thiol groups also can act as reversible donors of hydrogen, and thus participate in oxidation-reduction systems. They are concerned in several enzyme systems, including hexokinase, papain, urease, and succinic dehydrogenase. The chief biological thiols are the amino acid cysteine and the tripeptide glutathione.

The toxicity of mercurial and arsenical compounds, such as the war gas lewisite, $Cl.CH : CH.AsCl_2$, depends on the ability of the ·metal to replace hydrogen in tissue thiol groups. This can be overcome by anti-arsenicals, such as British anti-lewisite, or BAL, discovered by R. Peters (1945). BAL, which is 2,3-dithiolpropanol, $HS.CH_2.CH(SH).CH_2.OH$, competes for As or Hg, and diverts the metal from the tissue thiol groups.

Group VII: { **Manganese.**
                 { Halogens: **Fluorine, Chlorine,** Bromine, **Iodine.**

Manganese. Mn, a.n. 25, a.w. 54·93. The earth's crust contains about 1·0 gm. Mn per kg. Sea water has only about 0·001 mg. per litre.
Depending on soil conditions, the manganese content of plants, in mg. per kg. dry material, ranges from less than one up to 250. Representative values are: wheat bran, 100 to 200; beetroot, oats, spinach, wheat grain, 25 to 100; lettuce leaf, 216. The content in cereal grain often equals or exceeds the iron content. This is important, because the seed may be the only source of manganese for the growing plant in poor soil.
The element is unevenly distributed as a universal micro-constituent of animal tissues. Values for fresh material, in mg. Mn per kg. range from 0·1, in muscle, up to 2, in liver. A manganese protein, pinnaglobulin, occurs in the blood of the mussel *Pinna squamosa*.

Significance. Manganese is a constituent of the enzyme arginase, and can function as an activator of other enzymes, including phosphorylase, alkaline phosphatase, dipeptidase, and lactase. As a polyvalent metal, it can function in electron-transfer and oxidation-reduction reactions, and is able to display six different states of valency.
(1) *A Catalyst in Soil.* Manganese is an essential constituent of fertile soil. Its availability depends on the hydrogen ion concentration, and is decreased by soil alkalinity. Manganese ions take part in a soil respiration cycle in which manganous ions, Mn^{2+}, are oxidised to Mn^{3+} and Mn^{4+} by micro-organisms, and subsequently reduced to Mn^{2+} by oxidisable organic compounds in the soil. Manganese also regulates the state and availability of soil iron. The

optimum Fe/Mn ratio is 2/1, imbalance either way leads to deficiency of one or the other metal.

(2) *Plant Growth.* Manganese deficiency retards the synthesis of chlorophyll, and results in chlorosis of leaves and general failure of growth. Specific manganese-deficiency diseases include: " grey-speck " in oats, " speckled-yellow " in sugar beet, and " marsh-spot " in peas. Manganese is required also for assimilation and reduction of nitrate, the chief source of plant nitrogen. Excess of the element is harmful to plants, especially barley.

(3) *Animal Growth.* Manganese is necessary for growth, reproduction, and bone development in higher animals, including, by inference, the human subject. Manganese deficiency in avian nutrition results in perosis (a disorder of the joints, with subsequent deformities), delayed growth, and lowered egg production, with decreased fertility.

The adult human requirement is not known, but is assumed to be about 1 mg. in 24 hours. This is amply provided by the ordinary mixed diet, which supplies 3 to more than 8 mg. daily.

Tea, with a content of 150 to 900 mg. Mn per kg., a third of which is water-soluble, is the richest source in the diet.

Fluorine. F, a.n. 9; a.w. 19·00. Fluorine, the most electro-negative, or electron-attracting of all the elements, forms 0·3 gm. per kg. of the earth's crust. Sea water contains about 1·4 mg. per litre.

Fluorine is a micro-contaminant with no recognised function in the plant kingdom. Values, depending on environment, range from zero to 10 gm. per kg. dry weight. The halogen appears to be universal in higher animals. It accumulates in bone and teeth, where, by displacing OH from the bone salt, hydroxyapatite, $Ca_3(PO_4)_2 \, _3 . Ca(OH)_2$, it forms the more stable fluorapatite. Hence, skeletal fluoride tends to increase with age, in response to dietary intake. The fluoride content of buried bone similarly increases with time, by the slow absorption of soil fluoride; and, knowing the soluble fluoride content of the environment, it is possible to ascribe a date to fossil bone.

Representative values for fresh human bone are from 150 to 560 mg. F per kg. Values for bones and teeth of marine animals are much higher (6 to 16 gm. per kg.), because of the constant exchange-intake from the environment. Values for bone-ash of terrestrial animals range from 300 to 1,400 mg. per kg. Teeth are relatively poorer than bone in F, and enamel contains less than dentine.

Human blood contains 0·2 to 1·4 mg. per kg., which is the fluoride range for fresh, soft tissues.

Significance. (1) *Skeletal.* Fluoride contributes to the hardness of the bones and teeth, and the resistance of dental enamel to decay. In excess, the condition of fluorosis develops, the bones become more brittle, and the enamel acquires a rough and mottled surface. Deficiency can appear in districts where the fluoride content of the drinking water is less than 0·5 mg. per litre (0·5 parts per million), and can be remedied by fluoridation, so as to raise the value to the optimum range of 1·5 to 2 parts per million. Values above 4 lead to dental fluorosis. Dietary sources, in addition to water, are tea (100 mg. per kg.), sea fish, and baking powder made from bone-ash.

(2) *Metabolic.* The fluoride ion, F', in low concentration inhibits many enzymes (esterases, dehydrogenases, and some phosphatases), by combining with the metals necessary for their activation (calcium, magnesium, copper, iron, manganese, zinc). For this reason, fluoride has been used as an antiseptic and a food-preservative, but is not generally suitable. Chronic fluorosis in livestock can arise in high-fluorine areas, and is characterised by skeletal and dental abnormalities that impede the grazing ability of the animal.

Chlorine. Cl, a.n. 17, a.w. 35·46. The earth's crust contains about 0·48 gm. Cl per kg. Sea water contains about 19 gm. Cl per litre. Chloride has been detected in all plants, with the exception of the conifers.

Percentage values vary greatly with soil conditions, and range from 0·004 in wheat ash up to 9 in lettuce ash. There is no evidence that chloride is necessary for plant growth.

All animals contain chloride, concentrations being greatest in lower marine species, and least in some fresh-water fish.

The body of the new-born child contains about 5 gm. Cl, and that of the 70-kg. adult contains about 85 gm.

Values for fresh human tissues and secretions, in gm. Cl per kg., are: blood, entire, 2·8 to 3·2; plasma or serum, 3·4 to 3·8; red corpuscles, 1·8; cerebro-spinal fluid, 4·25; sweat, 0·7 to 5·2; urine, 1·2 to 6; milk, 0·4; gastric juice, 1 to 3; muscle, 0·5 to 1·3; cartilage, 2·5; brain, 1·3.

Significance. Biological chlorine is mostly in ionic form, as Cl', although organic chloro-compounds are known, notably, the antibiotic chloromycetin. The chloride ion is the chief anion of animal cells and tissue fluids, and serves to balance cellular K^+ and extracellular Na^+, and to contribute to the maintenance of the normal osmotic pressure within the organism. Cells readily take up Cl' and K^+, but expel Na^+ by operating a metabolic " pump " mechanism. As a result, Cl' is able to migrate between cell and surrounding fluid in response to changes in the concentration of other ions. This " chloride shift " takes place between the red corpuscles and the plasma during the transport of carbon dioxide in the blood.

Iodine. I, a.n. 53; a.w. 126·92. A micro-constituent of all plants and animals. Seaweeds are rich, and provide an industrial source of the halogen. The kelp ash of *Laminaria digitata* may yield 33 to 40 lb. per ton. Among land plants, values range from 5 mg. to 100 mg. per kg. fresh material, the concentration depending more on environment than on species.

In animals, the thyroid tissue is very rich in iodine. The adult human gland contains about 0·4 mg. per gm. fresh material, which amounts to 8 to 10 mg., or about 60 per cent. of all the iodine in the entire body. Blood contains 0·003 to 0·015 mg. per 100 ml.

Soil values usually fall within the range 0·6 to 8 mg. per kg. Values for sea water are from 0·017 to 0·05 mg. per litre.

Occurrence. Biological iodine occurs chiefly as iodinated derivatives of the amino acid tyrosine, or 4-hydroxyphenylalanine, $HO.C_6H_4.CH_2.CH(NH_2)$. COOH, namely iodogorgoic acid, 3-iodotyrosine, a component of spongin, the skeletal protein of sponges and the coral, Gorgonia. Thyroid iodine is represented by 3,5-diiodotyrosine, 3,5,3'-triiodothyronine, and 3,5,3',5'-tetraiodothyronine, or thyroxine, free or protein-bound as thyroglobulin.

Significance. Iodine is an essential micro-constituent of vertebrates and some invertebrates. Collected and elaborated into hormones by the thyroid gland, it determines the rate of the basal metabolism of the organism.

The minimum adult human requirement is 0·015 mg. I per 24 hours and is assured by the ordinary mixed diet, except in iodine-deficient districts or other goitrogenic circumstances.

Isotopes. The radioactive isotope, iodine-131 (half-life, 8·14 days), obtained by neutron bombardment of tellurium-130, is used as a tracer to measure uptake and distribution of iodine by the thyroid gland and to provide an intracellular source of radiation in the treatment of malignant diseases of the gland.

Group VIII: Iron, Cobalt, Nickel.

Iron. Fe, a.n. 26; a.w. 55·84. The earth's crust contains 50 gm. Fe per kg. Sea water contains about 0·03 mg. per litre.

Iron is a universal micro-constituent of all living organisms. Plant values, in mg. per kg. fresh material, range from less than 4 in fruits to more than 16 in leguminous plants and green leaves. Animal tissues contain 0·01 to 0·1 mg. per gm. cell substance. In addition, iron is an invariable secondary element in all red-blooded animals. The iron content of mammalian blood is about 50 mg. per 100 ml., mostly located in the red corpuscles as hæmoglobin, which contains 0·3 to 0·4 per cent. Fe. Blood plasma contains only 0·06 to 0·22 mg. per 100 ml.

The adult human body contains about 0·005 per cent., or 3 to 4 gm., of which 2 to 2·5 gm. circulate as blood pigment, 1 to 1·5 gm. are stored in liver, spleen, and red marrow, and the rest forms an easily-available " iron pool ".

Values for fresh material, in mg. Fe per kg., are: brain, 0·02; hair, 0·8; kidney, 0·05; liver, 0·08; muscle, 0·04; pancreas, 0·06; spleen, 0·1; milk, bovine, 0·002 to 0·01, human, 0·004; egg, hen, 0·025; egg yolk, 0·07.

Occurrence. Tissue iron exists chiefly in organic form, such as the iron porphyrans, from which are derived the cytochromes that occur in all aerobic cells, the oxygen-transport pigments of blood (hæmoglobins, chlorocruorins, hæmoerythrins), and the oxygen-storage pigment of muscle (myoglobin). Iron porphyrans from the prosthetic group of several enzymes: catalase, peroxidases, cytochrome oxidase, and the flavoprotein oxidases.

Higher animals also possess *ferritin*, an iron-storage protein, containing 20 to 50 per cent. of ferric iron, in liver and spleen; and *transferrin*, an iron-transport protein in blood plasma.

Significance. The primary biological function of iron is the transport of electrons in the respiratory chain of events that terminates in the oxidation of metabolic hydrogen. This is effected by alternate electronation (reduction) and de-electronation (oxidation) of the iron atom in the porphyrin complex (hæm) of the cytochromes: $Fe^{3+} + e' \rightleftharpoons Fe^{2+}$. In higher animals, iron, in the form of hæmoglobin, transports molecular oxygen from the lungs to the tissues.

Iron is necessary for the growth of all plants, and for the operation of the photosynthetic mechanism. A slight deficiency in the soil can diminish greatly the yield of a crop, without causing much change in appearance; a severe deficiency evokes a chlorosis, in which the leaves become poor in chlorophyll. In higher animals, insufficient iron in the diet results in anæmia. The condition is complicated by the fact that some forms of iron in the diet, notably hæmoglobin, are resistant to alimentary digestion, and may escape absorption. Inorganic iron, as sulphate, citrate, or glucuronate, is more readily assimilated.

The human requirement of iron varies with age and sex. It is greatest in growing children, recommended allowance 6–12 mg. daily, and in women during the child-bearing period, recommended allowance 12–15 mg. daily. The requirement of the adult male is normally met by an intake of 10 mg. daily.

The Iron Cycle. Iron occurs on the surface of the earth chiefly as ferrous oxide, FeO, and ferric oxide, Fe_2O_3. Ferrous silicate of rocks and soil are decomposed by atmospheric, CO_2, and yield ferrous carbonate. This is oxidised to ferric oxide, and the liberated CO_2 is returned to the atmosphere. Ferric oxide can act as an oxygen donator to the organic matter of the soil, producing CO_2 and being itself reduced to ferrous compounds. These are redistributed by the soil water and re-oxidised to ferric oxide. Iron thus maintains the circulation of carbon in soil by catalysing its conversion to CO_2, which can be assimilated in turn by soil organisms.

For assimilation by the plant, iron must be in the divalent ferrous state. Iron-uptake is inhibited by excess of manganese, which keeps the metal in the oxidised and unavailable ferric state. For optimum plant growth, the soil ratio Fe/Mn is between 3/2 and 5/2.

Isotopes. The artificial radioactive isotope iron-59 (half-life 47 days) is used as a tracer in metabolic studies.

Cobalt. Co, a.n. 27; a.w. 58·97. A widely distributed micro-constituent of the earth's crust, of which it forms about 0·0001 per cent. Soil values usually lie within the range 0·1 mg. to 100 mg. per kg. Values below 2 are associated with a deficiency syndrome.

Plant values, in mg. Co per kg. fresh material, are: wheat grain and bran, 0·01; rice, polished, 0·006; potato tuber, 0·06; onion bulb, 0·13; spinach leaf, 0·07 to 1·2; beetroot, 0·05 to 0·09; peas and beans, dry, 0·2 to 0·5; coffee bean, dry, 0·04; cacao bean, shelled and dry, 0·5; tea, dry leaf, 0·15; beech, dry leaf, 0·35; beech bark, 1·1.

Plant values are affected considerably by the environment; the element has not been shown to be necessary for growth. Among higher animals, cobalt is an invariable micro-constituent, being concentrated in pancreas, spleen, liver, and kidney, in which the ranges are 0·2 to 0·47 mg. per kg. fresh tissue.

Significance. Cobalt is a component of the cobalamins, or vitamins of the B_{12} group, which are necessary for the construction of the red corpuscles of the blood and which protect against pernicious anæmia. In addition, cobalt is specifically required by some animals, notably sheep and cattle, which develop a deficiency disease, *enzootic marasmus*, when fed on pastures where the soil has less than 0·07 mg. available Co per kg. dry weight. For sheep a 24-hour intake of 0·1 mg., and for cattle an intake of 0·3 to 1 mg. Co protects completely against the disease. Horses appear to be immune.

This cobalt effect is attributed to stimulation of the growth of beneficial micro-organisms in the alimentary tract of the ruminant, thereby providing an autogenous source of vitamins, including the cobalamins.

Isotopes. The radioactive isotope, cobalt-60 (half-life, 5·3 years), is used as a tracer in research, and a source of radiation in research and in therapy.
Only six elements occur in higher animals in concentrations of more than 1 per cent.; O, C, H, N, Ca, and P. About 1 per cent. of the total body weight is made up of K, S, Cl, Na, and Mg. Values for the chief micro-constituents, in mg. per 100 gm., are Zn 3; Mn, 0·3; Cu, 0·2; I, 0·04. The amount of an element present in the entire organism is no indication of its functional status; it may be concentrated chiefly in one region, like iodine in the thyroid gland, or it may activate enzymes that catalyse the production of hormones that govern the entire animal. In this way the mighty commonwealth of the organism is subject to the dictatorship of a few atoms.

General References
Asimov, I. (1954), "Elementary Composition of the Earth's Crust."
Black, D. A. K. (1952), "Sodium Metabolism in Health and Disease." Oxford.

Bear, F. E. (1955), " Chemistry of the Soil." American Chem. Soc. Monographs, No. 126.

Conway, E. J. (1943), " Chemical evolution of the ocean." *Proc. R. Irish Academy*, **48B**, 161.

Fearon, W. R. (1951), " Periodic classifications of the biological elements." *Sci. Proc. R. Dublin Soc.*, **25**, 235.

Glass, B. (1950), " Copper Metabolism." Baltimore.

Harvey, H. W. (1955), " Chemistry and Fertility of Sea Waters." Cambridge.

Henderson, L. J. (1924), " The Fitness of the Environment." London.

Kamen, M. D. (1948), " Radioactive Tracers in Biology." New York.

King, E. J. (1954), " Silicosis." Lectures on the Scientific Basis of Medicine. London.

Libby, W. F. (1952), " Radiocarbon Dating." Chicago.

Lotka, A. J. (1925), " Physical Biology." Baltimore.

Monier-Williams, G. W. (1949), " Trace Elements in Food." London.

Milton, R. F., and W. A. Waters (1949), " Methods of Quantitative Microanalysis." London.

McCance, R. A., and E. M. Widdowson (1951), " Composition of the body." *Brit. med. Bull.*, **7**, 297.

McElroy, W. D., and B. Glass (1951), " Phosphorus Metabolism," Vol. I. Baltimore.

" Potassium." *Proc. Internat. Colloquium* (1954). Paris.

Rankama, K., and Th. Sahuma (1950), " Geochemistry," Chicago.

Shohl, A. (1940), " Mineral Metabolism." New York.

Stiles, W. (1946), " Trace Elements in Plants and Animals." London.

Underwood, E. J. (1956), " Trace Elements in Human and Animal Nutrition." New York.

Vernadsky, V. I. (1929), " La biosphere." Paris.

Vinogradov, A. P. (1945), " Chemical study of the biosphere." *Pedology*, 348.

Webb, D. A. (1937), " Spectrographic analysis of marine invertebrates." *Sci. Proc. R. Dublin Soc.*, **21**, 505.

Webb, D. A., and W. R. Fearon (1937), " Studies in the ultimate composition of biological material." *Sci. Proc. R. Dublin Soc.*, **21**, 487.

Young, R. S. (1956), " Cobalt in biology and biochemistry." *Science Prog.*, **44**, 16.

" Bibliography of the Minor Elements and their Relation to Plant and Animal Nutrition." (1939–). Chilean Nitrate Educational Bureau, New York; London.

Chapter 3 Inorganic Compounds

" One may not doubt that, somehow, Good
Shall come of Water and of Mud;
And, sure, the reverent eye must see
A Purpose in Liquidity."

Rupert Brooke.

With the exception of small amounts of dissolved oxygen and nitrogen, elements do not occur free in living organisms, but are present as inorganic and organic ions and compounds. Inorganic compounds are non-combustible, and, with the exception of the carbonates, do not contain carbon. Organic compounds, on the other hand, are combustible, and all contain carbon and hydrogen.

Animal or vegetable ash after complete incineration is composed entirely of inorganic salts and oxides, and such compounds were the first investigated. Subsequently, analyses were made of tissue extracts and secretions after separation of organic compounds by dialysis or precipitation. Thus it has been shown that metals and other inorganic radicals occur as ions, as organic complexes, and as salts, both in hard tissues, such as bone, and in soft tissues, such as muscle.

Inorganic Biochemical Compounds. The most important are: water, carbon dioxide, the carbonates, carbamates, silicates, sulphates, phosphates, fluorides, and chlorides of the biochemical metals; the nitrogen derivatives, ammonia, nitrous and nitric acid.

Water. Water comes first in quantitative importance among biochemical compounds, and is the solvent in all vital reactions. The average water content of land animals is about 60 to 70 per cent. of the total weight. It may be as low as 10 per cent. in some insects, and in latent forms of life, such as seeds and spores; and may exceed 95 per cent. in lower forms of marine life, such as jelly fish.

The water content of mammalian tissue is roughly proportional to physiological activity, and inversely proportional to fat-content. It decreases with age. The human embryo at the end of the third month contains about 94 per cent. At birth, this has fallen to 67, and in adult life it is fairly constant between 60 and 63 per cent.

The 40 to 45 kg. of water incorporated in the human adult are located chiefly in the muscles. Adolph computes the total turnover of water between tissues, blood and alimentary tract, to range from 4·75 to 17·6 litres *per diem*, involving a loss of 1·05 to 7·8 litres, through the channels of the kidneys, colon, lungs and skin, the average daily output being 3·4 litres. This must be made good by the water obtained from the diet.

Estimation of Water. The water content of a living animal may be found by a " dilution " method, in which a known amount of some harmless, easily-detected solute is administered, and, after sufficient time to ensure uniform distribution has elapsed, its concentration in the plasma is estimated. To obtain values for total body water, solutes such as urea or deuterium oxide are used, since they penetrate the cells and are distributed uniformly in cellular and extracellular fluids.

Although the total water may vary from 50 per cent. of body weight, in obese subjects, to more than 70 per cent. in lean adults, the actual water content is almost a constant percentage of fat-free tissue, namely 82 for the newborn, and 73 for the human adult (McCance and Widdowson, 1951).

Free Water and Bound Water. The organism is a cellular, colloidal structure, and contains water in two chief forms: free water, or *water of solution*; and bound water, or *water of hydration*. Water in the liquid phase includes groups of 5 molecules, the central one being surrounded by four others tetrahedrally placed. Water of hydration consists of water molecules bound to *hydrophil* acceptors: proteins and other tissue colloids, soaps, and some inorganic ions, notably Na^+.

Free water circulates as a transport solvent, and varies according to diet, metabolism, and activity. Bound water is an integral part of the tissues, and reaches a constant value in mature life.

Functions of Water. (1) *Structure*. Water determines the bulk of tissues and organs, and renders them plastic while incompressible.

(2) *Nutrition*. All the food materials of plants and animals are assimilated in aqueous solution. Water, in addition, is the chief quantitative constituent of the dietary.

(3) *Anabolism*. In green plants, water provides the hydrogen used in the synthesis of carbohydrates and other compounds.

(4) *Catabolism*. Water is the major end-product of plant and animal metabolism.

(5) *Transport*. The food materials, the internal secretions, and the waste products of the organism are distributed and excreted in aqueous solution.

(6) *Temperature Stabilisation*. The high specific heat of water enables the organism to store heat and maintain a uniform temperature. The high latent heat of water renders it very efficient as a cooling agent when evaporating from the surface of the organism.

(7) *Solvent*. Water is a powerful ionising solvent, and ionisation is a preliminary state in many of the reactions taking place within the organism.

Ionic Systems. All aqueous solutions can be divided into (*a*) electrolytes, and (*b*) non-electrolytes. Electrolytes are characterised by their ability to conduct electricity, and by the fact that many of their physical properties, such as osmotic effect and boiling point, are in excess of those calculated from the molecular weight of the solute, showing that solution has been attended by an increase in the number of particles dissolved. Non-electrolytes have minimal electric conductivity, and their properties indicate that no increase has taken place in the units of solute. The difference is ascribed to the presence of *ions* in the electrolytes. These are derived spontaneously from the solutes, and their concentration determines the conductivity of the solution. Solutions containing no ions have zero conductivity.

Water is the most effective of the ionising solvents, and even when pure has a low conductivity of its own, indicating a slight degree of ionisation:

$$H_2O \rightleftharpoons H^+ + OH^-.$$

The H^+, or proton, being highly reactive, unites with a water molecule to form the *hydronium* ion, H_3O^+, which is also written $H_2O : H^+$, to show that a proton is in semi-polar union with H_2O, and can be removed easily by a proton acceptor.

Salts, even of weak acids or bases, are almost completely ionised in aqueous solution, consequently all the tissues and fluids of the organism contain a mixture of various ions. Some of these mixtures form natural systems of considerable importance in life. These include:

(1) *The hydrogen ion buffer system*, whereby the acidity and alkalinity of the tissues are kept within proper working range.

(2) *The oxidation-reduction systems* participating in tissue metabolism, and cellular electrolyte balance.

(3) Various *metallo-ionic systems* influencing tissue water content, and physiological sensitivity.

The H-ion Concentration of Living Tissues. Since all forms of life contain water, and all aqueous solutions contain H-ions and OH-ions, it follows that these are invariable constituents of living tissues. In pure water, or in other neutral solutions, the H-ion concentration, usually written $[H^+]$, exactly equals the OH-ion concentration, or $[OH^-]$. In acid solutions, $[H^+]$ is greater than $[OH^-]$. In alkaline solutions, $[OH^-]$ is greater than $[H^+]$. However they may vary individually, the product $[H^+] \times [OH^-]$ has a constant value for a given temperature. That is to say, neither $[H^+]$ nor $[OH^-]$ can ever equal zero. The strongest acid solution obtainable contains OH-ions; and the strongest alkaline solution contains H-ions, present as H_3O^+.

The activities of life are essentially acidogenic in that carbon dioxide is an end-product of the oxidation of organic compounds. In consequence, the H-ion concentration of the tissues and tissue fluids is continually tending to increase, and must be neutralised by appropriate bases if the chemical equilibrium of the organism is to be preserved.

Acids are substances capable of liberating H-ions.

Bases are substances capable of combining with H-ions.

It will be seen from this table that dihydro- and trihydro-acids only release one of their acidic hydrogens in $0.1\ M$ concentrations. By greatly increasing

Acid.	Ions Liberated.	Percentage Ionisation in 0·1 M Solution.	Dissociation Constant (K) $= \dfrac{[H] \times [A]}{[HA]}$.
Hydrochloric .	$H^+ + Cl^-$	>90	>10^6
Sulphuric . .	$H^+ + HSO_4{}^-$	>90	>10^6
Sulphurous .	$H^+ + HSO_3{}^-$	34	$1·7 \times 10^{-2}$
Phosphoric . .	$H^+ + H_2PO_4{}^-$	24	$7·6 \times 10^{-3}$
Acetic . . .	$H^+ + CH_3.COO^-$	1·33	$1·8 \times 10^{-5}$
Carbonic . .	$H^+ + HCO_3{}^-$	0·18	$3·1 \times 10^{-7}$
Hydrogen sulphide	$H^+ + HS^-$	0·09	8×10^{-8}
Boric . . .	$H^+ + H_2BO_3{}^-$	0·01	6×10^{-10}

the dilution of the acid, all the acidic hydrogen is ionised, whatever be the nature of the acid. Acid salts, such as NaH_2PO_4, $NaHSO_4$ and $NaHCO_3$, also liberate H-ions, but to a much lesser degree than the parent acid. The ionisation of very strong acids, such as HCl, can only be computed approximately in concentrated solutions, owing to ionic attraction effects.

In the anhydrous state, acids, such as HCl gas, pure HNO_3 and pure H_2SO_4, contain no free H-ions. On addition of water, or other ionising solvents, ionisation takes place to an extent determined by the *strength* of the acid. Strong acids are almost completely ionised; weak acids, except in great dilution, are only partially ionised. The degree of ionisation is expressed either as (i) the percentage of acid present in the form of free ions, or as (ii) the *dissociation constant* of the acid, K, which is the product of the concentrations of both component ions, $[H] \times [A]$, divided by the concentration of the unionised molecules of acid, $[HA]$.

Bases undergo a corresponding type of ionisation in aqueous solution, and liberate OH-ions, which are able to combine with H-ions to form water. The strength of a base is due to the number of OH-ions liberated at a given dilution. Thus, NaOH and KOH are almost completely ionised in N/10 concentrations, while N/10 NH_4OH, a weak base, is ionised only to the extent of 1·9 per cent.

Salts are compounds formed by the union of acidic and basic radicles. When dissolved in water they are ionised into their constituent positive and negative ions. If the positive ion is derived from a weak base, such as ammonia, it tends to lose a proton, and so increase the H-ion concentration of the solution.

$$NH_4.Cl \rightleftharpoons Cl^- + NH_4{}^+ \rightleftharpoons NH_3 + H^+$$

Ammonium chloride.   Ammonium ion.   Ammonia.

Conversely, the salt of a weak acid and a strong base forms an alkaline solution, owing to the tendency of the weak anion to abstract H-ions from the water, and so increase the OH-ion concentration of the mixture.

$$CH_3.COONa \rightleftharpoons Na^+ + CH_3.COO^- \longrightarrow CH_3.COOH + OH^-.$$
$$+ H_2O$$

Neutral solutions are those in which the H-ion concentration exactly equals the OH-ion concentration. Pure water is taken as the absolute standard of neutrality. At a temperature of 22° C., a litre of water has 10^{-7} *equivalents* of H^+ and 10^{-7} *equivalents* of OH^-. Otherwise expressed, there is 1 gm. of H^+ and 17 gm. OH^- in 10^7, or 10,000,000, litres of water at 22° C.

For brevity, these concentrations in gram-ions per litre are written C_H and C_{OH}. The C_H of pure water, or any neutral solution at 22° C., is 10^{-7}. Any solution with a C_H greater than 10^{-7} is acid; and any solution with a C_H less than this value is alkaline. The product $C_H \times C_{OH}$ always equals 10^{-14}, so either acidity or alkalinity can be expressed in terms of C_H, which is written $[H^+]$.

$$[H^+] \times [OH^-] = k \text{ (a constant)},$$
$$\therefore [H^+] = \frac{k}{[OH^-]}, \text{ and } [OH^-] = \frac{k}{[H^+]}$$

Electrometric Determination of C_H. The reaction, or H-ion value of a solution can be measured by three different types of instrument: (i) *the hydrogen electrode*, (ii) *the quinhydrone electrode*, and (iii) *the " glass " electrode*. In the first method, a platinum electrode with a layer of adsorbed hydrogen is immersed in a solution of known C_H, a similar electrode being immersed in the solution of unknown C_H. The two solutions are connected by a narrow tube containing an electrolyte, KCl, kept from diffusing by means of gelatin or agar. A similar arrangement is used in the quinhydrone electrode (Fig. 1).

H-ions tend to leave each electrode and pass into solution, the extent of their migration being opposed by the concentration of the H-ions already present in each solution. If the two solutions have the same C_H, the same number of H-ions will leave each electrode, and if the electrodes are connected with a suitable potentiometer, no difference in electropotential can be found to exist between them.

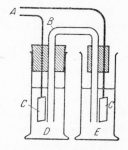

Fig. 1. Cell composed of two quinhydrone electrodes. A—leads to apparatus for measuring E.M.F. B—siphon filled with KCl in agar. C—platinum electrodes. D—solution of known p_H. E — solution of unknown p_H.

If, however, one solution has a lower C_H than the other, that solution will allow more H-ions to migrate from its electrode, which in consequence will become negatively charged when compared with the other electrode.

Knowing the potential difference, E, between the electrodes, and the value of C_H for one solution, the H-ion concentration in the other solution can be found from the formula, in which C_H^1 is the H-ion concentration in the more acid solution:

$$E = 0.0577 \, (\log_{10} C_H^1 - \log_{10} C_H^2) \text{ volts.}$$

It is now customary to employ the symbol pH instead of the more cumbersome $-\log_{10}C_H$, when the formula becomes

$$- E = 0{\cdot}0577\ (pH^1 - pH^2),\ \text{or}\ pH^1 = pH^2 - \frac{E}{0{\cdot}0577}.$$

In the quinhydrone method, the platinum electrodes are not kept coated with hydrogen, but, instead, a little quinhydrone $(C_6H_4O_2 . C_6H_6O_2)$ is added to each solution. Quinhydrone is a compound, the oxidation-reduction state of which depends on the C_H of its solvent, and this in turn affects the potential of the immersed electrode. The readings and calculation are similar to those of the hydrogen electrode method, and the procedure is more convenient, but has the serious limitation of being inapplicable to alkaline solutions, which destroy the quinhydrone.

In the " glass " electrode method, the two solutions are separated by means of a thin glass membrane, and the potential difference of the electrodes is measured by means of a specially sensitive potentiometer.

The pH Notation. The reaction of any solution or tissue can be expressed as 1×10^{-n} gm. H^+ per litre. In practice, this is abbreviated, and written in terms of the exponent n, which is called the pH of the solution. Otherwise defined, pH is equal to the logarithm of the volume in litres of solution that contains 1 gm. H^+, or, more briefly,

$$pH = -\log_{10}C_H, \text{ and } C_H = 10^{-pH}.$$

True neutrality at 22° C. is pH 7, and 7 is the logarithm of 10,000,000, the volume of water in litres that contains 1 gm. H^+. The more acid the solution the smaller will be the volume containing 1 gm. H^+, and the lower the pH. Hence, *all acidic solutions have a* pH *value below* 7, *and all alkaline solutions have a* pH *value above* 7.

To appreciate the pH notation it is important to remember that pH *decreases* with *increase* in acidity, and, furthermore, since pH is logarithmic, each change in a pH unit represents a ten-fold increase or decrease in C_H.

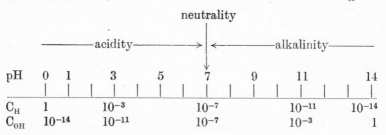

The pH Scale. H-ion concentration, or *actual acidity*, of a solution must be distinguished clearly from *available* or *titration acidity*, which is measured by finding the amount of alkali required to neutralise the solution. The pH value depends on the quality as well as the quantity of the acid; the titration value depends only on the quantity of total available acid. That is to say, pH is a measure of the number of acidic ions, while titration acidity is a measure of the number of acid molecules present, irrespective of whether they are ionised or not.

Decinormal HCl is ionised to the extent of about 90 per cent., and has a pH of about 1·04; decinormal acetic acid in only ionised to the extent of about 1·3 per cent. and has a pH of about 2·85.

Similarly, N/1 HCl (3·65 per cent., pH = 0·09) is a corrosive liquid, while N/1 $CH_3.COOH$ (6·0 per cent., pH = 2·37) resembles the weak vinegar that it so often impersonates.

Equal volumes of decinormal hydrochloric and acetic acid have the same neutralising power for alkalies, although one is a very strong acid and the other is a very weak acid.

Biologically, the actual reaction or pH of a solution is more significant than the neutralising power in terms of a standard acid or alkali.

Actual Acidity

Depends only on the concentration of free H-ions present.

Estimated electrometrically or colorimetrically.

Expressed in terms of [H+] or of pH.

Available Acidity

Depends on the number of acid molecules present, irrespective of ionisation.

Estimated by titration with standard alkali.

Expressed in terms of alkali required to neutralise a given volume.

Neutralisation Curves. When a strong acid is titrated with a strong base, and the accompanying changes in pH are measured, a characteristic curve is obtained showing an enormous alteration in pH near the neutral point. A single drop (0·05 ml.) of decinormal acid or alkali is sufficient to shift the pH value down or up by about six units. When a weak acid is titrated with a weak base, a different type of curve is obtained, in which the equilibrium point is reached gradually, and there are no sudden changes in pH.

Buffer Systems. Solutions of weak acids and their salts, or weak bases and their salts,

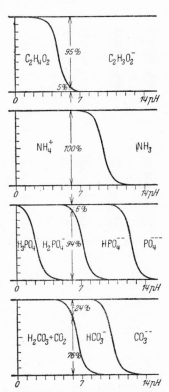

FIG. 2. State of acids and bases at different pH values for acetic acid, ammonia, phosphoric acid and carbonic acid.

constitute buffer systems, so called because they are able to neutralise alkalis or acids without undergoing marked change in pH. For example, sodium acetate can depress the acidity of HCl, and is used for this purpose in the phenyl-hydrazine test for sugars (p. 450).

The H-ion concentration of a typical buffer system can be found from the equation,

$$C_H = K\frac{[\text{free acid}]}{[\text{anion}]}$$

where K is the dissociation constant of the acid.

In a half-neutralised solution, the concentrations of free acid and anion are equal, and C_H becomes equal to K. Hence the dissociation constant of an acid (or a base) can be found by determining the C_H or pH of a half-neutralised solution. The pH of such a solution is termed the pK, or dissociation exponent of the acid (or the base, when an alkali is half-neutralised). Furthermore, the C_H of a half-neutralised solution is almost independent of dilution, since it is determined by the dissociation constant which, unlike the degree of dissociation, does not alter with dilution. Thus, a solution containing equivalent amounts of acetic and acetate ions has a pH of 4·75, and a solution containing equivalent amounts of ammonium ions and ammonia molecules has a pH of 9·48, (Fig. 2).

(1) *The Acid Carbonate System.*

$$HCO_3^- \begin{cases} + \text{ H}^+ \quad (\text{acid}) \rightarrow \overset{(\text{Weak acid.})}{H_2CO_3} \leftrightarrows H_2O + CO_2 \\ + \text{ OH}^- (\text{base}) \rightarrow CO^{2-}_3 + H_2O \end{cases}$$

(2) *The Acid Phosphate System.*

$$H_2PO_4^- \begin{cases} + \text{ H}^+ \rightarrow H_3PO_4 \\ + \text{ OH}^- \rightarrow HPO^{2-}_4 + H_2O \end{cases}$$

(3) *The Protein System*

Of these systems, protein buffers are probably of greatest importance in tissues and the blood; the carbonates come next and constitute the bulk of the alkaline reserve of the animal. Phosphate and phosphagen systems operate during muscular contraction. In blood plasma the normal ratio of HCO_3^-: H_2CO_3 is 20 : 1.

At the reaction of blood, pH 7·4, this acid carbonate system is not exerting its maximum effect, but as the pH of the blood decreases the buffer action becomes more powerful, and thus constitutes an important alkaline reserve of the organism. The acid phosphate system is more effective at pH 7·4, but the low concentration of phosphates in blood renders the system almost insignificant.

Proteins and amino acids, the structural units of the protein molecule, owe their buffering power to the fact that they exist in solution as dipolar or *zwitter*-ions, each of which carries positively charged —NH$^+_3$ groups and negatively charged —COO⁻ groups. The —NH^+_3 group acts as an acid by releasing H^+ to form H_2O by union with the OH^- ion provided by a base; while the —COO⁻ group acts as a base by combining with a proton, so as to form the un-ionised carboxyl group —COOH.

$$R\underset{\diagdown \text{COOH} \leftarrow \text{H}^+ +}{\overset{\diagup \text{NH}_3^+}{}} \qquad R\underset{\diagdown \text{COO}^-}{\overset{\diagup \text{NH}_3^+ + \text{OH}^- \rightarrow}{}} \qquad R\underset{\diagdown \text{COO}^-}{\overset{\diagup \text{NH}_2 + \text{H}_2\text{O}}{}}$$

Amino acid
(*dipolar ion*)

The modern definition makes it possible to arrange all acids and bases in one table in order of their dissociation, and their strength can be expressed either in pH units or in terms of [H^+] or of [OH^-].

Calculation of pH from K. By the law of mass action,

$$K[AC] = [A^-] \times [C^+].$$

The symbols in brackets denote *concentrations* in *mols* per litre, where a *mol* is the formula-weight in grams (gram-molecules or gram-ions). [AC] is the undissociated salt or acid, and the derived anions and cations are denoted by [A^-] and by [C^+], respectively.

For exact work, it is necessary to express concentration in terms of *activity*, obtained by multiplying each concentration by a special factor, the *activity constant*, which depends on the size and electric properties of the particles and the nature of the solvent.

K, the *ionisation constant, dissociation constant*, or, for acids and bases, the *affinity constant*, has a definite value for each electrolyte at a given temperature. When it refers to an acid or a base it is usually written K_a (acid dissociation constant) or K_b (base dissociation constant). Acids with more than one ionisable H have more than one K_a, each distinguished by a suffix to denote the ionisation of a second or third H^+.

From the table on p. 36 it will be seen that the K_a values for the common biological acids are very small numbers and, for simplicity in classification, it is now usual to express K_a and K_b in terms of their negative logarithms, pK_a and pK_b, as is done in the pH notation for expressing [H^+] and [OH^-]. Here, also, the lower the value of pK the greater the value of K and the stronger the acid or the base.

$$K = 10^{-pK} \; ; \; [H^+] = 10^{-pH}.$$

Representative pK_a values for biological acids at ordinary temperature are: formic, 3·75; lactic, 3·8; benzoic, 4·2; acetic, 4·75; uric, 5·8. Values for acids with more than one acidic hydrogen are: oxalic (pK¹) 1·23, (pK²) 4·19; phosphoric, (pK¹) 2·12, (pK²) 7·2, (pK³) 12·3.

Values of pK_b for common bases are: ammonium hydroxide, 4·74; methylamine, 3·36; calcium hydroxide, (pK²) 1·51.

No acid, or base, however strong, is completely ionised in concentrated solution. The effects of dilution in promoting ionisation can be shown by comparing the observed values for a strong acid, such as HCl (K > 10), and a weak acid, $CH_3.COOH$ (K = 1.8×10^{-5}), with values calculated for an imaginary acid (K = ∞), which is supposed to be completely ionised at all dilutions.

Concentration	Imaginary Acid [H⁺]	pH	HCl [H⁺]	pH	CH₃.COOH [H⁺]	pH
10 N . .	1×10^1	−1·0	?		?	
N . .	1×10^0	0·0	8×10^{-1}	0·1	4.3×10^{-3}	2·37
N/10 .	1×10^{-1}	1·0	9.1×10^{-2}	1·04	1.3×10^{-3}	2·88
N/100 .	1×10^{-2}	2·0	9.5×10^{-3}	2·02	4.3×10^{-4}	3·37
N/1,000 .	1×10^{-3}	3·0	9.7×10^{-4}	3·01	1.6×10^{-4}	3·87
N/10,000	1×10^{-4}	4·0	9.8×10^{-5}	4·01	4.3×10^{-5}	4·37

This table shows that a change in pH by one unit represents a ten-fold increase or decrease in [H⁺]. Although [H⁺] in aqueous solutions can never equal zero, since the product [H⁺] × [OH⁻] is a constant and has a real value, it is possible for pH to be 0·0, or even −1, if the solution is sufficiently rich in H⁺.

The strength of an acid is determined by the bond holding the proton, H⁺, to the base. The hydrogen atom contains one proton and one electron; if the electron be lost, the residual proton, H⁺, has a very small volume, and can pack more closely and be held more firmly than larger ions, such as Na^+. Hence, $CH_3.COONa$ ionises freely as $CH_3.COO^-$ and Na^+, while $CH_3.COOH$ has its H⁺ firmly attached, ionises feebly, and is a weak acid. In dilute acetic acid, the acetate anions and the water molecules compete for the H⁺, but since the acetate is more strongly basic, even in N/100 dilution over 90 per cent. of the protons remain attached to the acetate ion when equilibrium is reached.

$$CH_3.COOH + H_2O \longleftrightarrow CH_3.COO^- + H_2OH^+.$$

Calculation of pH from [H⁺]. Given that [H⁺] for N/10 HCl is 9.1×10^{-2}, find the pH.

$$10^{-pH} = [H^+] = 9.1 \times 10^{-2} \text{ for N/10 HCl,}$$
$$\text{pH N/10 HCl} = -\log_{10}[H^+] = -(\log_{10} 9.1 + \log_{10} 10^{-2})$$
$$= -(0.959 - 2) = 1.041.$$

Calculation of [H⁺] from pH. Since pH is the negative logarithm of a number, and the logarithm tables are of positive numbers, the pH value must be subtracted from the next highest integer, so as to give two terms, a negative integer and a positive fraction.

Given that the pH of N/10 $CH_3.COOH$ is 2·886, find the $[H^+]$.

pH = 2·886 = $-3 + 0·114$.
$[H^+] = 10^{-pH} = 10^{-2.886} = 10^{-3} \times 10^{0.114} = 10^{-3} \times 1·3$,
since 0·114 = $\log_{10} 1·3$.
Hence, the $[H^+]$ of N/10 acetic acid is $1·3 \times 10^{-3}$.

Calculation of pH of Buffer Systems. The mass action equation, $[H^+] = K_a[HA]/[A^-]$ may be written

$$\log_{10}[H^+] = \log_{10}K_a + \log_{10}\frac{[HA]}{[A^-]}, \text{ or } -pH = -pK_a + \log_{10}\frac{[HA]}{[A^-]}.$$

Rearranged, this becomes the *Henderson-Hasselbalch equation*,

$$pH = pK_a + \log_{10}\frac{[A^-]}{[HA]}.$$

For a buffer solution containing a weak acid and its ions, K_a is almost constant within a wide dilution range, and can be measured. Hence, knowing the components of a buffer mixture, the pH can be found, or conversely, knowing the pH, the composition can be calculated.

Maximum buffer effect occurs when $[A^-] = [HA]$, that is, when the acid is half neutralised.

Here, $[A^-]/[HA] = 1$, and $\log_{10}\frac{[A^-]}{[HA]} = 0$, and, by substitution

in the equation, $pH = pK_a$.

H-ion Indicators. These are reagents that change colour sharply at particular changes in H-ion concentration. A series has been prepared covering the entire range from extreme acidity, pH 0·1, to extreme alkalinity, pH 13·5 [*cf.* Appendix].

The H-ion Concentration of the Environment. (1) *The Ocean.* Sea water is slightly alkaline, the usual range being pH 7·75 to pH 8·25. It is increased by the photosynthetic activity of marine organisms, and Atkins has recorded a value as high as pH 9·7 in the waters of Plymouth Sound.

(2) *The Soil.* Fertile soil has a range of about pH 3 to pH 10. Values as acid as pH 1·7 have been found in America, and as alkaline as pH 11 in Egypt. Chalk soil can never be more alkaline than pH 8·4.

The pH of soil is of primary importance in determining the growth and distribution of plants. Sugar beet, for example, grows best between pH 8 and pH 6; flax grows best between pH 6 and pH 4.

The H-ion Concentration of the Organism. As a rule, plant tissues and fluids are acid, the average value being about pH 5·2; whereas animal tissue fluids, and resting tissues tend to be stabilised at a slight degree of alkalinity, about pH 7 to pH 7·5. Metabolism is generally acidogenic in character owing to the formation directly or indirectly of carbonic acid.

43

Representative pH values for human tissues and secretions at body-temperature, 37° C.: blood plasma, cerebro-spinal fluid, 7·35 to 7·45; gastric juice, 1 ± 0·3 (adult), 5 (infant); hepatic bile, 8·0 ± 0·5; intestinal juice, 7·3 ± 0·3; pancreatic juice, 7·8 ± 0·3; duodenal contents, 6·5 ± 0·5; saliva, 6·7 ± 0·4; milk, fresh, 6·8 ± 0·2; sweat, 6·0 ± 0·7; urine, 6·2 ± 1·7; intestinal excreta, 7 to 7·5; cellular contents, cytoplasm, 6·8 to 7·3, nuclei, 7·5 to 7·8.

Blood plasma is kept stabilised within the narrow range pH 7·4 ± 0·05; the extremes compatible with life are ± 0·4, hence blood is always a slightly alkaline medium.

Pure gastric juice is remarkable in having an acidity nearly as great as N/10 hydrochloric acid; conversely, egg-white, with a pH value of 8 to 9·5, is the most alkaline solution known to occur naturally.

Control of H-ion Concentration in Man. Four main factors operate:—

(1) The buffer systems of fluids and tissues.

(2) The respiratory excretion of CO_2 by the lungs.

(3) The compensatory excretion of acids or bases by the kidney.

(4) The metabolic formation of ammonia in the kidney and, probably, elsewhere.

Carbon Dioxide and Carbonic Acid. Oxidised carbon circulates in five forms within the organism: the anhydride CO_2, as a gas and as a solute; carbonic acid $(HO)_2CO$; acid carbonate, $HO.COO^-$; carbamate, $R.NH.COO^-$; and is immobilised in the skeleton as normal carbonates, MCO_3, where M is a divalent metal.

Gaseous carbon dioxide is the form in which the element carbon enters the plant and escapes from the animal. Within the organism it is dissolved in the tissue fluids, and hydrated to form carbonic acid, which in turn is neutralised by the buffer systems.

Under ordinary conditions of life, an adult man of 60 to 70 kg. excretes 750 to 900 gm. of CO_2 *per diem*. This corresponds to a level of 45 to 56 ml. CO_2 per 100 ml. arterial blood, and a CO_2 pressure in the alveolar air of the lungs of 40 mm. Hg.

Carbonic acid is the principal " volatile " acid produced in metabolism. It is sufficiently strong to form stable salts with the metals, and yet sufficiently weak to constitute one of the buffer systems whereby the neutrality of the organism is maintained.

The reaction of the blood is being thrust continuously towards the acid side by the CO_2 liberated during metabolism, and this increase in acidity, in turn, serves to stimulate the respiratory mechanism whereby CO_2 is eliminated. Hence, this waste product is utilised as long as it is in the organism.

Carbon Dioxide Transport by the Blood. If pure water is exposed to carbon dioxide at a partial pressure of 40 mm. Hg, which is the usual alveolar value, the gas dissolves until the resulting solution of carbonic acid has a pH of 4·7 for ordinary temperature. If, however, blood be exposed to the same partial pressure of gas the resulting solution has a pH of about 7·4, which is only slightly less than the value for untreated blood. That is to say, blood has a considerable buffering for H-ions. But blood is the transport medium for the elimination of carbon dioxide by the lungs, and must be provided with some mechanism for the rapid escape of the gas. When blood is exposed to reduced pressure, carbon dioxide is released in two ways: (i) rapidly from the carbonic acid, and (ii) slowly from the acid carbonates in solution. The speed of the first reaction led Meldrum and Roughton to suspect the existence of a catalyst, which they later isolated from the red corpuscles, and named **carbonic anhydrase** because it catalysed the reversible reaction,

$$H_2CO_3 \rightleftharpoons H_2O + CO_2.$$

When blood is previously treated with dilute cyanide or other appropriate enzyme inhibitors, and then exposed to a vacuum, the amount of rapidly-released carbon dioxide is diminished, whereas the slowly-released carbon dioxide is unaffected.

From this it is concluded that carbon dioxide is transported in the blood in three distinct forms: (*a*) as stable acid carbonate, (*b*) as unstable carbonic acid, readily dehydrated by an enzyme, and (*c*) as an unstable salt, not attacked by the enzyme. This salt has been identified as a carbamate produced by union between CO_2 and an uncharged —NH_2 group, such as occurs in hæmoglobin in slightly alkaline solution.

$$CO_2 + H_2N.R \rightleftharpoons HO.CO.NH.R$$
Carbamino derivative

Carbon Dioxide Assimilation. Green plants and a few specialised pigmented bacteria readily assimilate free CO_2 as their chief source of carbon, and subsequently elaborate it into organic compounds during photosynthesis. CO_2 is also assimilated, though to a much lesser extent, by many other cells and tissues, including those of the higher animal. Thus, by a reversible reaction of the type discovered by Wood and Werkman:

$$CO_2 + \underset{\text{Pyruvic Acid}}{CH_3.CO.COOH} \underset{\text{(decarboxylation)}}{\overset{\text{(carboxylation)}}{\rightleftharpoons}} \underset{\text{Oxaloacetic Acid}}{HOOC.CH_2.CO.COOH,}$$

CO_2 can re-enter the metabolic cycle.

A converse process is responsible for the liberation of CO_2 in plant and animal respiration.

IONIC SYSTEMS

Ions are electrically charged particles formed by the spontaneous dissociation of acids, bases and salts, when dissolved in water or other ionising solvents. Ions may be classified according to sign as: (i) positively-charged *cations*, R^+, which migrate to the cathode, or negative electrode; (ii) negatively-charged *anions*, R^-, which migrate to the anode, or positive electrode; and (iii) doubly charged dipolar, or *zwitter*-ions, $^+R^-$, which, when their charges are equal, migrate to neither electrode.

The principal biological ions are:—

(1) *Metallic cations*: Na^+, K^+, Ca^{2+}, Mg^{2+}.

(2) *Non-metallic cations*: H^+, NH_4^+, dipolar ions in acid solution.

(3) *Non-metallic anions*: Cl^-, HCO_3^-, $H_2PO_4^-$, aliphatic and other acid radicles ($R.COO^-$), dipolar ions in alkaline solution.

(4) *Dipolar ions*: Proteins and amino acids ($^+H_3N.R.COO^-$).

The other biological elements, such as Mn, Fe, Cu and I, occur as compounds or in very low ionic concentration.

The ionic composition of the tissues and tissue fluids determines: (*a*) conductivity, (*b*) buffering power and pH, (*c*) oxidation-reduction conditions, (*d*) membrane potential and, in part, (*e*) osmotic pressure.

Chloride Shift. Hamburger observed that when carbon dioxide enters the blood there is an accompanying migration of Cl^- from plasma to corpuscles. Conversely, when carbon dioxide escapes from blood there is a migration of Cl^- from corpuscles to plasma, although this change takes place against the concentration gradient for Cl^-. In outline, this " chloride shift " is due to (*a*) diffusion of carbonic acid into the corpuscle, where it is ionised by the intracellular buffer systems, which accept H^+ from the acid; (*b*) accumulation of HCO_3^- ions within the corpuscle until their concentration exceeds that of the HCO_3^- ions in the plasma; (*c*) diffusion of HCO_3^- ions from corpuscle to plasma, where they displace a corresponding number of Cl^- ions, which enter the corpuscle to balance the H^+ ions derived from the carbonic acid.

The Donnan Membrane Effect. When a simple electrolyte, such as sodium chloride, is separated from its solvent by a permeable membrane, ionic diffusion takes place until equilibrium is reached, when the product of the concentrations of the ions on either side of the membrane is the same, or $[Na^+] \times [Cl^-] = [Na^+] \times [Cl^-]$. Furthermore, by analysing samples from each side, it can be shown that the sodium concentration $[Na^+]$ on one side equals that on the other side of the membrane, $[Na^+]$, and also that $[Cl^-]$ equals $[Cl^-]$. If, however, a non-diffusible ion, such as a stearic acid radicle, $C_{17}H_{35}.COO^-$, be present on one side of the membrane it will inhibit the migration of some of the ions of the opposite sign, in this instance, Na^+. When equilibrium has set in, $[Na^+] \times [Cl^-] = [Na^+] \times [Cl^-]$, as before; but now $[Na^+]$ is greater than $[Na^+]$ and consequently $[Cl^-]$ must be greater than $[Cl^-]$.

$$\frac{Na^+ + Cl^-}{\underline{Na}^+ + \underline{Cl}^-} \qquad \frac{C_{17}H_{35}.COO^- + Na^+ + Cl^-}{\underline{Na}^+ + \underline{Cl}^-}$$

Simple equilibrium   Complex equilibrium

$$\left[Na^+\right] = \left[\underline{Na}^+\right] \qquad \left[Na^+\right] > \left[\underline{Na}^+\right] \qquad \left[\underline{Cl}^-\right] > \left[Cl^-\right]$$

This unequal concentration of the ions leads to a difference in potential between the solutions on either side of the membrane, which can be calculated or estimated electrometrically. The phenomenon was first predicted and experimentally verified by F. G. Donnan, in 1911, and is known as the Donnan Effect.

The physiological consequences of membrane potentials and ionic displacements are very great, and these processes modify or determine many forms of activity, including muscle contraction, nerve conduction, gland secretion, as well as general cell growth.

Every living cell has an endowment of ions, and its functioning is dependent on and modified by the ionic composition and balance of its environment, as shown by the cation relationship: Na^+ and K^+ are mutually antagonistic,

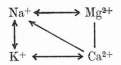

and may antagonise or be antagonised by Mg^{2+} or Ca^{2+}, which are themselves antagonistic or synergic according to conditions.

The recognition of metallo-ionic balance began with the work of Ringer on the maintenance of the heart beat by perfusion.

For the mammalian heart, a perfusion fluid must contain approximately: NaCl, 0·9 per cent.; KCl, 0·04 per cent.; $CaCl_2$, 0·024 per cent.; and $NaHCO_3$, 0·01 to 0·03 per cent. This mixture constitutes Locke's solution.

Isotonic NaCl by itself cannot maintain tissue function, but evokes toxic effects which are overcome by calcium when in the proportion of 1 Ca^{2+} to 50 Na^+.

Ca^{2+} affects the contraction process, and if excessive causes a decrease in relaxation, and ultimate cessation in a state of extreme contraction or " calcium rigor ".

K^+ is antagonistic to Ca, and if excessive causes a weakening of the beat, and cessation in a state of complete relaxation. Cl^- and Na^+ maintain the osmotic pressure of the fluid. $NaHCO_3$ forms a buffer system to keep the pH on the side of slight alkalinity. Rise in $[H^+]$ causes increased relaxation and weakening of beat; fall in $[H^+]$ causes decrease in relaxation.

Anion-Cation Balance. All tissues, secretions and mixed salt solutions contain a variety of electro-negative anions and electro-positive cations, and, however the composition may alter, the total number of ionic positive charges is balanced by an equivalent number of negative charges. If this were not so, the solution would be positively or negatively charged with respect to its environment. Electrolyte unbalance may occur locally during secretion, muscle-contraction, and the passage of a nerve impulse, and the resulting changes in electric potential can be recorded. A specialised example is seen in the electric organ of some fish, which is a modified form of muscle tissue capable, in the *Torpedo*, or *Stinging Ray*, of developing a brief potential of about 200 volts, when stimulated.

Electrolyte balance was formerly termed *acid-base* balance, in accordance with the old classification of all cations as basic and all anions as acidic. Since it refers to the actual concentrations of the ions, it is expressed not in terms of percentages but in terms of equivalent weights.

A **Mole,** or gram-molecule, is the molecular or ionic formula-weight of a substance in grams. A solution of molar concentration, M, contains one mole per litre.

An **Equivalent** weight, or equiv., is obtained by dividing the formula-weight by the valency of the ion, and may be in gram-equivalents, g.equiv., or in milligram-equivalents, milliequivalents, or m.equiv.

Thus, a Ca^{2+} solution of molar concentration denotes 40 gm. Ca^{2+} per litre, while a solution of 1 equiv. per litre is 20 gm. Ca^{2+} per litre, and one of 1 m.equiv. per litre is 20 mg. Ca^{2+} per litre.

Anion-Cation Concentration in Sea Water

	Na^+	K^+	Ca^{2+}	Mg^{2+}	Cl^-	CO_{23}^{2-}	SO_4^{2-}	PO_4^{3-}
Gm./litre .	11·0	0·4	0·4	1·3	19·3	0·09	2·7	0·015
M. equiv./litre	480	10	20	108	535	18	56	0·16

Total cation charge . . . 618	Total anion charge . 609

The failure of the anions and cations to balance shows that some values are incorrect in the analysis.

The calculation of anion-cation balance provides a check on chemical analysis. If the total charges do not balance, it shows that some species of ion has been overlooked, or wrongly estimated.

Solubility Product. When the solubility is less than 0·01 gm. molecule per litre, a salt is described as " sparingly soluble ". In saturated solutions, the product of the total concentrations of the ions is a constant value for a given temperature, and is termed the *solubility-product*, S_p. Thus, for the system:

$AgCl \rightleftharpoons Ag^+ + Cl^-$, $S_{AgCl} = [Ag^+] [Cl^-] = 1·2 \times 10^{-10}$, at 20° C.,

where S_{AgCl} is the solubility-product of silver chloride, and $[Ag^+]$ and $[Cl^-]$ are measured in g. ions per litre, and represent a solubility of about 1·5 mg. AgCl per litre.

A solution is not fully saturated until the product of the concentration of the ions reaches the value of the solubility-product of the parent salt. When this is exceeded, the solution is supersaturated and the salt tends to precipitate. Precipitation thus can be effected by increasing the concentration of either ion until the value of the S_p is reached. Solubility-products are of interest in animal biochemistry in regard to the deposition of calcium phosphate and carbonate during bone-formation, and the production of renal calculi.

Representative values for S_p at 20° C. are: CaF_2, $3\cdot2 \times 10^{-11}$; $BaSO_4$, $1\cdot2 \times 10^{-10}$; CaC_2O_4, $3\cdot8 \times 10^{-9}$; $CaCO_3$, $1\cdot7 \times 10^{-8}$; $MgCO_3$, $2\cdot6 \times 10^{-5}$; FeS, $1\cdot5 \times 10^{-19}$; $MgNH_4.PO_4$, $2\cdot5 \times 10^{-13}$.

The Inland Sea. In 1889, Bunge, the Swiss chemist, outlined a theory to explain the occurrence and distribution of the biological metals. Life, he assumed, arose in the tepid waters of a primæval ocean, and during the slow evolution of the invertebrates and primal vertebrates the tissues became adapted to a saline environment. When life eventually migrated from sea to land, the later vertebrates carried the chemical legacy of a marine ancestry. In the ocean the concentration of sodium chloride exceeds that of any other solute; consequently, it is the chief inorganic constituent of the tissue fluids of the animal. That is to say, the internal medium of life is not water, but diluted sea water.

In 1904, Macallum independently reached the conclusion that " the blood-plasma of vertebrates and invertebrates with a closed circulatory system is, in its inorganic salts, but a reproduction of the sea-water of the remote geological period in which the prototype representative of such animal forms first made their appearance."

He supported his conclusion by a series of analyses of blood-serum and sea water:—

Solution.	Percentage of Element.				
	Na	Ca	K	Mg	Cl
Sea water . .	1·072	0·042	0·038	0·136	1·932
Human serum . .	0·302	0·009	0·020	0·002	0·389
Sea water, diluted 1 : 3	0·357	0·014	0·012	0·045	0·644

The marked difference between the high concentration of magnesium in sea water and its low concentration in all vertebrate tissue fluids is explained by Macallum as being due to the selective action of the kidney, which stabilised the composition of the tissue fluids at a time when the magnesium content of the ocean was less than its present value.

The composition of the ocean in relation to organic evolution has been discussed by Conway (1943–7), according to whom the levels of H^+, Na^+, K^+, and HCO_3^- and Cl^- in the body fluids of higher animals are imposed by the composition, metabolism and general requirements of the surrounding tissues, while the levels of Ca^{2+}, Mg^{2+}, and HPO_4^{2-} are imposed by the composition of the skeleton, and the necessity for keeping the blood plasma saturated with the constituents of the bone salts. Nevertheless, the universal distribution and functional importance of the salts of the ocean in the blood and tissues of animals does suggest a long-continued historical association with an immemorial marine environment.

> " Hence in a season of calm weather,
> Though inland far we be,
> Our souls have sight of that immortal sea
> Which brought us hither."

General References

Bolam, H. T. S. (1942), " Donnan Equilibrium." London.

Britton, H. T. S. (1942), " Hydrogen Ions," 4th ed. London.

Conway, E. J. (1945), " Physiological significance of inorganic levels in the internal medium of animals." *Biol. Rev.*, **20**, 56. Cambridge.

Conway, E. J. (1947), " Exchanges of K, Na, and H ions between the cell and its environment." *Irish J. Med. Sci.*, October–November.

Gortner, R. A. (1949), " Outlines of Biochemistry." 3rd ed. New York; London.

Harvey, H. W. (1945), " Chemistry and Physics of Sea Waters," 2nd ed. Cambridge.

Macallum, A. B. (1926), " Palaeochemistry of the body fluids and tissues." *Physiol. Rev.*, **6**, 316.

McCance, R. A. (1936), " Experimental sodium chloride deficiency." *Proc. roy. Soc.*, B, 814, 245.

Pantin, C. F. (1931), " Origin of the composition of the body fluids in animals." *Biol. Rev.*, **6**, 459. Cambridge.

Peters, J. P. (1935), " Body Water." Springfield, Illinois.

" Progress in Biophysics and Biophysical Chemistry." Ed. by J. A. V. Butler. (1956).

Robertson, J. D., and Webb, D. A. (1939), " Micro-analysis of sea water and body fluids." *J. exp. Biol.* **16**, 155.

Robinson, J. R. (1952), " Active transport of water in living systems." *Biol. Rev.*, **28**, 158. Cambridge.

Chapter 4 Solutions and Colloidal Systems

All the chemical reactions associated with life take place between substances in aqueous solutions and aqueous colloidal systems, and the properties of these solutions and systems largely determine tissue organisation and function.

Solutions are micro-homogeneous mixtures the composition of which may vary within certain limits of saturation.

The characteristic of a micro-homogeneous mixture is that its constituents cannot be separated by mechanical methods, such as sedimentation or filtration. In the nomenclature of physical chemistry, a true solution is *monophasic*, all its constituents being present as part of the same physical state, or *phase*.

The constituent present in excess is termed the *solvent*, the other constituents being the *solutes*. In a true solution the solvent is usually a liquid, but may be a solid, as in the so-called " solid solutions " represented by glasses and alloys. The solutes, or dissolved constituents, may be gases, liquids or solids, the ultimate state of the solution (liquid or solid) being determined by the state of the solvent. The composition of a solution is limited by the solubility of the solutes, a critical point being reached when the solution is saturated in regard to a particular solute, the excess of which remains undissolved or separates out from the saturated solution, and may be removed by sedimentation or filtration. These heterogeneous mixtures are said to be *polyphasic* in that they contain mechanically-separable forms of matter.

Structure. The solute particles in a solution may be present as non-ionised molecules, such as sugar, or as electrically charged ions, three types of which exist: (i) positively charged cations, such as H^+, Na^+, and Ca^{2+}; (ii) negatively charged anions, such as OH^- and Cl^-; and (iii) dipolar, or *zwitter*-ions, such as amino acids, $^+R^-$, which carry charges of opposite electric sign.

Conductivity. The electrical conductivity of the solution is determined by the nature and concentration of the solute particles. Solutions of non-ionised molecules or dipolar ions have minimal conductivity and are termed non-electrolytes; solutions containing ions have a conductivity depending on the ionic concentration, and are termed electrolytes.

All aqueous solutions have some residual conductivity irrespective of the nature of the added solutes, owing to the fact that water itself is slightly ionised into H^+ and OH^-, and thus generates ionic solutes.

Osmotic Pressure. Solution is a spontaneous process and takes place whenever

51

a solute and an appropriate solvent encounter. If two solutions of different concentration are separated by a semipermeable membrane that restricts the passage of the solute particles, the solvent will diffuse across the membrane so as to equalise the concentrations. Similarly, if a solution is separated from some of its solvent it will undergo spontaneous dilution by diffusion of the solvent. The mechanical pressure that must be applied to the solution to prevent its expansion by dilution is termed the *osmotic pressure* of the system. This pressure can be measured in various ways, and affords information as to the number of solute particles present in a given volume of solution.

Semipermeability implies that a surface allows the passage of the solvent but restricts the passage of the solute responsible for the osmotic pressure. Semipermeability varies greatly with material structure. A filter paper is permeable to all solutes present in true aqueous solution, and also permits the passage of colloidal mixtures, such as milk and egg albumin. An animal membrane, such as parchment or peritonæum, will restrict the passage of proteins, soaps and other solutes of large molecular dimensions. Thin membranes can be constructed of collodion, cellophane, or gelatine of such degree of selectivity as to be permeable to ions but not to simple molecules.

Estimation of Osmotic Pressure. (i) *Direct*. The solution of known concentration is enclosed in a semipermeable container attached to a manometer tube. The container is immersed in a vessel containing an excess of the solvent, some of which diffuses into the container causing a rise of the solution in the manometer tube. When equilibrium is reached, the pressure of the diluted solution inside the container is balanced by the hydrostatic pressure of the liquid in the manometer, and can be measured in atmospheric units. Modifications of the apparatus include the use of a mercury manometer to avoid excessive dilution of the mixture, and the employment of metallic containers with frames to support the membranes.

(ii) *Indirect*. The boiling point of a solvent is raised and the freezing point is depressed by addition of solutes, the extent of the change being proportional to the concentration of solute particles.

It can be shown from the gas laws that an aqueous solution of an unionised solute in molecular concentration (1 gm. molecule of solute in 1 l. of solution) has osmotic pressure of 22·4 atmospheres at 0°, a boiling point of 100·52°, and a freezing point of −1·86°. Consequently, if the molecular weight of a non-ionising solute such as a sugar, is known, it is possible to calculate the osmotic effect, boiling point and freezing point of a solution of any given concentration.

Similarly, knowing the concentration of the solute it is possible to calculate the molecular weight from any one of the three properties of the solution. In practice, the easiest estimation is that of the freezing point, which is determined in a *cryoscope*, in which the value of Δ, the depression of the freezing point, is read by means of a sensitive Beckmann thermometer.

Osmotic pressure, in atmospheres $= \dfrac{22\cdot4 \times \varDelta,\ \text{in}\ ^\circ\text{C}}{1\cdot86}$.

The molecular weight, M, of a single solute can be calculated from the depression of the freezing point, $\varDelta$, of a solution containing w gm. of solute per litre, since

$$M = \frac{1\cdot86 \times w}{\varDelta}.$$

Solute.	M.	Osmotic value of a 10 per cent. Solution.	Freezing Point of a 10 per cent. Solution.
Urea . .	60	37·34 atm.	−3·1°
Glucose . .	180	12·4 ,,	−1·03°
Fructose .	180	12·4 ,,	−1·03°
Sucrose .	342	6·5 ,,	−0·54°

Sea water has an osmotic value of 13 to 26 atm. ($\varDelta = -1\cdot1$ to $-2\cdot2°$). Corresponding values are found for the blood plasma of lower marine animals; higher fish are less dependent on environmental levels. Land vertebrates, because of their mechanisms for osmotic regulation, have plasma values set about 6 atm.

The osmotic values of the blood plasma and tissue fluids are determined by a variety of solutes, the chief of which are Na^+ and Cl^-, and are kept in the region of 7 atmospheres (corresponding to a freezing point of $-0\cdot56°$) by the intake of water and the excretion of urine, the osmotic value of which may vary between 12 and 24 atmospheres during the day.

Milk, being a true secretion, has a constant freezing point range of $-0\cdot53°$ to $-0\cdot57°$ C.

COLLOIDAL SYSTEMS

Intervening between true solutions and unstable suspensions, which can be separated by simple mechanical methods, is a class of solutions termed *colloidal* by Graham, in 1856, to denote their glue-like non-crystallisable nature, as distinct from that of the *crystalloids*, or solutes present in true solutions. By selective *dialysis*, or filtration through parchment, he was able to separate colloids from accompanying diffusible crystalloids. Subsequently, it was found that the intrinsic difference between the two groups depended on the size of the solute particles and not on the crystallisability, and Ostwald suggested that colloids represented a state of matter rather than a class of compounds. In a true solution, the solute particles are less than 1 mμ in diameter; in a colloidal solution the particles range from 1 mμ to 100 mμ in diameter; in suspensions and emulsions the particles are greater than 100 mμ in diameter.*

* 1 mm. = 1,000 μ (microns).   1 μ = 1,000 mμ (millimicrons)

Colloidal solutions resemble true solutions in that they are homogeneous and are not resolved by simple filtration or sedimentation. The dispersed particles, however, display surface properties not shown by true solutes, and also may be separated by special methods involving the high-speed centrifuge or by ultra-filtration, and for this reason colloids are sometimes termed polyphasic solutions, the term phase being used to denote a mechanically separable form of matter.

To emphasise the distinction, the particles in a colloidal system are termed the *disperse* or *internal phase*, the solvent being the *continuous* or *external phase*.

Classification of Colloidal Systems. Unlike true solutes, the various components of a colloidal system can be any one or more of the three states of matter.

Representing the system as *solute/solvent*, the following arrangements are possible: gas/liquid, gas/solid, liquid/gas, liquid/liquid, liquid/solid, solid/gas, solid/liquid, solid/solid.

(i) *Gas/liquid* systems are represented by foams and froths, the permanence of which depends on the presence of stabilisers, such as soaps and saponin glucosides, which form froths when their aqueous solutions are shaken up with air.

Froth production is rare in nature, apart from fermentations, but an interesting example is afforded by the plant parasite that protects itself by means of a foam derived from leaf sap. Pathological and often fatal examples of froth formation in the higher animal are seen in air embolus, and pulmonary œdema.

(ii) *Gas/solid* systems in which gaseous particles are distributed through a solid external phase are of industrial importance in connection with the adsorption of vapours by means of charcoal filters, and their study has been encouraged by the introduction of gas as a weapon in civilised warfare. Many porous substances, including spongy platinum and palladium, adsorb and subsequently dissolve gases.

(iii) *Liquid/gas* systems, represented by mists and fogs, occur temporarily when air saturated with moisture is cooled suddenly. The stability of a mist depends on the size of the particles, being greatest when they are small, but stabilising factors, such as products of coal combustion, also operate to preserve the characteristic atmosphere of industrial towns in damp weather.

Cigarette smoke provides an example of two colloidal systems. The bluish smoke from the combustion is a dispersion of carbon particles carried upwards by the current of heated gas. The brownish exhalation is a fog formed by salivary moisture stabilised by products of tobacco combustion.

(iv) *Liquid/liquid* systems, or *emulsions*, are important biological colloids, and represent the form in which liquid fats are transported or secreted by the organism. Milk is a 3 to 4 per cent. emulsion of fat, stabilised by milk protein.

(v) *Liquid/solid* systems, or *gels*, are represented by natural and artificial jellies and mucoids, and by butter, all of which consist of a solid external phase retaining a dispersed liquid phase in its interstices. Cytoplasm is a gel.

(vi) *Solid/gas* systems are represented by colloidal smoke, the stability of which depends on the fineness of the particles and the presence of stabilisers.

(vii) *Solid/liquid* systems, sols or *suspensoids*, include the principal biological colloids, and are represented by the soluble proteins of the tissues and tissue fluids, and similar compounds of high molecular weight.

Metallic sols of gold, silver, copper, etc., form an important class of suspensoids, and are used industrially and therapeutically.

(viii) *Solid/solid* systems are often included among true solid solutions, but are of little biological interest, although it is possible to attribute the structure of bone and other metallo-skeletal tissue to the formation of solid solutions from calcium salts.

Properties of Colloidal Systems. Colloidal solutions resemble true solutions in that they exert an osmotic effect and have a lower freezing point than that of the solvent. These properties are usually slight, owing to the relatively greater size and smaller concentration of the dispersed particles. The osmotic effect of the plasma proteins, however, is an important factor in maintaining the volume of blood, and in man has a normal value of 305 to 307 mm. H_2O (0·03 atmospheres) at 22° C. This is significant, because the plasma proteins are unable to escape from the vascular system, and thus tend to retain tissue fluid.

(1) *Faraday-Tyndall Effect.* When a convergent beam of light is sent transversely across a true solution, and examined by an observer at right-angles to the path of the beam, the solution appears optically empty. When the observation is repeated using a colloidal solution, light is reflected from the surface of the disperse particles, and the path of the beam is seen as an illuminated cone. By using a strong source of light, colloidal particles can thus be detected in very low concentration.

A similar method of transverse illumination is used in the ultra-microscope whereby particles smaller than the shortest wave-length of visible light (400 mμ) are revealed as radiating points against a dark background.

When strongly illuminated by light of short wave-length, it has been found that molecules in true solution are able to scatter sufficient of the radiation to enable their structure to be studied spectroscopically. This *Raman effect* is employed in the elucidation of molecular architecture.

(2) *Brownian Movement.* When examined microscopically against a dark background, colloidal particles are observed to be in continual rapid irregular motion, a phenomenon first recorded in 1827 by the botanist R. Brown. Brownian movement is a form of perpetual motion, and is due to bombardment of the disperse particles by the molecules of the solvent.

(3) *Migration in an Electric Field, Electrophoresis.* Dispersed particles carry

an electric charge, and migrate to the anode or the cathode when the solution is electrolysed. Typical positively-charged colloids (cations) are: proteins in acid solution, hæmoglobin, ferric hydroxide and aluminium hydroxide suspensoids. Typical negatively-charged colloids (anions) are: proteins in alkaline solution, starch, soaps and metallic sols.

The colloidal charge is altered by addition of electrolytes, especially acids or bases, and may be neutralised or reversed owing to combination between the colloid and solute ions. A neutral disperse phase is said to be iso-electric, in which condition it migrates neither to anode nor to cathode.

(4) *Adsorption at the Phase Interface.* Solutes that lower surface tension tend to accumulate on the free surfaces of colloidal particles. This surface condensation is termed adsorption, and is of special significance in colloidal systems because of the enormous area presented by the disperse phase. Colloids often display preferential absorption for a particular class of solutes, and one solute may compete with another solute and displace it from the adsorbing surface.

This is exemplified in the use of tartrazol as an adsorption indicator in the estimation of chlorides (p. 350).

As a result of adsorption, the solute, or *adsorbate*, becomes highly concentrated on the colloid surface, and may undergo subsequent changes by chemical reaction with the colloid. Adsorption is a preliminary stage in enzyme catalysis, and is of primary importance in regulating the distribution of solutes among the tissue surfaces that make up the framework of structures associated with life.

Summary

True Solutions.	Colloidal Solutions.
1. One phase (mechanically homogeneous).	More than one phase (mechanically heterogeneous).
2. Optically empty. No Faraday-Tyndall cone.	Optically dense. Faraday-Tyndall cone when illuminated transversely.
3. Solute particles less than 1–5 mμ in diameter.	Disperse particles range from 5 mμ to 100 mμ.
4. No Brownian movement.	Particles show Brownian movement.
5. Solute particles show no surface properties other than the Raman effect.	Disperse particles show surface properties and carry a surface charge.

Colloidal Stability. The stability of a colloidal system depends on the combined effect of four factors:—

(1) *Diameter of Disperse Particles.* The sedimentation rate of a sphere falling in a liquid may be found by means of Stokes' law:

$$V = \frac{2\,r^2\,(s - s')g}{9\,u}$$

where V = rate of fall,
r = radius of particle,
s = density of particle,
s' = density of continuous phase,
g = gravity constant (981),
u = viscosity of solution.

From this it will be seen that rate of sedimentation is proportional to the square of the radius, and if the particle be sufficiently small, months, years, or even centuries, will be required for complete sedimentation.

(2) *Brownian movement* tends to keep the particles distributed throughout the system.

(3) *Electric surface charge* tends to keep the particles from flocculating and precipitating, since bodies of like charge are mutually repellant. The importance of the surface charge is shown by the fact that colloids are least stable when at the iso-electric point.

(4) *Surface stabilisation.* Metallic sols, although they have a disperse phase of very small dimensions, are so unstable that they are classified as *lyophobes*, owing to the readiness with which they lose their solvent phase. Emulsions and organic suspensoids, on the contrary, are examples of *lyophil* or hydrophil colloids, and are usually very stable. The difference is attributed to adsorption of the solute by the lyophil particles.

Colloid Stabilisers. These are substances which when added in small quantities promote the formation of colloidal systems and render them less liable to spontaneous precipitation. Gum acacia, gum tragacanth, soaps, saponins, gelatin and lecithin are representative stabilisers used industrially. Egg yolk, on account of the lecithin it contains, is used in pharmaceutical and in domestic preparations, such as the manufacture of mayonnaise by emulsification of vinegar in oil.

Precipitation and Coagulation of Colloids. Any operation that removes the stability factors in a colloidal system tends to bring about aggregation of the disperse particles. Violent agitation, as in the churning of milk, addition of colloids or electrolytes of the opposite electric charge, freezing and thawing, all promote flocculation of colloidal particles.

Analysis of Colloidal Systems. The average dimension of the disperse phase particles may be found in several ways.

(1) *Ultra-filtration* through surfaces of standard porosity. The colloidal disperse particles pass through ordinary filter papers (pore diameter, 2 to 5 μ) and through unglazed porcelain (pore diameter, 0·2 to 0·6 μ), but not through *ultra-filters*, such as sheets of collodion, cellophane, gelatin, or peritoneal membrane (parchment).

From the strength of a gelatin filter the size of the pores may be calculated, and depend on the concentration of gelatin present, irrespective of the thickness of the filter.

57

(2) *Rate of sedimentation* may be measured by means of a sedimentation balance, one pan of which is immersed in the solution, and acquires weight from the subsidence of the particles. The radius of the particles is then calculated by means of Stokes' law. The method is only applicable to suspensions and coarser suspensoids that subside rapidly.

Type.	Visibility.	Example.	Diameter.
Molecular	Not visible by ultra-microscope	True solutes	$0.5 \ m\mu$—$5 \ m\mu$
Ultra-microscopic	Not visible by microscope	Colloidal solutes	$5 \ m\mu$—$100 \ m\mu$
Microscopic	Not visible by the unaided eye	Fine suspensions	$200 \ m\mu$—$1 \ \mu$
Directly visible		Coarse suspensions	$> 10 \ \mu$ (0·01 mm.)

Average Diameter of Dispersed Particles.

0.1 mμ. 1 mμ.	10 mμ. 100 mμ.	1 μ. 10 μ.	100 μ. 1 mm. (1,000 μ).
True solutions	Colloids	Suspensions	Precipitates
Particles pass through ordinary filter paper		Particles retained by ordinary filter paper	
Brownian movement		No Brownian movement	

(3) *Ultra-centrifugal Methods.* By use of an air-stream that both supports and spins the rotor, speeds are obtainable up to 1,500,000 revolutions per minute, giving centrifugal forces 8 million times as great as that due to gravity. Such machines are used to separate nuclei and cytoplasmic inclusions from cells, and to fractionate the disperse phases in colloid mixtures. By employing a transparent solution-container, it is possible to photograph the meniscus of separation boundaries of the moving particles and to measure the sedimentation rates. From such data, Svedberg (1934–) has calculated the molecular weight, particle-size and shape of proteins and other natural colloids.

(4) *Electrophoresis.* When a positively- or negatively-charged colloid is submitted to an electric field at standard temperature and pH, the rate of migration of the particles is determined by their dimensions and the size of their electric charge. Migration data are found with great accuracy by the electrophoresis methods developed by Tiselius and other workers.

The container used is a U-tube, the upper limbs of which are of optical glass, rectangular in cross-section and detachable from the lower loop segment. At the start of operation the lower segment is filled with a buffer solution of the colloid, the limbs are filled with the same buffer and each is connected with a non-polarisable electrode. When a constant potential difference of 100 volts or more is set up between the limbs of the assembled container, the colloid gradually ascends one limb, forming a sharply-defined moving boundary between it and the supernatant buffer.

When more than one colloidal species is present, each one forms a separate boundary, migrating at its own rate. Hence, by electrophoresis, different colloids in a mixture can be detected, separated, and characterised, and from the data obtainable it is possible to calculate the molecular weights of the particles.

If the colloid is coloured or opaque the migration rate can be found by photographing the container at intervals. Migration of colourless, transparent colloids, such as simple proteins and polysaccharides, can be studied by projecting a narrow beam of light through a limb of the cell so as to reveal the streaks caused by local difference in the refractive index of the contents arising from the different colloidal boundaries. By an elaborate optical device this streak, or *schlieren* effect, can be scanned and the changes in refractive index with height in the vertical limb can be recorded as a shadow contour on a photographic plate.

For reproduction the record is usually turned sideways, so that each component of the colloid mixture is shown as a peak rising from a horizontal base-line.

Paper Electrophoresis. A strip of filter paper is soaked in buffer and the ends immersed in two troughs of buffer in which electrodes are placed, connected to a source of current. A minute amount of a solution containing two or more proteins, such as serum, is applied to the paper midway between the troughs and the current passed for a period. The separation of the protein fractions can be demonstrated by staining.

Methods of Preparing Colloidal Solutions. (1) *Solution.* Many organic compounds, such as proteins, soaps, and gums, form colloidal solutions spontaneously when treated with water, and occur as colloidal systems in their natural conditions.

(2) *Condensation of True Solute Particles.* By reduction or hydration it is possible to aggregate the ions of various metals so that they form particles of colloidal dimension.

(3) *Dispersion, or Peptisation, of Insoluble Particles.* By mechanical disintegration in a colloid mill it is possible to render insoluble substances, such as graphite or chalk, sufficiently fine to form colloidal solutions in water, oil and other liquids, while it is also possible by means of an electric arc formed between electrodes of a metal, immersed in water or other liquids, to disperse the metal in the form of a sol. These are industrial methods used for preparing colloidal lubricants and therapeutic agents.

Colloidal particles can be classified according to shape as linear and spherical. Linear colloids, such as cellulose, are fibrous, and dissolve with much swelling to form viscid solutions. Spherical colloids, such as glycogen, are powders in the solid state, and give solutions of low viscosity.

General References

Alexander, J. (1944), " Colloid Chemistry," 5th ed. New York; London.

Beutner, R. (1933), " Physical Chemistry of Living Tissues." London.

Buzagh, A. (1937), " Colloid Systems." (*Trans.* Darbishire.) London.

Ferry, J. D. (1936), " Ultrafilter membranes and ultrafiltration." *Chem. Rev.*, **18**, 373.

Fischer, M. H. (1933), " Lyophilic Colloids." Springfield, Ill.

Freundlich, H. (1926), " Colloid and Capillary Chemistry." London.

Frey-Wyssling, A. (1948), " Submicroscopic Morphology of Protoplasm." New York.

Langmuir, I. (1933), " Surface chemistry." *Chem. Rev.*, **13**, 147.

Lloyd, D. Jordan (1932), " Colloid structure and its biological significance." *Biol. Rev.*, **7**, 254.

Loeb, J. (1924), " Proteins and the Theory of Colloidal Behaviour." New York.

Michaelis, L., and P. Rona (1933), " Practical Physical and Colloidal Chemistry for Students of Medicine and Biology." (*Trans.* T. R. Parsons.) Cambridge.

Schmidt, F. O. (1939), " Ultrastructure of protoplasmic constituents." *Physiol. Rev.*, **19**, 270.

Schweyer, H. E. (1942), " Particle-size studies." *Chem. Rev.*, **31**, 295.

Svedberg, T. (1934), " Sedimentation of molecules in centrifugal fields." *Chem. Rev.*, **14**, 1.

Svedberg, T., and K. O. Pederson (1940). " The Ultracentrifuge." London.

Taylor, H. S., E. O. Lawrence and I. Langmuir (1942), " Molecular Films, the Cyclotron and the New Biology." New Jersey.

Ware, J. C. (1936), " Chemistry of the Colloidal State." 2nd ed., New York.

Chapter 5 Classification and Characteristics

of Organic Compounds

" Bear with me, gentlemen, while I remind you
of the incessant molecules that bind you."

Humbert Wolfe.

Living organisms may be divided into two classes: the *autotrophs*, represented by green plants and some pigmented micro-organisms; and the *heterotrophs*, represented by animals and by plants free from chlorophyll. Autotrophic organisms are able in the presence of sunlight to synthesise their
organic constituents from an inorganic environment providing water, carbon
dioxide, nitrate, ammonia and the additional biological elements. Heterotrophic organisms require organic food materials as well as water, oxygen and
the biological elements. In the collaboration that has made animal life possible
on earth, the autotrophs act as collectors and storers of energy in chemical
form available for the nutrition of the heterotrophs.

The bio-organic compounds associated with plants and animals are wide in
variety and often great in complexity, and no classification yet proposed is
entirely logical. Features of chemical structure, physiological significance
and biological distribution are selected according to convenience.

Classification by Family.		Classification by Function.	
1. Carbohydrates.	8. Carotenoids.	1. Plastics.	7. Buffers.
2. Proteins.	9. Terpenes.	2. Nutrients.	8. Storage products,
3. Lipids.	10. Flavins.	3. Hormones.	etc.
4. Steroids.	11. Flavones.	4. Catalysts.	
5. Porphyrins.	12. Alkaloids,	5. Vitamins.	
6. Purines.	etc.	6. Pigments.	
7. Pyrimidines.			

Neither of these classifications is exclusive or exhaustive, and each merely
serves to emphasise the biological significance of the included compounds.

ORGANIC TYPE FORMULÆ

Organic compounds, other than symmetrical hydrocarbons, can be represented as being composed of a linear or cyclic carbon *radical*, R, carrying one
or more reactive groups or side-chains. Cyclic radicals are represented chiefly
by phenyl, C_6H_5—, and indolyl, C_8H_6N—, rings, neither of which can be
assembled by the higher animal, but must be provided in the diet. Reactive

61

groups are represented chiefly by hydroxyl, —OH, carboxyl, —COOH, aldehyde, —CHO, keto, =CO, and amino, —NH$_2$, configurations.

(1) Systems Present in Biological Compounds.

(a) Derivatives of Open-Chain, or Linear Hydrocarbons.

Parent Hydrocarbon	Radical
Methane, CH$_4$	**Methyl,** *Me*, CH$_3$—, **Methylene,** CH$_2$=
Ethane, C$_2$H$_6$	**Ethyl,** *Et*, CH$_3$.CH$_2$—, **Vinyl,** CH$_2$: CH—
Propane, C$_3$H$_8$	**Propyl,** *Pr*, CH$_3$.(CH$_2$)$_2$—
	Allyl, CH$_2$: CH.CH$_2$—
Butane, C$_4$H$_{10}$	**Butyl,** CH$_3$.(CH$_2$)$_3$—
Pentane, C$_5$H$_{12}$	**Amyl,** CH$_3$.(CH$_2$)$_4$—
Hexane, C$_6$H$_{14}$	**Hexyl,** CH$_3$(CH$_2$)$_5$—

(b) Derivatives of Closed-Chain, or Cyclic Hydrocarbons

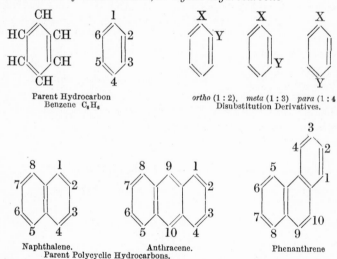

Parent Hydrocarbon
Benzene C$_6$H$_6$

ortho (1 : 2), *meta* (1 : 3) *para* (1 : 4
Disubstitution Derivatives.

Naphthalene.   Anthracene.   Phenanthrene
Parent Polycyclic Hydrocarbons.

(c) Heterocyclic Compounds. Cyclic structures containing other elements in the ring in addition to carbon are termed heterocyclic, and are represented chiefly by:—

Sugars in *pyranose* form ←   Pyran.   Furan.   → Sugars in *furanose* form

Porphyrins
Blood pigments
Bile pigments
Chlorophyll

←

$$
\begin{array}{c}
HC\text{——}CH \\
| \quad | \\
HC\diagdown\ \diagup CH \\
NH
\end{array}
$$
Pyrrole.

→

$$
\begin{array}{c}
CH \\
HC\diagup \diagdown C\text{——}CH \\
| \quad \quad | \\
HC\diagdown \diagup C\diagdown \diagup CH \\
CH \quad NH
\end{array}
$$
Indole
(Benzpyrrole).

$$
\begin{array}{c}
CH \\
HC\diagup \diagdown CH \\
| \quad \quad | \\
HC\diagdown \diagup CH \\
N
\end{array}
$$
Pyridine.

$$
\begin{array}{c}
N{=}CH \\
| \quad \quad | \\
HC \quad CH \\
|| \quad \quad || \\
N\text{——}CH
\end{array}
$$
Pyrimidine.

$$
\begin{array}{c}
N{=}CH \\
| \quad \quad | \\
HC \quad C\text{—}NH \\
|| \quad \quad \diagdown CH \\
N\text{——}C\text{—}N
\end{array}
$$
Purine.

$$
\begin{array}{c}
HC\text{—}NH \\
|| \quad \diagdown CH \\
HC\text{—}N
\end{array}
$$
Iminazole
(Glyoxaline).

Groups and Linkages Present in Biological Compounds.

Primary alcohol, $-CH_2.OH$

Secondary alcohol, $>CH.OH$

Amino, $-NH_2$ attached to $-CH_2-$ or $>CH-$

Amido, $-NH_2$ attached to $-CO-$

Carbamido, or uramido, $-NH.CO.NH_2$

Guanidino, $-NH.C(NH).NH_2$

Aldehyde, $-CHO$
Carboxyl, $-COOH$
Keto, $>CO$; **Imino,** $>NH$

Ether linkage, $>CH \qquad HC<$
$\quad\quad\quad O$

Ester linkage, $>CH \qquad OC-$
$\quad\quad\quad O$

Disulphide linkage, $-CH-S-S-CH_2-$
Thiol, or **sulphydryl group,** $-SH$

The position of a substituent group in a linear compound is denoted by numbering the C atoms from the functional group, or by the use of a Greek alphabet, the C atom next the characteristic group in the compound being described as the a-carbon. Confusion is liable to arise between the two types of nomenclature, and the numerical form is preferable.

Butyric acid
$$\overset{4}{C}H_3.\overset{3}{C}H_2.\overset{2}{C}H_2.\overset{1}{C}OOH$$
$$\quad \gamma \quad \beta \quad a$$

β-Hydroxy butyric acid,
or 3-*hydroxy butyric acid.*
$$CH_3.CH(OH).CH_2.COOH.$$

The position of a group in a cyclic compound is denoted numerically in reference to a particular carbon atom, C^1.

Double bonds, $-C=C-$, in organic compounds are denoted by the symbol

63

Δ with a pair of suffixes to indicate the position number of each C atom linked by the double bond.

The chief reactions undergone by organic compounds include *oxidation, reduction, condensation,* or union by elimination of water, *hydrolysis,* or resolution by addition of water, *polymerisation,* or combination of two or more similar molecules, *internal rearrangement* and *ring formation.*

Tautomerism, or dual configuration, is shown by certain organic groups and compounds, the structure of which differ under different conditions. Important biochemical examples are:—

. (*a*) *The Amide Group,*

$$\begin{array}{ccc} -CO & \rightleftharpoons & -C.OH \\ | & & || \\ NH_2 & & NH \end{array}$$

(*b*) *The Peptide Linkage,*

$$\begin{array}{ccc} {>}CH-\underset{\underset{O}{||}}{C}-NH-CH{<} & \rightleftharpoons & {>}CH-\underset{\underset{OH}{|}}{C}=N-CH{<} \end{array}$$

(*c*) *The Keto Compounds,*

$$\begin{array}{ccc} {>}CH-\underset{\underset{O}{||}}{C}-CH_2-CH{<} & \rightleftharpoons & {>}CH-\underset{\underset{OH}{|}}{C}=CH-CH{<} \end{array}$$

Mesomerism, or chemical resonance, is said to occur when a substance exists in an intermediate or *hybrid* state not capable of being exactly represented by a single structural formula.

For resonance to occur the compound must be capable of existing in two or more structural forms, differing only in the arrangement of the electrons. For example, in carbon dioxide, as oxygen is more electrophilic than carbon, each oxygen atom tends to pull away the electrons from the covalency bond, with the result that three structures are possible:

$$\ddot{:}\overset{..}{O}{}^{-}:C^{+}::\overset{..}{O} \rightleftharpoons \overset{..}{O}::C::\overset{..}{O} \rightleftharpoons \overset{..}{O}::C^{+}:\overset{..}{O}{}^{-}:$$
$$\text{I} \qquad\qquad \text{II} \qquad\qquad \text{III}$$

Formulæ I and III are polar compounds, in which the carbon atom has acquired a positive charge owing to loss of electrons, and one oxygen atom has gained a negative charge owing to electron rearrangement. Formula II is uncharged carbon dioxide.

As none of these formulæ accounts for all the properties of the compound, it is concluded that carbon dioxide exists in a condition of resonance, or very rapid electron change, between the three depictable structures. A resonating system has less energy than any one of its components, and hence increases the stability of the parent compound. In general, all tautomeric compounds can exist in a condition of resonance, in which they display properties not directly referable to any one tautomeric form. This is exemplified in urea and in the peptide linkages of proteins.

Hydrogen-Bonding. The hydrogen ion, because of its susceptibility to capture by a lone pair of electrons, can bind adjacent oxygen, nitrogen, or some other atoms in compounds or individual molecules. Thus water, which in the gaseous state is monomolecular H_2O, exists in the liquid state as the polymers $(H_2O)_n$, where n is 2, 3, 4, and 5. Union is effected by the sharing of H between a pair of molecules, and the resulting polymer is stabilised by resonance.

Co-ordination Complexes. Pairs of lone electrons in a single molecule or in several molecules can combine to form a semi-polar complex with an electropositive atom, such as a polyvalent metal. Complex formation of this kind is very important in biochemistry, and is found in the metallo-porphyrins present in chlorophyll and in hæmoglobin.

For example, the cupric ion forms a deep blue complex with four ammonia molecules, each of which contributes its lone pair of electrons to provide an electron octet for the denuded copper atom.

$$
\begin{array}{cc}
H_3N: \quad : NH_3 \\
Cu^{++} \\
H_3N: \quad : NH_3
\end{array}
\rightarrow
\left[
\begin{array}{cc}
H_3N. \quad .NH_3 \\
:Cu: \\
H_3N^{.} \quad ^{.}NH_3
\end{array}
\right]^{++}
$$

As a result of this subscription of electrons, the cupric ion loses its positive charge, which is distributed among the nitrogen atoms. Complexes of this type are unstable, and on acidification are resolved into ammonium ions, with release of the metallic ion. Where, however, the nitrogen atoms are present in the same molecule, as occurs in the porphyrins, the metallo-complexes are much more stable.

The presence of a lone pair of electrons taking part in a semi-polar bond is usually indicated by an arrow from the donor atom to the recipient, $D \rightarrow R$.

Cis-trans Isomerism. Geometrical isomers may arise through differences in the arrangements of atoms or groups around a double-bond linkage.

$$
\begin{array}{cc}
CH_3.(CH_2)_7 \quad (CH_2)_7.COOH \\
C = C \\
H \quad\quad H
\end{array}
\qquad
\begin{array}{cc}
CH_3.(CH_2)_7 \quad H \\
C = C \\
H \quad\quad (CH_2)_7.COOH
\end{array}
$$

Oleic Acid
(*Cis*-oleic acid)
m.p. 13–14° C.

Elaidic Acid
(*Trans*-oleic acid)
m.p. 45° C.

In the *cis*-isomer, the atoms or groups on one side of the horizontal axis are the same. Where more than one pair of double linkages occur in the molecule, more complex forms of *cis-trans* isomerism are possible. Natural oleic acid, thus, is a *cis*-form.

Simplified Structural Formulæ. Many natural compounds, such as steroids and alkaloids, have very complex formulæ, and it is convenient to simplify the diagrammatic representation of their structure. This is done by extending the convention adopted in organic chemistry for benzene and other aromatic, or benzenoid, derivatives, in which the carbon atoms and their attached hydrogens, —CH_2— and —$CH<$, are indicated by angles, the symbols for the elements being omitted.

$\bigwedge$ represents $\overset{CH_2}{\bigwedge}$, the saturated *ane*, or *methane* linkage.

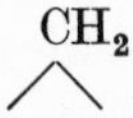

$\bigwedge\!\!\!\backslash$ represents $\overset{CH}{\bigwedge\!\!\!\backslash}$, the unsaturated *ene*, or *methene* linkage.

Where an unsaturated double or triple-linkage bond is not indicated, it is assumed that the bond C is carrying two H atoms, and the linkage is fully saturated. For this method of simplified representation to be unambiguous, special care must be taken to denote *every* unsaturated linkage in the diagram. Thus, benzene and its derivatives should be represented:—

not 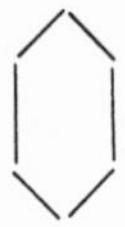 , which could denote

Benzene
C_6H_6

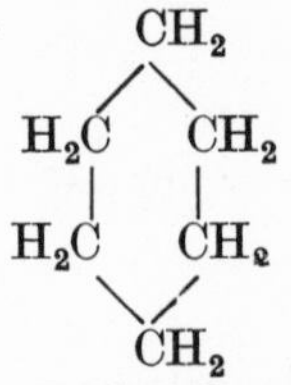

Hexahydrobenzene
C_6H_{12}

Reactive groups and short side-chains, —OH, —CH_3, —NH_2, =CO, —COOH, and the like, are denoted as such. Long side-chains may be written in simplified form.

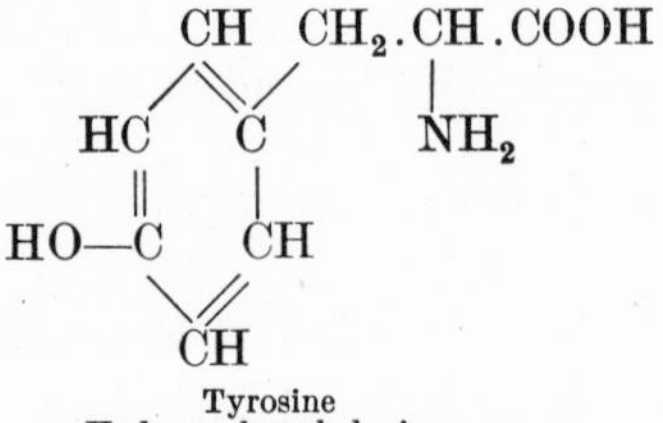

Tyrosine
p-Hydroxyphenyl alanine

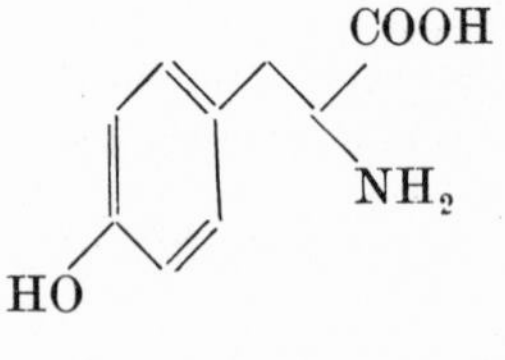

Tyrosine
(simplified formula)

The system may be applied to all types of organic compounds, including those in which N, O or another element forms part of a ring.

```
1  HN——CO  6
     |     |
2  OC    C——NH
     |    ||    ⟩CO  8
3  HN——C——NH
```
Uric Acid
2 : 6 : 8-trioxy purine

```
        O
        ||
1  HN      NH
    |
2  O=         O  8
      NH  NH
```
Uric Acid
(simplified formula)

The systematic nomenclature used in organic chemistry is gradually being adopted in biochemistry. According to this, the name of a compound is constructed to denote its chemical structure, type and characterising groups.

(1) The total number of C atoms is shown by a Greek numeral prefix:—

Pentane, a saturated hydrocarbon containing 5 carbon atoms.

Pentose, a sugar containing 5 carbon atoms.

(2) Saturation of all the carbon bonds is denoted by *ane*; unsaturation in any degree is shown by the vowel change of *a* to *e*, *ene*.

(3) The suffix shows either the general type of the compound or the presence of significant groups. Thus, the alcoholic groups, —$CH_2.OH$, =$CH.OH$, and ≡$C.OH$, are denoted by -*ol*, while *diol* or *triol* show the number of alcoholic hydroxyls present. The ketone group, =CO, is -*one*, and the amino group, —NH_2, is -*ine*, while the acidic carboxyl group, —$COOH$, is *ic* or *oic*.

Methods Used in Structural Analysis of Compounds

1. X-ray Difraction. When a beam of X-rays passes through a crystal, secondary rays are produced and can be recorded on a photographic film as a pattern of concentric rings of spots, the intensity and spacing of which depends on the atomic architecture of the crystal. Similarly, when a finely-ground crystalline powder is radiographed a pattern of concentric circles is obtained. By mathematical analysis of X-ray defraction patterns it is possible to calculate the shape and size of molecules, and the location and spacing of the constituent atoms.

2. Infra-red Spectrophotometry. Measurement of the radiations absorbed in the wave-length range $2 \cdot 5$ μ to 25 μ.

3. Raman Spectrophotometry. Measurement of the differences in frequency between the incident radiation and the scattered radiation when molecules are irradiated by waves of high intensity. Like the infra-red spectra, Raman spectra show the presence of groups, such as —CH_3, —C_6H_5, —SH, —OH, =NH, and various double-bond linkages.

4. Visible Spectrophotometry. Measurement of absorption in the visible spectrum, which extends from 760 mμ (red) to 400 mμ (violet).

5. Ultra-violet Spectrophotometry. This extends the absorption range surveyed to about 200 mμ, beyond which the quartz lens is opaque to short waves. Visible and ultra-violet spectra reveal the presence of specific *chromo-*

phores such as the CO group in molecules, and can be used also for the identification and estimation of compounds, such as hæmoglobin.

6. **Electrometric Titration.** By following the course of the change in pH when a substance is titrated, the various acidic and basic groups can be estimated. For very weak bases, such as amides, glacial acetic acid is used as solvent, and perchloric or sulphuric acid as titrating reagent.

7. **Polarography.** This electrometric method enables easily oxidised groups, such as —SH, or easily reduced functions, such as —S—S—, to be estimated and recorded.

Chromatography is the separation of individual solutes by selective adsorption and elution, interchange of ions, or partition between solvents, when the solution percolates through a porous column or sheet. The term was originally used to describe the separation of plant pigments (p. 168), but is applicable to any type of solute. Because of its great delicacy and versatility, chromatography is universally employed in all fields of analytical biochemistry.

Paper-partition Chromatography. A few drops of the solution are applied at a line drawn near one end of a long strip of filter paper. The strip is suspended vertically in a closed container so that the edge nearest the marked end is kept immersed in a small amount of a selected solvent on the floor of the container. Solvents commonly employed are phenol, *n*-propanol, *n*-butanol, or trimethyl pyridine (collidine), saturated with water prior to use. The solvent gradually ascends the paper at a rate of about 1 cm. per hour, carrying with it the solutes. When the solvent has advanced about two-thirds the length of the paper the strip is removed and the distance of the solvent front, D_s, from the starting line is measured. The paper is dried so as to remove the solvent, and the chromatogram is developed by spraying with an appropriate reagent, such as ammoniacal silver hydroxide for sugars; or ninhydrin for amino acids. On warming the paper the different solutes appear as scattered spots or zones of pigment. The distance, D_x, of each spot from the starting line is measured and its R_f value, or D_x/D_s ratio, is calculated. In this way, the number of solutes in a mixture can be found, and a solute can be identified by comparing its R_f value with that of those of known solutes obtained under the same conditions. There are many modifications of technique and apparatus, in some of which the solute flow is downward or horizontal (Kawerau, 1956). By applying constant-voltage electrodes to the sides of the paper, ionised solutes can be separated.

Vapour Phase Chromatography. The principle can be extended to a mixture of vapours. The mixture is carried through a heated column of suitable adsorbent in a stream of neutral gas, such as nitrogen. The constituents of the mixture are adsorbed on the column and are eluted soon afterwards in the same stream of neutral gas. As each component comes off it is carried by the stream through a detecting device, a commonly used example being a

Katharometer, in which it is detected by its effect on the thermal conductivity of the gas stream. Changes in thermal conductivity cause fluctuations in the current in a circuit which can be registered on a recording galvanometer. The tracing shows a peak corresponding to each component and the area enclosed between any peak and the base line is a measure of the amount of that component. The components can be identified by referring to a standard tracing.

General References

Biffen, F. M., and W. Seaman (1956), " Modern Instruments in Organic Analysis." New York.

Cowgill, R. W., and A. B. Perdue (1957), " Biochemical Research Technique." New York; London.

Fieser, L. F., and M. Fieser (1956), " Organic Chemistry," 3rd ed. New York; London.

Gero, A. (1952), " Biological Chemistry." New York; Toronto.

Mitchell, A. D. (1948), " British Chemical Nomenclature." London.

Weissberger, A. (1946), " Physical Methods of Organic Chemistry." New York.

Lederer, E., and M. Lederer (1953), " Chromatography." Elsevier: Amsterdam; London; New York.

Chapter 6 Carbohydrates

Three great families of organic compounds are associated closely with life: the Carbohydrates, the Proteins, and the Lipids. Carbohydrates, as sugars, are the principal form in which carbon is collected, transported, and utilised in the biosphere. As polysaccharides, carbohydrates account for about three-quarters of the total solids in the plant kingdom, and are the chief source of carbon in the diet of man, herbivora, and many lower organisms.

Definition and Nomenclature. A carbohydrate is a simple sugar or a compound formed by condensation of simple sugar units. A simple sugar, or mono-saccharide, is a neutral compound containing a free or potential aldehyde or ketone group, united to a primary alcohol group, $HO.CH_2$—, either directly or by a linkage of one or more secondary alcohol groups, —CH(OH)—. The general formula for a monosaccharide is $(CH_2O)_n$. The family name, *carbohydrate*, indicates that these compounds originally were regarded as hydrates of carbon, because most of them have the ratio H/O the same as that in water, H_2O. The systematic name of a carbohydrate ends in *ose*, although earlier names denoting source (alginic acid) or property (glycogen, dextrin) are in common use. For monosaccharides, the prefix denotes the number of carbon atoms in the molecule. Thus ribose, $C_5H_{10}O_5$, is a *pentose*; glucose, $C_6H_{12}O_6$, is a *hexose*. The terms *aldose* and *ketose* are employed to denote that a sugar contains an aldehyde, —CHO, or a ketone, —CO—, group.

Classification. Carbohydrates are divided into (I) saccharides, or sugars; and (II) polysaccharides, which occur as storage or structural compounds, and release saccharides on hydrolysis.

I. Saccharides

1. **Monosaccharides,** glycoses, or simple sugars. Non-hydrolysable carbohydrates. All are soluble in water, have a sweet taste, and display reducing properties in alkaline solution.

2. **Monosaccharide Derivatives.** Some of these are included among the carbohydrate family for convenience although they are not sugars.

(*a*) *Sugar alcohols*, aldoses in which the terminal aldehyde group has been hydrogenated to —CH₂.OH.

(*b*) *Glycosamines*, or amino sugars, in which —NH₂ replaces a hydroxyl group.

(*c*) *Sugar acids*, in which a carboxyl group, —COOH, represents one or other, or both, of the terminal groups of the sugar.

(*d*) *Deoxy sugars*, in which H replaces a hydroxyl group.

(*e*) *Sugar esters*, in which an acid radical replaces hydroxyl.

(*f*) *Sugar ethers*, of glycosides, formed by condensation between a sugar hydroxyl and a non-carboxylic hydroxyl group of another compound. Glycosides may be assembled from two sugar units, when the result is a disaccharide, or may contain a sugar and a non-sugar, or *aglycone*, unit.

3. **Oligosaccharides,** or compound sugars. Carbohydrates of low molecular weight formed by condensation of a small number (Gk. *oligos*, a few) of simple sugar units, not necessarily of the same species. All are water-soluble, and hydrolysable to simple sugars.

II. Polysaccharides

Chain-polymers of high molecular weight assembled from the same species of sugar unit, or from two or three different species, including an amino sugar or a sugar acid. They are insoluble in water, or form colloidal solutions, often of high viscosity.

Optical Properties of Carbohydrates. Simple sugars can be regarded as derivatives of the 3-carbon sugar glycerose, or glyceraldehyde, $C_3H_6O_3$, which contains an asymmetrically substituted or asymmetric carbon atom and exists in two isometric forms, *dextro-*, and *lœvo-*. Sugars lineally related to dextro-, or *d*-glycerose, are termed D-sugars, in distinction from L-sugars, which are related to *l*-glycerose.

The H—C—OH link furthest from the aldehyde or ketone group is the reference group. All D-sugars have a terminal configuration similar to that in *d*-glycerose.

In higher sugars, with lengthening of the chain, the number of optical isomers, or epimers, increases in accordance with van't Hoff's rule, $n = 2^c$, where n is the number of possible isomers, and c is the number of asymmetric carbon atoms in the compound. Thus, a ketohexose has four asymmetric carbons and can exist in any one of sixteen isomeric forms.

Confusion can arise from indiscriminate use of the small prefix, *d* or *l*, to denote relationship as well as direction of optical rotation. It is now usual to employ the prefix $(+)$ or $(-)$ to indicate if a compound is dextro- or lævo-rotatory. The capital prefix D or L is used to denote structural relationship to the $(+)$ or $(-)$ reference compound. Thus D-aldopentose, or, more explicitly, D $(-)$ aldopentose, is the lævorotary 5-carbon aldose related to *d*, or $(+)$ glycerose; L $(+)$ ascorbic acid, is the dextrorotatory compound

71

related to $l-$, or $(-)$ glycerose. The direction of optical rotation is not necessarily the same as that of the reference compound.

The close physical and chemical relationship between pairs of optical isomers renders them similar in many of their properties, but in the region of molecular dimensions, ruled by the enzymes, the difference between isomeric forms is fundamental in determining their susceptibility to biological attack. The carbohydrates and the proteins are the outstanding examples of compounds assembled from optically-active units.

The Natural Sugars

The commonest monosaccharides in the biosphere are the pentoses and the hexoses. Glycolaldehyde, $HO.CH_2.CHO$, a diose, is the simplest sugar. It takes part in pentose metabolism. The trioses are represented by d-glyceraldehyde and the ketotriose, dihydroxyacetone, $HO.CH_2.CO.CH_2.OH$, both of which are intermediates in the metabolism of hexoses. A heptose, $C_7H_{14}O_7$, is associated with pentose metabolism. Higher sugars of infrequent occurrence include octoses, $C_8H_{16}O_8$, nonoses, $C_9H_{18}O_9$, and a decose, $C_{10}H_{20}O_{10}$. Sugars higher than trioses tend to occur in stable ring-form.

Examples

Pentose

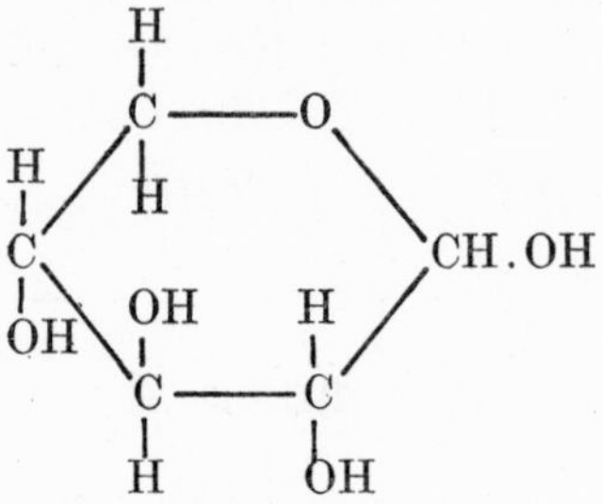

D-Arabinopyranose

Hexose

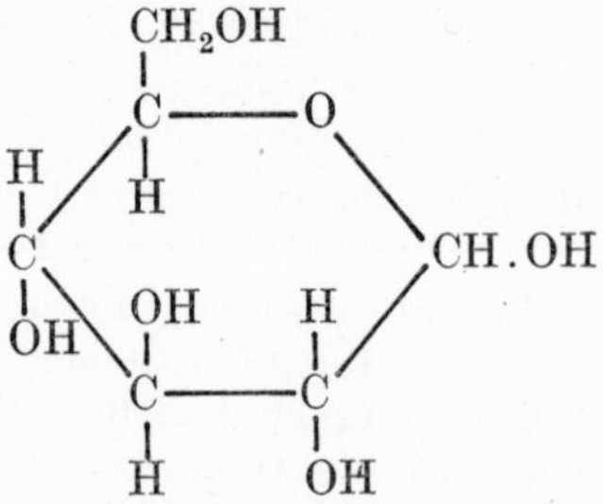

D-Glucose

Pentoses, $C_5H_{10}O_5$, and Deoxypentose, $C_5H_{10}O_4$

Sugar.	Sources.
D-Arabinose	The glycoside *aloin*; tubercle bacilli.
L-Arabinose	The polymer *araban*, in bran, husks, fruit skin; gum arabic, cherry and other gums; pectins; beet pulp.
D-Ribose	Ribonucleosides and ribonucleic acids of all organisms.
D-Ribulose	Widespread in animal and plant tissues.
D-Xylose	The polymer *xylan*, in straw, husks, wood gum.
L-Xyloketose	Urine, in conditions of pentosuria.
Deoxyribose (2-deoxy-D-ribose)	Deoxyribonucleosides and Deoxyribonucleic acids of all cell nuclei.

Pentoses occur chiefly as polymers, or *pentosans*, from which they are obtained quantitatively by acid hydrolysis. They also occur as glycosides, or *pentosides*, of which the nucleic acids are of unique importance since they constitute the self-reproducing units by means of which cells and viruses are perpetuated. D-ribulose is an intermediate in pentose metabolism.

Hexoses, $C_6H_{12}O_6$

Sugar.	Sources.
D-Glucose	Free in fruits, flowers, honey, blood, and diabetic urine. As a glycoside in oligosaccharides and other compounds. As a polymer in cellulose, starch, dextrins and glycogen.
D-Fructose	Free in fruits, flowers, honey, and fœtal blood. As a glycoside in sucrose and raffinose. The polymer *inulin*, in dahlia starch.
D-Galactose	As a glycoside in lactose and in glycolipids. The polymer *galactan*, in seaweeds.
L-Galactose	Flax seed mucilage.
D-Mannose	In some proteins (ovomucoid, serum globulin). The polymer *mannan*, in Ivory nut.

Out of twenty-four possible hexoses, only four are capable of being utilised by higher animals. They are the aldoses, D-glucose, D-galactose, and D-mannose, and the ketose, D-fructose. Some of the other hexoses occur in, or are utilised by, some plants and micro-organisms.

D-**Glucose,** *grape sugar*, or *dextrose* occurs free in fruit and plant juices and in blood and tissue fluids of animals. Pure glucose is a white, crystalline solid. It melts at 100° C., losing one molecule of water of crystallisation at 110° C. Anhydrous glucose melts at 146° C. Further heating produces a brown mixture of decomposition products, termed *caramel*.

Glucose is very soluble in water, the solution being about one-third as sweet as sucrose of the same concentration. It is dextro-rotatory, $[a]° = + 52 \cdot 2_D$. Glucose is a typical aldose sugar in all its reactions. It reduces alkaline copper

73

reagents, forms a characteristic osazone with phenylhydrazine, and is readily fermented by yeasts and bacteria.

D-Fructose, *fruit sugar*, or *lævulose*, accompanies glucose in fruits, flowers, and their product, honey. It is obtained also from the hydrolysis of fructosides, the chief of which is sucrose, and from the polysaccharide, inulin. It crystallises with difficulty in fine, colourless needles, m.p. 110° C. Fructose differs from the other three fermentable hexoses in being a ketose, and in being lævo-rotatory, $[a]_D = -92 \cdot 0°$. It is much sweeter and more reactive than glucose.

The Constitution of the Monosaccharides. All the aldohexoses can be represented by the *linear* formula,

$$HO.CH_2.CH(OH).CH(OH).CH(OH).CH(OH).CHO$$
$$6 \quad\ 5 \qquad 4 \qquad\ \ 3 \qquad\ \ 2 \qquad\ 1$$

in which the carbon atoms are numbered from the right, starting with the aldehyde group.

The natural, or 2-ketohexoses, can be formulated similarly,

$$HO.CH_2.CH(OH).CH(OH).CH(OH).CO.CH_2.OH$$

Such linear formulæ are inadequate in that they do not distinguish between the isomeric forms of the sugars. This can be done by means of *projection* formulæ, in which the hydroxyl group of each —CH(OH)— link projects to the right or the left of a vertical axis. In this way sixteen different arrangements of the aldohexose structure can be obtained. The sugar corresponding to each of these arrangements, and to the eight possible ketohexoses, has been synthesised, and appropriate structures have been assigned to the natural hexoses.

CHO	CHO	CHO	CH₂.OH
H.C.OH	HO.C.H	H.C.OH	CO
HO.C.H	HO.C.H	HO.C.H	HO.C.H
H.C.OH	H.C.OH	HO.C.H	H.C.OH
H.C.OH	H.C.OH	H.C.OH	H.C.OH
CH₂.OH	CH₂.OH	CH₂OH	CH₂.OH
D-glucose.	D-mannose.	D-galactose.	D-fructose.

Important features of these formulæ are: (i) the arrangement of the terminal groups at carbons 5 and 6, which is the same as that in *d*-glycerose, and indicates that the four chief natural hexoses are all D-sugars; (ii) the similarity of the pattern involving carbons 3, 4, 5, and 6, which partly explains the ready interconvertability of the four hexoses.

All linear formulations, however, fail to account for the relative stability of the pentoses and hexoses, and the concealment of the aldehyde or ketone function. Thus, the Raman spectra of sugars in solution do not display the characteristics of the carbonyl group, $:CO$; and aldohexoses do not give a positive reaction with Schiff's aldehyde reagent. This is explained by the assumption that the aldehyde group in the aldohexoses has entered into the formation of an oxygen bridge with carbon 5, to produce a stable 6-membered ring of the pyran type. Similarly, the ketone group of the ketohexoses can link up with carbon 5 to produce a 5-membered ring of the furan type, or with carbon 6 to produce a 6-membered ring of the pyran type. The 6-membered ring being the more stable, natural hexoses occur chiefly in *pyranose* form.

Aldopentoses, similarly can exist as pyranose or furanose rings; ketopentoses can only form furanose rings.

D glucose
(open form).

D-glucose
(pyranose form).

α- and β-sugars. When ring closure occurs, the oxygen of the aldehyde or ketone group acquires a hydrogen atom, and becomes a hydroxyl group. This hydroxyl group can project either below, (α), or above, (β), the plane of the ring; consequently, two isomeric forms are possible for each pyranose or furanose sugar, and the corresponding derivatives are described as α- or β-glycosides. Conversion of an α- to a β-sugar requires opening and reclosing of the ring. This occurs to some extent when a sugar is dissolved in water, and is responsible for the *mutarotation*, or change in optical activity, which continues until a constant value is reached, and the solution contains an equilibrium mixture of α- and β-forms.

α-Glucose.

α-Glucoside.

β-Glucose.   β-Glucoside.

In the perspective formulæ, attached H and OH are represented as projecting either above or below the plane of the ring. This allows for the existence of the sixteen isomeric aldohexoses.

Ring-flexion. These formulations do not take into account the valency strains that flex or crumple ring compounds into " boats " and " chairs." Thus, the pyranose rings assume a " chair " configuration, in which the oxygen bridge forms the upper angle, and the hydroxyl groups are set axially or equatorially, according to the particular sugar.

Oligosaccharides

The natural oligosaccharides, or compound sugars are assembled from two to four simple sugar units, and are named according to the number of units they contain.

Disaccharides, or Bioses, $C_{12}H_{22}O_{11}$, and **Trisaccharides, or Trioses,** $C_{18}H_{32}O_{16}$,

Sugar.	Sources.	Components.
Maltose	Starch, glycogen	D-Glucose
Lactose	Milk	D-Glucose and D-Galactose
Cellobiose	Cellulose	D-Glucose
Gentiobiose	The glycoside, *amygdalin*	D-Glucose
	The triose, *gentianose*	D-Glucose and D-Fructose
Melibiose	The triose, *raffinose*	D-Glucose, D-Fructose and D-Galactose
Sucrose	Fruits and sugar-storing plants, cane and beet	D-Glucose and D-Fructose
Turanose	The triose, *melezitose*	D-Glucose and D-Fructose
Trehalose	The polymer, *trehalum*, in ergot and moulds	D-Glucose

Tetrasaccharides $C_{24}H_{42}O_{21}$, are represented by Stachyose (leguminous seeds), assembled from two D-glucose units and a unit of D-galactose and D-fructose.

The properties of an oligosaccharide depend on the type of components and the manner of their linkage. If all aldehyde or ketone groups are involved, the compound sugar is non-reducing. As, for example: sucrose, trehalose, raffinose, gentianose, stachyose. This distinction is of considerable analytical importance.

A. **Reducing Disaccharides** (potentially active groups present).

MALTOSE

Maltose, or *malt sugar*, a glucose-glucoside produced during the hydrolysis of starch and glycogen by acids or enzymes. It is the characteristic sugar of *malt*, or germinating barley, being formed by the breakdown of the reserve starch. It is very soluble in water, and is dextro-rotatory, $[a]_D = + 137 \cdot 5°$. The sugar is a typical aldose and gives a characteristic osazone. Maltose is easily hydrolysed by acids or the enzyme *maltase* into two molecules of glucose.

Since maltose is not attacked by the enzymes sucrase, lactase, or emulsin, all of which hydrolyse β-glucosides, it is inferred that it is an α-glucoside of α-glucose.

LACTOSE

Lactose, or *milk sugar*, is found in the milk of all mammals. Its percentage ranges from about 2 in the rabbit, to about 7·5 in the elephant. Human milk has a lactose range of 5 to 7 per cent. Cow's milk contains 3·5 to 4·8 per cent. The sugar appears in the blood and the urine during lactation. It has not been detected conclusively in plants or in lower animals. Lactose is much less soluble and less sweet than the other common sugars, and is not fermented by ordinary yeasts. It is dextro-rotatory, $[a]_D = + 52 \cdot 5°$, has the properties of an aldose, and gives a characteristic osazone. Oxidation with nitric acid converts it, *via* galactose, into mucic acid, a sparingly soluble crystalline compound. This reaction serves to distinguish lactose, galactose, and their derivatives from all other sugars.

Lactose readily undergoes lactic fermentation by many organisms found infecting milk, notably *Streptococcus lactis*. This leads to the formation of lactic acid, and the consequent " souring " of the liquid. Lactose is hydrolysed by a specific enzyme, *lactase*, found in the mammalian intestine, in emulsin (from almonds), and in some yeasts. It is not attacked by maltase, sucrase, or diastase, and is somewhat more resistant to acid hydrolysis than maltose or sucrose. The products of hydrolysis are the monosaccharides, glucose and galactose, showing that it is a galactoside, actually, 4-β-galacto-sido-glucose.

Reactions of Lactose.

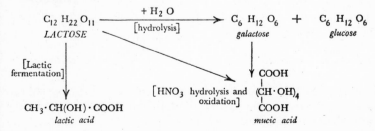

77

CELLOBIOSE

Cellobiose, or *cellose*, a β-glucose-glucoside obtained indirectly when the polysaccharide *cellulose* is acetylated and hydrolysed; the yield shows that at least one-half of cellulose is composed of cellobiose units. Cellobiose is hydrolysed by acids, by emulsin, lactase, and the specific enzyme, *cellobiase*, but not by maltase. The end-products are two molecules of glucose. In its properties cellobiose resembles maltose, but is less sweet and less soluble.

Maltose is 4-α-glucosido-glucopyranose and cellobiose is 4-β-glucoside-glucopyranose.

Cellobiose has not been found to occur free in nature.

B. Non-reducing disaccharides

SUCROSE

Sucrose, *saccharose, cane sugar, beet sugar*, the most important industrial sugar, is widely distributed in plants, notably the stems of the sugar-cane and sugar millet, the root of the sugar-beet, and the trunks of some palms and maples. Sucrose crystallises readily as large, colourless monoclinic crystals, m.p. 160° C., which are soluble in water to the extent of 67 gm. per 100 gm. of solution at 20° C. The sugar is non-reducing, and does not show mutarotation in solution. It is readily hydrolysed by dilute acids, forming a molecule of glucose and one of fructose. Chemically, sucrose is an α-glucoside of fructose. Sucrose is dextro-rotatory, $[a]_D = + 66 \cdot 5°$, but after hydrolysis the resulting mixture of monosaccharides is lævo-rotatory (owing to the liberation of fructose), and this mixture is termed " invert sugar ". Consequently, hydrolysis of sucrose is often described as *inversion*. The enzyme capable of causing it is called *invertase*, the systematic name being *sucrase*, which shows the particular sugar it attacks.

Structure of the Disaccharides. Maltose is a glucose glycoside, in which the units are held in α linkage between carbon 1 and carbon 4 of the respective sugars. Lactose is a galactose glycoside in which the units are in 1,4-β-linkage.

α-**Maltose.**
1,4-α-D-glucosido-D-glucose.

Lactose (α-, or β-).
1,4-β-D-galactosido-D-glucose.

These and other reducing oligosaccharides, like their constituent sugars, can exist in α- and β-forms, as indicated by the formulation >CH. OH for the grouping at carbon-1 in the glucose unit in lactose.

Sucrose is a fructose glucoside, in which the carbon 1 of the glucose is in α-β-linkage with carbon 2 of the fructose. As this linkage involves the reducing group in each sugar, sucrose is non-reducing. The fructose unit in sucrose is in the 5-membered ring, or furanose, form; and when released by hydrolysis rapidly changes to the more stable 6-membered ring or pyranose form.

Sucrose.
1-α-D-glucosido-2-β-D-fructofuranose.

Fructopyranose.

POLYOSES, OR POLYSACCHARIDES

These carbohydrates differ profoundly from the sugars. Of high molecular weight, they do not form true solutions in water, but are either colloidal or insoluble. They have no sweet taste. They give none of the sugar reactions characteristic of aldose or ketose grouping.

Instead, many of them react chromatically with iodine, a property not possessed by the sugars. The carbohydrate nature of the polysaccharides is shown by their conformity to the type formula, $C_m(H_2O)_n$, and by their cleavage into simple sugars on complete hydrolysis. Biologically, polysaccharides constitute the food reserve (starch), and structural material (cellulose, lignose, pentosan) of plants, and the easily mobilised carbohydrate reserve (glycogen) of animals. Substituted polysaccharides (heterosaccharides) are found as structural carbohydrate in the chitin of crustaceans and insects, and the pectin of fruits.

Hexosans

Type.	Structural Unit.	Source.
Cellulose	D-Glucose	Cell walls of plants, tunicates, and some micro-organisms
Dextrins	D-Glucose	Starch and glycogen hydrolysis
Dextrans	D-Glucose	Bacterial synthesis
Glycogens	D-Glucose	Liver, muscle, placenta, algæ, fungi, yeasts
Galactans	D-Galactose	Marine algæ
Inulin	D-Fructose	Roots of *Compositæ*: dahlia, artichoke
Levans	D-Fructose	Bacterial synthesis
Lichinins	D-Glucose	Cell walls of lichens
Mannan	D-Mannose	Shells of hard seeds: ivory nut, yeasts
Starches	D-Glucose	Seeds and tubers

79

HOLOSACCHARIDES. Polysaccharides composed entirely of sugar units.
(1) **Pentosans.** $(C_5H_8O_4)_n$, polymers of a pentose unit. Chiefly *arabans* (from arabinose) and *xylans* (from xylose). Pentoses occur mostly in combination with other materials in vegetable gums and mucilages.
(2) **Hexosans.** $(C_6H_{10}O_5)_n$, polymers of a hexose unit. The most important members are the *glucosans*, or polymers of glucose, including cellulose, starch, and glycogen.

Cellulose, the chief product of vegetation, is the skeletal material of the cell wall of plants, and in fibrous form, free or associated with lignin, occurs in cotton, flax, hemp, ramie, jute, straw, esparto, and wood.
After cleansing by alkali, cotton, either as wool or as filter-paper, is nearly pure cellulose. Insoluble in water and common organic solvents, cellulose may be dissolved in (a) ammoniacal cupric hydroxide, (b) acetic anhydride, (c) alkaline carbon disulphide and some other reagents, yielding important industrial products: artificial silks (rayon), and plastics (viscose, cellophane). Dissolved in a mixture of nitric and sulphuric acids, cellulose forms the basis of gun-cotton, celluloid, collodion. As plants age, the cellulose becomes lignified by incorporation of *lignin*, a polymer of phenol units. Ligno-cellulose, chief constituent of wood, is used in the manufacture of " low-grade " papers that become yellow and friable on exposure to air and light.
Cellulose is a chain-polymer of D-glucose units held in 1,4-β-linkage. Hydrolysed progressively by the enzyme cellulase, it yields cellodextrins and, ultimately, the disaccharide cellobiose, which in turn is hydrolysed by the enzyme cellobiase, or by acids, to D-glucose. These enzymes occur in germinating seeds, lower plants and micro-organisms, but are absent from the digestive secretions of higher animals. As a result, cellulose is unavailable for human nutrition. The abundant cellulose in the diet of ruminants is made available by a partnership involving the micro-flora of the paunch and cæcum which degrade the polysaccharide, with production of assimilable short-chain fatty acids.

Cellulose
Molecular weight, 300,000 to 500,000.
Number of C_6 units, 2,000 to 3,000. Length of chain, 1 to $1 \cdot 5\mu$.

Cellulose fibres are formed from threads of chain molecules held together by cross-linkages, involving hydrogen-bonding between sugar units in adjacent chains.

STARCH

Starch, or *Amylum*, is present in quantity in many vegetable foodstuffs, in cereals, and their products, such as bread. It is characterised by giving a blue-purple colour with iodine. It does not occur in animal tissues.

Starch is found in solid granules throughout plant tissues in leaves, stems, roots, fruits, and seeds. The granules are usually made up of concentric layers formed round a hilum, suggesting that the material is deposited during cycles of activity. When viewed by polarised light, a black cross is seen branching from the hilum.

The shape and size of the granule is characteristic of the plant, being oval in beans, ovoid and irregular in potato and arrowroot, discoid in wheat and barley, and polyhedral in rice and maize.

The starch granule is an aggregation of starch molecules which can be resolved and rendered water-soluble by mild acid or enzyme hydrolysis, yielding " soluble starch ".

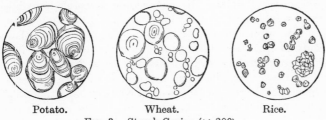

Potato.   Wheat.   Rice.

Fig. 3.—Starch Grains (× 200).

Average diameters in μ of common starches are: potato, 140 to 180; arrowroot, 155; haricot bean, 65; pea, 45 to 55; wheat, 45 to 55; maize, 30; oat (composite granules), 35 to 45; oat (single granules), 6 to 8; rice (single granules), 4 to 6.

Amylose and Amylopectin. Natural starches are mixtures of two polysaccharides: (*a*) *Amylose*, an unbranched chain of up to 300 glucopyranose units in 1,4-*a*-linkage; and (*b*) *Amylopectin*, a glucopyranose chain with branches attached by 1,6-linkage. Amylose separates out as a complex when starch paste is saturated with thymol and cyclohexanol. It forms 15 to 25 per cent. of most starches, gives a pure blue iodine reaction, and has been crystallised. Amylopectin, which is the total polysaccharide in some " waxy " starches, when pure gives a purple iodine reaction.

Dextrins are intermediate products of hydrolysis of starch and glycogen. They differ from starch in being soluble in cold water, and from sugars in being more readily precipitated by alcohol. The higher members, *e*-dextrins (erythro-dextrins), give red colours with iodine, the lower members, *a*-dextrins (achroo-dextrins), give no colour with iodine. All have a high dextrorotation in solution, hence the group name, and all are completely hydrolysable to sugar. The copper-reducing power depends on the method of preparation, and non-reducing dextrins have been obtained. Dextrins do not occur free in Nature. Their presence imparts a characteristic flavour to bread crust, toast, and partly charred cereal foodstuffs.

DEXTRIN

Dextrin, or *starch gum*. Industrial dextrin is made by heating dry potato starch to 210° C., or by autoclaving starch paste in presence of 1 per cent. citric acid. The product is chiefly *a*-dextrin, and is an important adhesive. Maltodextrin is the general term applied to non-crystalline copper-reducing intermediate products of the action of diastase on starch.

GLYCOGEN

Glycogen, or *animal starch*, is found principally in liver and muscle, and also in placenta, in all fœtal tissues, in many fungi, and in maize seed. It is a rapidly mobilised source of glucose. Glycogen closely resembles amylopectin. It is a white, water-soluble powder, $[a]_D = + 196 \cdot 6°$. It gives a mahogany red with iodine, and is precipitated from aqueous solution by addition of alcohol up to 60 per cent., or by saturation with solid ammonium sulphate. It does not reduce alkaline copper solutions. Hydrolysis by acids, diastase or amylase, converts it first into lower dextrins, then maltose, and finally glucose.

Glycogen is relatively stable in hot 30 per cent. KOH or NaOH, and may be extracted by these reagents from fresh, finely minced tissues. It is purified by alcoholic reprecipitations, and by dialysis. It is quantitatively precipitated from aqueous solutions by addition of four volumes of glacial acetic acid.

Glycogen Distribution in Animals. Mammalian liver contains 3 to 7 per cent. of glycogen, or about a quarter to a half of the total in the animal. The remainder is chiefly in muscle, which contains up to 1 per cent. Starvation rapidly lowers the liver glycogen value, but not the muscle glycogen.

Because of its branched structure the molecule of amylopectin or glycogen can extend or shorten its many branch chains by addition or removal of glucose units and thus act as a very labile sugar reservoir. As a result of variation in chain lengths, number of branches, and state of aggregation, the molecular weights of these polysaccharides can range from less than 10,000 in the unbranched amyloses to more than 4 million in the glycogens.

Starch (amylose) and Glycogen Chain

Chain-branching starts by condensation between a terminal carbon 1 in a glucose molecule and a carbon 6 in a pre-existing chain, or stem.

Each branch thus formed can extend into a chain of about twenty glucose units in 1,4-α-linkage, and may give rise to secondary branches, starting from one of its —$CH_2.OH$ groups.

Evidence for structure is chemical and biological. Methylation, followed by complete hydrolysis, yields 2,3,6-trimethylglucose derived from the units of the unbranched chains which, therefore, must have had their carbons 1 and 4 involved in linkage. Oxidation by periodic acid, HIO_4, attacks free terminal carbons 1 and 4, with production of formic acid, and can be used to estimate the number of end-groups, or chain-ends present.

The enzyme, α-amylase, a 1,4-α-glucosidase in malt, hydrolyses amylum completely to maltose, showing that the polysaccharide is a chain of disaccharide units in α-linkage. α-amylase is unable to break the 1,6-linkages in amylopectin and in glycogen, consequently, hydrolysis stops when all the branches have been removed, and up to half the polysaccharide has been converted to maltose. The residue consists of a mixture of short-chain dextrins. If it is treated with 1,6-α-glucosidase, present in pancreatic juice, the resistant glucose units will be split off, and the action of the α-amylase will continue, until the next 1,6-linkage points are encountered.

The progressive hydrolysis of starches by mixed enzymes results in the intermediate formation of long-chain dextrins by terminal erosion of the amylose chains, and short-chain dextrins from the debranched stems of amylopectins.

$$\text{Starch} \begin{cases} \text{amylopectin} \to \text{short-chain dextrins} \to \text{maltose} \\ \text{amylose} \quad \to \text{long-chain dextrins} \to \text{maltose} \end{cases} \searrow \text{glucose}$$

amylopectin → short-chain dextrins → maltose
Starch
amylose   → long-chain dextrins → maltose → glucose
             +   +   +
          maltose maltose maltose

HETEROSACCHARIDES

Heterosaccharides are polysaccharides containing two to six different species of structural unit, which may be a pentose, a hexose, an amino sugar, a sugar acid, or a sugar ester. Plant heterosaccharides include heteropentosans (gums, pectic substances, hemi-celluloses) which contain pentose units; and heterohexosans (lignocellulose, pectocellulose, lipocellulose) which contain hexose units.

Pectins, or vegetable mucilages, occur in roots, fruit pulp and rind and the peel of apples, oranges and lemons. They are not extracted by cold water, but when boiled with weak acids such as accompany them in fruits, or when attacked by the enzyme *pectase*, they are hydrolysed to substances that form characteristic jellies. Agar, from some red seaweeds (*Rhodophyceae*), and carrageen, from the alga *Chondrus crispus*, are assembled from galactose units, some of which occur as sulphate esters. Industrially important heterosaccharides from seaweeds include *alginic acid* (a polymer of D-mannuronic acid), *carrageen*, and *agar* (polymers of galactose and galactose sulphate).

Animal Heterosaccharides

Name.	Units.	Sources.
Chitin	N-acetylglucosamine $(CH_3.CO.NH.C_6H_{11}O_5)$	Crustacean shell, insect cuticle, fungi
Chondroitin sulphates, A, B, C	N-acetylchondrosamine, glucuronic acid, sulphuric acid	Connective tissues, cartilage, lung
Heparin	Glucuronic acid, glucosamine, sulphuric acid	Liver, lung, thymus, spleen
Hyaluronic acid	N-acetylglucosamine, glucuronic acid	Skin, umbilical cord, vitreous humor, synovial fluid, streptococci

Mucopolysaccharides. The characteristic viscosity of secretions, such as saliva, bile, and other biological fluids was formerly attributed to the presence of *mucins* (L. *mucus*, slime) and *mucoids*. Mucins, as a class, are flocculated by acetic acid; mucoids are not. These substances are heterosaccharide in structure and may be classified as mucopolysaccharides when they occur free, and as mucoproteins when they occur associated with proteins. An alternative term, " glycoprotein ", is applied to proteins containing carbohydrate units.

Representative examples are: salivary mucoproteins; gastric mucins; mucoids of blood serum, urine, and egg white; gonadotropic hormones of the pituitary gland; the mucoproteins of the red corpuscles that constitute the A, B, O(H), and Rh blood-group antigens.

Mucopolysaccharides contain nitrogen entirely or chiefly in the form of hexosamine units or N-acetylhexosamine, which can be detected by colour tests.

Sialic acid, or neuraminic acid, occurs in many secretions, and appears to be a component of some mucoproteins and other proteins. It is characterised by the development of a purple colour with p-dimethylaminobenzaldehyde (Ehrlich's aldehyde reagent) in cold, acid solutions. Sialic acid appears to be the N-acetyl derivative of a 9-carbon sugar amine. It is a constituent of the blood-group mucoproteins and the complex lipids of brain and spleen.

SUGAR DERIVATIVES

Polyols, polyhydroxyalcohols, or sugar alcohols, can be regarded as being derived from simple sugars by reduction of the aldehyde or ketone group. Like the sugars, they are water-soluble and sweet, but are stable non-reducing compounds and are widely distributed in plants. They are not fermented by common yeasts, but are attacked by some moulds and bacteria, and are used analytically as a means of differentiating micro-organisms.

Examples are: *glycerol*, $C_3H_5(OH)_3$, in fats and complex lipids; *erythrol*, $C_4H_6(OH)_4$, in algæ and mosses; D-*mannitol*, $C_6H_8(OH)_6$, a polyol corresponding to D-mannose, in fungi and manna from larch and other tree saps. D-*ribitol* $C_5H_7(OH)_5$, corresponding to D-ribose, is universally distributed as riboflavin, or vitamin B_2, in the flavin coenzymes.

Sugar polyols are linear compounds of the type $HO.CH_2.(CH.OH)_n.CH_2OH$. Inositols, or cyclic polyols, are 6-membered ring compounds, $C_6H_6(OH)_6$ assembled from —CH(OH)— units. They resemble the linear polyols, in solubility and sweetness, but, because of their ring structure, are much more stable. Like the hexoses, they have the general formula $C_6H_{12}O_6$, but having no potential aldehyde or ketone group, they are non-reducing.

Inositol, or *myo*-inositol, is widespread in plant and animal tissues: leaves, citrus fruit, cereal grain, yeasts, fungi, bacteria, muscle, liver and central nervous system. Because of its original source it was termed " muscle sugar ". In plants it occurs chiefly as a hexaphosphate ester, phytic acid, $C_6H_6(O.PO(OH)_2)_6$, which forms a sparingly soluble calcium-magnesium salt, *phytin*, that is concentrated in the outer coat of seeds, and provides a reserve of metals for the growing plant.

Neither phytic acid nor phytin is attacked by the enzymes of the human alimentary tract, so they are unavailable as sources of phosphate, calcium, or magnesium. In excess, free phytic acid is harmful, as it immobilises the available calcium in the diet, and may " decalcify " the animal.

Phytic acid, free or as phytin, can account for two-thirds to three-quarters of the total phosphorus of the important food cereals. Representative values in mg. phytic acid per 100 gm. dry material, are: wheat, 263; oatmeal, 239; bran, 487 to 1,150; beans, 495; grass, 7; yeast, 4·7.

Myo-inositol is included among the vitamins required by higher animals; it is necessary for the growth of some yeasts, moulds, insects, and other organisms. By substitution of Cl for OH the powerful insecticide hexachlorocyclohexane, or *gammexane*, $C_6H_6Cl_6$, is obtained which induces inositol starvation in the organism by competing with the available polyose.

Structure. Nine *cis-trans* isomeric forms of inositol are possible, of which four occur naturally, including the relatively common *myo*-inositol. Of these nine isomers only two are optically active.

Sugar Acids. Sugars on partial oxidation yield mono- and dicarboxylic acids having the same number of carbon atoms as the parent sugar. Oxidation of a terminal aldehyde group yields an *aldonic acid*, $HO.CH_2.(CH.OH)_n.COOH$.

Oxidation of a terminal alcohol group in an aldose yields a *uronic acid*, $HOOC.(CH.OH)_n.CHO$. This requires that the aldehyde group be protected or masked in ring form during the oxidation. If both terminal groups be oxidised the result will be a *saccharic*, or *aldaric acid*, $HOOC.(CH.OH)_{n2}.COOH$.

COOH ←	CHO	CHO →	COOH	COOH
H—C—OH	H—C—OH	H—C—OH	H—C—OH	CH₂
HO—C—H	HO—C—H	HO—C—H	HO—C—H Reduction	CH₂
H—C—OH	H—C—OH	H—C—OH	H—C—OH ---→	CH
H—C—OH	H—C—OH	H—C—OH	H—C—OH	CH₂
CH₂OH	CH₂OH → COOH	COOH	COOH	COOH
D-gluconic acid.	D-glucose	D-glucuronic acid.	Saccharic acid.	Adipic acid.

(open forms).

D-glucuronic acid, which exists in pyran ring form, is the most important of the uronic acids. It is a structural unit in many heterosaccharides, and is employed also to make more soluble or to detoxify substances prior to excretion in the urine.

L-*galacturonic acid* occurs in pectic acids. D-*mannuronic acid* is a structural unit in *alginic acid*, which is extracted from *Laminaria* and other algæ, by alkalis. Sodium alginate is used industrially as an adhesive and a thickening agent. It is of no nutritional value to man.

Sugar Esters. One or more of the hydroxyl groups in a sugar can condense with acids to give a variety of esters, some of which are of value in structural analysis. Important natural esters are the sugar phosphates, which are obligatory intermediates in many paths of carbohydrate metabolism.

The Sugar Phosphates

Phosphate esters of sugars are of fundamental importance in biology. They are generated by the phosphorolysis of polysaccharides, or by transfer of phosphate radicals from high-energy polyphosphate, such as adenosine triphosphate.

Glucose 1-Phosphate. Glucopyranose in which the hydroxyl at carbon 1 has been replaced by $-O-PO(OH)_2$. It is a non-reducing high-energy ester, first isolated by the Cori in 1937.

Glucose 6-Phosphate (Robinson, 1931). Glucopyranose in which the primary alcohol hydroxyl at carbon 6 has been replaced by phosphate. It retains the reducing properties of the parent sugar.

Fructose 6-Phosphate (Neuberg, 1918), the corresponding fructofuranose ester, and **Fructose 1,6-diphosphate** (Harden and Young, 1905), like the glucose phosphates are intermediates in hexose degradation and construction.

Pentose Phosphates. Ribose and deoxyribose phosphates occur as chain units in the nucleic acids. Ribulose phosphates are intermediates in the photosynthesis of carbohydrates and the metabolism of pentoses.

Triose Phosphates. Glyceraldehyde 3-phosphate and dihydroxyacetone phosphate, fission products of fructose 1,6-diphosphate, are intermediates in sugar metabolism.

Amino Sugars. Sugars in which an amino group replaces one of the primary or secondary hydroxyls are represented chiefly by the 2-aminohexoses, D-*glucosamine* and D-*galactosamine*, both of which occur as structural units in heterosaccharides. Other amino sugars have been detected in antibiotics. Amino sugars are reducing compounds, with basic properties due to the exposed amino group, which is usually masked by acetylation when the amino sugar forms a unit in a heterosaccharide.

Glucopyranose type.

D-**glucose:** $X = Y = -OH$; $Z = -CH_2.OH$
D-**glucuronic acid:** $X = Y = -OH$; $Z = -COOH$
D-**glucosamine:** $X = -OH$; $Y = -NH_2$; $Z = -CH_2.OH$
N-**acetyl-D-glucosamine:** $X = -OH$; $Y = -NH.CO.CH_3$; $Z = -CH_2.OH$
Glucose 1-phosphate: $X = -O-PO(OH)_2$; $Y = -OH$; $Z = -CH_2.OH$
Glucose 6-phosphate: $X = Y = -OH$; $Z = -CH_2.O-PO(OH)_2$

Glucose Derivatives.

Deoxy sugars contain one atom of oxygen less than the parent carbohydrate, and are represented by 2-deoxy-D-ribose, and by the ω-deoxy sugars, in which the ω-, or terminal group, $-CH_2.OH$, has become $-CH_3$, forming a methyl sugar.

87

Examples of ω-deoxy sugars are: 3-deoxyglyceric aldehyde, or lactic alde-hyde, $CH_3.CH(OH).CHO$, found in poplar leaves; 6-deoxy-D-galactose, found as a polymer in Japanese seaweed and in gum tragacanth; 6-deoxy-D-allose, or digitalose, found in the glycoside digitalin; and 6-deoxy-L-mannose, or L-rhamnose, found in many glycosides.

2-deoxyribose has not been found free, but is universally distributed in plants and animals as a component of the deoxyribonucleic acid of nuclear chromatin.

D-ribopyranose.   D-deoxyribopyranose.

Chapter 7 Identification and
Estimation of Carbohydrates

Furfural Reactions. Sugars higher than tetroses are dehydrated by strong acids with production of furfurals which can be detected colorimetrically by condensation with phenols. Pentoses are quantitatively converted into furfuraldehyde on distillation with $N/5$ sulphuric or hydrochloric acid. Hexoses yield the less stable 5-hydroxymethyl furfural which breaks down to levulinic, $H_3C.CO.CH_2.CH_2.COOH$, and formic acids. Oligosaccharides and polysaccharides are hydrolysed by the acid to their component sugars and react accordingly. Amino sugars and uronic acids, and their polymers, also yield furfurals.

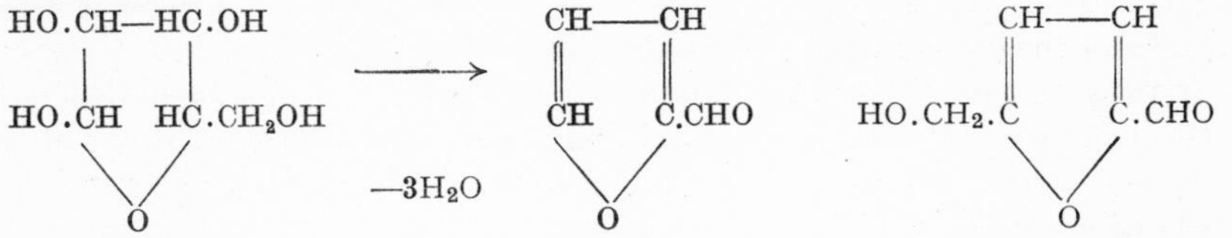

HO.CH—HC.OH   CH——CH   CH——CH

HO.CH   HC.CH$_2$OH   CH   C.CHO   HO.CH$_2$.C   C.CHO

O   —3H$_2$O   O   O

Pentose   **Furfura**   **Hydroxy-methylfurfural.**
(furanose type).   (furfuraldehyde).

A. Furfural Tests

(1) **Thymol Test.** Mix 2 ml. of the sugar solution with 2 drops of a 2 per cent. ethanol solution of thymol. Add an excess, 5 ml., of concentrated, or about 10 N hydrochloric acid (30 to 35 per cent. w/v HCl). Immerse tube in boiling water. If a carbohydrate is present, a purple colour will develop; rapidly with pentoses and ketohexoses, slowly with polysaccharides. The thymol can be replaced by other phenols: α-naphthol (Molisch test), resorcinol, orcinol, phloroglucinol. The pigments can be extracted with amyl or butyl alcohol, and characterised spectrometrically.

(1a) **Sulphuric Ring Test.** The reagent is a recently prepared 0·1 per cent. solution in pure, concentrated sulphuric acid of thymol, α-naphthol, carbazole (Dische test), or anthrone (Dreywood test). To not more than 1 ml. of sugar solution add carefully 2 ml. of the reagent, so as to form a lower layer. Let the tube stand at room temperature. A positive test is shown by the development of a coloured zone between the layers, which varies from red-purple (thymol) to blue-green (anthrone). Should no colour appear within ten minutes, gently mix the contents. A positive delayed reaction is given by

89

insoluble carbohydrates, such as starch and cellulose. If the solution is too concentrated, charring occurs and obscures the test. Some non-sugars, notably glycerol and ascorbic acid, give orange or red colours with the reagents in the ring test.

B. Selective Furfural Tests

(1) **Pentoses and Ketohexoses.** (*a*) Apply the general test (A1) in the absence of thymol or other phenol. Pentoses, ketohexoses, and their compounds, including sucrose, develop orange-red colours; aldohexoses and their compounds do not. (*b*) Apply the general test (A1), including the phenol, but reducing the amount of acid to 2 ml., instead of 5 ml. Under these conditions, aldohexoses and their compounds (maltose, lactose, starch, glycogen, cellulose) fail to react, or only do so after prolonged heating.

(2) **Uronic Acids.** Apply test A1, using naphthoresorcinol as the phenol. Colours ranging from red to blue are given by the carbohydrates, but the uronic acids yield blue-violet pigments, which, unlike the sugar pigments, are soluble in benzene, and thus may be extracted. This test is used to detect glycuronic compounds in urine.

(3) **Aniline Test for Pentoses.** Mix 2 ml. of the solution with 2 drops of aniline and 5 ml. of glacial acetic acid. Immerse in boiling water. Pentoses develop a red colour, other carbohydrates do not react.

(4) **Urea Test for Fructose.** To about 0·3 g. of solid urea in a small dish, add 6 drops of concentrated hydrochloric acid, and not more than 2 drops of the sugar solution. Mix until most of the urea has dissolved. Evaporate on a boiling water bath. If fructose or a fructoside (sucrose, inulin) is present a bright blue colour will develop. Water inhibits the test, which is very delicate, and will reveal fructose in one drop of a 0·1 per cent. solution. In high concentration, aldoses develop red colours after prolonged heating.

Rearrangement to Enediols. In alkaline solution, the oxygen bridge in simple sugars and reducing oligosaccharides is broken by hydrolysis. This opens the ring, and exposes the aldehyde or ketone group, which rearranges by accepting a hydrogen atom from the adjacent alcohol group, and forms the very reactive *enediol* system.

$$R\text{—}CH(OH).CHO \rightleftharpoons R\text{—}C(OH) = CH(OH) \rightleftharpoons R\text{—}CO.CH_2.OH$$

Aldose   1,2-Enediol   Ketose

Structurally related sugars yield the same enediol as, for example, glucose, fructose, and mannose, which have the same pattern apart from the groupings at carbons 1 and 2. Consequently, in alkaline solution any one of these hexoses can give rise to an equilibrium mixture that includes the other two sugars and the enediol common to all three.

An enediol is a powerful reducing agent, and gives a violet colour with alkaline *o*-dinitrobenzene, bleaches methylene blue, and reduces ferric, cupric, silver, and mercuric ions, as may be seen in the familiar tests for reducing sugars.

At higher temperatures, or in more alkaline solution, when protected from

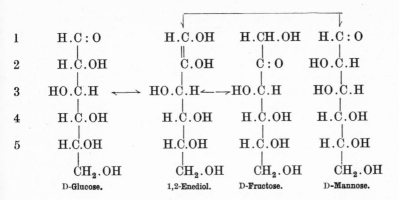

	D-Glucose.	1,2-Enediol.	D-Fructose.	D-Mannose.
1	H.C : O	H.C.OH	H.CH.OH	H.C : O
2	H.C.OH	C.OH	C : O	HO.C.H
3	HO.C.H ⟶	HO.C.H⟵ ⟶	HO.C.H	HO.C.H
4	H.C.OH	H.C.OH	H.C.OH	H.C.OH
5	H.C.OH	H.C.OH	H.C.OH	H.C.OH
	CH₂.OH	CH₂.OH	CH₂.OH	CH₂.OH

oxidation, the enediol double-bond is transferred to carbons 3 and 4, with subsequent cleavage of the hexose into two trioses. Accompanying polymerisations impart a yellow-brown colour.

3,4-Enediol $\quad$ HO.CH$_2$.CH(OH).C(OH)=C(OH).CH(OH).CH$_2$.OH

Trioses $\quad$ HO.CH$_2$.CH(OH).CHO $\quad$ HO.CH$_2$.CO.CH$_2$.OH
$\qquad\qquad\qquad$ Glyceraldehyde. $\qquad\qquad$ Dihydroxy acetone.

C. Enediol Reactions

(1) **Alkali Test.** Boil 5 ml. of the solution. Remove from flame, and make alkaline with 5 drops of 20 per cent. sodium hydroxide or concentrated ammonium hydroxide. Allow to cool, without shaking. If a reducing sugar is present the solution will become yellow, deepening into brown, as the enediol polymerises. Non-reducing oligosaccharides (sucrose, raffinose) and polysaccharides do not react.

(2) **Methylene Blue Test.** Add a couple of drops of very dilute (0·1 per cent.) methylene blue to 5 ml. of the solution. Make alkaline with 5 drops of 20 per cent. sodium hydroxide. Warm gently. The blue colour will be discharged if a reducing sugar is present, but returns on aerating the contents of the tube by shaking. This reaction can be used to provide an " internal indicator " for sugar estimation by copper reduction methods.

(3) *o*-**Dinitrobenzene Test.** Apply test C2, substituting a few drops of 5 per cent. *o*-dinitrobenzene, C$_6$H$_4$(NO$_2$)$_2$, in ethanol. On warming, a deep violet colour will develop if a reducing sugar is present. The test is very delicate and will detect 6 parts of reducing sugar in a million. If the sugar solution is too concentrated the test may be obscured by the development of the yellow enediol pigments.

(4) **Copper-reduction Tests.** (*a*) *Trommer.* To 5 ml. of solution add 2 drops of 5 per cent. copper sulphate and 10 drops of 20 per cent. sodium hydroxide. A light blue precipitate of cupric hydroxide forms, and will dissolve to form a blue solution if sufficient sugar, or any other polyol is present. Boil. The blue

91

will be replaced by an orange-red suspension of cuprous oxide if a reducing sugar is present. In the absence of reducing agents the cupric hydroxide is dehydrated to black cupric oxide; for this reason excess of copper should be avoided, as it may obscure a slight positive reduction effect.

(b) *Fehling.* Mix equal volumes (2 ml.) of Fehling's reagent A and B. A deep blue colour forms. Boil; no change will be observed. Add 2 ml. of the test solution, and warm gently. An orange-red suspension will appear if a reducing sugar is present.

(c) **Benedict Qualitative Test.** Mix 8 drops of the solution with 5 ml. of Benedict's qualitative reagent. Boil for 90 seconds or immerse in boiling water for 2 to 3 minutes. Remove and allow to cool. A green turbidity with a yellow precipitate indicates 0·1 to 0·3 per cent. of reducing sugar in the original solution. A dense orange-red precipitate and a clear supernatant liquid indicates more than 1·5 per cent. sugar. The reagent is designed specially for the detection of sugar in urine; it must not be confused with Benedict's quantitative reagent, which is used only for sugar estimation.

MECHANISM OF THE COPPER REDUCTION TESTS

$$CuSO_4 + 2NaOH \longrightarrow Cu(OH)_2 + Na_2SO_4$$
Cupric hydroxide
(Blue precipitate)
= **Trommer Reagent.**

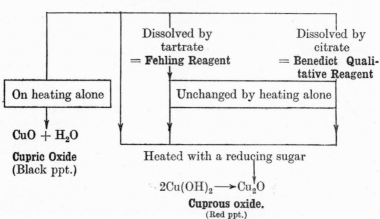

| | Dissolved by tartrate = **Fehling Reagent** | Dissolved by citrate = **Benedict Qualitative Reagent** |

On heating alone | Unchanged by heating alone |

CuO + H₂O
$$CuO + H_2O$$
Cupric Oxide
(Black ppt.)

Heated with a reducing sugar

$$2Cu(OH)_2 \longrightarrow Cu_2O$$
Cuprous oxide.
(Red ppt.)

(d) *Hydrolysis Test for Sucrose.* Apply Trommer's test to 5 ml. of solution. If there is no reduction acidify the mixture with a few drops of concentrated hydrochloric acid, as shown by discharge of the blue colour. Let the warm solution stand for a couple of minutes to allow acid hydrolysis to take place. Regenerate the Trommer reagent by adding sufficient 20 per cent. sodium hydroxide to restore the blue colour. Heat gently. If reduction now takes place, the original solution will have contained sucrose or some other non-reducing oligosaccharide or ester. Starch and other polysaccharides will give the test if boiled with acid for a few minutes.

(e) *Methylamine Test for Maltose and Lactose.* Add 5 drops of 5 per cent. methylamine hydrochloride to 5 ml. of the neutral solution. Boil briefly, remove from the flame, and while still warm make alkaline by addition of sufficient (10 drops) 20 per cent. sodium hydroxide. Let the tube stand without shaking. If a yellow colour develops (alkali enediol reaction) a reducing sugar is present; if the yellow changes to bright carmine the sugar is maltose, lactose, cellobiose or other reducing oligosaccharide.

(f) *Tetrazolium Test.* To 2 ml. of solution add 5 drops of a 2 per cent. aqueous triphenyltetrazolium chloride and 5 drops of 20 per cent. sodium hydroxide. Warm gently. If a reducing sugar is present the mixture will turn red and eventually yield a red precipitate of triphenylformazan. The test is given rapidly in the cold by free enediols, including ascorbic acid, and has been adapted to show the viability of seeds and cells.

C. Hydrazone and Osazone Formation

Compounds containing a free or potential carbonyl group (aldehydes, ketones, reducing sugars) condense with hydrazines to yield *hydrazones*:

$$\diagdown\!\!C : O + H_2N.NH.R \longrightarrow \diagdown\!\!C = N.NH.R$$
Hydrazine.   Hydrazone.

In this way, by use of the reagent phenylhydrazine, $C_6H_5.NH.NH_2$, phenyl-hydrazones can be obtained from all the reducing sugars. Phenylhydrazones of the common sugars, with the exception of mannose, are soluble in water.

CHO + H₂N—NH.C₆H₅   CH=N—NH:C₆H₅
| |
H—C—OH   H—C—OH   + H₂N.NH.C₆H₅
| |
(CH.OH)₃ ———→   (CH.OH)₃ + H₂O
| |
CH₂OH   CH₂OH
D-glucose.   D-glucosehydrazone.   CH = N.NH.C₆H₅
CHO   CH = N—NH.C₆H₅ |
| | C = N.NH.C₆H₅
HO—C—H ———→   HO—C—H ———→ |
| | (CH.OH)₃
(CH.OH)₃   (CH.OH)₃ |
| | CH₂OH
CH₂OH   CH₂OH   Osazone
D-mannose.   D-mannosehydrazone.   common to all three
CH₂OH   CH₂.OH   sugars
| | (Glucosazone).
CO   C = N—NH.C₆H₅
| |
(CH.OH)₃ ———→   (CH.OH)₃
| |
CH₂OH   CH₂OH
D-fructose.   D-fructosehydrazone.

93

However, when boiled with an excess of phenylhydrazine an additional condensation takes place, forming an osazone which is sparingly soluble and separates in characteristic crystalline form. The sugar osazones provide a method for the identification of sugars, alone and in mixtures. D-glucose, D-mannose, and D-fructose yield different hydrazones, but all form the same osazone, showing that their structure is similar, when the individuality of the carbon 1 and 2 arrangement has been lost by combination with the second molecule of the hydrazine.

Test. Mix 5 ml. of the solution with 2 ml. phenylhydrazine reagent. Immerse the tube in boiling water for 30 to 60 minutes. If the test is positive, the contents of the tube will become bright yellow. Allow the tube to cool slowly at room temperature. The osazone will separate as a yellow, crystalline precipitate. Transfer to a slide, apply a cover glass, and examine microscopically.

Characteristics of the Commoner Osazones. *Glucose, fructose,* and *mannose* yield the same osazone, **glucosazone,** which crystallises in yellow brushes or sheaves of slender needles; m.p. 231° C.

Galactosazone forms elongated strips and plates; m.p. 214° C.

Maltosazone occurs in stellate clusters of broad-bladed crystals; m.p. 206° C.

Lactosazone forms close tufts of short, fine crystals; m.p. 200° C. It is fairly soluble in hot water, and only separates out slowly on cooling. Osazone preparations from disaccharides are liable to be contaminated with osazones formed from monosaccharides liberated by acid hydrolysis if boiling has been prolonged. Pentose osazones include *arabinosazone*, which forms long, curved threads and wisps; m.p. 143° C., and *xylosazone*, which forms long needles; m.p. 166° C. Non-reducing sugars and polysaccharides do not yield hydrazones or osazones.

The osazones can be identified by microscopic inspection and by determination of the melting-point after recrystallisation from hot water or methanol.

Enzyme Tests for Sugars

Yeasts, fungi, and bacteria contain enzyme systems that convert sugars into products that can be used for sugar identification. Examples are the alcoholic fermentation of sugars by yeast, and the lactic fermentation of lactose by *Lactobacillus.* The enzyme *notatin*, a dehydrogenase from moulds (*Penicillium notatum, Aspergillus niger*), in presence of atmospheric oxygen specifically oxidises D-glucose to gluconic acid and hydrogen peroxide, and provides a selective test for the sugar (p. 230).

Fermentation by Yeast. The yeast organism decomposes fermentable sugars into alcohol and carbon dioxide in accordance with the general equation:

$$C_6H_{12}O_6 \rightarrow 2\ C_2H_5.OH + 2\ CO_2.$$

(*a*) *Acid Formation.* Shake up about 25 to 30 ml. of sugar solution with 2 to 3 gm. of baker's yeast (*Saccharomyces cerevisea*). Transfer about 5 ml. into a test tube, and add a few drops of the indicator phenol red. The reaction of

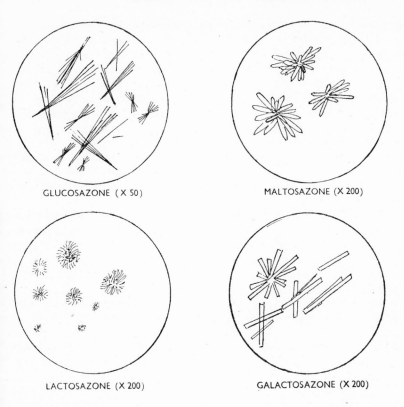

GLUCOSAZONE (× 50)

MALTOSAZONE (× 200)

LACTOSAZONE (× 200)

GALACTOSAZONE (× 200)

the mixture is acid (yellow). Add a drop or two of N/10 NaOH until the mixture is just alkaline (pink), and incubate the tube at 45° to 50° C. for a few minutes. The contents gradually become acid owing to liberation of carbon dioxide from the fermenting sugar. On neutralising again, the process is repeated, and continues until all the sugar is fermented.

(b) *Alcohol Production.* Fill the closed limb of a fermentation tube with the yeast-sugar mixture so as to leave no air bubbles. Place tube in an incubator at 40° to 50° for 1 hour, or leave for 24 hours at room temperature. If a fermentable sugar be present it is broken down into alcohol and carbon dioxide, which collects as a gas in the closed limb of the tube.

(1) *Detection of Carbon Dioxide.* Add 2 to 3 ml. of 20 per cent. sodium hydroxide to the tube; close the orifice, and invert the tube so as to mix the contents. The gas is rapidly absorbed by the alkali, and a negative pressure develops in the tube.

(2) *Detection of Alcohol.* Transfer about 2 ml. of the contents of the tube to a petri dish. In the centre of the dish place a watch-glass containing about 5 drops of concentrated nitric acid and a drop of 5 per cent. potassium chrom-

ate. Avoid any overflow. Cover the dish and let it remain at room temperature. Alcohol vapour diffuses from the fermentation mixture and is oxidised by the chromic acid. The contents of the watch-glass gradually change in colour from orange to blue, owing to formation of chromium nitrate.

Fermentable Sugars. Four hexoses only are fermented by ordinary yeast, namely: *glucose, mannose, galactose,* and *fructose.* Of the commoner disaccharides, *maltose* and *sucrose* are attacked while *lactose* is not. Pentoses as a class are non-fermentable by yeast.

The test thus serves to distinguish pentoses and lactose from all other common reducing sugars. It is frequently applied to urine to distinguish *glucose* from (1) *lactose,* (2) *urinary pentose,* and (3) *glycuronic acid,* all of which reduce alkaline copper solutions.

Iodine Test for Polysaccharides. Starches, glycogens, and higher dextrins form deeply pigmented adsorption compounds with iodine in neutral or acid solution. This can be demonstrated by adding the carbohydrate solution, drop by drop, to 5 ml. of water coloured yellow by addition of a few drops of 1 per cent. iodine: dark blue, amylose; red-brown to purple, amylopectin, glycogen, higher dextrins (erythrodextrins). Alkalies and proteins inhibit the test by combining with the iodine, as shown by the bleaching of the yellow colour. This can be overcome by acidification with acetic acid.

The pigment is an iodine adsorption complex of variable composition. It dissociates on warming or addition of alkali, but reforms on cooling or on acidification. The reaction is not given by the fructose polysaccharide inulin, or by lower dextrins, or by saccharides.

Rotation of Polarised Light. By use of the polarimeter, all carbohydrates can be divided into a dextro-rotatory class and a lævo-rotatory class. The sugar D-fructose is the commonest lævo-rotatory saccharide, and for this reason is termed *lævulose.* Each pure saccharide has a specific rotatory constant, which is determined under equilibrium conditions so as to avoid confusion due to mutarotation.

Specific Rotation. This is defined as the rotation in angular degrees produced by a length of 1 decimetre of solution containing 1 gm. of solute in 1 ml. It may be expressed: $[a] = \dfrac{100a}{lc}$,

in which $[a]$ = specific rotation;

a = observed angular rotation;
l = length of the column of solution, in decimetres;
c = concentration, in grams per 100 ml. of solution.

The value of the specific rotation depends on the temperature, which is fixed for reference purposes at 20° C. It also depends on the nature of the light source employed. The bright yellow D lines of the sodium spectrum or the yellow-green mercury line, 5461Å, are the usual illuminants. The light used is indicated by affixing D or Hg to the symbol denoting the specific rotation.

Sugar in Aqueous Solution.	$[\alpha]_D$	Sugar in Aqueous Solution.	$[\alpha]_D$
L-Xylose . .	+ 19·0	D-Fructose .	− 92·0
D-Arabinose .	−105·0	Lactose . .	+ 52·5
L-Rhamnose .	+ 8·9	Maltose . .	+137·5
D-Glucose . .	+ 52·2	Sucrose . .	+ 66·5
D-Galactose .	+ 80·5	Invert sugar .	− 20·6
D-Mannose .	+ 14·6	Raffinose . .	+105·2

CHROMATOGRAPHIC SEPARATION OF CARBOHYDRATES

The application of chromatography to the separation and identification of sugars was introduced by Partridge in 1946, and has been widely extended. For microanalysis, where a milligram or less of material is available, the paper technique is popular; column-separation methods are employed.

In the paper technique, a drop of the sugar solution is applied to one end of the strip, and allowed to dry. The chromatogram is then developed in the usual way by means of a moving solvent, such as water-saturated phenol or water-saturated n-butanol. After separation, individual sugar spots are located by spraying. Thus reducing sugars can be revealed by one of the enediol reactions, of which the silver reduction is the most sensitive. Paper chromatography can be adapted also to the separation of various sugar derivatives, notably the important phosphate esters.

ESTIMATION OF CARBOHYDRATES

Methods employed for the estimation of carbohydrates can be classified as (1) Physical, (2) Chemical, and (3) Biological. Physical methods include measurement of the optical rotation and the refractive index, and are employed principally in the sugar industries. Chemical methods include the reduction of cupric or ferric ions in alkaline solution. These methods have been highly developed for special purposes, such as the estimation of sugar in blood (Folin-Wu, Hagedorn-Jensen, Haynes). Chemical methods, based on furfural or enediol reactions, have been devised for colorimetric or spectro-photometric analysis, and, in micro-form, can be used to estimate chromato-graphically-separated sugars. Biological methods include the use of specific selective enzymes or cultures of sugar-selective organisms. In this way, individual sugars can be detected in mixtures or, alternatively, organisms can be identified by their behaviour to individual sugars.

Method for Identifying the Common Carbohydrates

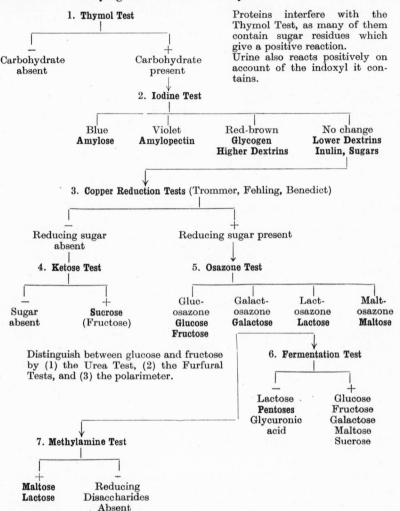

1. Thymol Test

Carbohydrate absent   —   +   Carbohydrate present

Proteins interfere with the Thymol Test, as many of them contain sugar residues which give a positive reaction. Urine also reacts positively on account of the indoxyl it contains.

2. Iodine Test

| Blue Amylose | Violet Amylopectin | Red-brown Glycogen Higher Dextrins | No change Lower Dextrins Inulin, Sugars |

3. Copper Reduction Tests (Trommer, Fehling, Benedict)

— Reducing sugar absent   + Reducing sugar present

4. Ketose Test   **5. Osazone Test**

| — Sugar absent | + Sucrose (Fructose) | Glucosazone Glucose Fructose | Galactosazone Galactose | Lactosazone Lactose | Maltosazone Maltose |

Distinguish between glucose and fructose by (1) the Urea Test, (2) the Furfural Tests, and (3) the polarimeter.

6. Fermentation Test

— Lactose Pentoses Glycuronic acid   + Glucose Fructose Galactose Maltose Sucrose

7. Methylamine Test

+ Maltose Lactose   — Reducing Disaccharides Absent

General References (Chapters 6 and 7)

" Advances in Carbohydrate Chemistry." Ed. by W. W. Pigman and M. L. Wolfram. Vol. I (1945–). Academic Press, New York.

Armstrong, E. F., and K. F. Armstrong (1931), " Glycosides." London.

Armstrong, E. F., and K. F. Armstrong (1934), " Carbohydrates." London.

Barger, G. (1930), "Organic Chemistry in Biology and Medicine." New York; London.

Barton-Wright, E. (1933), " Recent Advances in Plant Physiology." London.

Bell, D. J. (1952), " Introduction to Carbohydrate Chemistry." 3rd Ed., London.

Browne, C. A., and F. W. Zerban (1941), " Physical and Chemical Methods of Sugar Analysis." New York.

Evans, W. L. (1942), " Less familiar aspects of carbohydrate chemistry." *Chem. Rev.*, **31**, 537.

Fearon, W. R. (1942), " Detection of lactose and maltose by methylamine." *Analyst*, **67**, 130.

Fearon, W. R., and D. Mitchell (1932), " Nitro-chromic acid reaction." *Analyst*, **57**, 372.

Fearon, W. R., and E. Kawerau (1943), " Oxidation of ascorbic acid by o-dinitrobenzene." *Biochem. J.*, **37**, 326.

Fearon, W. R., and J. A. Drum (1950), " Detection of fructose." *Analyst*, **75**, 56.

Grönwall, A. (1957), " Dextran." New York; Oxford.

Hassid, W. Z. (1944), " Carbohydrates." *Ann. Rev. Biochem.*, **13**, 59.

Haworth, W. N. (1929), " Constitution of the Sugars." London.

Haworth, W. N. (1944), " Structure, Function and Synthesis of Polysaccharides." Bakerian Lecture. Royal Society, London.

Heuser, E. (1938), " Cellulose." *Organic Chemistry*, Ed. Gilman, **2**, 1534.

Honeyman, J. (1948), " Chemistry of the Carbohydrates." London.

Irvine, J. C. (1927), " Structural study of carbohydrates." *Chem. Rev.*, **4**, 203.

Kent, P. W., and M. W. Whitehouse (1955), " Biochemistry of the Amino Sugars." London; New York.

Levene, P. A. (1925), " Hexosamines and Mucoproteins." London.

Mark, H. (1940), " X-ray investigation of carbohydrates." *Chem. Rev.*, **26**, 169.

Marsh, J. T., and F. C. Wood (1942), " Chemistry of Cellulose." London.

Norman, A. G. (1937), " Biochemistry of Cellulose." London.

Percival, E. G. (1953), " Structural Carbohydrate Chemistry." London.

Pigman, W. W., and R. M. Goepp (1948), " Chemistry of the Carbohydrates." New York.

Pringsheim, H. (1932), " Chemistry of the Monosaccharides and the Polysaccharides." New York.

Pryde, J. (1931), " Recent Advances in Biochemistry." London.

Radley, J. A. (1940), " Starch and its Derivatives." 2nd Ed. London.

Raymond, A. L. (1942), " Carbohydrates." *Organic Chemistry*. Ed. Gilman.

Whittier, E. O. (1925), " Lactose." *Chem. Rev.*, **2**, 85.

Wolfrom, M. L. (1942), " Carbohydrates." *Organic Chemistry*, Ed. Gilman, **2**, 1399.

Chapter 8 Proteins

" Undoubtedly the most important of the known components of living matter, without which life would not be possible."

G. J. Mulder, 1844.

Definition. A protein is a compound containing one or more chains of α-amino acid units combined in peptide linkage.

$$H_2N.CH(R).COOH \quad —HN.CH(R).COO— \quad —CH(R)—CO—HN—CH(R)—$$
α-Amino Acid.   Amino Acid Unit.   Peptide Linkage.

At least forty different natural amino acids are known, of which about twenty are represented in proteins and are responsible for the high percentage of nitrogen, 15 to 19, which is a feature of the protein family.

In alkaline solution all proteins form red to violet complexes with cupric ions. This copper-peptide, or " biuret " reaction is characteristic of the peptide linkage.

Molecular weights range from less than 1,000 for the simpler peptides, to more than 5×10^6, for some conjugated proteins. Where the molecular weight is greater than 10,000 the protein exists as a typical colloid.

The properties and individuality of a protein are determined by the variety, number, and order of arrangement of the amino acid units in the peptide chains, and the way in which the chains are folded, coiled, and cross-linked. Because of these possibilities for permutation, the protein family is vast in membership and versatile in functions. Proteins represent the chief form assumed by the element nitrogen during its association with life.

Classification. The protein family is divisible into (A) Simple Proteins, (B) Conjugated Proteins, and (C) Derived Proteins.

A. SIMPLE PROTEINS

Simple proteins are assembled entirely or chiefly from α-amino acid units. They are classified, provisionally, according to solubility in water, dilute salt solutions and concentrated solutions of ammonium sulphate. Lower members of the group are non-colloidal and diffusible; higher members are macro-molecules or aggregates of high molecular weight.

(1) **Natural Peptides.** Soluble in water and saturated solutions of ammonium sulphate; not coagulated by heat. They range from short-chains of two units (dipeptides) to polypeptides of eight or more units, which may be ring-closed, as in the pituitary hormones, *oxytocin* and *vasopressin*, and in the antibiotics, *gramicidin, tyrocidine* and *polymixin*; or cross-linked in pairs, as in the

100

pancreatic hormone, *insulin*. Apart from a few non-reacting dipeptides, the peptides as a class give a characteristic pink copper reaction.

(2) **Gliadins** or **Prolamins**. These are peculiar to plants, and occur largely in the seeds of cereals. They are insoluble in water, soluble in dilute acid and alkali, and have the special property of being soluble in 70 to 80 per cent. aqueous alcohol. They are not coagulated by heat. Important prolamins are: *hordein*, from barley; *zein*, from maize; and *gliadin*, from wheat and rye. As a class, gliadins are characterised by their high content of proline, which confers alcohol-solubility on the class.

(3) **Glutelins.** Vegetable proteins found chiefly in cereal grain. They are insoluble in water and aqueous alcohol in all concentrations, but may be dissolved by dilute acids or alkalies. They are not coagulated by heat. *Glutenin*, from wheat, and *oryzenin*, from barley, are members of the class. When wheat flour is made into a paste with water the gliadin present forms an adhesive and binds together the glutenin. The mixture is termed *gluten*, and is responsible for the production of dough. Gluten makes up about 6 to 12 per cent. of wheat flour.

(4) **Scleroproteins,** or *Albuminoids*. Insoluble fibrous proteins found in the skeletal, connective, and epidermal tissues of animals. They do not occur in plants. Scleroproteins are very stable, and resist acid and alkaline hydrolysis, but ultimately are resolved into amino acids.

(i) *Collagens* or *gelatin precursors*, found in bone, cartilage, and the " white fibres " of connective tissue. Collagens are hydrolysed by boiling with concentrated acids or alkalies, or by superheated steam. They are attacked by the gastric enzyme pepsin, but not by trypsin. *Gelatin* is the characteristic early product of hydrolysis. Collagens are rich in the simple amino acid glycine, the yield of which may be as high as 25 per cent. They lack the biologically important amino acids, cystine, tyrosine, and tryptophan.

(ii) *Elastins*, found in the " yellow " or elastic fibres of connective tissue, in cartilage and ligaments. They differ from collagens in being readily attacked by both pepsin and trypsin. The end-products of hydrolysis are especially rich in glycine (25 per cent.) and leucine (20 per cent.).

(iii) *Keratins*. These scleroproteins are characteristic of epidermal tissue, and occur in hair, wool, feathers, claws, horns, and nails. They are the most stable of all proteins, and are well adapted to withstand the environment. Insoluble in water, dilute acids and alkalies, they resist many proteoclastic enzymes, including pepsin and trypsin. Keratins are dissolved by concentrated alkalies, and by metallic sulphides, a property that underlies the use of barium or calcium sulphide as a depilatory. They are rich in the amino acids histidine, lysine, and arginine, which are present in the ratio 1 : 4 : 12. The tyrosine and cystine contents also are usually high; tyrosine being about 3 to 4 per cent., and cystine reaching values of 8 to 14 per cent. in wool, and 15 to 20 in human hair.

(5) **Albumins.** Water-soluble, **heat-coagulable** proteins found in animals and plants. Important members are *ovalbumin*, from egg-white; *serum albumin*,

101

from blood; *lactalbumin*, from milk; *myoalbumin*, from muscle; *leucosin*, from wheat, rye, and barley; *legumelin*, from pea, bean, and lentil.

As a class they undergo a characteristic irreversible coagulation when heated to about 75° C. in solution. Coagulation is most marked in slightly acid solutions (pH 6 to pH 5), and is retarded by alkalis. It forms an important test for higher proteins.

(i) *Ovalbumin* constitutes 10 to 13 per cent. of egg-white. It can be obtained in crystalline form by half-saturation with ammonium sulphate at pH 4·58. It is lævo-rotatory in solution, $[a]_D = -35·5°$.

(ii) *Serum albumin* occurs in serum (4 to 6 per cent.), lymph, and other tissue fluids. Like ovalbumin it coagulates about 75° C., but differs in being more lævo-rotatory, $[a]_D = -56°$.

(6) **Globulins.** Higher proteins insoluble in water, but soluble in dilute salines. They accompany albumins and have corresponding names: *ovoglobulin* (egg-white), *serum globulin* (blood), *lactoglobulin* (milk). *Fibrinogen*, the clot-forming protein in blood plasma, is a globulin. The majority of vegetable tissue and seed proteins are globulins: *legumin* (seeds of pea, bean, and lentil), *excelsin* (Brazil nut), *edestin* (hemp seed). Unlike the animal globulins, the vegetable globulins are not heat-coagulable.

Distinction between Globulins and Albumins. Albumins and animal globulins are distinguished from all other proteins in being coagulated by heat when in solution. Globulins, unlike albumins, are not removed from tissues by water-extraction, but require the use of dilute salines as solvents, such as 2 to 5 per cent. sodium chloride. When a globulin solution is dialysed or diluted with excess of water, the globulin is flocculated, owing to reduction in the concentration of the solvent salts. All animal globulins are flocculated by full-saturation with magnesium sulphate, or half-saturation with ammonium sulphate; vegetable globulins are not completely flocculated by these reagents. When the concentration of ammonium sulphate is raised to full saturation (about 80 per cent.) all albumins and globulins separate from solution and can be removed and purified by redissolving and fractional flocculation with inorganic salts, alcohol, or acetone. By electric separation methods it has been shown that most of the native albumins and globulins are mixtures of closely related proteins.

B. CONJUGATED PROTEINS

Conjugated, or compound, proteins are proteins in combination with non-protein, or *prosthetic* units.

(1) **Phosphoproteins** contain 0·1 to 1·0 per cent. phosphorus in the form of phosphate esters of serine and threonine units in the peptide chain. They include the important food proteins of young vertebrates.

Casein (caseinogen), a mixture of phosphoproteins, α-, β-, and γ-, present in the milk of all species, percentage values ranging from less than 1 in the human subject, to 9 in the cat and the reindeer. The caseins are insoluble in water and occur as solubilised complexes in milk. These are decomposed by weak acids, with liberation and flocculation of the casein, as occurs when milk becomes " sour ", owing to bacterial conversion of the lactose to lactic acid.

The isoelectric point of the caseins is about pH 4·6, in which region they flocculate, but redissolve in alkali or excess acid.

Casein is not heat-coagulable; when milk is acted on by the enzyme chymase, or rennin, in gastric juice, it is degraded to *paracasein*, which forms an insoluble complex, or clot, with the calcium ions that are always present in milk. This curdling by rennin can be distinguished from the flocculation caused by acids in being irreversible, and requiring the presence of calcium ions.

Vitellin and **Livetin**, two phosphoglobulins that account for about three-quarters of the total protein which forms 16 per cent. of the weight of avian egg yolk.

(2) **Glycoproteins** contain about 0·2 to 4 per cent. of sugar, and thus differ from the mucoproteins which have a carbohydrate content in excess of 5 per cent. in the form of heterosaccharides.

Agreement is not yet reached on the classification of the glycoproteins. Many common proteins, such as the albumins and globulins of egg-white and blood serum, give positive reactions with the general carbohydrate tests, and analyses of recrystallised proteins give constant percentage values: oval-bumin, 1·7 (mannose); ovoglobulin, 4·0 (mannose); serum albumin, 0·47 (mannose and galactose); serum globulins, 1·8 (mannose and galactose); casein, 0·3 (galactose). Hence, these proteins should be classified as glyco-proteins, but for convenience most of them are included in the group of simple proteins.

(3) **Nucleoproteins.** Conjugates of basic protein and nucleic acid. In an environment that provides the necessary ingredients, nucleoproteins display the unique property of self-reproduction and are employed for this purpose in all cells: as nuclear genes for the transmission of inheritance; as plasma genes for the construction of enzymes and other proteins. Nucleoproteins also enter into the composition of viruses and bacteriophages.

(6) **Chromoproteins.** Conjugates of a protein, usually a globin or a globulin, with a pigment that can be detached by warm acids or alkalies.

(*a*) **Metalloporphyrin proteins** are represented by the hæm proteins, in which the pigment is ferrous protoporphyrin, or hæm.

Hæmoglobins occur as oxygen-transport proteins in the red corpuscles of all vertebrates, and in the blood plasma of some invertebrates, and the root nodules of leguminous plants.

Myoglobins, oxygen-storage pigments of vertebrate and invertebrate muscle.

Cytochromes, electron-transport cellular pigments present in all aerobic organisms.

Catalases and **Peroxidases,** enzymes concerned in the decomposition of peroxides.

(b) *Flavoproteins*, in which the pigment is an orange-red flavin derivative (flavin phosphate, flavin adenine dinucleotide), are represented by at least fifteen widely distributed respiratory enzymes.

Miscellaneous chromoproteins include: rhodopsin and iodopsin, visual pigments of the retina; erythrocruorins and chlorocruorins, iron-containing respiratory pigments of invertebrate blood; ferritin, an iron-storage pigment of liver and spleen; hæmocyanins, copper-containing oxygen-transport pigments in the blood of crustaceans; tyrosinase, a copper-containing enzyme.

(7) **Lipoproteins.** Conjugates of a protein and a lipid or a steroid that can be removed by organic solvents. Lipoproteins occur in cell-inclusions, chloroplasts, " acid-fast " bacteria, and in blood plasma, where they transport fats and cholesterol. Typical lipoproteins are: thromboplastin (blood platelets), lipovitellin (egg yolk).

Protein Components of Conjugated Proteins

Protamins are peptides that, so far, have only been obtained from the nucleoproteins in fish sperm. They contain 4 to 10 different species of amino acid units, and are strongly basic because of the high content of diamino acid (arginine) residues.

Salmin, from salmon sperm, has a molecular weight of 8,000, and contains 58 units: arginine, 40; serine, 7; proline, 4; glycine, 3; valine, 2; alanine, 1; isoleucine, 1.

Other protamines are: *clupein* (herring), *cyprinin* (carp), *percin* (perch), *scombrin* (mackerel), *sturin* (sturgeon).

Histones are basic proteins, soluble in water and dilute acids, and flocculated by ammonia and higher proteins. They differ from the protamines in containing a greater variety of amino acid units, including tyrosine.

Nucleohistones occur in combination with nucleic acid in the nuclei of plant and animal cells.

Globins occur in combination with hæm in the hæmoglobins. They are flocculated by half-saturation with ammonium sulphate and rendered insoluble by subsequent heat-denaturation.

C. DERIVED PROTEINS

Products obtained by the denaturation and cleavage of natural proteins. They represent stages in protein digestion and synthesis.

(1) **Denatured Proteins.** Many native proteins, especially those of the albumin and globulin types, undergo a " denaturation " when exposed at ordinary temperatures to the action of acids, alkalis, alcohols, or concentrated solutions of urea, guanidine salts or some organic bases. Denaturation involves a rearrangement within the protein molecule, resulting in decreased solubility, change in viscosity, exposure of reactive thiol groups, and loss of some

specific biological properties. Some forms of denaturation can be reversed by removing the agent by dialysis. Heat-coagulation is an example of an irreversible thermal denaturation.

Heat-Coagulation. Albumins and globulins differ from all the other proteins in being coagulated when heated in aqueous solution. The change is preceded by heat-denaturation, which is favoured by an acid reaction; then the insoluble protein particles flocculate and coagulate, a change that is promoted by neutral electrolytes, such as NaCl, about pH 5·7 to pH 5·9.

Heat-coagulation will not take place in an alkaline solution, or in a strongly acid solution deficient in salts. Hence, in testing for albumin or globulin the solution is first slightly acidified with dilute acetic acid, and treated with sodium chloride. The coagulation temperature depends on the nature of the protein, the reaction of the mixture, and the electrolytes present.

Blood serum at pH 5·7 coagulates about 75° C.; egg-white coagulates about 62° C. Heat-coagulation is an important group test, and a means of detecting traces of higher protein in urine.

(2) Protein Cleavage Products. In denaturation and coagulation the protein molecule is rearranged but not decomposed; in the subsequent changes of cleavage, the molecule is fragmented in stages until the final end-products are reached. Four intermediate and somewhat artificial levels of hydrolysis are recognised:

(*a*) *Metaproteins.* Cleavage products not coagulable by heat, insoluble in water at pH 6·0, but soluble in greater concentrations of acid or alkali. When dissolved in either of these reagents they are termed acid metaprotein and alkali metaprotein respectively. They resemble higher proteins in giving a violet colour reaction with copper sulphate and sodium hydroxide. Metaproteins from albumin and globulin give a positive Thiol test (p. 166) owing to the unmasking of — SH groups during early hydrolysis.

(*b*) *Proteoses.* Cleavage products not coagulable by heat, soluble in water, and not precipitated at pH 6·0, but completely precipitated by saturation with sodium sulphate at 33° C. Unlike metaproteins and higher proteins, the proteoses give a rose colour reaction in the copper protein test.

(*c*) *Peptones.* Cleavage products resembling proteoses, but not precipitated by saturation with sodium sulphate. They give a rose colour reaction in the copper protein test, and are completely precipitated by strong tannic acid. Peptones resist the action of the proteoclastic enzymes, pepsin and pure trypsin, but are attacked by the peptidases, such as erepsin, found in the small intestine.

(*d*) *Peptides.* Simple hydrolytic products, mostly soluble in water and not precipitated by tannic acid. They give a rose colour in the copper protein test, and are precipitated by excess of alcohol.

Proteoses, peptones and peptides constitute the sub-group of **lower proteins,** as distinct from the precursors, the higher proteins.

Chapter 9 Amino Acids

All the natural amino acids are colourless, crystalline solids. All except cystine, leucine and tyrosine, are readily soluble in water; and all except proline and hydroxyproline are sparingly soluble in ethanol.

Dipolar Form of the Amino Acids. The monoamino-monocarboxylic acids of the type $H_2N.CH(R).COOH$ are neutral in solution, and are very weak electrolytes. Nevertheless, they are buffer solutes capable of neutralising acids and bases. In this they are said to be *amphoteric*, the property depending on the presence of an acid and a basic group in the same molecule. This can be regarded as the result of a hydrogen ion migrating from the carboxyl to the amino group of the acid, so as to form a dipolar ion having two equal charges of opposite electric sign and tending to migrate neither to the anode nor the cathode when a current is passed through the solution.

$$
\begin{array}{ccc}
\text{R—CH.COOH (acidic)} & & \text{R—CH.COO}^- \\
| & \rightleftharpoons & | \\
\text{NH}_2 \text{ (basic)} & & \text{NH}_3{}^+ \\
\text{Amino acid} & & \text{Amino acid} \\
\text{(non-ionised form).} & & \text{(dipolar form).}
\end{array}
$$

Acids are neutralised by the —COO$^-$ group of the amino acid, which can combine with H$^+$ to form —COOH. Alkalis are neutralised by the —NH$_3^+$ group, which can donate H$^+$ by reverting to —NH$_2$.

Optical Activity. All of the amino acids, are optically active, except glycine, the α-carbon of which is not asymmetric.

These optically-active acids can belong either to a D- or L-series, depending on the configurational arrangement of the three radicals, H, NH$_2$ and —COOH, which are attached to the *alpha* carbon atom. Glyceraldehyde, the referent for the sugars, can be related formally to the amino acid *serine* and thus used as a referent for the other α-amino acids. As with the sugars, these D- and L-relationships denote molecular configuration and not direction of optical rotation, which is indicated by the prefixes (+) or (−).

$$
\begin{array}{cccccc}
\text{COOH} & \text{COOH} & \text{COOH} & \text{CHO} & \text{CHO} & \text{COOH} \\
| & | & | & | & | & | \\
\text{H}_2\text{N.C.H} & \text{H}_2\text{N.C.H} & \text{HO.C.H} & \text{HO.C.H} & \text{H.C.OH} & \text{H.C.NH}_2 \\
| & | & | & | & | & | \\
\text{CH}_3 & \text{CH}_2\text{OH} & \text{CH}_2\text{OH} & \text{CH}_2\text{OH} & \text{CH}_2\text{OH} & \text{CH}_2\text{OH} \\
\text{L(+)} & \text{L(−)} & \text{L(+)} & \text{L(−)} & \text{D(+)} & \text{D(+)} \\
\text{Alanine.} & \text{Serine.} & \text{Glyceric Acid.} & \text{Glyceraldehydes.} & & \text{Serine}
\end{array}
$$

The common amino acids, irrespective of their optical rotation, belong to the L-series. Members of the rare D-series occur in some antibiotics (gramicidins and penicillins), capsular material of bacilli (anthrax) and ergot alkaloids.

CLASSIFICATION OF THE AMINO ACIDS

(1) Acids derived from Acetic Acid: $CH_3.COOH$

$$CH_2.COOH \qquad CH_2.COOH \qquad CH_2.COOH \qquad CH_2.COOH$$
$$| \qquad\qquad | \qquad\qquad | \qquad\qquad |$$
$$NH_2 \qquad\quad NH.CH_3 \qquad NH.CO.C_6H_5 \qquad N(CH_3).C(:NH).NH_2$$

Glycine   Sarcosine   Hippuric acid   Creatine
(amino acetic acid).   (Methyl glycine).   (Benzoyl glycine).   (Methyl guanidino acetic acid).

Glycine is the only one of these that occurs as a protein unit. Sarcosine is a hydrolysis product of creatine. Hippuric acid is present in urine. Creatine occurs in muscle.

(2) Amino Acids derived from Propionic Acid: $CH_3.CH_2.COOH$

$$CH_3.CH.COOH \qquad HO.CH_2.CH.COOH$$
$$| \qquad\qquad\qquad\qquad |$$
$$NH_2 \qquad\qquad\qquad\quad NH_2$$

(+) **Alanine.**   (−) **Serine.**
α-amino propionic acid)   (β-hydroxy alanine).

$$CH_2.CH.COOH \qquad HOOC.CH.CH_2 \quad CH_2.CH.COOH$$
$$| \quad\ | \qquad\qquad\quad | \qquad\quad\ | \qquad |$$
$$HS \quad NH_2 \qquad\qquad H_2N \quad S——S \quad NH_2$$

(+) **Cysteine**   (−) **Cystine**
(β-thio alanine).   (β-dicysteine).

Penicillamine, β,β'-dimethyl cysteine, a component of the penicillin antibiotics, is a representative of the D-series of amino acids.

$$\begin{array}{c} C—CH_2.CH.COOH \\ // \qquad\qquad | \\ HC \quad CH \quad NH_2 \\ | \qquad || \\ 5\ HC \quad CH\ 3 \\ \backslash / \\ CR \\ 4 \end{array}$$

Phenylalanine, R = H
Tyrosine, 4-hydroxy phenylalanine, R = OH
Thyronine, R = —O.C_6H_4.OH

3,5-Diiodotyrosine occurs in the thyroid gland and in many marine organisms, sponges and corals, including Gorgonia, from the skeleton of which it was originally isolated and named iodogorgoic acid. It can be prepared by the action of iodine on tyrosine in alkaline solution.

Thyronine, the phenyl ether of tyrosine, is the parent of the thyroid hormones **3,5,3'-triiodothyronine** and **thyroxine.**

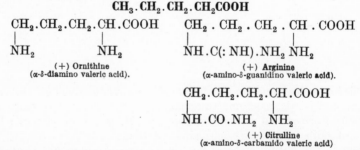

HO—[ring]—O—[ring]—$CH_2.CH.COOH$
                                      |
                                     NH_2

(I positions labeled on rings)

(−) **Thyroxine**, 3,5,3′,5′-tetraiodothyronine.

$$
\begin{array}{c}
CH \quad CH_2\!-\!CH.COOH \\
HC \quad C\!-\!C \quad NH_2 \\
HC \quad C \quad CH \\
CH \quad NH
\end{array}
$$

(−) **Tryptophane**
(3-indolyl-2-alanine).

$$
\begin{array}{c}
CH_2.CH.COOH \\
HC=C \quad NH_2 \\
HN \quad N \\
CH
\end{array}
$$

(−) **Histidine**
(β-iminazole alanine).

(3) Amino Acids derived from Butyric Acid: $CH_3.CH_2.CH_2.COOH$

$CH_3.CH_2.CH.COOH$
                    |
                   NH_2

(+) **Butyrine**
(α-amino butyric acid).

$CH_3.CH(OH).CH.COOH$
                      |
                     NH_2

(−) **Threonine**
(β-hydroxy butyrine).

$CH_2.CH_2.CH.COOH$
  | |
$S.CH_3$ NH_2

(+) **Methionine**
(γ-methylthiol-butyrine).

$CH_2.CH_2.CH(NH_2).COOH$
  |
$O\!-\!NH.C(:NH).NH_2$

(+) **Canavanine.**

Methionine, like cystine, is a sulphur-containing amino acid, and an essential source of methyl groups in human nutrition.

Canavanine, from Jack bean and other seeds. Jack bean, resembles arginine in being a guanidine derivative and yielding urea on alkaline hydrolysis.

(4) Amino Acids derived from Valeric Acid:

$$CH_3.CH_2.CH_2.CH_2COOH$$

$CH_2.CH_2.CH_2.CH.COOH$
  | |
NH_2 NH_2

(+) **Ornithine**
(α-δ-diamino valeric acid).

$CH_2.CH_2.CH_2.CH.COOH$
  | |
$NH.C(:NH).NH_2$ NH_2

(+) **Arginine**
(α-amino-δ-guanidino valeric acid).

$CH_2.CH_2.CH_2.CH.COOH$
  | |
$NH.CO.NH_2$ NH_2

(+) **Citrulline**
(α-amino-δ-carbamido valeric acid)

Arginine occurs in many proteins, and may be an essential part of the molecular pattern of all proteins; on hydrolysis it yields ornithine and urea.

Citrulline occurs free in the melon (*Citrullus*); and also as an intermediate in the hepatic synthesis of urea.

(5) Amino Acid derived from iso-Valeric Acid.

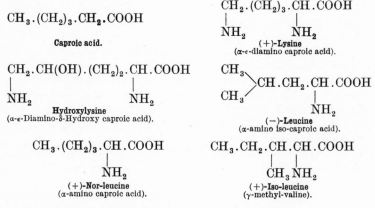

$$CH_3 > CH.CH_2.COOH$$
Iso-valeric
acid.

$$CH_3 > CH.CH.COOH$$
$$|$$
$$NH_2$$
(+)-**Valine**
(α-amino iso-valeric acid).

(6) Amino Acids derived from Caproic Acids.

$$CH_3.(CH_2)_3.CH_2.COOH$$
Caproic acid.

$$CH_2.(CH_2)_3.CH.COOH$$
$$| \qquad\qquad |$$
$$NH_2 \qquad\qquad NH_2$$
(+)-**Lysine**
(α-ε-diamino caproic acid).

$$CH_2.CH(OH).(CH_2)_2.CH.COOH$$
$$| \qquad\qquad\qquad\qquad |$$
$$NH_2 \qquad\qquad\qquad\qquad NH_2$$
Hydroxylysine
(α-ε-Diamino-δ-Hydroxy caproic acid).

$$CH_3 > CH.CH_2.CH.COOH$$
$$|$$
$$NH_2$$
(−)-**Leucine**
(α-amino iso-caproic acid).

$$CH_3.(CH_2)_3.CH.COOH$$
$$|$$
$$NH_2$$
(+)-**Nor-leucine**
(α-amino caproic acid).

$$CH_3.CH_2.CH.CH.COOH$$
$$| \quad |$$
$$CH_3 \; NH_2$$
(+)-**Iso-leucine**
(γ-methyl-valine).

(7) Amino Acids and Amides derived from Succinic Acid.

$$CH_2.COOH$$
$$|$$
$$CH_2.COOH$$
Succinic acid.

$$H_2N.CH.COOH$$
$$|$$
$$CH_2.COOH$$
(−)-**Aspartic acid.**
(amino succinic acid).

$$H_2N.CH.COOH$$
$$|$$
$$CH_2.CO.NH_2$$
(−)-**Asparagine**
(β-amino succinamide).

(8) Amino Acids and Amides derived from Glutaric Acid.

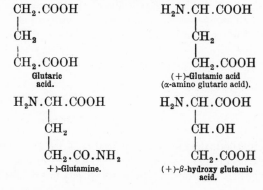

$$CH_2.COOH$$
$$|$$
$$CH_2$$
$$|$$
$$CH_2.COOH$$
Glutaric
acid.

$$H_2N.CH.COOH$$
$$|$$
$$CH_2$$
$$|$$
$$CH_2.COOH$$
(+)-**Glutamic acid**
(α-amino glutaric acid).

$$H_2N.CH.COOH$$
$$|$$
$$CH_2$$
$$|$$
$$CH_2.CO.NH_2$$
+)-**Glutamine.**

$$H_2N.CH.COOH$$
$$|$$
$$CH.OH$$
$$|$$
$$CH_2.COOH$$
(+)-β-**hydroxy glutamic**
acid.

109

(9) Cyclo-Imino Acids derived from Pyrrolidine.

$$\begin{array}{ccc}
\text{H}_2\text{C}\!-\!\text{CH}_2 & \text{H}_2\text{C}\!-\!\text{CH}_2 & \text{HO.HC}\!-\!\text{CH}_2 \\
| \quad\; | & | \quad\; | & | \quad\; | \\
\text{H}_2\text{C} \quad \text{CH}_2 & \text{H}_2\text{C} \quad \text{CH.COOH} & \text{H}_2\text{C} \quad \text{CH.COOH} \\
\diagdown\!\diagup & \diagdown\!\diagup & \diagdown\!\diagup \\
\text{NH} & \text{NH} & \text{NH}
\end{array}$$

| Pyrrolidine. | (−)-Proline (α-carboxypyrrolidine). | (−)-Hydroxyproline (β-hydroxyproline). |

Notes on the Amino Acids. Hydroxylysine appears to be restricted to the collagens and gelatins, where it represents about 1 per cent. Hydroxyproline also is of limited distribution, but is well-represented in collagens and gelatins (10 to 14 per cent.) and elastins (1 to 2 per cent.). Proline is the only ethanol-soluble amino acid present in proteins.

Naturally-occurring amino acids that have not been found in proteins are represented by: β-alanine (carnosine, anserine, pantothenic acid), α-amino-butyric acid (*Corynebacterium diphtheriæ*), γ aminobutyric acid (bacteria, yeasts, brain tissue), canavanine, or α-amino-γ-guanidinoxy-n-butyric acid (Jack bean, " bladder senna "); octopine (octopus and scallop muscle), djenkolic acid (Djenkol bean), " dopa ", or 3,4-dihydroxyphenylalanine (plant and animal tissues). α,ε-diaminopimelic acid (cell walls of certain Gram-positive bacteria).

In the dicarboxylic acids, aspartic and glutamic, the presence of the second carboxyl group renders them acid in solution. Conversely, the diamino acids, lysine, hydroxylysine, and arginine, and the imidazolyl acid, histidine, are basic.

General Reactions of Amino Acids. The α-amino group can be removed by deamination or masked by combination with aldehydes. The carboxyl group can be destroyed by decarboxylation: these reactions are common to all free amino acids, and provide methods for their estimation.

(1) *Deamination by Nitrous Acid.* Free nitrous acid, HO.NO, but not the nitrite ion, ONO⁻, combines with free amino groups to form an unstable *diazo* compound, R—NH—NO, that hydrolyses spontaneously into R.OH, H_2O and N_2, which escapes as a gas, and can be measured.

When an amino acid is deaminated in this way the corresponding hydroxy acid is produced:—

$$CH_3.CH(NH_2).COOH + HO.NO \longrightarrow$$

Alanine
(α-amino propionic acid).

$$CH_3.CH(OH).COOH + H_2O + N_2$$

Lactic acid
(α-hydroxy propionic acid.)

In Van Slyke's method, the amino compound is added to a mixture of 30 per cent. sodium nitrite and glacial acetic acid contained in a special apparatus, which can be shaken vigorously. The evolved gas is expelled, treated with alkaline permanganate to absorb nitric oxide, which forms as a by-product, and the residual nitrogen is estimated in a manometer. Under standard conditions, the α-amino groups lose all their nitrogen within five minutes.

(2) *Formaldehyde Condensation.* When an amino acid in neutral solution is mixed with excess of neutral formaldehyde solution, the mixture becomes acid, and can be titrated (Sörensen's reaction), thus affording an important method for the estimation of amino acids and ammonium salts. By the action of the alkali during titration, the ionised amine groups are changed from the protected form, $-NH_3{}^+$, into the free form, $-NH_2$, by removal of H^+, which is neutralised by the OH^- of the alkali. The free amino group rapidly combines with the formaldehyde to produce a substituted amino alcohol, $R-NH-CH_2.OH$, which is neutral to the indicator. Thus, the amount of alkali used is a measure of the amino groups originally present in the mixture.

$$R-NH_3{}^+ \begin{cases} H^+ \; (+ \; OH^- \rightarrow H_2O) \\ R-NH_2 + OCH_2 \longrightarrow R-NH-CH_2.OH \end{cases}$$

Proteins treated with formaldehyde lose the properties associated with their terminal amino groups, and by this means diphtheria and similar bacterial toxins can be converted into harmless *toxoids*, or *anatoxins*, which, however, still retain the power of acting as antigens when injected into animals, and thus are of value in conferring immunity.

(3) *Miscellaneous Amino Reactions.* Phenyl isocyanate, $C_6H_5.N : CO$, even at $0°$ C., reacts readily with free amino groups to yield substituted ureas of low solubility and easy identification, $C_6H_5.NH.CO.NH.R$.

Quinones and cyclic ketones, such as ninhydrin and alloxan, condense with amino compounds in alkaline or slightly acid solution to yield pigments, some of which are suitable for colorimetric estimation.

o-Quinone.　　　Ninhydrin.　　　Alloxan.　　　:2-Naphthoquinone 4-sulphonic acid.

The Ninhydrin Reaction. In 1911, Ruhemann showed that ninhydrin (triketo-hydrindine hydrate) quantitatively decarboxylated certain amino acids, with formation of CO_2, NH_3, and an aldehyde:

$$R.CH(NH_2).COOH \longrightarrow R.CHO + CO_2 + NH_3.$$

If the reaction occurs at a pH higher than 4, the NH_3 combines with the excess reagent to give a blue pigment. The imino acids, proline and hydroxyproline, react to yield a red pigment, and evolve CO_2 but not NH_3. Protein hydrolysates give various shades of violet, owing to the presence of both α-amino and imino groups, while ammonium salts and amines may yield blue

111

colours. The liberation of CO_2 is restricted to free α-amino acids, in that it requires the presence of both —COOH and an adjacent —NH_2 or —NH—CH_2— group. When such compounds are boiled with water and excess of ninhydrin, at pH 1 to 5, all the CO_2 of the carboxyl groups is evolved in a few minutes, and can be measured volumetrically or titrated after absorption by alkali.

(4) *Decarboxylation*. In addition to the ninhydrin reaction, amino acids can be decarboxylated by enzyme systems present in many micro-organisms, with production of the corresponding amine.

$$CH_2(NH_2).COOH \longrightarrow CH_3.NH_2 + CO_2$$
$$\text{Glycine.} \qquad\qquad \text{Methylamine.}$$

Many of these amines, notably *tyramine*, from tyrosine, and *histamine* from histidine, are much more physiologically active than the parent amino acid, and their liberation is an important factor in shock and similar conditions.

SUMMARY OF AMINO ACID REACTIONS

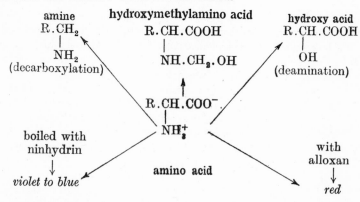

Sources of the Amino Acids

(1) *Synthetic*. All the amino acids are now obtainable as synthetic products, which from the method of their manufacture appear as equimolecular mixtures of the l and d isomers.

(2) *Natural*. Amino acids in their natural isomeric form are obtained in quantity from the complete hydrolysis of proteins by boiling with concentrated acids or by the action of mixtures of protein-splitting enzymes (pepsin, trypsin, peptidases). Acid hydrolysis can be effected by dissolving the protein in concentrated (up to 10 N) hydrochloric acid, and boiling for about 8 hours under a reflux condenser, or until a sample of the hydrolysate no longer gives a copper peptide test. While most of the free amino acids withstand this drastic treatment, a few, notably tryptophan, serine, threonine, and cystine, are completely or partially destroyed.

Alkaline hydrolysis is more rapid and more destructive than acid hydrolysis, and is only used for special purposes.

Enzymatic hydrolysis can be used to obtain intermediate peptides as well as amino acids.

As the enzymes, themselves, are proteins, errors may arise from reversion synthesis of peptide artefacts, known as *plasteins*, and the process requires the use of purified enzymes and control of pH and sterility.

Separation of the Products of Protein Hydrolyses. Methods in general use include: 1, *Column Chromatography*, using a neutral carrier, such as starch, or an ion-exchanger, such as a sulphonated polystyrene resin; and 2, *Paper Chromatography*, followed by colour development. Column chromatography, employing sets in series, can be used for the separation of amino acids from mixtures in which the amounts may range from 2·5 mg. upwards; paper chromatography can be used for the microanalysis of samples of 1 ml., or less, containing only a few mg. of amino acids.

(1) Column Chromatography. A small amount of a mixed amino acid solution is delivered on to the top of a column of adsorbent, and as it percolates downwards the constituents are differentially adsorbed. A suitable eluant is allowed to flow through the column at a constant slow rate and the outflow collected in successive fractions. Each of the amino acids is differentially eluted and appears in the outflow at different times; each can be identified and estimated in the successive samples.

It is usual to plot the amount of amino acid in each sample against the total volume that has flowed through the column when the sample was collected. The resulting graph shows a series of peaks each representing a separate amino acid. An example from the work of Moore and Stein (1951) will serve to illustrate this technique. The granulated absorbent was a sulphonated polystyrene resin, Dowex-50, in the sodium form, used in a 0·9 × 100 cm. column. About 6 mg. of amino acid mixture was delivered on to the column and the eluants were buffers of varying pH. The temperature of the column could also be varied by means of a surrounding water jacket. The eluant flowed through at a rate of 4 ml. per hour. At pH 3·41 and 37·5° C. eight amino acids were separated in the first 220 ml. of effluent and the stages in the flow at which these fractions were obtained, presented in a table instead of a graph, were as follows:

Stages in flow of *Effluent*.	*Amino Acid.*
60 to 75 ml.	Aspartic acid
75 ,, 85 ,,	Threonine
85 ,, 100 ,,	Serine
115 ,, 130 ,,	Glutamic acid
130 ,, 145 ,,	Proline
155 ,, 170 ,,	Glycine
170 ,, 185 ,,	Alanine
185 ,, 215 ,,	Cystine

(2) **Paper Chromatography.** A very small volume, say 0·01 ml., of a solution containing a minute amount of amino acid mixture is applied to a strip of filter paper near one end, and dried. The paper is suspended vertically so that this end dips into the eluant, the whole being enclosed in a tank to prevent evaporation. The eluant, ascending past the amino acid spot, differentially elutes the constituents which are carried upwards at varying speeds. After some hours the paper is removed and dried, and the location of the several amino acids made apparent by spraying with some colour reagent, like ninhydrin. The coloured areas can be identified by comparing their positions with those on a chromatogram from a known mixture. Alternatively, the areas can be cut out and the acids dissolved and identified chemically, but the amounts are usually too small to make this feasible.

Amino Acid Distribution in Proteins. The amino acid content of the chief proteins is known and many tabulations are available. Variations in results are attributable to sub-species varieties among well-established types. For example, the milk protein, β-lactoglobulin, obtainable in crystalline form, and once regarded as a pure substance, has been shown by chromatography, to be a mixture. Again, proteins that are continually being built up or broken down may resemble the glycogens in having no absolute molecular composition, but may vary slightly in accordance with the activities of the tissue whence they came.

The amino acid content of a protein may be specified in several ways: (1) Percentage yield obtained by complete hydrolysis. When completely hydrolysed 100 gm. of protein yields about 120 gm. of mixed amino acids owing to uptake of water of hydrolysis. Alternatively, amino acid content may be expressed as: (2) Number of individual units present per molecule of protein, or, when the molecular weight is uncertain, per kg. of protein.

Codification of the Amino Acids. For brevity, amino acids can be denoted by a code derived from the initial letters of their common or trivial names: alanine, **Ala**; arginine, **Arg**; aspartic acid, **Asp**; cysteine, **CySH**; cystine, **CyS**, or **(CyS)₂**; glutamic acid, **Glu**; glycine, **Gly**; histidine, **His**; hydroxyproline, **Hypro**; leucine, **Leu**; isoleucine, **Ileu**; lysine, **Lys**; methionine, **Met**; phenylalanine, **Phe**; proline, **Pro**; serine, **Ser**; threonine, **Thr**; tryptophan, **Try**; tyrosine, **Tyr**; valine, **Val**. This code is used chiefly to denote the amino acid residues in simple peptides and peptide chains.

By convention, a peptide is described as a derivative of the amino acid unit carrying the terminal free carboxyl group, which is written so as to appear on the right-hand of the formula:

Glycyl-alanine, $H_2N.CH_2.CO.NH.CH(CH_3).COOH$, or Gly-Ala.
Alanyl-glycine, $H_2N.CH(CH_3).CO.NH.CH_2.COOH$, or Ala-Gly.

In peptide codification, a dot before the symbol denotes that the amino group is involved in the linkage, and a dot after the symbol shows that the carboxyl group is involved. Thus, .Gly represents $—NH.CH_2.COOH$, and Gly. represents $H_2N.CH_2.CO—$. Expressed in this way, the peptide glycyl-alanine is

114

Amino Acid Content of Representative Proteins
Values in gm. per 100 gm.

Amino Acid.	Ovalbumin.	Casein.	Myosin.	Gelatin.	Gliadin.	Zein.
Alanine	6·7	3·2	6·5	9·3	2·1	10·5
Arginine	5·7	4·1	7·3	8·5	2·7	1·7
Aspartic Acid	9·3	7·1	8·9	6·7	1·3	2·6
Cysteine	1·3	0·0	1·4	0·0	2·4	0·0
Cystine	0·5	0·3	1·4	0·0	2·4	0·8
Glutamic Acid	16·5	22·4	22·1	11·2	45·7	26·9
Glycine	3·0	2·0	1·9	26·9	0·0	0·0
Histidine	2·3	3·1	2·4	0·7	1·8	1·3
Hydroxylysine	0·0	0·0	0·0	1	0·0	0·0
Hydroxyproline	0·0	0·3	?	14·5	?	?
Isoleucine	7·0	6·1	15·6	1·8	11·9	5
Leucine	9·2	9·2	?	?	?	21
Lysine	6·3	8·2	11·9	4·6	0·6	0·0
Methionine	5·2	2·8	3·4	0·9	1·7	2·4
Phenylalanine	7·6	5·0	4·3	2·5	6·4	7·3
Proline	3·6	10·6	1·9	14·6	13·5	10·5
Serine	8·1	6·3	4·3	3·2	4·9	7·0
Threonine	4·0	4·9	5·1	2·2	2·1	3·4
Tryptophan	1·2	1·2	0·8	0·0	6·6	0·1
Tyrosine	3·7	6·3	3·4	1·0	3·5	5·2
Valine	7·0	7·2	2·6	3·3	2·6	4
Amide N	1·0	1·6	1·2	0·1	4·5	3
Total N	15·7	15·3	16·7	18·0	17·6	16·2
Total S	1·6	0·7	1·1	0·1	1·0	0·7

Values expressed as percentages do not show the quantitative importance of each amino acid as they do not take into account differences in the molecular weights of the individual acids, which range from 75 (glycine) to 240 (tryptophan) and reach 777 in the iodinated acid, thyroxine. By dividing the percentage value by the molecular weight of the amino acid residue, composition tables can be expressed more significantly as numbers of each molecule per kg. protein, or per protein molecule.

written Gly.Ala; and Ala.Gly denotes the peptide alanyl-glycine. Care must be taken to avoid confusion with ordinary punctuation marks.

THE ARCHITECTURE OF THE PROTEIN MOLECULE

(I.) **Molecular Weights.** Proteins and their cleavage products down to the smaller polypeptides form colloidal solutions in water; this implies that they are compounds of much greater molecular size and weight than, say, the simple sugars and the amino acids, and the ordinary thermal methods used for determining molecular weights are inapplicable, since colloids undergo changes when boiled or frozen in solution. The methods employed are (i) *stoichiometric*, according to which the molecular weight is deduced from the content of a particular amino acid or element such as iodine, sulphur or iron, present in the molecule, on the assumption that the protein contains a simple multiple of the unit; (ii) *physical*, depending on measurements of osmotic pressure, sedimentation equilibrium and sedimentation rate, using an ultracentrifuge.

115

The results obtained by different methods may be at variance because of the liability of some proteins to undergo reversible dissociation or aggregation in response to changes in concentration or pH. Nevertheless, for the homogeneous proteins, the data are in reasonable agreement, and can be used to check and supplement each other. With some techniques the experimental finding is a reproducible multiple of the molecular weight; the term " particle weight " has been used in such cases.

For example: the percentage of iron in the enzyme catalase, from liver, is 0·1. In order to contain at least one iron atom per molecule, catalase must have a minimum molecular weight of 55·84 × 1,000, since the atomic weight of iron is 55·84. Sedimentation rate measurements indicate that the molecular weight of catalase is about 225,000, which is 4 × 55·84 × 1,000, and shows that the catalase molecule must contain 4 atoms of iron.

Approximate Molecular Weights of Proteins

1,000 to 2,000: oxytocin, vasopressin, gramicidins.
2,000 to 3,000: tyrocidins, clupein, cobra neurotoxin.
5,000 to 8,000: secretin, salmin, insulins.
12,000: cytochrome *c*, ribonuclease.
15,000: histones, lysozyme.
38,000 to 44,000: β-lactoglobulin, chymotrypsin, ovalbumin.
68,000 to 73,000: serum albumin, hæmoglobin.
10,000 to 150,000: gelatins.
200,000 to 300,000: excelsin, edestin.
483,000: urease.
5,000,000: hæmocyanin (snail).

II. Molecular Structure

(1) **The Peptide Chain.** The simplest structure a protein can have is that of a chain of amino acid units joined in peptide or amide linkage.

$$-\text{CO}-\underset{\underset{R_1}{|}}{\text{CH}}-\text{NH}-\text{CO}-\underset{\underset{R_2}{|}}{\overset{\overset{R_2}{|}}{\text{CH}}}-\text{NH}-\text{CO}-\underset{\underset{R_3}{|}}{\text{CH}}-\text{NH}-\text{CO}-\underset{}{\overset{\overset{R_4}{|}}{\text{CH}}}-\text{NH}-$$

R represents the various monovalent groups that form side-chains to a common main-chain.

Evidence in Support of the Peptide Theory. (i) All proteins give a violet or rose colour with copper salts in alkaline solution (the copper protein test), which is characteristic of the peptide linkage >CH—CO—NH—CH<, and not given by any individual amino acid other than serine, threonine and histidine, which have a somewhat similar arrangement in their molecules.
(ii) During protein hydrolysis there is little change in the reaction. The basic

116

amino and the acid carboxyl groups are exposed at an equal rate, showing that they were originally present in combination.

(iii) Peptides of known structure can be built up from amino acids by several methods (Bergmann, Boissonas), and shown to be identical with peptides from protein sources.

(iv) *End-group Characterisation.* The reagent 2,4-dinitrofluorobenzene in alkaline solution reacts readily with terminal amino groups in peptide chains, yielding bright yellow dinitrophenyl, or *DNP*, derivatives.

$$O_2N - \underset{\displaystyle}{\bigcirc}{}^{NO_2} - F + H_2N{-}R \longrightarrow O_2N \underset{\displaystyle}{\bigcirc}{}^{NO_2} {-}HN{-}R + .HF$$

On hydrolysis, the *DNP*-labelled amino acid is split off and identified, and the procedure of labelling then re-applied to the residual peptides. By this technique, Sanger and others have shown that the insulin molecule is assembled from two peptide chains, of which one has glycine, and one phenylalanine at the amino terminus of the chain. When insulin is oxidised by performic acid (H.COOOH), the chain cross-linkages are broken, and by progressive application of the *DNP*-labelling technique, it is possible to determine the sequence of the amino acid units in each chain.

For example, the glycyl-terminating, or *A* chain has the structure:
Gly . Ileu . Val . Glu . Glu NH$_2$. CySH . CySH . Ala . Ser . Val . CySH . Ser . Leu . Tyr . Glu NH$_2$. Leu . Glu . AspNH$_2$. Tyr. CySH . Asp NH$_2$.

(2) **Chain Folding.** Higher proteins can be divided into two groups: *fibrous* and *globular*; a distinction that is confirmed by the results of X-ray and electron diffraction analysis. When a crystalline structure is irradiated by a narrow beam of X-rays, secondary rays are reflected from each plane within the structure, and form interference patterns that can be photographed. These patterns show shadow spots and segments caused by individual atoms or groups of atoms, indicating an internal periodicity or regularity of construction. By comparing patterns from crystals of known composition it is possible to measure inter-atomic distances and valency angles, and data thus obtained has been applied to the elucidation of protein structure by Meyer, Astbury, Pauling and many other workers. As Astbury has demonstrated, two extreme types of proteins exist: (1) the visibly crystalline but not fibrous, such as insulin, ovalbumin, and hæmoglobin; and (2) the visibly fibrous but not visibly crystalline, such as the proteins of hair, tendon, and silk. These fibrous proteins can be subdivided into: (1) a keratin, myosin, fibrin, elastin, or KMF group, the fibres of which are elastic, and give a characteristic α-diffraction patterns; and (2) a collagen, silk-fibroin group, the fibres of which are relatively inelastic, and give a characteristic β-diffraction pattern.

The structure of the β-form proteins is the simpler. X-ray diagrams indicate a repeating unit of 3·3 to 3·5 Å in length, at regular intervals along the chains; these are the amino acid residues, —NH—CHR—CO—. The side-chain groups, R, of the residues project alternately to either side of the peptide main chain. The residues are linked by peptide bond formation, —NH—CHR—CO—NH—CHR—CO—, the distance between the C and the N in the amido group, —CO—NH—, that constitutes the bond, is 1·32 Å. The chains are woven into sheets by cross-linkages at various points, and hydrogen-bonding between peptide —NH—, and —CO— groups, in closely adjacent chains.

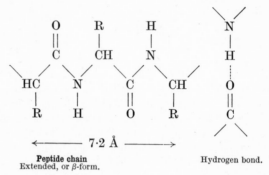

Peptide chain
Extended, or β-form.

Hydrogen bond.

The α-Helix. When proteins of the KMF group, or α-form, are stretched they display diffraction patterns characteristic of proteins of the β-form, and regain their original α-form, when allowed to recoil. This indicates that the peptide chains in the KMF protein fibres must be more closely folded or twisted in a way that allows them to stretch reversibly when under tension. This is explained by hydrogen-bond formation between appropriate amido groups in the same peptide chain, with the result that each chain in the unstretched fibre is twisted into a helix, like a one-strand rope, in which each individual amino group is hydrogen-bonded to the amido group in the turn of the helix immediately above it. Of the various possible types of peptide arrangement, the so-called α-helix has been the most successful in explaining protein structure.

The α-helix is as closely twisted as possible. The helix is right-handed, with 3·7 amino acid residues per turn, each amido group being bonded to the amido group three residues beyond it.
When sufficient tension is applied, the hydrogen-bonds are separated, and the chains in the protein fibre open-out into the extended, β-form.

Cross-linkage. Helices and lamina are held together by linkages between special units in the chains. Of these, the disulphide bond is the most familiar.

118

It is formed between two cysteine residues in adjacent chains, or within the same chain.

$$R.CO.NH.CH.CO.NH.R \qquad\qquad R.CO.NH.CH.CO.NH.R$$

$$
\begin{array}{ll}
\text{R.CO.NH.CH.CO.NH.R} & \text{R.CO.NH.CH.CO.NH.R} \\
\quad | & \quad | \\
\quad CH_2 & \quad CH_2 \\
\quad | & \quad | \\
\quad SH & \quad S \\
\qquad\qquad \xrightarrow[+2H]{-2H} & \quad | \\
\quad SH & \quad S \\
\quad | & \quad | \\
\quad CH_2 & \quad CH_2 \\
\quad | & \quad | \\
\text{R.CO.NH.CH CO.NH.R} & \text{R.CO.NH.CH.CO.NH.R}
\end{array}
$$

The disulphide bond can be unlocked by reduction and reformed by mild oxidation, which may take place spontaneously in alkaline solution. Stronger oxidisers convert it to sulphonic acid residues, $>CH.SO_2.OH$, and destroy the linkage system.

Other cross-linkages claimed to occur in peptide assemblages are: hydrogen bonding, phosphate esterification, carboxylic esterification, and polar valencies between positively- and negatively-charged centres in the chain.

An interesting example is that of the free thiol groups, which are unmasked when ovalbumin and some other proteins are denatured by saturation with urea. The origin of these —SH radicals is uncertain. They cannot arise from disulphide bonds, as the system —S—S— in cystine and cystine-linked peptides is stable to urea.

Globular Proteins. The architecture of the globular proteins is obscure. The diffraction patterns usually show an inner halo, ascribed to reflection from systems of side-chains; and an outer halo, ascribed to main-chain, or " backbone " reflection.

Many different types exist and profound differences in properties are found amongst such proteins as enzymes and viruses even when closely related chemically.

Titration Curves for Amino Acids and Proteins. When a solute is titrated by an acid or a base, and the resulting changes in pH are plotted for each unit of acid or alkali added, a titration curve is obtained, showing the buffering power of the solute. With water or solutions of neutral salts, such as NaCl, the pH change on either side of neutrality is abrupt; with amino acids or proteins, the change is gradual, owing to the acid-buffering power of the —COO⁻ groups, which combine with H⁺, and the base-buffering power of the —NH₃⁺ groups, which release H⁺. A protein solution in water has as many amino groups in the acidic or base buffering form —NH₃⁺ as it has carboxyl groups in the basic or acid buffering form —COO⁻. The protein molecule is electrically neutral and the pH of the solution is said to be at the *isoelectric point.*

119

In the presence of salts complexes may be formed and the behaviour may be different. The pH at which the protein-salt complex has no net charge is usually different from the isoelectric point and has been termed the isoionic point.

The isoelectric points of native proteins usually lie between pH 4 and pH 7 with the exception of pepsin, fibroin, the nucleoproteins and some muco-proteins, which lie between pH 2·7 and pH 3·5; and the basic proteins, such as protamines, histones, trypsin, and secretin, which lie between pH 7·5 and pH 12·2.

ANALYTICAL REACTIONS OF PROTEINS

A. General Colour Reactions given by all Proteins

(1) **The Copper Peptide Test,** or " Biuret " Test. Mix 5 ml. of solution with 1 ml. of 20 per cent. NaOH, and 1 or 2 drops of dilute (1 per cent.) $CuSO_4$. If a protein is present the solution will become purple. Using the minimal quantity of copper sulphate, it is possible to distinguish two shades of colour:

(i) *Violet,* given by all higher proteins and also by gelatin.

(ii) *Rose-pink,* given by all lower proteins (proteoses, peptones, peptides), except gelatin. Excess of copper renders these shades indistinguishable.

Add 20 per cent. acetic acid until the colour is discharged. A precipitate will form if the solution contains a higher protein, not if it contains a lower protein.

The colour depends on the presence of the peptide linkage

$$>CH-CO-NH-CH<$$

in the protein molecule. A somewhat similar colour is given by other compounds containing this grouping, such as *biuret,* $H_2N-CO-NH-CO-NH_2$, hence the older and misleading name for the test. Proteins do not contain biuret.

Acidification is of use in distinguishing between a doubtful violet or rose colour. Proteins (except gelatin) that give a violet copper reaction are precipitated on subsequent acidification of the mixture. No protein giving a rose colour is precipitated on subsequent acidification.

Ammonia inhibits the test by forming a deep blue colour with the $CuSO_4$; this may be overcome by addition of a large excess of NaOH, but it is a common source of error in testing filtrates after saturation with ammonium sulphate.

(2) **Ninhydrin Test.** To 2 ml. of solution, which must be neutral, add a few drops of 0·1 per cent. ninhydrin. Boil gently. A colour ranging from red-purple to blue will develop if a protein or an amino acid is present.

(2a) *Paper Test.* Allow a couple of drops of the solution to dry on a strip of filter paper. Apply a couple of drops of 0·1 per cent. ninhydrin in pH 5 buffer (2 per cent. citric acid in N/5 NaOH). Heat carefully over a small flame.

Under these conditions, a positive result can be obtained with 0·01 to 0·001 mg. of an amino acid, or a primary or secondary amine.

B. Colour Tests for Individual Amino Acids

(1) **Xanthoprotein Reaction.** Mix 5 drops of concentrated nitric acid with 5 ml. of the solution. A precipitate may form if a higher protein, such as albumin, is present. Heat the mixture. If the test is positive, a yellow colour will develop. Cool, and make alkaline with ammonium hydroxide. The colour will deepen to orange. The test is given by the aromatic amino acids, tyrosine and tryptophan, both free and protein-bound. Phenylalanine does not react under these conditions.

(2) **Mercury Test for Tyrosine.** Mix 5 drops of Millon's reagent with 5 ml. of the solution. A precipitate will form if a higher protein is present. Heat the mixture carefully. If the test is positive, the coagulum or solution will become dark red. The test is given by phenols, including tyrosine, free or protein-bound. Chloride or excess of alkali inhibit the test by precipitating the mercury. This can be overcome by using an excess of the reagent.

(3) **Aldehyde Tests for Tryptophan.** Mix 2 ml. of the solution with 1 ml. of light-activated glacial acetic acid. Add excess (> 5 ml.) of concentrated hydrochloric acid. Immerse tube in boiling water. If the test is positive, a deep, stable violet colour will develop. The test can also be performed as a " ring " reaction, in the cold, using concentrated sulphuric acid to form a lower layer.

The active ingredient is glyoxylic acid, $HOOC.CHO$, which forms slowly when glacial acetic acid is kept exposed to sunlight. Recognition of this led to the subsequent discovery of tryptophan by Hopkins and Cole in 1899. If the acetic acid is replaced in either form of the test by a few drops of Ehrlich's aldehyde reagent (2 per cent. para-dimethylaminobenzaldehyde in N H_2SO_4), a violet colour, becoming deep blue, will be obtained.

These tests are given by tryptophan, both free and protein-bound. Positive reactions are obtained with most of the common proteins, notable exceptions being protamines, insulin, zein, and gelatins, the molecules of which do not contain tryptophan units.

(4) **Naphthol Test for Arginine.** Mix 5 ml. of the solution with 5 drops of 20 per cent. sodium hydroxide and either 2 drops of 2 per cent. α-naphthol in ethanol or 1 ml. of saturated aqueous thymol. Add 5 to 10 drops of 2 per cent. sodium hypochlorite. A positive result is shown by the development of a colour, either carmine (α-naphthol) or golden-yellow (thymol). The test is given by monosubstituted guanidines, $H_2N.C(:NH).NH.R$, including arginine, both free and protein-bound.

α-Naphthol, used by the discoverer of the test (Sakaguchi, 1925) has the disadvantage that it deteriorates in solution, and gives extraneous colour. Aqueous thymol is more stable, but, because of the low solubility of thymol, more of the reagent must be employed.

(5) **Lead Test for Labile Sulphur.** Add 5 drops of 5 per cent. lead acetate to 5 ml. of the solution, followed by sufficient 20 per cent. sodium hydroxide to redissolve the white precipitate of lead hydroxide that forms at first. Boil the mixture. A positive test is shown by the development of a yellow colour deepening into dark brown, as lead sulphide forms in the mixture. The test is given by compounds that liberate sulphur, including cysteine and cystine, both free and protein bound. Methionine does not give the test.

(6) **Nitroprusside Test for Thiols.** Sodium nitroprusside in alkaline solution gives purple colours with sulphides and compounds containing a free thiol or sulphidryl group, —SH, including cysteine and glutathione. The commoner proteins do not give this reaction because the thiol groups, when present, are masked by involvement in bond-formation, such as —S—S—, in cystine. These bonds can be opened by reducing agents and by denaturing agents, such as urea. Mix 2 ml. of a solution of egg albumin with 2 drops of freshly prepared 2 per cent. sodium nitroprusside. Make alkaline with a couple of drops of ammonium hydroxide. Then add an excess of solid urea to the tube and let it dissolve without shaking. As the urea dissolves it denatures the protein, unmasking the thiol groups, which give a purple colour with the reagent. Denaturation requires a high concentration of urea, as can be shown by the reversible bleaching of the colour on addition of water drop by drop and its restoration on addition of more urea. Acid metaproteins which are produced in the early stages of peptic digestion, or when albumins and globulins are dissolved in N/10 HCl and incubated at 45° C. for some hours, give a direct thiol reaction.

GROUP TESTS FOR PROTEINS

(1) **Heat-Coagulation** (Albumins and Animal Globulins)
Add a few drops of " Universal " or other appropriate indicator to 5 ml. of the protein solution, and adjust to the isoelectric region, pH 5–6, either by dilute acetic acid or sodium carbonate. Add a drop of 5 to 10 per cent. sodium chloride. Boil gently. A white coagulum shows the presence of albumin or globulin.

If metaproteins are present, they will be precipitated at pH 5–6 before heating and must then be removed by filtration before continuing the test.

(2) Fractional Separation by Neutral Salts

(a) *Half-saturation.* Mix 5 ml. of solution with an equal volume or slightly more, of saturated ammonium sulphate.

A white flocculation is given by globulins, caseinogen and other higher proteins, with the notable exception of albumins.

(*b*) *Full-saturation.* Filter the mixture after half-saturation and add 5 ml. of the filtrate to a test tube containing about one-third its volume of solid ammonium sulphate. Mix well. All higher proteins and lower proteins, except peptones and peptides, are flocculated, as is shown by the appearance of a turbidity in the liquid above the layer of undissolved ammonium sulphate.

Fractional flocculation, or " salting-out ", is used in the separation and identification of mixed proteins. Unlike heat-coagulation, it is a reversible process, and the protein flocculate can be redissolved on addition of water or removal of the salt by dialysis.

$MgSO_4$, Na_2SO_4 and $NaCl$ are also used as neutral flocculants, but are not as effective as $(NH_4)_2SO_4$ or $ZnSO_4$.

(3) **Flocculation by Special Reagents**

Acids, Metals, and Alkaloidal Reagents. Concentrated strong acids, notably nitric and trichloracetic, $CCl_3.COOH$, flocculate most proteins higher than peptones; concentrated tannic acid flocculates gelatins and peptones, as well as higher proteins.

Detection of Proteins in Simple Mixtures

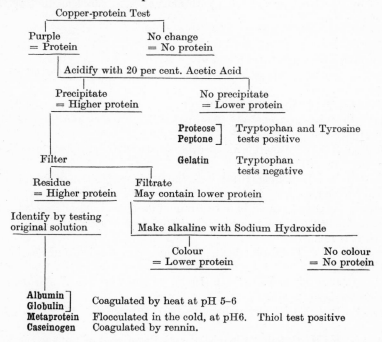

This scheme of analysis is useful for the examination of artificial mixtures and peptic and tryptic digestion products. It does not differentiate between albumin and globulin or between proteose and peptone when present along

Flocculation Tests

Protein.	Heat-coagulation.	Ammonium Sulphate.	
		Half-saturation.	Full saturation.
Albumin . . .	+	−	+
Animal globulin . .	+	+	+
Plant globulin . .	−	−	+
Acid Metaprotein. .	Flocculates at pH 6; coagulates if heated in this state	−	+
Proteoses . . .	−	±	+
Peptones and peptides .	−	−	−
Casein . . .	−	+	+
Gelatin . . .	−	+	+

with other higher and lower proteins. Such differentiation can be accomplished by fractional precipitation with neutral salts, supplemented by the foregoing tests.

General References (Chapters 8 and 9)

"Advances in Protein Chemistry," Vol. I. Ed. M. L. Anson and J. T. Edsall (1945–). New York.

Astbury, W. T. (1939), " X-ray study of proteins." *Science Progress*, **34**, 1; (1941); " Proteins," *Chem. Ind.*, **60**, 491 (1942); " X-rays and the stoichiometry of proteins." *J. chem. Soc.*, 1942, 337.

Block, R. J. (1945), " Isolation and synthesis of the natural and amino acids." *Chem. Rev.*, **38**, 504.

Block, R. J., and D. Bolling (1944), " Amino Acid Composition in Protein and Foods." London.

Cannan, R. K. (1942), "Acid-base titration of proteins." *Chem. Rev.*, **30**, 395.

Chibnall, A. (1942), " Amino acid analysis and protein structure." *Proc. roy. Soc.*, **B, 131**, 136.

Cohn, E. J., and J. T. Edsall (1942), "Proteins, Amino Acids, and Peptides." New York.

Dawson, C. R., and M. F. Mallette (1945), " Copper proteins." *Advances in Protein Chemistry*, **2**, 179.

Fearon, W. R. (1939), " The carbamido-diacetyl reaction." *Biochem. J.*, **33**, 902.

Gustavson, K. H. (1956), " Chemistry and Reactivity of Collagen." N.Y. Academic Press. New York.

Huggins, M. L. (1943), " Structure of fibrous proteins." *Chem. Rev.*, **32**, 195.

" Lipo-proteins " (1949). Faraday Society discussion.

Longworth, L. G. (1942), " Study of proteins by electrophoresis." *Chem. Rev.*, **30,** 323.

Neurath, H., and K. Bailey (1953), " The Proteins." Academic Press Inc. New York.

" Nomenclature of amino acids." *Biochem. J.*, (1948), **42,** 1.

Pickels, E. G. (1942), " Ultra-centrifuge analysis of proteins." *Chem. Rev.*, **30,** 341.

Smith, K. M. (1940), " The Virus: Life's Enemy." Cambridge.

" Symposium on Amino Acid Metabolism " (1955). John Hopkins Press, Baltimore.

Synge, R. M. L. (1943), " Products of partial hydrolysis of proteins." *Chem. Rev.*, **32,** 135.

Van Slyke, D. D. (1942), " Physiology of the amino acids." *Science*, **95,** 259.

Vickery, H. B., and C. L. Schmidt (1931), " History of the discovery of the amino acids." *Chem. Rev.*, **9,** 169.

Chapter 10 Lipids

Living organisms are not soluble in water; they may be drowned but they are not dissolved. External resistance in plants and animals is conferred by the use of coverings of polysaccharides or scleroproteins. Internal resistance is maintained by the presence of water-repelling compounds incorporated into tissues and cell membranes. In this way monocellular and higher forms of life are protected from the solvent action of their aqueous environment; otherwise, water could be a dangerous beverage.

By the extraction of dried animal or plant tissue with " fat solvents " these water-repelling substances can be separated. In their solubility and other physical properties they differ sharply from carbohydrates and proteins, and constitute the third great family of biological compounds, the lipids.

Definition. Lipids are simple or complex esters or amides of long-chain carboxylic acids. They are characterised by insolubility in water, and solubility in the " fat solvents ": ether, light petroleum (petrol), chloroform, carbon tetrachloride, carbon disulphide, benzene, toluene and hot acetone or alcohol. All lipid esters can be saponified, or hydrolysed by alkalies, into their constituent acids and alcohols.

Classification. Lipids are mutually intersoluble, and are universally distributed as mixtures, partly as structural lipid of cell membranes and cell contents, and partly as storage lipid in adipose tissue, liver and in plant seeds rich in oil. The family is conveniently divided into: (A) Simple Lipids, including the true fats; (B) Phospholipids; (C) Glycolipids; and (D) Lipoids, or non-saponifiable lipids, which are included in a larger group: the Lipid Derivatives.

A. **Simple Lipids.** Esters of lipid acids with glycerol or a long-chain alcohol or a sterol. They contain only carbon, hydrogen and oxygen. The commonest simple lipids are glyceryl esters, or *glycerides*.

B. **Phospholipids.** Glycerides in which one organic acid radical has been replaced by phosphoric acid, forming a *phosphatidic acid*.

(1) *Lecithins*. Choline esters of phosphatidic acids.

(2) *Cephalins*. Ethanolamine esters of phosphatidic acids.

C. **Sphingolipids.** Amides of lipid acids and sphingosine derivatives.

(1) *Sphingomyelins*. Sphingolipids in which the sphingosine is combined with choline phosphate.

(2) *Galactolipids*, or cerebrosides. Sphingolipids in which the sphingosine is combined with galactose.

D. **Lipid Derivatives.** Final products of hydrolysis include:

(1) *Lipid Acids.* Higher members of the acetic series and the unsaturated oleic, linoleic, linolenic, arachidonic and clupadonic series.

(2) *Alcohols.* Glycerol. Higher members of the ethanol series.

(3) *Bases.* Ethanolamine, choline, sphingosine.

(4) *Sugar.* Galactose, from galactolipids.

(5) *Phosphoric acid,* from phospholipids and sphingomyelins.

LIPID COMPONENTS

(A) **Acids.** At least eight different series of organic acids are represented in the natural lipids. One of these, the acetic series, is saturated; the others are all more or less unsaturated.

(1) **The Acetic or Stearic Series,** $C_nH_{2n+1}COOH$. The chief members are:—

Acid.	Formula.	Solubility in H_2O.	Occurrence.
Formic	$H.COOH$	Miscible	Stings of insects and plants.
Acetic	$CH_3.COOH$	,,	Vinegar.
Butyric	$C_3H_7.COOH$	,,	Butter fat.
Caproic	$C_5H_{11}.COOH$	4 : 100 at 15° C.	Coconut oil.
Caprylic	$C_7H_{15}.COOH$	9 : 1000 at 15° C.	Palm oil.
Capric	$C_9H_{19}.COOH$	1 : 1000 at 100° C.	Laurel oil.
Myristic	$C_{13}H_{27}.COOH$	Insoluble	Nutmeg oil.
Palmitic	$C_{15}H_{31}.COOH$	,,	Most animal and vegetable fats and oils.
Stearic	$C_{17}H_{35}.COOH$	,,	Most animal and vegetable solid fats.
Arachidic	$C_{19}H_{39}.COOH$	,,	Peanut (Arachis) oil.
Lignoceric	$C_{23}H_{47}.COOH$	,,	Glycolipides.
Cerotic	$C_{25}H_{51}.COOH$	,,	Beeswax.
Melissic	$C_{29}H_{59}.COOH$	,,	Beeswax.

Tuberculo-stearic (10-methyl stearic), $C_{18}H_{37}.COOH$ and phthioic acid, $C_{25}H_{51}COOH$, occur in the lipids of the human-type tubercle bacillus.

Palmitic Acid, $CH_3(CH_2)_{14}.COOH$, m.p. 62° C., occurs in many plant and animal fats and waxes, especially palm oil, Japan wax, and myrtle wax. It is present in spermaceti as cetyl palmitate and in beeswax as myricyl palmitate. The acid is insoluble in water, slightly soluble in cold alcohol, and easily soluble in boiling alcohol.

Stearic acid, $CH_3(CH_2)_{16}.COOH$, m.p. 69·3° C., is very widely distributed, especially in the body fat of higher animals as tallow, lard, and suet. It is prepared in quantity by the catalytic hydrogenation or " hardening " of the corresponding unsaturated acids, oleic, linoleic, linolenic, and clupadonic, all of which have the same number of carbon atoms. Stearic acid is a white solid, with a faint but characteristic smell. It is insoluble in water, but easily soluble in boiling alcohol.

(2) **The Oleic Series,** C_nH_{2n-1}.COOH. Unsaturated acids having one double bond, —CH : CH—.
Oleic acid, $C_{17}H_{33}$.COOH, m.p. 14° C., the most widely distributed of all the fatty acids. The free acid is a colourless liquid that turns yellow on exposure to air and light. It is a typical example of an *unsaturated* compound, and its presence in glycerides is shown by its property of reducing osmium tetroxide ("osmic acid"), OsO_4, with the formation of a black deposit, easily recognised in histological preparations.
The Structure of Oleic Acid. (i) Combustion shows that the empirical formula is $C_9H_{17}O$.
(ii) Molecular weight determination gives the formula, $C_{18}H_{34}O_2$.
(iii). Titration shows that a single carboxyl group is present, $C_{17}H_{33}$.COOH.
(iv). On reduction, oleic acid takes up two atoms of hydrogen, and is converted into the corresponding saturated acid, *stearic acid*, $C_{17}H_{35}COOH$. This shows that there must be one double bond, or —CH=CH— link, in the oleic acid molecule, and that the acid has a straight chain.
(v). On oxidation, oleic acid breaks up into nonylic acid and azelaic acid, both of which are C_9 acids, indicating that the double bond in oleic acid is midway in the chain.

$$CH_3.(CH_2)_7.CH_2{-}CH_2.(CH_2)_7COOH \qquad \text{Stearic acid}$$

$$CH_3.(CH_2)_7CH{=}CH.(CH_2)_7.COOH \qquad \textbf{Oleic acid}$$

$$CH_3(CH_2)_7COOH \longleftarrow\!\!\longrightarrow HOOC.(CH_2)_7.COOH$$
$$\text{Nonylic acid} \qquad\qquad\qquad \text{Azelaic acid}$$

This shows that oleic acid is a $\triangle^{9:10}$ unsaturated acid; the suffix denoting that a double bond occurs between the ninth and tenth carbon atoms, as numbered from the right.
Other examples of the oleic series are: tiglic acid, C_4H_7COOH, from croton oil; erucic acid, $C_{22}H_{43}$.COOH, from mustard oil; and vaccinic acid, the $\triangle^{7:8}$ isomer of oleic acid, from bacteria and animal tissues.
Each member contains one double bond and is converted on reduction into a corresponding member of the stearic series.
(3) **The Linoleic Series,** C_nH_{2n-3}.COOH. The natural acids are all C_{18} compounds with two double-bonds. In human storage fat they are found mostly as phospholipids and as esters of cholesterol. Linoleic acid, the chief member, is a constituent of linseed and other "drying oils", which harden to form a film on exposure to the air. Its formula is

$$CH_3.(CH_2)_4.CH : CH.CH_2.CH : CH.(CH_2)_7.COOH.$$

(4) **The Linolenic Series** is represented by linolenic acid, $C_{17}H_{29}$.COOH, which makes up about 20 per cent. of linseed oil, and occurs in all vegetable drying oils. Members of this series have three double-bonds.
(5) **The Arachidonic Series,** having four double-bonds, is represented by arachidonic acid, $C_{19}H_{31}$.COOH, found in lecithin and cephalin.

(6) **The Clupadonic Series,** represented by clupadonic acid, $C_{17}H_{27}$.COOH, in cod-liver oil, and probably all marine oils.

(7) **Hydroxy acids** are represented by the **Cerebronic Series,** including phreno-sinic or cerebronic acid from phrenosin of brain tissue; and the **Ricinoleic Series,** including ricinoleic acid, the glyceride of which is the chief constituent of castor oil.

(8) **The Cyclic acids** include the two members, chaulmoogric acid from chaulmoogra oil and hydnocarpic acid from hydnocarpus and chaulmoogra. They are used in the treatment of leprosy.

(B) **Alcohols.** Natural fats and oils are esters of the trihydroxy alcohol gly-cerol; the other aliphatic alcohols occur either free as solutes in oils and fats or combined as *waxes*. Five groups of these alcohols may be recognised, four of which belong to the straight-chain type of compounds.

(1) Alcohols of the *Ethyl Alcohol Series*, C_nH_{2n+1}.OH; these contain one hydroxyl group. Being higher members of the series, they are all odourless and tasteless solids, insoluble in water but soluble in fat solvents. They are characteristic constituents of the waxes. The chief examples are: cetyl alcohol, $C_{16}H_{33}$.OH, from spermaceti; carnaubyl alcohol, $C_{24}H_{49}$.OH, from wool wax; melissyl, or myricyl alcohol, $C_{30}H_{61}$.OH, from beeswax.

(2) Dihydroxy alcohols of the *Glycollic Series*, represented by coryphyl alcohol, $C_{24}H_{48}(OH)_2$, from carnauba wax.

(3) Trihydroxy alcohol of the *Glycerol Series*. Only one member is known, glycerol, a basic constituent of all true fats.

Glycerol, or glycerin, CH_2OH.CH(OH).CH_2OH, is quantitatively the most important of the lipid alcohols, and is obtained during the saponification of fats and oils. It is a colourless, odourless, viscid liquid, with a sweet, pungent taste. It is a good solvent, and is very hygroscopic, absorbing about 50 per cent. of its weight of water from the atmosphere. For this reason it is used in cosmetics and " vanishing creams " designed to keep skin moist and sticky.

Free glycerol is not a lipid. It is insoluble in most of the fat solvents, and is miscible in all proportions with water and with alcohol.

Reactions of Glycerol. (1) *Dehydration*. On being heated rapidly along with an anhydrous salt, such as $NaHSO_4$, glycerol loses two molecules of water, and is dehydrated to form the unsaturated aldehyde acrolein, which imparts the characteristic acrid smell to burning fat.

$$
\begin{array}{lcl}
CH_2.OH & & CH_2 \\
| & & || \\
CH.OH & \longrightarrow & CH \quad + 2H_2O \\
| & & | \\
CH_2.OH & & CHO \\
\text{Glycerol.} & & \text{Acrolein}
\end{array}
$$

(2) *Esterification*. Glycerophosphoric acid, $CH_2OH.CH(OH).CH_2O.PO:(OH)_2$, is prepared by heating glycerol in 60 per cent. phosphoric acid at 100° C. It is a characteristic constituent of the phospholipids, such as lecithin. **Nitroglycerin,** glyceryl trinitrate, $CH_2(O.NO_2).CH(O.NO_2).CH_2(O.NO_2)$, is prepared by adding glycerol to a cooled mixture of nitric and sulphuric acids. It is an ingredient in many high explosives, and is also used therapeutically as a general vaso-dilator.

Compound alcohols or **alcohol ethers** occur in fish-liver oils and bone marrow. *Batyl alcohol*, $C_{21}H_{42}O(OH)_2$, is a monoglycerol ether of octadecyl alcohol.

Sterols, or **Alcohols of the Cholane Series.** These differ from the other lipid alcohols in the possession of a complex cyclic structure. They are represented by the zoosterols, including *cholesterol*, $C_{27}H_{45}.OH$, found in animals, and the phytosterols and zymosterols, found in plants.

SIMPLE LIPIDS

Oleo-lipids, or Lipid Oils: Glyceryl esters liquid at 20° C.

Fats: Glyceryl esters solid at 20° C.

Waxes: Esters of lipid acids and higher alcohols, usually solid at 20° C.

Oils. The term " oil " emphasises a physical property and is applied to the liquid fats and to other classes of chemically unrelated compounds, notably: the liquid paraffins, which are hydrocarbons of no significance in animal or plant nutrition or construction; and the " essential oils ", which are volatile, cyclic compounds of plant origin.

The most important of the simple lipids are the lipid oils and the fats. They are tri-glyceride in structure, being esters of the trihydroxy alcohol, glycerol, and three molecules of a lipid or aliphatic acid. On hydrolysis the glyceride is resolved progressively into its components.

$$
\begin{array}{ccc}
R_1.CO.O.CH_2 & R_1.COOH & HO.CH_2 \\
| & | & | \\
R_2.CO.O.CH \quad +\ 3H_2O \longrightarrow & R_2.COOH\ + & HO.CH \\
| & | & | \\
R_3.CO.O.CH_2 & R_3.COOH & HO.CH_2 \\
\text{Glyceride.} & \text{Acids.} & \text{Glycerol.}
\end{array}
$$

Hydrolysis can be accomplished by the fat-splitting enzymes, or lipases, by superheated steam or by alkalis. Alkaline hydrolysis of a lipid is termed saponification, because the liberated acid is neutralised and forms a soap.

The acid radicals in a fat or oil may be of the same, or different species, as in the mixed glycerides.

Significance. Oleo-lipids and fats form a large group of natural compounds that occur in plants and in all terrestrial and marine animals, and provide an important class of food material. The component lipid acids are long, straight-chain members of an ascending series from C_{14} to C_{24}, increasing by 2C at a time. The glyceride structure of common fat was discovered by Chevreul, in 1823; since then, some 600 different natural fats have been recognised

(Hilditch, 1948). Acids as low as C_{10} and as high as C_{30} occur in specialised lipid secretions.

A characteristic of natural fats is the predominance of fatty acids with an even number of total C atoms in the molecule, suggesting that fat-synthesis proceeds by addition of C_2 units to a C_{2n} nucleus.

Lard, obtained from the pig, is the mixed glyceride of stearic acid (40 per cent.), oleic acid (50 per cent.), linoleic acid (10 per cent.).

Tallow, or beef and mutton fat, contains mixed glycerides of stearic acid (33 to 50 per cent.), palmitic acid (10 to 20 per cent.), and oleic acid (50 to 60 per cent.).

Butter, or milk fat, occurs to the extent of 3 to 5·5 per cent. in mammalian milk, and is a complex mixture of the glycerides of oleic, lauric, myristic, palmitic, stearic, and arachidic acids. It is characterised by the presence of butyric acid, which makes up 4 to 6 per cent. of the total fatty acid present.

Human fat resembles tallow in many respects; its fatty acid content is largely determined by the fatty acids in the diet. At body temperature, human fat is almost liquid, because of its high percentage of glycerides of oleic acid.

Vegetable Fats. The principal members of a large group are:—

Cacao butter (cocoa butter), from the beans of the cocoa tree (*Theobroma cacao*), is made of glycerides of stearic and oleic acids. It is used in pharmacy and in confectionery.

Cocoanut oil, from the fruit of the cocoanut tree (*Cocos nucifera*), is used largely in the preparation of edible fats, margarines, and " nut butter ". Glycerides of lauric, myristic, decanoic, hexanoic, stearic and oleic acids are included in its composition. It is used in the preparation of marine soap.

Vegetable oils are divided into *drying oils*, which harden on exposure to light and air, and *non-drying oils*, which do not. Various intermediate forms are grouped as *semi-drying oils*. The property of " drying " depends on the presence of highly unsaturated acids in the glyceride.

Important non-drying oils are *rape seed oil* or *colza oil*, from the mustard; *almond oil, olive oil*, and *castor oil*, from seeds of *Ricinus communis*. Many of these are used as lubricants.

The commonest drying oils are *linseed oil*, from flax seed (*Linum usitatissimum*), *tung oil, hempseed oil, soya bean oil*, and *walnut oil*.

Marine oils include the *fish oils*, found almost uniformly distributed in the tissues of most fish; *liver oils*, chiefly from cod, shark, ling, halibut and skate, are of great therapeutic value as sources of the vitamins A and D; *blubber oils*, from the oleaginous tissues of the seal and the whale.

ANALYTICAL REACTIONS OF SIMPLE LIPIDS

Alkaline Hydrolysis (Saponification). Shake up 5 ml. of olive oil or melted fat with 5 ml. of 20 per cent. sodium hydroxide. A white emulsion forms, consisting of a disperse phase of liquid fat in a continuous aqueous phase. Immerse the tube in boiling water. The emulsion is unstable and resolves into a layer of oil on a layer of alkali. Hydrolysis takes place at the interface, and is aided by shaking the tube occasionally. After at least half an hour, remove and cool the tube. The contents show three layers: a lower one of alkali and glycerol, an upper one of unchanged oil, and an intermediate solid layer of soap, sodium oleate, which has been " salted-out " of the lower layer by the excess of alkali. Carefully pour off the liquid layers, and test for glycerol by means of the nitro-chromic test. Rinse the small cake of soap with cold water to remove excess of alkali. Then add about 10 ml. of water, and boil till the soap dissolves.

Detection of Soap. (a) Acidify about 3 ml. of solution with a few drops of HCl. The soap is decomposed and the liberated fatty acid separates out.
(b) Add a few drops of 5 per cent. $CaCl_2$ to 3 ml. of soap solution. A white precipitate of calcium soap separates out. This reaction takes place in " hard " water when soap is added, and renders washing uneconomical.
(c) Add about 1 ml. of saturated NaCl to 3 ml. of soap solution. The soap is displaced, or " salted-out ", and rises to the top of the liquid. This process is employed industrially in the purification of soap.
(d) Add about 1 ml. of 1 per cent. $CuSO_4$ to 2 ml. of soap solution. Mix well. A pale blue precipitate of copper soap separates. Add 2 ml. of benzene or toluene, and shake gently. The copper soap is extracted as a blue solution in the organic solvent.
Copper salts of aliphatic acids higher than butyric are soluble in benzene.
Detection of Glycerol. Add a few drops of 5 per cent. potassium chromate and an excess of concentrated nitric acid to the mixture of oil and alkali after separation of the soap. A blue colour develops in the aqueous layer owing to the presence of glycerol liberated from the hydrolysed fat. This is a general test for compounds containing primary or secondary alcohol groups (p. 95).

SOAPS

A soap is the salt of a higher aliphatic acid, and is formed whenever fats are hydrolysed in an alkaline medium. Potassium, sodium, and ammonium soaps are dissolved readily by water to form colloidal solutions, and are used in washing. Calcium and magnesium soaps are insoluble, and represent a form in which these metals are excreted by the intestine.

Soluble soaps form alkaline solutions, owing to removal of H^+ by the aliphatic anions to produce the feebly ionised aliphatic acid:

$$R.COONa + H_2O \rightarrow R.COO^- + Na^+ + H_2O \leftarrow \rightarrow R.COOH + Na^+ + OH^-.$$

Micelle Formation. Soaps and long-chain aliphatic acids are unsymmetrical electrolytes: the carboxyl groups are hydrophilic, with a strong affinity for water; the hydrocarbon chains are hydrophobic and repelled by water. Hence, soaps and higher aliphatic acids can only form true solutions of very low concentration, M/1,000 to M/50. Above this, aggregation occurs, producing *micelles*, or spheroidal clusters, each having a liquid core of converging carbon chains and an exterior shell of carboxyl or other hydrophilic groups, which keeps the micelles solvated and dispersed. These lipid micelles can act as grease-removers, because of the fat-dissolving property of the cores. Long-chain acids in which the carboxyl is replaced by a sulphonic or other strongly acid radical are used industrially as synthetic detergents of high efficiency.

WAXES

Waxes are esters formed from a higher alcohol and an aliphatic acid, and are non-glycerides. All are insoluble in water but soluble in fat solvents. They are much more resistant to hydrolysis than true fats, and are not attacked by the lipoclastic enzymes, hence, waxes are not utilisable in animal nutrition. When hydrolysed they show their ester structure by giving rise to an aliphatic acid, and an alcohol.

The chief waxes are wool wax, beeswax, spermaceti, chinese wax, and carnauba wax.

Wool wax, or *lanolin,* comes from the fleece of sheep. It is a mixture of esters and free alcohols, including the sterol cholesterol, also lanosterol and agnosterol, which are derivatives of a five-ring hydrocarbon, *picene.*

Lanolin may absorb up to 80 per cent. of its weight of water, and is an important agent for the dermal administration of drugs. It is absorbed by the skin, and for this reason is hopefully described as a " skin food " by makers of cosmetics.

Beeswax, secreted by the honey-bee during digestion, is used for building the comb. It is chiefly myricyl palmitate, and is largely employed in the manufacture of polishes.

Spermaceti, obtained as a solid from the head oil of the sperm and other whales, is chiefly cetyl palmitate. Its principal industrial use is the manufacture of candles.

COMPLEX LIPIDS: PHOSPHOLIPIDS AND SPHINGOLIPIDS

Phospholipids resemble the fats physically and, like them, yield glycerol and lipid acids on hydrolysis. They differ in containing a phosphoric acid radical, usually in combination with a nitrogen base. Phospholipids are much less soluble in cold acetone than are the other lipids, and can be separated from ethereal extracts by addition of acetone.

Structure. The phospholipids are derived from α-glycerophosphoric acid, $HO.CH_2.CH(OH).CH_2.O.PO(OH)_2$, in which each of the glycerol hydroxyls is esterified with a lipid acid, forming a phospho-diglyceride, or phosphatidic acid. The lipid acid radicals are not necessarily of the same species, and one usually is unsaturated.

Phosphatidic acids accompany lipids in seeds, fruits and leaves. **Lecithins** occur chiefly in egg yolk, the medullary sheaths of nerves and in liver. The 50-gm. egg of the domestic fowl contains about 1 gm. of lecithin in its 15 gm. of yolk.

R .CO.O.CH$_2$ R.CO—, and R′.CO— = Lipid acid radicals
 | Phosphatidic Acid: X = H
R′.CO.O.CH   Lecithins: X = (CH$_3$)$_3$N$^+$.CH$_2$.CH$_2$—O—
 | Cephalins: X = NH$_2$.CH$_2$.CH$_2$—O—,
X .PO.O.CH$_2$ or NH$_2$.CH(COOH).CH$_2$—
 OH

Phospholipid.

The lecithins are phosphatidyl esters of the quaternary nitrogen base *choline*, or N-trimethyl-ethanolamine, HO.CH$_2$.CH$_2$.N$^+$(CH$_3$)$_3$, and provide a reserve of this important agent.

The lipid acid radicals differ in lecithins from different sources. Yolk lecithins contain stearic and oleic, liver lecithins contain in addition palmitic or arachidonic radicals. Partial hydrolysis of lecithin can be effected by enzymes: lipase liberates lipid acids; phosphatase liberates phosphoric acid; cobra venom esterase liberates the unsaturated acid radical, leaving a residual *lysolecithin*. Lysolecithins are powerful hæmolytic agents, and contribute to the harmful effects of injection of snake venom. They are antagonised by cholesterol, with which they form non-hæmolytic complexes.

Cephalins accompany lecithins, and are widely distributed in plants and animals. They include: colamine cephalins, or phosphatidyl-ethanolamines, in which the base in ethanolamine, or colamine, HO.CH$_2$.CH$_2$.NH$_2$; and serine cephalins, or phosphatidyl-serines, in which the base is the amino acid L-serine, HO.CH$_2$.CH(NH$_2$).COOH. Serine by decarboxylation forms ethanolamine, so the two cephalin types may be interchangeable.

Acetal Phospholipids, or plasmalogens, form about 10 per cent. of the phospholipids of brain and liver. They can be regarded as choline or ethanolamine esters of α-glycerophosphoric acid, in which the two glyceryl hydroxyls are combined in acetal union with stearic or palmitic aldehyde, forming a 5-membered ring. On treatment with mercuric chloride the aldehyde is set free and can be detected by Schiff's reagent (Feulgen, 1924).

Lipositols. Phospholipids in which inositol is esterified with the phosphoric radical. Lipositols have been found in brain, soy bean, and tubercle bacilli.

Sphingolipids are derivatives of the base sphingosine, an 18-carbon amine containing two hydroxyl groups.

Sphingomyelins constitute 1 to 1·5 per cent. of fresh brain and nerve tissue, and about one-third of the total phospholipid of lung and spleen. Brain sphingomyelin contains a stearic, lignoceric, or nervonic acid radical in amide union with the amino group in the sphingosine molecule, the terminal hydroxyl group of which is linked by phosphoric acid to choline.

Galactolipids, or cerebrosides, constitute 2 to 4 per cent. of fresh brain, and are concentrated in the medullary sheaths of nerves. Unlike the other lipids, they are sparingly soluble in ether, but can be removed from ether-extracted residues by boiling ethanol. On fractional crystallisation, four types can be separated: phrenosin, kerasin, nervone, and hydroxynervone.

Galactolipids differ from other compound lipids in being free from a phosphoric radical, and differ amongst themselves in the lipid acid radical present, which is lignoceric, or tetracosanoic, $H_3C.(CH_2)_{22}.COOH$, in kerasins; α-hydroxylignoceric, or cerebronic, in phrenosins; nervonic, $H_3C.(CH_2)_7CH : CH.(CH_2)_{13}.COOH$, in nervones; and α-hydroxynervonic in hydroxynervones.

Sphingolipids

$$H_3C.(CH_2)_{12}CH : CH.CH(OH).CH.CH_2.O—X$$
$$|$$
$$NH—Y$$

Sphingosine: $X = Y = H$

Sphingomyelin: $X = —PO(OH).O.CH_2.CH_2.N^+(CH_3)_3$
$Y = $ Lipid acid radical in amide union, $R.CO.NH—$, with the sphingosine amino group.

Galactolipid: $X = C_6H_{11}O_5$, a galactose unit in carbon 1 glycoside linkage.
$Y = $ Lipid acid radical.

More complex lipids are represented by Gangliosides, which accompany galactolipids in nerve tissue. On hydrolysis they yield a molecule of sphingosine, three of hexose (glucose and galactose), an aliphatic acid of the C_{22} or C_{24} series, and neuraminic acid.

Other lipids are the sulphatides from brain, which contain sulphuric acid radicals, and the phospholipids of bacterial origin, of which those from the tubercle bacillus are noteworthy in that they yield *phthioic acid*, a branched-chain acid that stimulates tubercle formation in tissues.

Significance of the Lipids. (1) *Structural.* Phospholipids are universally present in micro-organisms and in all cells of plants and animals, being localised in boundaries, mitochondria and other inclusions, where they may be employed in organising various enzyme systems. The myelin that forms the sheath of medullated nerve fibres is constructed of protein, cholesterol, and sphingolipids. Non-medullated nerves also have coatings of complex lipids.

(2) *Food Reserve.* Aided by their insolubility in aqueous media, lipids are stored readily as reserve material in seeds and nuts, and in liver and adipose tissue. The amount can vary greatly with species and with diet and activity. The adult human subject in health has a fat content of 100 to 200 gm. per Kg. of body weight, more than half of which is storage fat.

(3) *Food Material.* Fats and oils together represent one of the three great sources of carbon and hydrogen in the animal dietary. Containing less oxygen than the carbohydrates or the proteins, they are concentrated sources of energy, yielding about 9·3 kilocalories per gram.

(4) *Solvents.* Dietary and storage fats carry in solution important solutes, notably the fat-soluble vitamins A, D, and E, and their precursors.

135

(5) *Essential Nutrients.* Small amounts of the polyene, or highly-unsaturated acids, linoleic, linolenic, arachidonic, are required in the diet of the higher animal. These accompany the common food fats. In addition, the lecithins are sources of choline, which prevents excessive accumulation of storage fat in the liver.

SEPARATION AND CHARACTERISATION OF LIPIDS

After successive extraction of the dried material with alcohol and ether, or other solvent, the combined extracts are saponified by boiling with aqueous alkali. This results in the separation of the unsaponifiable lipoids (sterols, higher alcohols, carotenoids, hydrocarbons), which can be removed by skimming or ether-extraction. The aqueous mixture is acidified with hydrochloric acid. This results in the separation of the water-insoluble lipid acids, which can be extracted by ether. The water-soluble lipid derivatives (glycerol, phosphoric acid, choline, and other bases) remain in the aqueous phase, and are separated individually.

The natural lipids, because of their intersolubility, occur in mixtures that, for the purpose of analysis, are submitted to a routine series of estimations.

(1) *Acid Value.* The amount of potassium hydroxide, in mg., required to neutralise the free fatty acids present in 1 gm. of the material.

This value measures the rancidity and degree of hydrolysis of the fat.

(2) *Saponification Value.* The amount of potassium hydroxide, in mg., required to saponify completely 1 gm. of the fat. This measures the total fatty acids present in ester and free form, and varies inversely with the molecular weight of the fatty acids.

(3) *Iodine Value.* The amount of iodine, in gm., that is decolourised by combining with 100 gm. of fat. This measures the degree of unsaturation of the acids present in the fat. The process is catalysed by using the iodine as a monobromide or monochloride.

(4) *Volatile Acid Value,* or Reichert-Meissl Number. The amount of N/10 KOH required to neutralise the volatile fatty acids obtained when 5 gm. of hydrolysed fat is distilled by a current of steam. This measures the total fatty acids of low molecular weight up to C_{12}.

(5) *Thiocyanogen Value* (Kaufmann, 1925). The weight of thiocyanogen,

Analytical Constants for Common Fats (Plimmer, 1938)

Fat.	Saponification Value.	Iodine Value.	Reichert Value.
Lard	195	46–70	0·6
Olive oil	185–196	79–88	0·6
Linseed oil . . .	192–195	173–201	0·0
Butter	220–233	26–50	26–33

$(SCN)_2$, absorbed by 1 gm. of fat. This is a better index of the degree of unsaturation than the iodine method, which is often inadequate for fatty acids with more than one double-bond.

Mixed glycerides, such as make up animal fats, are described briefly in terms of their component acids. Thus, *tristearin* is the glyceride containing three stearyl residues, while *β-palmito- αα-distearin* has a palmityl unit in the central, or *β*-position, and a stearyl unit at each of the ends of the glyceryl residue.

Fats are also characterised by their *refractive index* and by their *specific gravity*, which for a solid fat is about 0·85 and for an oleo-lipid about 0·91 to 0·94. After liberation by hydrolysis and acidification, the fatty acids are isolated by repeated fractionation of their lithium or lead salts, or by low-temperature crystallisation. Thus, when an acetone solution of mixed acids from a natural fat is cooled to about −30° C., the saturated acids separate, while further cooling from −40° to −80° C. removes unsaturated acids.

Fats as a class have lower melting-points than those of their constituent acids, and re-solidify at temperatures below their m.p. Human fat melts about 17° C., and, hence, is in the liquid state at body-temperature.

Fatty acids can be separated and identified by chromatographic methods, and by the counter-current diffusion technique (Craig, 1950).

General References

Anderson, R. J. (1939–40), " Chemistry of the Lipids of Tubercle Bacilli." *Harvey Lectures*, 35.

Bloor, W. R. (1943), "Biochemistry of the Fatty Acids."

Craig, L. C. (1950) in " Techniques of Organic Chemistry." Ed. by A. Weissberger. Interscience Publishers, New York.

Dawson, R. M. C. (1957), "Animal phospholipids." *Biol. Rev.*, **32**, 188. Cambridge.

Eckey, E. W. (1954), " Vegetable fats and oils." *American Chem. Soc. Monograph*, No. 123.

Hilditch, T. P. (1953), " Chemical Constitution of Natural Fats." 3rd Ed. London.

" Progress in the Chemistry of Fats and Other Lipids." Ed. by R. T. Holman *et al.* Vol. I (1952–). New York; London.

Ralston, A. W. (1948), " Fatty Acids and Their Derivatives." New York; London.

Thannhauser, S. J., and G. Schmidt (1946), " Lipins and lipidoses." *Physiol. Rev.*, **26**, 275.

Chapter 11 Sterols and Steroids

The fraction obtained when tissues are extracted with fat-solvents contains, in addition to simple and complex lipids, a varying amount of lipoid material that is not saponified by alkalies. Prominent among these lipoids are the sterols and the steroids. They can be regarded as derivatives of a saturated tetracyclic hydrocarbon, sterane, $C_{17}H_{28}$. The first sterol to be recognised was obtained from biliary calculi, and was named " cholesterine " (Gk. *solid bile*), later changed to *cholesterol*, when an alcohol group was shown to be present in the compound. Related substances obtained from plants were described generally as *sterols*. Subsequently, it was discovered that many important biological compounds, including bile acids, sex hormones, and vitamin-precursors contain a tetracyclic nucleus similar to that in the sterols: these compounds are termed *steroids*.

Sterane.
Cyclo-Pentano-13 : 14-perhydrophenanthrene.

Sterane. The systematic name for this hydrocarbon is *cyclo*-pentano-13 : 14-perhydrophenanthrene, which shows that it can be regarded as assembled from a phenanthrene unit in which the double-bonds are hydrogenated, forming perhydrophenanthrene; together with a fully-saturated 5-membered cyclic hydrocarbon, *cyclo*-pentane, C_5H_{10}, which is fused with ring C of the perhydrophenanthrene by sharing carbon atoms at positions 13 and 14.

Definition. The natural sterols and steroids are a family of hydrocarbons derived from a sterane ring-system which has a methyl group at carbon 13 and, with the exception of the œstrogens, a methyl group at carbon 10. According to their source, sterols are divided into zoosterols, phytosterols, and zymosterols. Steroids are grouped according to function or source, such as : bile acids, saponins, cardio-active aglycones, bufotalins, sex hormones, metabolic hormones.

STEROLS

Sterols occur universally in animals and plants, but are absent usually from bacteria. They are associated, free and as esters, with the tissue lipids. Chemically, the natural sterols all contain a hydroxyl group at carbon 3, usually a double-bond in ring A, and a long side-chain at carbon 17. They all are optically active.

Representative Sterols

Sterol.	Formula.	Double-Bonds.	Source.
Cholesterol	$C_{27}H_{45} \cdot OH$	5 : 6	All animal tissues
7-Dehydrocholesterol	$C_{28}H_{43} \cdot OH$	5 : 6, 7 : 8	Liver oils
β-Cholestanol	$C_{27}H_{47} \cdot OH$	none	Animal tissues
Coprostanol	$C_{27}H_{47} \cdot OH$	none	Fæcal lipid
Stigmasterol	$C_{29}H_{47} \cdot OH$	5 : 6, 22 : 23	Soya bean
β-Sitosterol	$C_{29}H_{49} \cdot OH$	5 : 6	Higher plants
Ergosterol	$C_{28}H_{43} \cdot OH$	5 : 6, 7 : 8, 22 : 23	Yeasts, ergot

Cholesterol, isolated from biliary calculi in 1775, has attracted continuous attention because of its medical importance, its wide distribution, and its chemical structure.

Cholesterol, accompanied by 1 to 2 per cent. β-cholestanol, occurs normally free or combined (usually as an oleate or a palmitate) in tissues and secretions, notably brain, bile, blood and adipose deposits; it accumulates pathologically in biliary calculi, sebaceous cysts and atheromatous blood vessel walls. The 70-kg. adult human body contains about 210 gm.

Human blood plasma contains about 200 mg. cholesterol per 100 ml., mostly esterified and combined with protein.

Representative cholesterol values, expressed as percentage, are: human brain, fresh, 2·2; human brain, dried, 10·9; suprarenal gland, fresh, 5 to 7; sciatic nerve, dried, 5·6; spleen, kidney and lung, fresh, 0·3 to 0·5; animal fats, 0·1 to 0·35; human bile, 0·06 to 0·16; human milk, 0·03; egg-yolk, fresh, 0·49; liver oils, 0·5 to 1·5.

The cholesterol content of the plasma is often increased in renal disease, the highest levels being reached in the more chronic types. In lipoid nephrosis it may be as high as 1000 mg. per 100 ml. plasma.

Cholesterol has not yet been found in any plant tissues, and its presence in a vegetable oil is evidence of adulteration with fat of animal origin.

Cholesterol is obtained readily by extracting powdered biliary calculi with boiling alcohol. On cooling, the sterol crystallises out in characteristic flat plates with one corner notched.

Sitosterol and **Stigmasterol** are characteristic of higher plants, and are concentrated in tissues rich in lipids, especially the germ of the seeds. These sterols are restricted to the plant kingdom, and although they necessarily

139

occur in the animal diet, there is no evidence either of their utilisation or conversion to zoosterols by higher animals, although it is possible that certain molluscs unable to manufacture cholesterol may obtain their characteristic *ostreaosterol* from the isomeric phytosterols that occur in the algæ on which they feed.

Ergosterol, Provitamin D$_2$. This sterol was isolated from the fungus Ergot by Tanret, but attracted little attention until 1927, when it was shown to be convertible into **vitamin D$_2$,** or **ergocalciferol,** by solar or ultra-violet irradiation. Ergosterol occurs in moulds, yeasts and some fungi. It can be separated from cholesterol by fractional crystallisation from ethanol. Unlike cholesterol, it has an additional double-bond, 7 : 8, in ring B, and its ultra-violet spectrum has three distinct absorption bands.

Selective oxidation of cholesterol, by removing an H atom from carbons 7 and 8, generates a second double-bond in ring B, producing **7-dehydrocholesterol.** Like ergosterol, 7-dehydrocholesterol is a vitamin-precursor and on ultra-violet irradiation is degraded to **vitamin D$_3$,** or **cholecalciferol.** Cholesterol is dehydrogenated to 7-dehydrocholesterol by enzymes in the liver, intestinal wall and skin, and thus provides an indirect source of the vitamin.

Structure and Formulation of the Sterols. Cholesterol and other sterols on oxidation yield a long-chain ketone and a residual C$_{19}$ nucleus. Thus, from cholesterol is obtained methyl-*iso*-hexyl ketone,

$$CH_3.CO.CH_2.CH_2.CH_2.CH(CH_3)_2,$$

which indicates that the parent side-chain is

$$-CH(CH_3).CH_2.CH_2.CH_2.CH(CH_3)_2,$$

oxidation having taken place at the point of attachment of the —CH— group to the nucleus.

By a similar procedure, the side-chains of the other sterols, and the steroid *cholic acid*, were separated and identified, and the following semi-structural formulæ were deduced:—

Cholesterol $R.CH(CH_3).CH_2.CH_2.CH_2.CH(CH_3)_2$.
Stigmasterol $R.CH(CH_3).CH=CH.CH(C_2H_5).CH(CH_3)_2$.
Ergosterol $R.CH(CH_3).CH=CH.CH(CH_3).CH(CH_3)_2$.
Cholic acid $R.CH(CH_3).CH_2.CH_2.COOH$.

The tetracyclic structure of the nucleus is shown by the production of 17-methylpenteno-phenanthrene (Diels, 1927) when a sterol is degraded by heating with Se at 320° C.

The natural sterols and steroids differ in the attached side-chains and in the position and number of the double-bonds, but all appear to conform to a general pattern.

In ring A, carbon 3 is always attached to oxygen, either as an hydroxyl, —OH, or an oxo group, : O; this is denoted by -*ol* or -*one*, respectively, in the name of the compound.

17-Methylpenteno-phenanthrene
(Diels' hydrocarbon).

Cholesterol.

Carbon 13 always carries a methyl group.

Carbon 17 in ring D is joined to a long side-chain, in the sterols; or carries —OH, : O, or —CO—, in the steroids.

Carbon 10 carries a methyl group in the sterols, bile acids, adrenal cortex hormones and testicular hormones; but in the female sex hormones all its valencies are occupied by the ring bonds.

Rings A and B may be unsaturated in varying degrees; rings C and D are saturated and stable.

While the possibilities of isomerism among these structures is very great, in the natural compounds it appears to be restricted to the configuration at carbon 5, and at carbon 3 whenever this carbon carries an —OH group. Isomerism can be referred to the orientation of the methyl groups at 10 and 13. These groups are in *cis* relationship in that they both project in the same direction as regards the general plane of the tetracyclic nucleus. Conventionally, in formulation, they are assumed to project forward towards the observer. Other groups of hydrogen atoms that project in the opposite direction to these methyl groups, or *away* from the observer, are in the *trans*, or α-configuration, and denoted by a dotted line of attachment. Groups and atoms that project in the same direction as the reference methyl groups are in the *cis*, or β-configuration, and are denoted by unbroken line attachment. In cholesterol the hydroxyl group at carbon 3 is in the β-configuration; the single hydrogen atoms at carbons 9, 14, and 17 are in α-configuration. On hydrogenation, the double-bond between carbons 5 and 6 in ring B is saturated, producing **dihydrocholesterol,** or 3β-**cholestanol,** $C_{27}H_{47}$.OH, which accompanies cholesterol to the extent of 1 to 2 per cent. in tissues. In 3β-cholestanol the hydrogen atom that has become attached to carbon 5 has assumed a trans, or α-configuration. **Coprostanol,** or **coprosterol,** an isomer of cholestanol, occurs in bacteria, and in fæcal lipids, being formed in the intestine by bacterial attack on sterols. It differs from cholestanol in having the hydrogen at carbon 5 in β-configuration, so it cannot arise by direct hydrogenation of cholesterol.

141

The *cis-trans* relationships between the methyl group at carbon 10 and the hydrogen at carbon 5 are determined by the *cis-trans* flexure of rings A and B, and represent an important difference in the structure of the sterol or steroid. **Sterol Provitamins.** Unsaturated sterols that have double-bonds at 5 : 6 and 7 : 8 in ring B are converted to vitamins of the D class by solar or ultra-violet irradiation in the region 256 mμ to 313 mμ. Because of their function as calcium distributors in the animal, these vitamins are termed **calciferols.** Ergosterol was the first sterol to be recognised as a provitamin. On irradiation it yields a series of $C_{28}H_{43}$.OH isomers: lumisterol, tachysterol, calciferol, toxisterol, and suprasterols I and II. Of these, calciferol is the only one that displays vitamin activity; it is formed from tachysterol by the opening up of ring B. The active fraction first obtained by irradiation was termed vitamin D; later this was shown to be a conjugate of lumisterol and the actual vitamin, which was renamed D_2 or calciferol. D_2 is known now as ergocalciferol to denote its sterol source. It is prepared in quantity for therapeutic use. The most important natural vitamin D is cholecalciferol, or D_3, which is an irradiation product of 7-dehydrocholesterol, and occurs in liver oils and in the skin. D_3 differs from D_2 only in the structure of the side-chain.

Provitamins D.   Vitamins D.

Ergosterol and $\mathbf{D_2}$, $C_{28}H_{43}$.OH:

R = —CH(CH₃).CH : CH.CH(CH₃).CH(CH₃)₂.

7-Dehydrocholesterol and $\mathbf{D_3}$, $C_{27}H_{43}$.OH:

R = —CH(CH₃).CH₂.CH₂.CH₂.CH(CH₃)₂.

Other less important vitamins D exist, differing in the structure of the side-chain that is attached to the nucleus common to all vitamins of this class.

Analytical Reactions of the Sterols

(1) **Acetic Anhydride Test** (Liebermann and Burchard, 1899). Mix 5 drops of acetic anhydride with 2 ml. of a solution of the sterol in chloroform, and add concentrated sulphuric acid, drop by drop. A positive result is shown by the development of a violet colour that changes to a stable emerald green, which may be used for the colorimetric estimation of the sterol. The test is given by cholesterol and sterols with a 5 : 6 double-bond in ring B. Saturated sterols, such as cholestanol and coprosterol, do not react.

(2) **Chloral Hydrate Test** (Rosenheim, 1929). When about 1 mg. of ergosterol is dissolved in 1 gm. of chloral hydrate, melted in a water-bath at 100° C., a carmine colour will develop, showing an absorption band at 500 mμ. This colour changes to green, and then becomes deep blue. A few natural sterols produce red colours when warmed with chloral hydrate, but the change to blue is selective for ergosterol.

(3) **Digitonin Test.** The glycoside digitonin, from *Digitalis purpurea*, forms a precipitate with cholesterol, ergosterol, and other sterols that have a hydroxyl group at carbon 3 in the *cis*, or β-configuration.

THE BILE ACIDS

The bitterness of gall is proverbial, and is a property of the " bile salts " which are present in the bile of all higher animals. These bile salts are conjugates of a bile acid and glycine or taurine.

Representative Bile Acids

Acid.	Formula.	Source.
Cholic	$C_{23}H_{36}(OH)_3.COOH$	Man, ox, goat, sheep
Deoxycholic	$C_{23}H_{37}(OH)_2.COOH$	Man, ox, goat, sheep
Lithocholic	$C_{23}H_{38}(OH).COOH$	Man, ox
Hyodeoxycholic	$C_{23}H_{37}(OH)_2.COOH$	Pig
Chenodeoxycholic	$C_{23}H_{37}(OH)_2.COOH$	Man, ox

Cholic Acid. 3.7,12,tri (α) hydroxycholanic acid,

The bile acids can be regarded as hydroxy derivatives of a saturated steroid, cholanic acid, $C_{23}H_{39}.COOH$, obtained when H replaces OH at 3, 7, and 12 in cholic acid. Its constitution is shown by its preparation from coprostanol by oxidative shortening of the side-chain. Lithocholic acid is 3-hydroxycholanic acid; deoxycholic acid is 3,12-dihydroxycholanic acid; hyodeoxycholic acid is 3,6-dihydroxycholanic acid; chenodeoxycholic acid is 3,7-dihydroxycholanic acid. In all these acids, the hydroxyl groups are in α-orientation, or *trans* to the methyl groups.

Oxidation of the three hydroxyl groups to oxo groups, : O, in cholic acid produces *dehydrocholic acid*, a powerful cholagogue. The bile acids occur chiefly in bile as glycocholides and taurocholides, amides formed by condensation with glycine and taurine, respectively, and the carboxyl group at the end of the side-chain.

$$R—CO.NH.CH_2.COOH + H_2O \rightarrow R.COOH + H_2N.CH_2.COOH$$

Glycocholide. Bile acid. Glycine.

$$R—CO.NH.CH_2.CH_2.SO_2.OH + H_2O \rightarrow R.COOH + H_2N.CH_2.CH_2.SO_2.OH$$

Taurocholide. Bile acid. Taurine.

Taurine, aminoethylsulphonic acid, can be formed from the amino acid cysteine by oxidation to cysteic acid followed by decarboxylation.

Human fistula bile contains 1·0 to 1·5 per cent. of glycocholides and 0·3 to 0·5 per cent. of taurocholides; the relative proportions of the bound acids being: cholic, 3; deoxycholic, 1; chenodeoxycholic, 1; lithocholic, 1.

Taurocholides are the most widely distributed of the bile acid conjugates; the cholic derivative, *taurocholic acid*, occurs in the bile of snakes, teleosts, birds, and mammals. Glycocholides appear to be restricted to mammalian bile, the cholic derivative, *glycocholic acid*, being the commonest. The bile acids and their more soluble conjugates are surface active compounds, and by lowering interfacial tensions promote the liberation of adsorbed substances and the diffusion of solutes through membranes. By forming water-soluble complexes, or *choleic acids*, the bile acids solubilise lipids, and aid in alimentary absorption.

Preparation of Bile Acids. Mix a paste made of 50 ml. of ox bile and 10 gm. of animal charcoal, and evaporate to dryness on a water-bath, stirring at intervals. Powder the residue, and boil with 100 ml. of 95 per cent. alcohol for about half an hour. Cool, and filter into a dry dish. Add ether until the mixture begins to form a permanent cloud. Cover, and leave overnight at low temperature. A crystalline mass of bile acid conjugates separate out, and may be filtered off, and purified by reprecipitation from alcohol.

They can be separated by fractional crystallisation from water, in which taurocholic acid is much more soluble than glycocholic acid. Taurocholic acid is very bitter; glycocholic acid has a characteristic bitter-sweet taste. It is toxic, being cytolytic and hæmolytic. It slows the heart by stimulating the vagus.

When the bile acid conjugates are dissolved in a minimum amount of N.HCl, and kept at room temperature, hydrolysis occurs, and the free bile acids separate out.

STEROID GLYCOSIDES

Neutral Saponins. Soapwort (*Saponaria*) and other plants contain a class of glycoside characterised by high surface activity. They form soap-like froths in aqueous solution, act as emulsifiers and detergents, and can hæmolyse blood corpuscles even in very low concentration. On hydrolysis, saponins yield a sugar and a steroid aglycone, or *genin*. Thus, the common foxglove, *Digitalis purpurea*, contains a group of saponins, one of which, digitonin, yields digitogenin, $C_{27}H_{44}O_5$.

Cardio-active Glycosides. Saponins often are associated with glycosides having a powerful action on the heart; notably, those of the digitalis group, used for over a century in medicine, and those of the strophanthus group, employed as arrow poisons. Both the saponin genins and the cardio-active aglycones have tetracyclic nuclei of the steroid type, carrying the side-chain that determines the special properties of the compound. Thus, cardio-activity is associated with the presence of an unsaturated lactone ring attached to carbon 17 in the steroid nucleus.

Toad Venoms. The " ugly and venomous " toad owes its reputation to the presence of bufotoxin in the secretion of its skin glands.

On hydrolysis, bufotoxin yields arginine, suberic acid, and a toxic steroid, bufotalin, $C_{26}H_{36}O_6$. Related toxic steroids, or bufagins, occur in other species of toad. In their effects they resemble the digitalis glycosides.

STEROID HORMONES

Physiologically active substances with the steroid structure are elaborated by the gonads and the adrenal cortex and many of them and their products are excreted in the urine. During the earlier phases of our knowledge of the endocrine aspects of sex it was assumed that a special substance or group of substances manufactured in the testis and excreted in the urine controlled the sex characters of the male, and that those of the female were similarly controlled by specifically ovarian products. This simple view is no longer tenable. Both types of hormone are manufactured by each type of gonad and are excreted in the urine of each sex. Hormones of both kinds can be extracted from the adrenal cortex, which is the source of these substances in the urine of castrates and of the very young. Furthermore, many vegetable sources of substances with sex hormone activity are known.

It is now usual to classify the sex hormones according to their action on the secondary sexual characters; those that influence the male sex characters are called androgens, whether they are produced in the testis, the ovary or the adrenal cortex, and the corresponding determinants of female characters, irrespective of their site of manufacture, are called gynæcogens or œstrogens. The most potent androgen is testosterone, manufactured by the interstitial cells of the testis, but the product excreted in the urine, androsterone, was recognised earlier. It is also manufactured by the adrenal cortex, perhaps as a by-product in the metabolism of other steroids. Ostradiol, produced in the follicle, is the most potent œstrogen but, again, œstrone, the urinary excretory product, was recognised earlier and it, like androsterone, can be isolated from the adrenal cortex.

The corpus luteum of the ovary also manufactures a steroid hormone, progesterone, which assists in preparing the uterine mucosa for the fertilised ovum but is not classified with the œstrogens.

The hormones of the adrenal cortex, the corticoids, are primarily metabolic but certain androgens and œstrogens show metabolic activities. Testosterone encourages protein anabolism and is a factor in the ease with which muscle

145

hypertrophy can be induced in the young, healthy male. Non-masculinising derivatives in which this metabolic property is retained are used clinically and termed anabolic steroids.

Œstrogens, female sex hormones. These hormones promote the development and maintenance of the secondary sexual characters, including the œstrus cycle. All are derived from 13-methylsterane, or œstrane, in which ring A contains three double-bonds, and a hydroxyl group in β-configuration at carbon 3. As a result, they are phenolic in character, and their consequent solubility in alkalis enables them to be separated from other steroid hormones.

Œstrane Nucleus.

Hormone.	Double-bonds.	Structure.
Œstrone .	1 : 2, 3 : 4, 5 : 10	OH, 3 ; 0, 17
Œstradiol .	1 : 2, 3 : 4, 5 : 10	OH, 3, 17
Œstriol .	1 : 2, 3 : 4, 5 : 10	OH, 3, 16, 17
Equilin .	1 : 2, 3 : 4, 5 : 10, 7 : 8	OH, 3 ; 0, 17
Equilenin .	1 : 2, 3 : 4, 5 : 10, 6 : 7, 8 : 9	OH, 3 ; 0, 17

Œstradiol, the actual hormone of the ovarian follicle, also occurs in the placenta, and the urine of pregnancy, along with its derivatives, œstrone and œstriol. Equilin and equilinin occur principally in the urine of pregnant mares. The formulæ of these compounds is given on p. 412. Urinary œstrogens are excreted in solubilised form as glycuronides and sulphates of low biological activity.

Corpus Luteum Hormone. Only one form is known to exist, *progesterone* (progestin, luteosterone), $C_{21}H_{30}O_2$, obtained from the corpus luteum, placenta, and urine of pregnancy, where it is accompanied by inactive reduction derivatives, *pregnanediol*, $C_{21}H_{33}O_2$, and *allo-pregnanediol*. Progesterone is a 17-acetyl ($CH_3 . CO$—) derivative of a steroid nucleus carrying a methyl group at 10 and 13, and an oxygen at 3, and having a double-bond at 4 : 5 (p. 412).

Androgens

Testicular Hormones. From male urine, (1) *androsterone*, and (2) *dehydroisoandrosterone*, can be isolated; *testosterone* (3) has been obtained from testicular extracts, and has been prepared, also, from cholesterol. *Androstanediol* (4) has been obtained by reduction of androsterone; it is the diol corresponding to œstradiol, and is about three times as potent as the parent androsterone, but, unlike œstradiol, it has not yet been isolated from natural sources. The androgens resemble the gynæcogens in general structure, but differ in their degree of saturation. Testosterone is the most powerful. Chemically, the androgens are simple oxo or hydroxy derivatives of a parent steroid, *androstane*.

146

All three testicular hormones, and the androgen, adrenosterone, from adrenal cortex, are 10,13 dimethyl steroids.

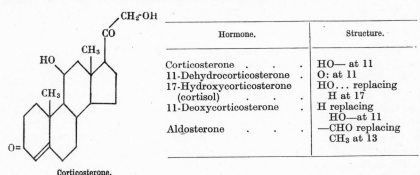

Androstane Nucleus.

Hormone.	Double-bonds.	Structure.
Androsterone	none	α-OH at 3, : O at 17
Dehydro-*iso* androsterone	4 : 5	β-OH at 3, : O at 17
Testosterone	4 : 5	: O at 3, —OH at 17
Adrenosterone	4 : 5	: O at 3, 11, 17

Adrenal Cortex Hormones

Corticoids. Lipid extracts of the adrenal cortex contain a mixture of steroid hormones, including œstrogens, androgens, and regulators of metabolic processes. The term corticoid is applied to such hormones as are believed to be manufactured exclusively in the adrenal cortex. All can be regarded as derived from 10,13-dimethylsterane, in which ring A has a double-bond at 4 : 5, an oxygen atom at carbon 3, and, with the exception of adrenosterone, a ketol side-chain, —CO—CH$_2$.OH, at carbon 17.

Corticosterone.

Hormone.	Structure.
Corticosterone . . .	HO— at 11
11-Dehydrocorticosterone .	O: at 11
17-Hydroxycorticosterone (cortisol) . . .	HO... replacing H at 17
11-Deoxycorticosterone .	H replacing HO—at 11
Aldosterone . . .	—CHO replacing CH$_3$ at 13

Other corticoids include 11-dehydro-17-hydroxycorticosterone, or cortisone (Kendall compound E); 11-deoxy-17-hydroxycorticosterone; and adrenosterone, which resembles corticosterone in structure but for the replacement of HO at 11 by O, and —CO—CH$_2$.OH at 17 by O. The relationships and functions of the corticoids are discussed in Chapter 24.

Analytical Reactions of the Steroid Hormones

(1) **Sterone Reactions.** Steroids containing a —CO— unit in ring A or ring D in alkaline solution form coloured co-ordination compounds with picrate (orange) and with *m*-dinitrobenzene (purple). The second of these reagents has been applied by Zimmermann (1935) to the estimation of 17-oxosteroids, or " 17-ketosteroids ", in urine.

(2) **Ketol Reactions.** The ketol side-chain at 17 in the corticoids forms an enediol in alkaline solution, —C(OH)=CH(OH), and thus can be estimated by phosphomolybdate or copper reduction methods.

Where there is in addition a hydroxyl group at 17, as in cortisone, the steroid gives a purple colour with phenylhydrazine in sulphuric acid (Porter and Silber, 1950).

(3) **Phenolic Reactions.** Steroids, such as the œstrogens, in which ring A is unsaturated and carries a hydroxyl group, react as phenols, and develop red colours when warmed with phenol in concentrated sulphuric acid (Kober, 1931).

General Significance of the Sterols and Steroids

The occurrence of the tetracyclic sterane system in such a variety of compounds of different biological importance, the universal distribution and persistence of certain features, suggest that the molecular shape and profile of the nucleus is of special significance in cell architecture and activity.

Thus, by their ability to form conjugates with lipids and with proteins, the sterols may impose a pattern on cell membranes, and act as valves in the regulation of cell imports and exports. Within the cell, the steroid hormones, as has been suggested by Peters (1956), may form or modify the framework that holds in place the mitochondria, microsomes and other operational units.

Carcinogenic Hydrocarbons

In 1915, Yamagiwa showed that application of tar was capable of evoking malignant changes in the skin of rodents. The production of these skin cancers was verified by many workers, although it was realised that animals differed in their susceptibility and tars differed in their carcinogenic property. In 1924, Kennaway obtained and isolated active carcinogens from the mixture of tars produced when pure acetylene or pure isoprene is heated with hydrogen, thus showing that the agent was a hydrocarbon, and not a contaminant. The synthetic and natural carcinogenic tars resembled one another in the possession of an intense fluorescent spectrum, which suggested the presence of polycyclic nuclei.

A number of such compounds were prepared and examined, and at least four were found to possess unmistakable carcinogenic properties. They are: (1) 1 : 2-benzanthrene, (2) 3 : 4-benzpyrene, (3) 5 : 6-*cyclo*-pentano-1 : 2-benzanthrene, and (4) methyl cholanthrene, which was obtained from desoxycholic acid, and is very active.

1 : 2-Benzanthrene.   3 : 4-Benzpyrene.

5: 6-*cyclo*-Pentano-
1 : 2-benzanthrene.

20-Methyl cholanthrene.

Now, although none of these compounds is a true steroid, they all contain polycyclic nuclei, and, furthermore, the fact that methyl cholanthrene has been prepared from a naturally occurring bile acid suggests that they must be considered as possible types of compounds produced in abnormal sterol metabolism.

9 : 10-dimethyl benzanthrene is a powerful carcinogen, and its local application may induce a skin cancer within thirty-five days.

Two at least of the synthetic carcinogens, namely 1 : 2-benzpyrene and 5 : 6-*cyclo*-pentano-1 : 2-benzanthrene are also active œstrogens.

Carcinogenesis is now recognised as a metabolic perversion evoked by many apparently unrelated compounds and agencies, including prolonged exposure to ultra-violet irradiation, X-rays and radio-active substances. Carcinogenic compounds may have two types of action:—

(1) *Local*. By injuring cell nuclei, and thus inhibiting normal growth, or by evoking a mutation that leads to a new race of cells. An industrial cancer, first recognised in the late eighteenth century as a disease of occupation among chimney sweeps, has been traced to prolonged exposure to soot, the active agent, later isolated from coal tar, being 3 : 4-benzpyrene.

(2) *Distant*. Continued exposure to aniline or β-naphthylamine, under industrial conditions, may lead to bladder tumours. The incidence of some animal cancers can be increased by excessive and prolonged administration of sex hormones. Conversely, administration of *stilbœstrol*, the artificial œstrogen discovered by Dodds, may check cancers of the prostate by its indirect inhibiting effect on the output of androgens by the testicle. These distant effects are distinct from local actions. Thus, *p*-dimethyl amino azo benzene, $(CH_3)_2N.C_6H_4.N : N.C_6H_5$, has no obvious action when applied directly to the liver, but when given in small amounts daily in the diet results in a cancer of the liver; the compound was formerly used, for colouring foodstuffs, under the name of " butter yellow ".

According to Darlington (1948), the plasmagenes, or self-reproducing nucleoprotein units in the cells, are the targets of the carcinogens. Normally the plasmagenes are concerned with the synthesis of enzymes and cell proteins, cell-growth being governed by the nucleus. Aggravated by a carcinogen, an abnormal type of linkage forms in the plasmagene, and reproduces itself as a malignant tissue. Some carcino-plasmagenes are diffusible, and the tumours can be transmitted from animal to animal by injection of cell-free extracts of tumour tissue. Otherwise, direct grafting of tissue is required.

149

The fact that some mammalian cancer cells retain their carcinogenic activity after freezing, drying, and pulverising, suggests that " cancer has a continuing cause, and that this, in mammals as in birds, is a virus " (Gye, 1949).

General References

Barry, G., and J. W. Cook, *et al.* (1935), " Pure hydrocarbon carcinogens." *Proc. roy. Soc.*, B. **117, 318**.

Crowfoot, D. (1944), " X-ray crystallography and sterol structure." *Vitamins and Hormones*, **2, 409**. New York.

Darlington, C. D. (1948), " Plasmagene theory of the origin of cancer." *Brit. J. Cancer*, **2, 118**.

Fieser, L. F., and M. Fieser (1949), " Chemistry of Natural Products Related to Phenanthrene." 3rd ed., New York.

Friedmann, E. (1937), " Sterols and Related Compounds." Cambridge.

Greenstein, J. P. (1948), " Biochemistry of Cancer." New York; London.

Morton, R. A. (1942), "Absorption Spectra of Vitamins, Hormones and Coenzymes." 2nd ed. London.

Schoppee, C. W. (1956), " Steroids." *Perspectives in Organic Chemistry.* Ed. by A. Todd. New York; London.

Sobotka, H. (1938), " Chemistry of the Steroids." Baltimore; London.

Stern, K., and R. Willheim (1943). " Biochemistry of Malignant Tumours." New York; London.

" Steroids." Elsevier's Encyclopædia of Organic Chemistry Vol. 14, Supp. 1 (1956). Ed. by F Radt.

Chapter 12 Biological Pigments: Pyrrole Derivatives, Carotenoids, Flavins, Melanins

PYRROLE DERIVATIVES

The red inner world of the animal and the green world of the plant owe their colours to pigments derived from a simple heterocyclic compound, pyrrole, $C_4H_5.NH$, which occurs in tetrapyrrole groups of four units. Two great classes of these pigments exist: the *linear tetrapyrroles*, represented by the bile pigments; and the *cyclic tetrapyrroles*, or porphyrins, found in the blood pigments and in chlorophyll.

Tetrapyrrole skeleton (a,c-biladiene).

Natural Linear Tetrapyrroles, or Bilirubinoids

Name.	Formula.	Source.
Bilirubin . . .	$C_{33}H_{36}O_6N_4$	Bile
Biliverdin (Dehydrobilirubin) .	$C_{33}H_{34}O_6N_4$	Bile
Mesobilinogen . . .	$C_{33}H_{44}O_6N_4$	Reduced bilirubin
Urobilinogen . . .	$C_{33}H_{48}O_6N_4$	Urine
Mesobilin (Urobilin IXα) .	$C_{33}H_{42}O_6N_4$	Urine
Urobilin (stercobilin) .	$C_{33}H_{46}O_6N_4$	Urine, Intestinal contents
Uteroverdin . . .	$C_{33}H_{34}O_6N_4$	Dog placenta
Bilipurpurin (phylloerythrin) . .	$C_{34}H_{36}O_6N_4$	Bile

The hepatic secretion of man and other animals is deeply coloured owing to the presence of pigments, notably *bilirubin* and *biliverdin*. Bilirubin is the chief pigment in human bile, to which it imparts a golden-yellow colour. Biliverdin, an oxidation derivative of bilirubin, is found in herbivora and other animals, and imparts an emerald green colour to the bile. When both

151

pigments are present, as in ox bile, the colour may vary from brown to green. These pigments are waste products derived from hæmoglobin.

Bilirubin, $C_{33}H_{36}O_6N_4$, occurs in bile as a soluble bilirubinate; in biliary calculi it is present as an insoluble calcium salt. It can be prepared from evaporated bile residues or powdered gallstones by the following method of successive extraction: (i) ether, (ii) hot water, (iii) 10 per cent. acetic acid, (iv) alcohol, and (v) hot glacial acetic acid. By this process the following substances are removed: sterols, bile salts, biliverdin, and inorganic salts. The residue is dried and extracted with hot chloroform, which removes the bilirubin. On cooling, bilirubin crystallises out.

Bilirubin is a red-brown tetrapyrrole, insoluble in water, dilute acids, and the common fat-solvents. It is soluble in hot chloroform, acetone, and in alkalies. The solutions show no characteristic visible absorption spectrum.

Structure. Mild oxidation converts bilirubin into the green pigment, *biliverdin*; more powerful oxidants resolve it into four pyrrole units. Bilirubin does not combine with metals to form porphyrans, thus suggesting that the formula is an open chain of pyrrole units, not a closed tetrapyrrole or porphyrin.

When bilirubin is reduced by sodium amalgam it is converted to a colourless derivative, mesobilinogen, which is reoxidised by atmospheric oxygen to a yellow compound, *mesobilin*, that resembles *urobilin* (stercobilin), the waste pigment present in urine and intestinal contents.

Bilirubin $R = -CH_2.CH_2.COOH.$

By reduction of the two vinyl groups —CH : CH$_2$, to ethyl groups, Et, —CH$_2$.CH$_3$, mesobilin is formed from bilirubin.

Biliverdin $R = -CH_2.CH_2.COOH.$

Urobilinogen (stercobilinogen). $R = -CH_2.CH_2.COOH.$

Biliverdin, or dehydrobilirubin, is derived from bilirubin by loss of two hydrogen atoms in the region of the central linkage of the tetrapyrrole chain. It is formed spontaneously when bilirubin is oxidised by exposure to air in alkaline solution, or treated with hydrogen peroxide. The pigment is precipitated by acidification, and any unchanged bilirubin removed by chloroform extraction.

Biliverdin is a dark green amorphous solid, insoluble in water, ether or chloroform. It dissolves in alkalies to form salts, and is freely soluble in glacial acetic acid. These solutions have a bright green colour, but no characteristic visible spectrum. Biliverdin is the precursor of bilirubin in the formation of bile pigment from hæmoglobin.

$$\text{Me.CH—C.Et} \quad \text{Me.C——C.}R \quad R.\text{C}═\text{C.Me} \quad \text{Me.C—HC.Et}$$

Urobilin (stercobilin). $R = -CH_2.CH_2.COOH.$

Urobilin, or stercobilin, is a brown pigment derived from bilirubin by bacterial reduction in the intestine. It is reabsorbed into the blood, and reduced still further to the colourless chromogen, *urobilinogen*, in which form it is excreted in the urine. Urobilin is separated from urine by saturation with ammonium sulphate and extraction with alcohol. In solution, it shows a distinct absorption band in the region $b-\text{F}$ (486 mμ—508 mμ). Addition of zinc chloride or acetate to the neutral solution causes a green fluorescence and the appearance of an additional absorption band near the b line. Fæcal or urinary urobilin (stercobilin) is strongly lævorotatory, and thus differs from the artificial mesobilin, or urobilin IXa

Urobilinogen, the colourless precursor of urobilin, is a normal constituent of fresh urine, and may be greatly increased in amount in conditions of intestinal stasis and increased intestinal putrefaction. When urine is exposed to air, or treated with mild oxidising agents, urobilinogen is converted to urobilin, and the colour of the urine darkens. Like urobilin, it is precipitated by saturation with ammonium sulphate, but, unlike urobilin, it is soluble in ether, and thus may be extracted. When pure, urobilinogen is a colourless crystalline solid. In solution it shows no absorption bands and no fluorescence on addition of zinc salts.

Urobilinogen, unlike urobilin, gives an immediate red colour with Ehrlich's aldehyde reagent (p. 447).

Urobilin and urobilinogen do not usually occur free in urine, but in some loosely combined forms. It is possible that *urochrome*, the characteristic yellow pigment of urine, is a urobilin derivative.

Systematic Nomenclature. The bilirubinoids of higher animals are derived from the cyclic tetrapyrrole, protophorphyrin IX, present in hæmoglobin and other hæm compounds. Hence, common bilirubin is denoted bilirubin IXa, to show that is comes from protoporphyrin IX by fission of the a-linkage between the pyrrole rings. In the linear tetrapyrroles the rings are linked by hydrocarbon bridges in various states of hydrogenation: three methylenes, $-CH_2-$, in the bilans; two methylenes and one methyne, $-CH<$, in the bilenes; two methynes and one methylene in the biladienes, and three methynes in the bilatrienes.

Thus the urobilinogens are bilans; urobilin is a *b*-bilene; bilirubin is an *a,c*-biladiene; and biliverdin is a bilatriene.

Colour Reactions of the Bilirubinoids. (1) *Oxidation.* When " fuming " nitric acid, which is yellow in colour owing to dissolved nitrogen peroxide, is added carefully so as to form a lower layer, a characteristic zone-sequence of colours develops, depending on the oxidation and hydroxylation of the hydrocarbon bridges (Gmelin reaction, 1826). In order of oxidation the colours are: green (biliverdin), blue, violet (bilipurpurin), red, yellow (choletelin). Finally, the compound is fragmented into colourless pyrrole units. Milder oxidisers, such as mercuric chloride, iodine, and ferric chloride, also can be used.

(2) *Acid Diazo-Reaction.* Aromatic diazo compounds, such as diazobenzene sulphonic acid, form bright purple or blue pigments with bilirubin in acid solutions (Ehrlich, 1883); the test is selective for biladienes, other bilirubinoids are non-chromogenic. Biliverdin, urobilins, and urobilinogens do not react, and the test has been applied to the recognition and estimation of bilirubin in blood plasma by van den Bergh.

In alkaline solution, diazo reagents form coloured diazo pigments with many compounds, including the amino acids, histidine, tryptophan, and tyrosine (Pauly reactions, 1904), and various phenols, and thiochrome.

(3) para-*Dimethylaminobenzaldehyde Reaction.* This aldehyde in acid solution (N.HCl) gives a red colour with urobilinogens, but not with other bilirubinoids, including urobilin (Ehrlich, 1901).

Similar colours are given by pyrrole and some pyrrole derivatives, including indole. These pigments usually can be extracted by chloroform or light petroleum, and thus differ from the red pigment given by porphobilinogen (red), tryptophan (violet to blue), and urea (yellow).

(4) *Fluorescence with Zinc Ions.* The *b*-bilenes, such as urobilin and stercobilin, produce a green fluorescence with zinc acetate in presence of ethanol (Jaffé, 1869). The test is very delicate, and the zinc complex has a characteristic fluorescent spectrum.

Dipyrrole Pigments. Pigment-precursors and pigments formed from two pyrrole units in methylene or methyne linkage occur in small quantities in normal and pathological urines. These compounds are of interest as possible metabolites in the construction or break-down of the natural tetrapyrroles. (*a*) *Pentadypents.* Red pigments formed by the action of hydrosulphite in alkaline solutions. The spectra show an absorption band about 525 mμ, hence the name, " penta-dy-pent ". Propentadypents are formed when hæmoglobin, hæm, or bilirubin is bleached by excess of hydrogen peroxide. (*b*) *Porphobilinogen,* a dipyrryl methyne found in the urine in conditions of acute porphyria. Like urobilinogen, it forms a red pigment with *p*-dimethylaminobenzaldehyde, but can be distinguished by its insolubility in chloroform.

(c) *Mesobilifuscin*, or Myobilin, a methyne-linked dipyrryl derived from the muscle pigment, myoglobin, is excreted in conditions of progressive muscular dystrophy and during the involution of the uterus during the first week of the puerperium.

Macro-Cyclic Tetrapyrroles, or Porphyrins

Porphyrins are widely distributed pigments of high stability. The nitrogen in the tetrapyrrole cluster readily combines with metals, such as Fe, Cu, Mg, and Mn, to form metallo-porphyrins, or *porphyrans*, having catalytic properties.

Porphyran proteins, such as hæmoglobin, participate in oxygen transport; others, such as cytochrome, are concerned in the oxidation mechanisms of all living tissues.

Name.	Formula.	Source.
Protoporphyrin	$C_{34}H_{34}O_4N_4$	Hæmoglobin
Hæmatoporphyrin	$C_{34}H_{38}O_6N_4$	Hæmoglobin
Ætioporphyrin I.	$C_{32}H_{38}N_4$	Chlorophyll
Ætioporphyrin III.	$C_{32}H_{38}N_4$	Hæmoglobin
Coproporphyrin	$C_{36}H_{38}O_8N_4$	Urine, yeast
Uroporphyrin	$C_{38}H_{38}O_{16}N_4$	Urine, Turacou feathers

General Structure of the Porphyrins

Knowledge of the porphyrins has been reached by the convergence of work on chlorophylls, chiefly by the Willstätter school, and on the blood pigments, by Hans Fischer; and important contributions have been made by Stoll, Conant, Marchlewski, Kuhn, and Küster. The properties of the porphyrins as a class suggest a ring structure composed of four stable units. On oxidation of a porphyrin, these units are obtained in the form of di-substituted pyrroles, one substituent of which is always a methyl group.

Pyrrole.

Di-substituted pyrrole.

Porphin, $C_{20}H_{14}N_4$
(Parent nucleus of porphyrins)

155

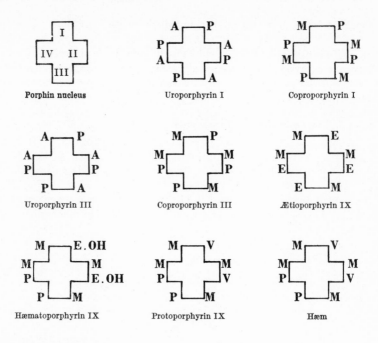

Porphin nucleus   Uroporphyrin I   Coproporphyrin I

Uroporphyrin III   Coproporphyrin III   Ætioporphyrin IX

Hæmatoporphyrin IX   Protoporphyrin IX   Hæm

Codification of the Porphyrins

M, methyl, CH_3—.   V, vinyl, $H_2C : CH$—.

E, ethyl, $CH_3.CH_2$—.   A, acetic, $HOOC.CH_2$—.

E.OH, hydroxyethyl, $HO.CH_2.CH_2$—.   P, propionic, $HOOC.CH_2.CH_2$—.

Natural porphyrins belong to two types, designated I and III, according to the arrangement of the substituent groups in the porphin nucleus. In type I an acetic or a methyl group replaces H in the angular positions 1, 3, 5, 7. In type III, there is an acetic or a methyl group at 1, 3, 5, 8. Most of the natural porphyrins belong to type III, and can be converted chemically to a reference compound, 1,3,5,8-tetramethyl-2,4,6,7-tetraethyl porphin, also known as ætioporphyrin-IX, or -9. Because of this relationship, protoporphyrin (type III) and its immediate derivatives are alternatively described as -IX or -9 compounds.

Coproporphyrin I occurs in small amounts in normal bile and urine, accompanied by uroporphyrin I. The urinary output is characteristically increased in the condition of congenital porphyria, pernicious anæmia, hæmolytic jaundice, and poisoning by lead, sulphonamides, or barbituric derivatives. *Coproporphyrin III* occurs in some bacteria and may appear in the urine as a result of lead or sulphonamide poisoning.

156

Uroporphyrin III is a micro-constituent of normal urine and is greatly increased in some forms of porphyrinuria. Its copper derivative, turacin, is present in the feathers of some tropical birds.

Protoporphyrin IX $C_{34}H_{34}O_4N_4$, is universally distributed and its iron complex, **hæm**, combined with a protein, appears as the respiratory pigments: hæmoglobins, myoglobins, cytochromes, and helicorubins, and enzymes, including cytochrome oxidase, catalase.

Porphyrin Proteins

The outstanding porphyrin compounds found in the animal body are: (i) the *hœmochromes*, or oxygen-transport pigments of the blood, and (ii) the *cytochromes*, or respiratory pigments of the tissues. The hæmochromes include the iron-containing chromoproteins, hæmoglobin, erythrocruorin, chlorocruorin and hæmoerythrin, and the copper-containing chromoprotein, hæmocyanin. The cytochromes are four in type, and are found in all aerobic cells.

THE HÆMOCHROMES, OR BLOOD PIGMENTS

	Hæmoglobin	Erythrocruorin	Chlorocruorin	Hæmocyanin	Hæmoerythrin
Distribution .	Vertebrates	Many invertebrates	Polychate worms	Molluscs Arthropods	Gephyreans
Colour .	Red	Red	Green	Blue	Red
Prosthetic group	Hæm	Hæm	Hæm	Hæmocuprin	Hæmoferrin
Metal .	Fe	Fe	Fe	Cu	Fe
Location	Corpuscles, Muscle	Corpuscles	Plasma	Plasma	Corpuscles or plasma
M. Wt.	68,000	17,000 to 5×10^6	300,000 to 5×10^6	300,000 to 5×10^6	17,000 to 68,000

Hæmoglobin, the dominant pigment of animal life, occurs in the red cells of all vertebrates. It is a chromoprotein, made up of 94 per cent. of globin and 4 to 5 per cent. of the porphyran, **hæm,** the residue being mostly lipid material. Not only does the hæmoglobin differ in different species but fœtal hæmoglobin differs from maternal, although adult hæmoglobin in normal human subjects is the same, irrespective of sex or race (Munro Fox, 1945). In sickle-cell anæmia, a condition found in African natives and people of African origin, the abnormal shape of the red cell is associated with the replacement of glutamic acid in the hæmoglobin molecule by valine. Species differences among lower animals are ascribed to difference in the protein component of the pigment. Crystalline hæmoglobin can be obtained directly from the blood of horses, dogs, and rats, after " laking ", or hæmolysis of the red cells by addition of water or ether.

Derivatives of hæmoglobin.

A. *Addition compounds:* oxyhæmoglobin, nitroxyhæmoglobin, carbon monoxyhæmoglobin or carbonylhæmoglobin, (otherwise known as carboxyhæmoglobin), sulphæmoglobin, cyanohæmoglobin.

B. *Decomposition products:* hæmochromogen, hæmin, hæm, hæmatin, hæmatoporphyrin.

Oxyhæmoglobin, HbO_2, a scarlet compound of hæmoglobin containing two atoms of displaceable oxygen for each atom of iron in the molecule. It forms spontaneously when a solution of hæmoglobin is shaken with air, and it is responsible for the transport of oxygen in the blood stream.

In concentrations of 1 : 1,000 to 1 : 10,000, oxyhæmoglobin has a characteristic spectrum with two absorption bands between the D and the E lines. The α-band is the narrower and more distinct, and lies on the D line, the middle of the band being at 579 mμ. The middle of the β-band is about 542 mμ. Oxyhæmoglobin has a third band (Soret's band), located in the ultra-violet region of the spectrum between G and H, its centre being at 415 mμ. When oxyhæmoglobin is reduced, this band is displaced towards the visible spectrum. On exposure to low atmospheric or oxygen pressure, or when treated with reducing agents such as hydroxylamine, sodium hydrosulphite, ammonium sulphide, oxyhæmoglobin is readily reconverted into hæmoglobin, which shows a single diffuse band between the D and E lines.

The Interaction between Hæmoglobin and Oxygen. Crystallised hæmoglobin, irrespective of its source, contains about 0·335 per cent. of iron, in the ferrous form. One gram of hæmoglobin combines with 1·34 ml. of oxygen, at 0° C. and 760 mm. Hg (atmospheric pressure), a ratio corresponding to two atoms of O for each atom of Fe. The union is molecular; oxygen unites and dissociates in the form of O_2, without oxidising the Fe. Assuming that a molecule of Hb contains only one atom of Fe, the molecular weight is approximately 16,700. But direct determinations of sedimentation rate and osmotic pressure indicate a value of about 68,000, which is four times as large. Hence, the formula for oxyhæmoglobin is HbO_8, and the reversible *oxygenation* process is:

$$Hb_4 + 4O_2 \rightleftharpoons Hb_4(O_2)_4.$$

Methæmoglobin, HbOH, or $Hb(OH)_4$, forms when hæmoglobin is oxidised in alkaline solution with permanganate or peroxide, or when ferricyanide is added to oxyhæmoglobin. The colour of the solution turns chocolate-brown, and the characteristic spectrum of methæmoglobin develops. In acid solution there is an absorption band towards the red end of the spectrum, between C and D, its centre being about 634 mμ. In alkaline solution two additional bands are seen, resembling those of oxyhæmoglobin but differing in that the β-band is sharper than the α-band. Methæmoglobin is formed also by the action of nitrobenzene, pyrogallol, acetanilide, and other phenols and amines, and may appear in the urine in cases of poisoning by chlorate, nitrate, or phenols.

In methæmoglobin, the iron has been oxidised to the ferric form, and the pigment is no longer able to take part in oxygen transport. By the action of reducing agents, or by intravenous injections of glucose into the circulation, methæmoglobin is converted into hæmoglobin, and thus restored to physiological utility.

Carbon monoxyhæmoglobin or carbonylhæmoglobin, HbCO, is formed by the action of CO on hæmoglobin or oxyhæmoglobin, from which it displaces the oxygen. The spectrum shows two absorption bands resembling those of oxyhæmoglobin but shifted more towards the violet end; the centre of the a-band being at 570 mμ, and the β-band at 535 mμ.

Distinction between oxy- and carbon monoxyhæmoglobin:—

(1) Carbon monoxyhæmoglobin is more pink or " cherry red " than oxyhæmoglobin solutions of the same concentration, and on dilution the colour of the carbon monoxy compound remains pink, while the oxyhæmoglobin turns yellowish.

(2) On treatment with ammonium sulphide or similar reducing agents, carbon monoxyhæmoglobin is unchanged, while oxyhæmoglobin is converted to hæmoglobin. This test can best be followed by means of a spectroscope. By the action of a strong reducing agent, such as sodium hydrosulphite, aided by heat carbon monoxyhæmoglobin can be converted into hæmoglobin.

(3) By means of the reversion spectroscope, carbon monoxyhæmoglobin can be detected and estimated in presence of oxyhæmoglobin.

The terms *carbon monoxyhæmoglobin* and *carbonylhæmoglobin* are preferable to the usual *carboxyhæmoglobin*, which implies the presence of a carboxy, or —CO_2 group, rather than the —CO, or carbonyl group, actually present.

Human blood commonly contains $0 \cdot 15 \pm 0 \cdot 05$ ml. CO per 100 ml, the value being raised by tobacco smoking, or other exposure to CO-contaminated air.

DECOMPOSITION PRODUCTS OF HÆMOGLOBIN

Hæmochromogen is a chromoprotein formed by the action of alkalis and reducing agents on hæmoglobin. When a dilute solution of blood is warmed with an alkali the colour changes from red to greenish-brown. This is due to (1) formation of methæmoglobin, and (2) its decomposition into the protein *globin* and the iron porphyran *hæmatin* or *methæm*. At the same time, the alkali denatures the liberated protein. If now a reducing agent be added, such as hydrosulphite, the hæmatin will be converted to reduced hæmatin or **hæm.** Hæm rapidly recombines with the denatured globin to form a new chromoprotein *hæmochromogen*.

In alkaline solution this hæmochromogen has a bright carmine colour, and shows two bands somewhat like those of oxyhæmoglobin but nearer the violet end of the spectrum. The a-band is the darker and narrower, and its centre is at 556 mμ, almost midway between the D and the E lines. The β-band covers the E and the b lines, and has its centre about 528 mμ.

The pigment can be distinguished from oxyhæmoglobin by its stability to reducing agents.

Hæmochromogens are also formed readily by union of hæm with pyridine, nicotine, and similar bases.

Takayama's Test. Spread a very small drop of blood on a slide so as to form a film. Let dry in air. Add 2 to 4 drops of the reagent, and cover with a slip to prevent evaporation. After 10 to 15 minutes, examine microscopically for the small pink crystals of pyridine hæmochromogen.

Hæmatin, methæm, or oxidised hæm, $C_{34}H_{32}O_4N_4FeOH$, a base which in reduced form occurs united to protein in hæmochromogens. It is a dark, amorphous powder, insoluble in water and many organic solvents, but dissolves in alkalies or in glacial acetic acid forming solutions termed *alkaline* and *acid hœmatin*, respectively. The change of colour blood undergoes when warmed with alkalies or acids is due to the formation of the corresponding hæmatin.

When a mixture of alcohol and ether is added to dilute blood which has been acidified with a few drops of hydrochloric acid, the chromoprotein is decomposed and the liberated hæmatin passes into the alcohol-ether layer.

As ordinarily prepared, " hæmatin " is a mixture of a ferric porphyran, *methœm*, and a ferrous porphyran, *hœm*. Hæmoglobin, itself, is a chromoprotein formed by the union of globin and hæm, and when oxidised to oxyhæmoglobin, the hæm component is converted into a labile form, oxy-hæm. Drastic oxidisers change the ferrous oxy-hæm into the ferric methæm, as occurs when methæmoglobin is prepared.

Hæmatin chloride, or **hæmin,** $C_{34}H_{32}O_4N_4FeCl$, a purple-brown crystalline salt that forms spontaneously in old blood clots. It can be prepared by simmering a fragment of dried blood, or stained material, with acetic acid containing 1 per cent. NaCl.

The hæmin crystals are dark brown elongated rhomboids or spindles, occurring singly or grouped as crosses or rosettes. Hæmin is insoluble in water, dilute acids, and neutral organic solvents, but dissolves with decomposition in alkalies, forming hæmatin, which may be precipitated in a pure condition by acidification.

Hæmin is important chemically as it is the starting-point for the study of the hæmatoporphyrin compounds.

Structure of the Hæms. The iron-porphyrans, or hæms, like the other porphyrans are mono-metallic derivatives of a porphyrin. In hæm the iron is ferrous (divalent) and bound by the pyrrole nitrogens, conventionally regarded as belonging to rings I and II, or I and III. In hæmatin (methæm) and in hæmatin chloride, the iron is ferric (trivalent) and can combine with an anion, such as OH' (in methæm) or Cl' (in hæmin).

Me.C——C.V   Me.C══C.V
‖   ‖ | |
C   C—CH══C   C
/ N   N \
HC   Fe   CH
\ N   N /
C   C—CH══C   C
| | | |
Me.C══C.R   R.C══C.Me

Haem, $C_{34}H_{32}O_4N_4Fe$ $R=-CH_2.CH_2.COOH$
(Ferrous protoporphyran).

Me.C——C.V   Me.C══C.V
‖   ‖ | |
C   C—CH══C   C
/ N   N \
HC   Fe.OH   CH
\ N   N /
C   C—CH══C   C
| | | |
Me.C══C.R   R.C══C.Me

Methaem, $C_{34}H_{32}O_4N_4FeOH$
(Ferric protoporphyran).

Hæmatoporphyrin, $C_{34}H_{38}O_6N_4$, an iron-free derivative of hæm, is obtained by the action of strong acids on hæmoglobin, or by dissolving hæmatin chloride in glacial acetic acid saturated with HBr. After four days, the mixture is diluted and the porphyrin precipitated by exact neutralisation. Hæmatoporphyrin is a dark violet powder, almost insoluble in water, but soluble in alcohol, alkalis, and concentrated sulphuric acid. It is a di-hydroxy derivative of **Protoporphyrin,** in which each vinyl side-chain, —CH : CH_2, has become —$CH_2.CH_2.OH$.

The acid solution has a very distinctive pair of absorption bands, one on either side of the D line. These may be demonstrated by the addition of 1 to 2 drops of undiluted blood to 10 ml. of concentrated sulphuric acid, and spectroscopic examination of the resulting purple mixture.

Derivatives of Protoporphyrin. On heating with soda-lime, carbon dioxide is lost and *ætioporphyrin III* is formed. This porphyrin resembles one originally obtained from chlorophyll, and its preparation from the blood pigments is of great biochemical interest.

When protoporphyrin is oxidised in acid solution it is resolved into four pyrrole residues, the *hæmopyrroles,* from the study of which the structure of the original porphyrin has been confirmed.

The Phototoxic Properties of Hæmatoporphyrin. Small intravenous injections of hæmatoporphyrin have no ill-effect on albino mice, rats, and guinea-pigs, as long as the animals are kept in the dark. On exposure to light, however, a severe dermatitis develops, often followed by œdema and death. The response persists for some weeks after sensitisation. It is not referable to foreign protein accompanying the injection, as animals are equally sensitive to autogenous hæmatoporphyrin.

Structure of Hæmoglobin. Hæmoglobin is a compound of the colourless, basic, protein globin and the dicarboxy acid hæm, which contains a carboxyl group at the end of one side-chain in rings III and IV of the parent protoporphyrin. Hæmoglobin is only stable in neutral solutions, and relatively slight degrees of acidity or alkalinity are sufficient to resolve it into globin and hæm. As the constitution of globin is not known, it is only possible to represent hæmoglobin by a semi-structural formula.

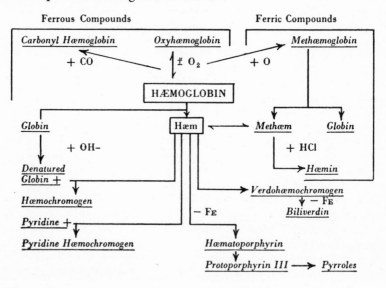

Hæmoglobin
(Globin hæmochromogen).

In oxyhæmoglobin, the additional oxygen molecule is assumed to be held loosely by a residual valency to the Fe atom.

Relationship of the Hæmoglobin Derivatives

Conversion of Hæmoglobin Pigment into Bilirubin. Lemberg has shown that oxidation of a hæmochromogen opens up the tetrapyrrole ring to form a green verdohæmochromogen, which has a linear tetrapyrrole, *verdohæmatin*, convertible into biliverdin by removal of the iron atom by acids.

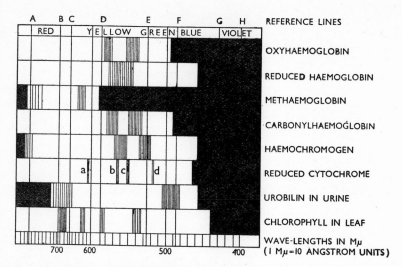

Absorption Spectra of Pyrrole Pigments
The sodium reference line is D, 590 mμ.

Hæmochromogen. Verdohæmochromogen. Biliverdin.

Subsequent reduction of the biliverdin forms bilirubin.

THE CYTOCHROMES

Cytochrome. In 1884, MacMunn observed that muscle and many other animal tissues possessed a sharply defined four-banded spectrum, which he attributed to a special pigment, *myohæmatin* or *histohæmatin*, so-called from its spectrographic resemblance to blood hæmatin. Hoppe-Seyler, the discoverer of hæmochromogen, opposed MacMunn's conclusion, and the work remained neglected until, in 1925, Keilin, using an intense system of illumination which allowed the examination of thick layers of tissue, showed that histohæmatin was universally distributed in all aerobic cells, and renamed the pigment *cytochrome*.

Cytochromes are universal micro-constituents of plant and animal cells, and aerobic unicellular organisms, including yeasts and bacteria. Located chiefly in mitochondria, the cytochromes form a sequence that constitutes the main causeway in the final stages of aerobic respiration, terminating in the reaction between transferred hydrogen atoms and molecular oxygen, to form water. This is effected by the reversible oxidation and reduction of the iron atoms successively in each member of the cytochrome sequence, the last of which, *cytochrome oxidase*, is concerned with the reaction with molecular oxygen. The spectrum shows several absorption bands, the position of which differs in cytochromes from different sources, but the general pattern of which shows a fundamental constancy. The position of maximum density of each band is:

Cytochrome a: α-band, 600 mμ; β-band, 513 mμ.

Cytochrome b: α-band, 564 mμ; β-band, 530 mμ.

Cytochrome c: α-band, 550 mμ; β-band, 520 mμ.

Various related types have been detected spectroscopically, and are classified as a or b, according to absorption band maxima. Thus, cytochrome a_3 (characteristic band, 445 mμ) is the terminal oxidase in baker's yeast, pig heart, and some tumor cells. Cytochrome b_2 is associated with the enzyme *lactic dehydrogenase* from yeast.

Oxidation of cytochrome causes a disappearance of the characteristic spectrum, reduction, which occurs spontaneously in living tissue, causes its reappearance.

Cytochrome c, m.w. 11,800, is very widely distributed, and has been isolated as a red, crystalline hæmochromogen from heart muscle and avian pectoral muscle. It contains 0·46 per cent. of iron as hæm, protein-bound by combination of a thiol group with each of the vinyl groups in the protoporphyrin IX nucleus. Unlike the hæmoglobins, cytochrome c does not form a loose oxygenation compound with molecular oxygen; but, in presence of a catalyst, it is oxidised to the ferric form, which no longer displays the characteristic reduced cytochrome spectrum.

Representative cytochrome c values for dry rat tissue, in mg. per gm., are: heart, 2·34; kidney, 1·36; skeletal muscle, 0·68; brain, 0·35; liver, spleen, 0·22; embryo, 0·03 (early), 0·18 (late).

THE MAGNESIUM PORPHYRANS

Chlorophyll, the green pigment of plant life, can be extracted easily from leaves by alcohol, acetone, ether and similar organic solvents. The yield is about 1 to 2 gm. per kg. of fresh leaves, and 5 to 10 gm. per kg. of dried leaves. By subsequent extraction with a mixture of light petroleum and methyl alcohol, the pigment can be resolved into about 80 per cent. of chlorophyll a (soluble in petroleum) and about 20 per cent. of chlorophyll b (soluble in methyl alcohol). Both pigments are green, but they differ in their spectra in ethereal solution; chlorophyll a has a broad band in the red, 675 to 640 mμ, and a narrower band in the orange, 615 to 605 mμ, chlorophyll b has a band to the right of the C line, 655 to 635 mμ.

In more dilute solutions over the wide absorption range, the absorption maxima are: chlorophyll a, 663, 623, 607, 577, 534, 507, 494, and 423 mμ; chlorophyll b, 644, 614, 597, 567, 542, 503, 456 and 428 mμ.

Chlorophylls a and b occur associated with lipoproteins, and are restricted to the chloroplasts of the plant; related chlorophylls, c, d, and e, are found in some pigmented bacteria and in algæ.

Structure. Willstätter has shown that when chlorophyll is extracted from leaves by ethyl alcohol, an enzyme, *chlorophyllase*, present in the leaf, catalyses an alcoholysis of the pigment, splitting off phytyl alcohol, $C_{20}H_{39}$.OH, which is replaced by a —C_2H_5 group to give a mixture of a and b chlorophyllides. By alkaline hydrolysis, these chlorophyllides are converted into chlorophyllins, which are tricarboxy acids derived from a magnesium porphyran, *ætiophyllin*. Treatment with acid removes the magnesium, leaving an *ætioporphyrin* closely related to the protoporphyrin found in hæmoglobin and hæm pigments. Chlorophyll is the methyl phytyl ester of a tricarboxy magnesium porphyran, the carboxyl group of which is closed to form a ring.

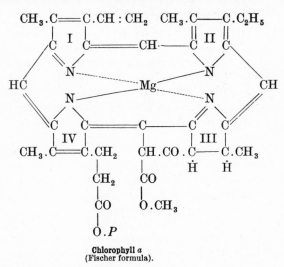

Chlorophyll a
(Fischer formula).

P represents the phytyl radicle, $C_{20}H_{39}$, which on hydrolysis of chlorophyll is liberated as phytyl alcohol, or phytol.
In chlorophyll b, the —CH_3 group in ring II has been oxidised to —CHO.

Phytol is a monohydroxy alcohol derived from the linear hydrocarbon hexadecane. Its origin and significance is unknown, but it is a probable precursor of the carotenoid pigments, and is a component of vitamin K.

$$\begin{array}{c} \text{H} \quad \text{H} \;\; \text{CH}_3 \;\text{H} \;\; \text{H} \quad \text{H} \;\; \text{CH}_3\,\text{H} \;\; \text{H} \quad \text{H} \;\; \text{CH}_3\,\text{H} \;\; \text{H} \quad \text{H} \;\; \text{CH}_3 \\ | \quad | \quad | \quad | \quad | \quad | \quad | \quad | \quad | \quad | \quad | \quad | \quad | \quad | \quad | \\ \text{HO—C—C=C—C—C—C—C—C—C—C—C—C—C—C—C—CH}_3 \\ | \qquad\quad | \quad | \quad | \quad | \quad | \quad | \quad | \quad | \quad | \quad | \quad | \\ \text{H} \qquad\quad \text{H} \;\, \text{H} \;\, \text{H} \;\, \text{H} \;\, \text{H} \;\, \text{H} \;\, \text{H} \;\, \text{H} \;\, \text{H} \;\, \text{H} \;\, \text{H} \;\, \text{H} \end{array}$$

Phytol, $C_{20}H_{39}.OH$
2 : 6 : 10 : 14-Tetramethyl-16-hydroxy-Δ^{14}-hexadecene

Function of Chlorophyll. The chief absorption band of chlorophyll, in the leaf, is in the red, about 678 mμ, which is in the region of maximum solar energy during the day. The radiant energy thus trapped is used to effect the reduction of the absorbed and bound CO_2, by means of H derived from H_2O.

SIGNIFICANCE OF THE PORPHYRINS

A characteristic of the porphyrin ring system is its ability to encage an atom of a metal in the centre of the nitrogen cluster. Thus held, the metal retains its catalytic properties, which may be enhanced or made selective when the metallo-porphyran forms the prosthetic group in a conjugated protein. Consequently, the porphyrins provide a mechanism for employing biological metals. In green plants a magnesium porphyran apparatus is used to absorb and divert solar energy for the purpose of splitting water molecules, possibly by electrons liberated from the irradiated metal:

$$\text{R.Mg} \rightarrow \text{R.Mg}^+ + e^- \; ; \; \text{H} \overset{..}{:} \overset{..}{\text{O}} : \text{H} + e^- \rightarrow (\text{H}) + \overset{..}{:} \overset{..}{\text{O}} : \text{H}.$$

In higher animals an iron porphyran apparatus, the hæmoglobin of the red corpuscles, is used for the capture, transport, and release of molecular oxygen within conditions prescribed by biological requirements. Finally, in all aerobic organisms, that is to say, the greater part of the biosphere, the cellular lifeline with free oxygen is maintained by the cytochrome apparatus of iron porphyrans.

The porphyrin ring system is very stable. Vanadium porphyrans, originally derived from chlorophyll, occur up to 0·4 per cent. in coal, asphalt, shale oil, and petroleum, showing the biological origin of such materials. Some of these fossil porphyrans contain carboxyl groups and, therefore, cannot have been exposed to temperatures much above 200° C. during the long periods of their geological formation, otherwise the porphyrin acid would have been decarboxylated. Porphyrin synthesis must have been an early as well as a universal endowment of life. In the higher animal, tracer studies, using amino acids labelled with ^{15}N, have shown that the simple amino acid, glycine, is the source of the protoporphyrin nitrogen in hæmoglobin.

Vestigial Porphyrans. The chief natural porphyrans, blood and muscle hæmoglobins, chlorophylls, cytochromes, all belong to Type III. The urinary porphyrin, coproporphyrin, belongs to Type I. Although the human adult output is minute, about 50 mg. per 24 hours, it is greatly increased in conditions of congenital porphyria. As conversion of Type III into Type I porphyrin involves opening up, rearranging, and reclosing the macro-cyclic tetrapyrrole nucleus, it seems unlikely that coproporphyrin I is derived from hæm, or some other Type III prophyrin. An alternative possibility is that coproporphyrin I, and the uroporphyrin I that sometimes accompanies it, are relics of a Type I tradition from a remote ancestry. The presence in early fœtal life of uroporphyrin I, which is subsequently replaced by Type III, similarly, may be a vestigial chemical survival.

Chlorophyll is quantitatively an important constituent in the diet of herbivora, and a constant constituent in the human diet, and the suggestion has often been made that it is of value in nutrition.

There are, however, objections to this. Chlorophyll is not attacked by any of the enzymes of the human alimentary tract, and its utilisation has to depend on bacterial decomposition. This may be significant in ruminants, where the parasitic factor in digestion is recognised, but is hardly so in man. It must not be forgotten that chlorophyll when it is degraded forms an important source of magnesium, in addition to providing porphyrins.

Marchlewski (1924) has shown that bilipurpurin, or cholehematin, a pigment present in the bile and biliary concretions of ruminants, is identical with *phylloerythrin*, a porphyrin pigment which he obtained by the biological degradation of chlorophyll or the acid hydrolysis of chlorophyllides. His discovery of phylloerythrin thus leads to the conclusion that the chlorophyll molecule may enter into the metabolic processes of herbivorous animals.

An Evolutionary Link between Plants and Animals. When investigators first realised that all flesh is grass, as far as its pigments are concerned, it was hoped that a path of chemical evolution might be traced between the two kingdoms. Verne, for example, suggested that the hæm of animals may arise from vegetable chlorophyll, and, in consequence, the development of vertebrates was delayed until green plants had appeared in abundance. But, as Barcroft points out, the respiratory pigment cytochrome may be a much more ancient porphyrin than chlorophyll.

Yeast and bacteria, for example, grown on media entirely free from chlorophyll exhibit the spectral bands of cytochrome and hæm, which suggests that the chlorophyll has been evolved from hæm by the organism, and not hæm from chlorophyll.

" Every detail points to something, certainly; but generally to the wrong thing. Facts point in all directions, it seems to me, like the thousands of twigs on a tree. It's only the life of the tree that has unity and goes up—only the green blood that springs, like a fountain, at the stars."

G. K. Chesterton.

CAROTENOIDS

Carotenoids are fat-soluble hydrocarbon pigments widely distributed in low concentrations throughout the animal and plant kingdoms. They are orange or red in colour, crystallisable, freely soluble in light petroleum, chloroform and similar fat-solvents, but insoluble in water. They are easily bleached by oxidation, and give a deep blue colour in presence of concentrated sulphuric acid (the carotenoid reaction). Since they accumulate in oils and fats, they are also termed *lipochromes*. Carotenoids impart the typical colour to egg-yolk, the corpus luteum of the ovary, butter fat, liver oils, carrot, turnip, maize, tomato, " the sere and yellow leaf ", and many fruits and flowers.

History. The group name is derived from that of the first member discovered, *carotin* or carotene, which, in 1831, was isolated from carrots, and subsequently was found to occur along with another yellow pigment, *xanthophyll*, in all chlorophyll-containing foliage. Between 1906 and 1914, Willstätter isolated nearly a dozen different carotenoids, and Palmer showed that the pigment of milk and butter fat is carotene derived from the diet of the cow (1922). The pigment of egg-yolk, originally termed " lutein ", was shown to be a mixture of carotene and leaf xanthophyll, the latter being now re-named *lutein*.

Plant Carotenoids

In Order of Adsorption from Petroleum Solutions

Name.	Formula.	Chief Sources.	Adsorbent.
Alcohols :			
Flavoxanthin	$C_{40}H_{56}O_3$	Buttercup	$CaCO_3$
Violaxanthin	$C_{40}H_{56}O_4$	Pansy	,,
Taraxanthin	$C_{40}H_{56}O_4$	Dandelion	,,
Lutein	$C_{40}H_{56}O_2$	Green leaves	,,
Zeaxanthin	$C_{40}H_{56}O_2$	Maize	,,
Ketone :			
Rhodoxanthin	$C_{40}H_{50}O_2$	Rose fruit	,,
Hydrocarbons :			
γ-Carotene	$C_{40}H_{56}$	Carrot	$Al(OH)_3$
β-Carotene	$C_{40}H_{56}$	Carrot	,,
α-Carotene	$C_{40}H_{56}$	Carrot	,,

Carotene, $C_{40}H_{56}$. Fresh carrot has 0·005 to 0·01 per cent. of carotene, and fresh grass contains about 0·01 per cent. of carotene and 0·02 per cent. of lutein (xanthophyll). The pigment is easily obtained by extracting dried carrot scrapings or dried leaves with light petroleum (which does not extract the chlorophyll). The extract is evaporated in a dish at room temperature, and the residue freed from lipids by rinsing with small quantities of the solvent. The carotene fraction remains as a crop of dark red micro-crystals, which by chromatographic adsorption, can be resolved into three isomers.

α-Carotene, m.p. 175°, $[a]_D = + 323°$, forms brilliant rhomboidal crystals, copper-red in colour.

β-Carotene, m.p. 185°, $[a]_D = 0°$, resembles the α-form, but is slightly less soluble. *β-Carotene* occurs almost pure in spinach and in red pepper (paprika).

The carotene fraction from palm-nut oil contains about 60 to 70 per cent. of the β-form, the rest being α-carotene.

γ-Carotene is rare in higher plants, but has been found in the acid-fast bacteria. It differs from the other isomers in having only one ring in its molecule.

Lycopene, $C_{40}H_{56}$, the colouring matter of tomatoes, differs from the carotenes structurally in having non-cyclic end-groups.

Chromatographic Analysis

The Russian botanist, Tswett, found in 1906 that a tube packed with powdered calcium carbonate could be used to separate pigments from solution in non-polar solvents, such as light petroleum. When the solution was allowed to flow down the tube, the pigments tended to be adsorbed at different stages, thus producing a striated *chromatogram*. Twenty years later, Kuhn and his colleagues applied this method to the resolution of the carotenoids, and were able to fractionate crude carotene into (i) an optically inactive β-carotene, and (ii) a dextro-rotatory α-carotene, the latter being adsorbed below the former. A narrow zone of pigment above the β-carotene layer proved to be a third isomer, γ-carotene, 34 mg. of which were obtained from 35 gm. of crude carotene, which, in turn was got from 300 kg., or about 6 cwt., of raw carrots. Chromatographic adsorbability is increased by the presence of hydroxyl groups and unsaturated linkages in the adsorbent, and thus affords information about the structure of the compounds.

Structure of the Carotenoids

On reduction, lycopene was found by Karrer to accept 26 hydrogen atoms

Lycopene. $C_{40}H_{56}$.

α-Carotene. $C_{40}H_{56}$.

β-Carotene. $C_{40}H_{56}$.

169

and give rise to a paraffin hydrocarbon, $C_{40}H_{82}$, which led him to conclude that the pigment is a linear compound containing 13 unsaturated linkages. Carotene, although an isomer of lycopene, was found by Zechmeister to accept only 22 atoms of hydrogen, from which he concluded that it contained two cyclic groups separated by an unsaturated chain. These groups were subsequently identified as being derived from β-ionone, a constituent of the essential oil of the violet.

The hydrocarbon carotenoids differ from each other in the arrangement of the terminal groups, both of which may be open, as in lycopene, or both closed to form 6-membered rings, as in α- and β-carotene.

The xanthin carotenoids are ketones or alcohols derived from carotenes by substitution of H in the terminal rings.

Vitamin A

In 1919, Steenbock suggested that the fat-soluble vitamin A was related in some way to the carotenoids because of the similarity of distribution in natural sources. Inadequate knowledge of the properties of the vitamins delayed confirmation of the hypothesis, until, in 1929, von Euler showed that although carotene was not identical with vitamin A, it could replace the vitamin in the diet. Moore subsequently demonstrated that the pigment is transformed into the vitamin within the animal. Meanwhile, the carotenes had been resolved into their isomers, and it was found that β-carotene had twice the provitamin potency of α-carotene. Since the formula of vitamin A was known to be $C_{20}H_{29}.OH$, it was suggested that the vitamin was hydroxy-*semi-β*-carotene, two molecules of which were derived from one molecule of β-carotene by hydrolytic fission.

α-Carotene, γ-carotene, cryptoxanthin and myxoxanthin and aphanin (from algæ) each contain a *semi-β*-carotene residue, and can give rise to one molecule of vitamin A. At least ten natural carotenoids are provitamins of A, and β-carotene is taken as the international standard for comparison (p. 185).

Structurally, vitamin A contains a β-ionone nucleus carrying a side-chain with four unsaturated linkages and a terminal primary alcohol group. A related form, vitamin A_2, $C_{20}H_{27}O$, is in livers of fresh-water fishes. It differs from A, in having an additional double bond in the ring. Neither vitamin has been found in plants.

Vitamin A.

β-Ionone.

Animal Carotenoids. The carotenoids found in higher animals are usually plant carotenoids derived from the diet; the grass of the field being the prin-

cipal source of the provitamins necessary for human life. Although the carotene: xanthophyll ratio in grass is 1 : 2, both cows and horses preferentially
absorb the carotene to the exclusion of the xanthophyll. Birds accumulate
xanthophyll almost exclusively, and it reappears in the egg-yolk, body fat and
plumage, a fact known empirically by canary breeders. Man absorbs carotene
and xanthophyll with equal facility, and both pigments occur in human
plasma. Milk fat, the commonest dietetic source of carotene, contains from
1 to 20 parts per million, depending on the nature of the food consumed.

Among the lower animals, carotenoids occur as special body pigments. The
shells of the lobster and other crustacea contain a blue chromoprotein, which
on hydrolysis by boiling liberates *astacene*, $C_{40}H_{56}O_4$, a tetra-keto-β-carotene.
Astacene is the typical pigment of echinoderms, gold-fish skin and the flesh
of salmon. *Violerythrin*, $C_{40}H_{56}O_6$, is the carotenoid that as an ester, *actino-
erythrin*, imparts the brilliant colour to sea anemones.

Biogenesis of the Carotenoids. According to Karrer, the alcohol *phytol*,
$C_{20}H_{39} \cdot OH$, which forms about one-third of the chlorophyll molecule, is the
parent substance of the carotenoids. Desaturation of two phytol residues
would in theory yield lycopene, from which the other carotenoids could arise
by closure of the terminal groups to form rings. The symmetry of the
carotenoid molecule suggests an origin from such a precursor.

The structural unit of both phytol and the carotenoids is *isoprene*,
$H_2C=C(CH_3)—CH=CH_2$, which presumably arises during the photosynthesis
of carbohydrates.

Analytical Reactions of the Carotenoids

Examine microscopically a thin section of carrot. In the cortical region
minute needle-shaped orange crystals can be seen in the cells. These are
stearate coloured by carotene. Cover the preparation with a glass slip, and
carefully instil a drop of concentrated sulphuric acid. The crystals develop a
deep blue colour.

Apply the following tests to a specimen of fish-liver oil diluted 1 : 10 with
chloroform, or to a solution of carotene in chloroform.

(1) *Sulphuric Acid Test*. Careful addition of a couple of drops of concentrated
sulphuric acid to a water-free solution of a carotenoid produces a transient
blue-violet colour, which is very marked if the mixture contains vitamin A.

(2) *Antimony Trichloride Test*. When 2 to 5 ml. of a chloroform solution of
a carotenoid are treated with an excess of a 30 per cent. solution of antimony
trichloride in chloroform a stable blue colour develops. The reagent gives
colours also with steroids containing a double-bond at $C_1=C_2$ in Ring I, and
with pyrrole and furfural derivatives, so the test requires to be controlled
spectroscopically.

A blue colour is given by vitamin A (Carr-Price test), but the vitamin blue
can be distinguished by the presence of an absorption band in the region of
562 to 583 mμ, which is not shown by any of the carotenoids. A maximum

absorption band is shown by vitamin A_1 at 617 mμ; and by vitamin A_2 at 693 mμ.

FLAVINS

It has been known for many years that animal tissues display a greenish fluorescence on exposure to ultra-violet radiation. In 1929, Ellinger, during an exploration by means of his " intra-vital microscope ", observed that the fluorescent pigment was concentrated chiefly in the liver and upper renal tubule epithelium of all species of animals examined. Using the fluorescence as a guide, he succeeded in extracting and purifying the compound by absorption on Fuller's earth, and subsequent elution with aqueous pyridine. Milk whey proved to be a good source of the pigment, which was eventually obtained in crystalline form, and was termed a *lyochrome*, since it was water-soluble, thus differing from the fat-soluble lipochromes, or carotenoids.

Meanwhile, two groups of investigators working along different lines had also recognised the existence of this new type of pigment. Warburg and Christian had shown that their " yellow ferment " or respiratory catalyst, originally obtained from brewer's yeast, on hydrolysis liberated a lyochrome apparently identical with one obtained by Ellinger; and Kuhn, during a study of the vitamin B complex, found that one member, vitamin B_2, was itself a lyochrome.

In addition, lyochromes were obtained from a variety of animal and plant sources, and were named by affixing the termination *flavin*, to indicate the yellow colour of the pigment: *lactoflavin*, from whey; *ovoflavin*, from egg-white; *hepatoflavin*, from liver; *renoflavin*, from kidney; *uroflavin*, from urine; *maltoflavin*, from malt; and *zymoflavin*, from yeast.

Definition. Flavins are nitrogenous pigments derived from *iso*-alloxazine, and characterised by: (1) solubility in water and insolubility in fat-solvents; (2) yellow colour in solution, and orange-red colour in crystalline form; (3) greenish-yellow fluorescence in neutral aqueous solutions, the fluorescence being extinguished by addition of acid or alkali; (4) stability to oxidising agents; and (5) reversible reduction to leuco-compounds.

The concentration of these flavins in their natural sources is very low. Fresh liver or kidney contains 10 to 20 mg. per kg., whey contains up to 80 mg. per litre, consisting of a mixture of related lactoflavins, *a—d*.

Riboflavin, lactoflavin or vitamin B_2, $C_{17}H_{20}O_6N_4$, the most important of the lyochromes, occurs in free and bound forms.

(1) *Riboflavin-5′-phosphoric acid*, or *riboflavin mononucleotide*, was isolated from heart muscle, in 1932, by Banga and Szent-Györgyi, and later shown to be the coloured prosthetic group in Warburg's original " yellow enzyme ". In riboflavin mononucleotide, the —O—PO(OH)$_2$ group replaces —OH in the terminal or 5′ position in the ribityl side-chain.

(2) *Riboflavin-adenine dinucleotide* is the necessary prosthetic group in several flavoproteins that have catalytic properties.

(3) *Free Flavins.* Principally riboflavin, which is identical with the ovoflavin, hepatoflavin, and lactoflavin *d*.

(4) *Flavoproteins*, containing riboflavin mononucleotide or dinucleotide, occur chiefly as the " yellow enzymes " and hydrogen-carriers in tissue respiration: amino acid oxidase, xanthin oxidase, etc.

Structure of the Flavins. When riboflavin is irradiated in alcohol, a sugar, D-ribose, is split off, leaving a crystallisable residue, *lumichrome*. Alkaline hydrolysis of lumichrome yields urea and a dimethyl benzpyrazine, which suggests the presence of three rings in the original flavin, one of which has yielded the urea. This has led to the *iso*-alloxazine formula now adopted for the lyochromes, according to which lumichrome is the 6 : 7-dimethyl derivative.

Benzypyrazine.

iso-Alloxazine.

Riboflavin, vitamin B₂
(6 : 7-dimethyl-9-D-ribityl *iso*-alloxazine).

MELANINS

Melanin Pigments. Tyrosine is oxidised by the enzyme tyrosinase to a red indole compound formed by closure of the side-chain. This red compound is reduced spontaneously to an indole base, *melanogen*, which subsequent oxidation polymerises to a dark-brown pigment, *melanin*. Melanin, or closely related melanoids, impart the characteristic colour to brown or black hair, the fur of animals, the choroid coat of the eye, the ink secretion of the cuttle fish *Sepia*, and the malignant melanotic sarcomata. The pigments are very stable, and are insoluble in water, acids, and organic solvents, but bleached by oxidising agents, including hydrogen peroxide. The changes involved in melanin formation have been elucidated by Raper (1928).

This series of reactions is of importance in establishing a relationship between tryptophane and tyrosine. The colourless melanogen is excreted in the urine of patients suffering from melanotic sarcoma, and may be recognised by its

173

oxidation to melanin, which occurs spontaneously on exposure to the atmosphere, or after addition of any mild oxidising agents. A corresponding melanin is obtained from the plant amino acid, 3 : 4-dihydroxy-phenyl-alanine, by the specific enzyme, " *dopa* " oxidase, which has no action on tyrosine. The condition of albinism is ascribed to the lack of one or more of these oxidising enzymes.

Melanin formation in the deeper layers of the epidermis is responsible for the racial and climatic pigmentation of the skin, and may have some protective effect against excess of harmful solar radiation.

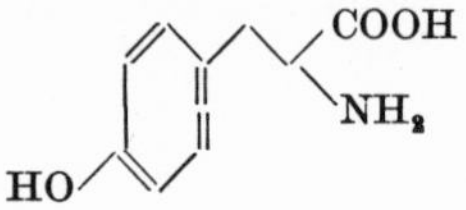

Tyrosine.

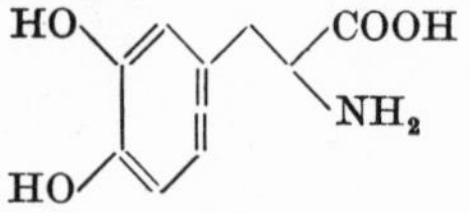

"Dopa"
3 : 4-dihydroxy-phenylalanine.

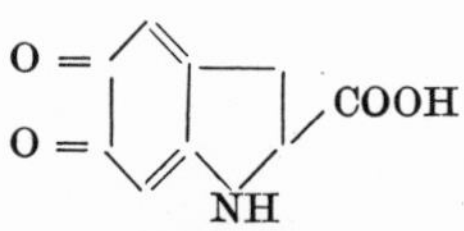

Dopachrome
(red)

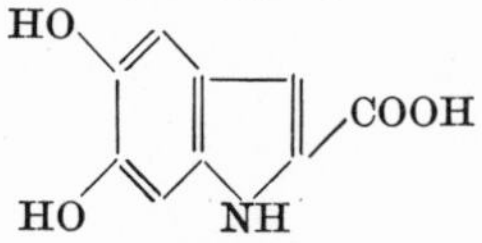

Melanogen

Dopachrome seems to be identical with a pigment of red hair that can be extracted by boiling with N/10 HCl.

PTERIDINES

In 1889, Hopkins showed that the yellow pigment of butterfly wings is a cyclic nitrogen compound. Forty years later, the observation was confirmed and extended by Wieland, and by Hopkins, and it was established that these pterins, or wing-pigments, including one from the yellow bands of the wasp, are derivatives of a base, pteridine, which is formed by union of a pyrimidine and a pyrazine ring. Simple pterins are almost entirely restricted to insects, pteridines occur as micro-constituents of plant and animal tissues, especially green leaves, yeasts, fungi, liver and kidney, where they represent a vitamin complex, **Folic acid,** a polypeptide of glutamic acid units combined with **Pteroic acid,** which is assembled from *para*-aminobenzoic acid and a pterin **Xanthopterin.** Pteroic acid is a growth-stimulant for *Streptococcus lactis*

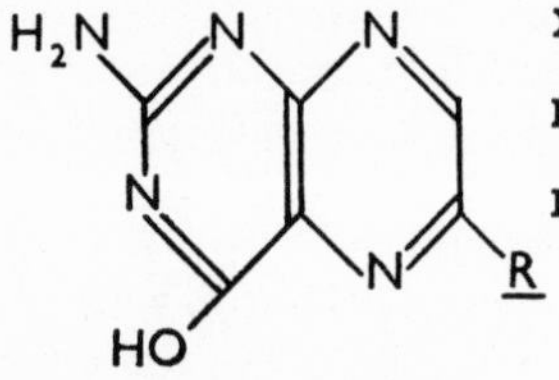

Xanthopterin, R = —OH

Pteroic acid,   R = —CH$_2$.NH.C$_6$H$_4$.COOH

Pteroyl glutamic acid,
R = —CH$_2$.NH.C$_6$H$_4$.CO—NH.CH.CH$_2$.CH$_2$.COOH
                                            |
                                          COOH

Pteridine Nucleus

174

R, *Lactobacillus casei*, yeast, and other organisms; combined with glutamic acid, it is also an essential factor for growth, feathering, and hæmoglobin-formation in chickens.

FLAVONES AND ANTHOCYANINS

The widely distributed yellow or orange pigments of flower petals and some fruits are glycosides of a phenyl derivative of chromone, termed **flavone,** or *anthoxanthin*. These flavones are entirely different in structure and properties from the *flavin* pigments; but like them, are of interest in animal physiology, since the anti-sterility vitamins E are chromone derivatives, and the capillary-maintenance vitamin P is closely associated with the flavone fraction of citrus peel, and may be a flavone derivative.

The familiar red, purple or blue colours of flowers, fruits and some leaves are due to glycoside pigments formed from anthocyanins, also indirectly derived from chromone.

General References

Booth, V. H. (1957), " Carotene." Cambridge.
" Chemical Pathology of the Animal Pigments." Ed. by R. T. Williams (1954). *Biochem. Soc. Symposia*, No. 12. Cambridge.
Dartnall, H. J. A. (1957), " The Visual Pigments." London.
Goodwin, T. W. (1952), " Comparative Biochemistry of the Carotenoids." London.
Gray, C. H. (1953), " Bile Pigments." London.
" Hæmoglobin." Ed. by F. J. W. Roughton and J. C. Kendrew (1948). London.
Lemberg, R., and J. W. Legge (1949), " Hæmatin Compounds and Bile Pigments." New York.
MacMunn, C. A. (1914), " Spectrum Analysis Applied to Biology and Medicine." London.
Mayer, F. (1943), " Chemistry of natural colouring matters." *American Chem. Soc. Monographs*, No. 89.
Morton, R. A. (1942), "Application of Absorption Spectra to the Study of Vitamins, Hormones, and Coenzymes." London.
" Porphyrins: Biosynthesis and Metabolism." (1956). *CIBA Foundation Symposia*.
" Pteridines: Chemistry and Biology." (1956). *CIBA Foundation Symposia*.
Roche, J. (1936), " La biochemie générale et comparée des pigments respiratoires." Paris.
Zechmeister, L., and L. Cholnoky (1942), " Chromatography." *Trans. A. L.* Bacharach and F. A. Robinson. London.

Chapter 13 Nutrients

" 'All flesh is grass ' is not only metaphorically but literally true; for all those creatures we behold are but the herbs of the field, digested into flesh in them, or more remotely carnified in ourselves; . . . this frame we look upon hath been upon our trenchers; in brief, we have devoured ourselves."

Thomas Browne (1605–1682).

Nutrition is the process whereby an organism incorporates material from its environment for the purposes of growth, maintenance and repair. A nutrient is a substance capable of being assimilated and utilised by an organism.

Foodstuffs are natural or manufactured products of plant or animal origin, used as sources of nutrients.

Green plants and some pigmented micro-organisms are **autotrophic,** or self-feeders, in that they are not dependent on imported organic nutrients, but obtain their carbon, hydrogen, and nitrogen from inorganic sources: carbon dioxide, water, ammonia, and nitrate. The energy required is captured from solar radiation by a photosynthetic mechanism. A few autotrophic organisms, notably the hydrogen bacteria and the sulphur bacteria, obtain their necessary energy by the oxidation of molecular hydrogen, hydrogen sulphide, or other inorganic reductants.

All animals, fungi, and most bacteria are **heterotrophic,** or food-importing, in that they are unable to synthesise some or all of their organic food requirements, and, directly or indirectly, are dependent on the activity of autotrophic organisms.

Nutrients may be classified: (1) *chemically*, according to structure; or (2) *biologically*, according to need. Specifically essential nutrients are constructive and provide components of cells and secretions that otherwise could not be made. Many are also combustible and contribute energy for the maintenance of life. Essential nutrients include water, certain inorganic ions, amino acids, vitamins and growth-factors, the precise needs of which differ in different species. Combustible nutrients are chiefly the carbohydrates, proteins, and lipids, which, though not specifically essential, must be in sufficient quantity to supply enough energy for the working life of the organism. Furthermore, most proteins and some lipids contain essential nutrients incorporated into their structures.

Animals, green plants, and many micro-organisms are **aerobic,** in that they require molecular oxygen for the completion of their energy-releasing respiratory processes. Other organisms are **anaerobic,** and can obtain all their necessary energy from reactions not involving free oxygen.

Nutritional Requirements of the Higher Animal

(1) **Oxygen.** Oxygen is unique among the nutrients. It is taken in as a free element, in gaseous form; it is not assimilated by the alimentary tract; and it acts as the ultimate acceptor of hydrogen in aerobic metabolism. So important is the continuous provision of oxygen that a special apparatus, the pulmonary system has been evolved for this purpose, and carriers of molecular oxygen, the hæmoglobins, are present in the blood of all vertebrates. The adult human lungs have a capacity of about 4·5 litres, and normally contain about 0·5 litres of oxygen, which suffices for the body at rest for about two minutes. If the supply is not maintained, a condition of anoxæmia will develop rapidly, and death will follow acute oxygen starvation in about three minutes.

(2) **Water.** Water is not regarded popularly as a food material because it yields no energy to the organism. It is, however, the chief constituent of most of the tissues, and thus contributes to the structure of the body.

The total water intake of the normal adult is between 2 and 3·5 litres *per diem*, more than half of which is eaten in the form of solid food.

A 3,000-kilocalorie diet as consumed contains about 2,000 ml. of preformed and potential water and must be supplemented by the further consumption of 1 to 1·5 litres in a liquid form.

A satisfactory daily water intake for the adult is 1 ml. per kilocalorie of food. Circumstances of marine warfare have shown that 500 ml. (18 oz.) represent the smallest daily supply of water capable of maintaining individual life in occupants of boats adrift.

The consumption of water is regulated by the composition of the blood plasma. When the concentration of Na^+ and Cl' rises above the normal level, the sensation of thirst is evoked.

(3) **Metals.** The biological metals are widely and unevenly distributed in the dietary. Some, such as iron and magnesium, occur chiefly in organic combination and are not easily absorbed. Others occur as salts, such as chloride and phosphate, and yield assimilable ions. The human requirements of many of the individual metals are known approximately from surveys of satisfactory diets, and can be expressed in terms of a *minimum demand*, M.D., below which health cannot be maintained; and an *optimum demand*, O.D., which ensures a safety margin.

(4) **Carbohydrates.** More than 65 per cent. of the solids of the human diet are carbohydrates. Starch, the chief constituent, occurs in cereals (wheat, oats, barley, rice, rye, and maize, or Indian corn), of which it forms 60 to 80 per cent. It is present also in tubers and roots: potato, 18 to 20 per cent.; parsnip, carrot, turnip, 3 to 11 per cent. In the average diet of the human adult, starch indirectly provides 300 to 500 gm. of glucose daily. Sucrose, from cane or beet (13 to 15 per cent.), is the common sweetening agent, supplemented by industrially-prepared glucose, or " starch sugar ", in the manufacture of preserves. Glucose and fructose occur in honey, fruits and syrups. Lactose

Inorganic Nutrients

Element.	Adult 24-Hour Need.		Chief Sources, in mg. per kg.
	M.D.	O.D.	
Na	4 gm.	6·5 gm.	Table salt, animal products.
K	1·5 gm.	3 gm.	Vegetable and animal products.
Ca	0·8 gm.	1·5 gm.	Cheese, milk, egg-yolk, " hard " water.
Mg	0·3 gm.	1 gm.	Green vegetables.
Fe	10 mg.	20 mg.	Liver, treacle, currants, raisins, egg-yolk (80 plus); peas and beans (50 to 150, dry); wheat, entire (50); oatmeal (50); lean meat, prunes, spinach (20 to 30); white flour, potato, polished rice (10).
Cu	2 mg.	3 mg.	Shell fish, crustaceans (up to 400); cocoa shell (200); lamb or calf liver (100); yeast (50 to 100); tea, coffee, cocoa, chocolate, nuts, currants, tomato pulp (10 to 30).
Mn	2 mg.	7 mg.	Tea leaves (150 to 900, dry); bran (50 to 150); liver, kidney, shell fish (up to 100); wholemeal flour (10 to 70); spinach, lettuce, blackberry, cereals, nuts, dry peas and beans (10 to 50).
Co	+	0·1 mg.	Sheep and calf pancreas and liver (0·3, dry); tea leaves (0·1, dry); wholemeal flour (0·1).
Zn	1 mg.	12 mg.	Oysters (250 to 600); wheat germ (140); wheat bran (75 to 140); yeast (up to 200); beef liver (30 to 85), wholemeal bread, oatmeal, cocoa, egg yolk, tea leaves, dry peas, beans, and lentils (20 to 50).
Cl	6 gm.	10 gm.	As for sodium.
S, as HS—	0·5 gm.	1 gm.	Sulphur-containing amino acids in proteins of milk, eggs, and meat.
P, as PO_4^{3-}	3 gm.	4·5 gm.	Phosphoproteins, phospholipides.
I	0·055 mg.	0·2 mg.	Crude table salt, fish, liver.
F	+	+	Tea leaves, drinking water.

occurs in milk (3 to 4 per cent.) but, apart from the diet of children, the amount consumed is small.

Cellulose, or vegetable fibre, does not contribute energy since it is not attacked by the enzymes of the human alimentary tract. It may have some value as an irritant in promoting peristalsis, and in the form of bran and under the name of " roughage " it is prescribed, if not consumed, with enthusiasm.

Calorific Value. Carbohydrates have a heat equivalent of about 4 kilogram calories per gram and contribute about two-thirds of the total energy requirements of the adult. They are the cheapest food materials and predominate in the diets of the poor and the parsimonious.

(5) **Proteins.** The nitrogenous foods make up 10 to 15 per cent. of the solids of the human diet, and may reach 30 per cent., if the consumer can afford them. They are the most expensive and most palatable part of the dietary, and are well represented in lean meat and fish (18 to 20 per cent.), cheese (10 to 40 per cent.), egg-white (12 per cent.), egg-yolk (16 per cent.), liver (29 per cent.), kidney (26 per cent.), milk (3 to 4 per cent.), bread (6 per cent.),

potato (1 to 2 per cent.), green vegetables (1 to 2·5 per cent.), beans and peas (6 to 20 per cent.). Proteins form the only dietary source of amino acids, the content of which differs in different proteins. For this reason, about half of the food protein should be derived from animal sources to ensure getting a sufficient supply of the indispensable acids, and several sorts of protein should be included in the dietary, so as to provide an adequate selection.

Calorific Value. When completely oxidised to carbon dioxide, nitric acid, and water, 1 gm. of dry protein yields 5·8 kilocalories of energy. In the organism, however, oxidation of the nitrogen is only carried as far as urea, and for this reason the calorific value of food protein is only 4·1 kilocalories per gram.

Protein Requirement. The optimum 24-hour requirement for the human subject is rated at 1 gram protein per kg. body weight, on the assumption that the protein is of good quality and capable of providing all the essential amino acids. For children, the need, in gm. per kg. body weight is relatively greater.

Year . .	1–3	3–5	5–15	15–17	21
Amount . .	3·5	3·0	2·5	1·5	1·0

For the lactating mother, the requirement is 2 gm. per kg. body weight. Protein requirement, as calculated from nitrogen-balance data, represents the intake of protein nitrogen sufficient to maintain the normal growth-rate in young animals, or to equal the total nitrogen output in adults in a state of constant body weight. With good quality protein, nitrogen-balance can be maintained in healthy adults by intakes of 30 to 36 gm. per 24 hours, or 2·9 gm. protein nitrogen per square metre of body surface.

Amino Acids Essential in Human Nutrition. When an animal is fed on a diet deficient in an essential amino acid, it compensates by breaking down tissue proteins to provide the missing nutrient. Nitrogen-imbalance results, the output exceeds the import, and the body weight falls. By this means, Rose and his colleagues have been able to identify the amino acids necessary in human nutrition, and to estimate the minimum amount of each that is required to maintain nitrogen-balance in adults. Expressed in gm. per 24 hours, the minimum necessary intake, m, and the " safe " intake, s, for the individual amino acids are: L-leucine, 0·5 to 1·1 (m), 2·2 (s); L-lysine, 0·4 to 0·8 (m), 1·6 (s); L-isoleucine, 0·7 (m), 1·4 (s); D- or L-methionine, 0·8 to 1·1 (m), 2·2 (s); L-phenylalanine, 0·8 to 1·1 (m), 2·2 (s); L-threonine 0·3 to 0·5 (m), 1·0 (s); L-tryptophan, 0·15 to 0·25 (m), 0·5 (s); L-valine, 0·4 to 0·8 (m), 1·6 (s).

Biological values of food proteins in terms of their relative ability to maintain nitrogen equilibrium, where 100 represents maximum ability: egg, entire, 91; egg albumin, 91; milk, 74; casein, 68; beef muscle, 67; soy flour, 65; peanut flour, 56; yeast, 52; wheat gluten, 42; white flour, 41.

Data such as these show that the biological value of a protein depends primarily on its content of essential amino acids, though other factors, such as digestibility, must be taken into account.

The pioneer investigations of Rose are of historical interest in that they led to the discovery of the amino acid *threonine*, when it was observed that casein and casein hydrolysates were more effective in maintaining growth than were equivalent mixtures of the then-known amino acids.

Inter-relationships exist among the amino acids, because of the sparing effect of related units. Thus, tyrosine can replace about half the phenylalanine requirement, but by itself has no growth-promoting properties in the absence of phenylalanine.

Cystine, because of its available sulphur, can replace about one-sixth of the methionine requirement, but has no growth-promoting effect in the absence of methionine.

Young animals, including the child, the rat and the chick, cannot synthesise arginine sufficiently rapidly to meet their growth demands, and for them it is an essential amino acid. Histidine also appears to be necessary for the growing rat. Glutamine and proline, but not hydroxyproline, can replace arginine to some extent.

(6) **Lipids.** The simple and complex lipids represent 10 to 20 per cent. of the diet in temperate countries, depending on food habits and season of the year. The chief sources are: (i) *Animal fats*, lard, suet, butter (83 per cent.), cream (20 to 40 per cent.), milk (3 to 4 per cent.) meat (1 to 20 per cent.), mackerel and herring (7 per cent.), salmon, 12 per cent.). (ii) *Vegetable fats*, oils, oleo-margarine (84 per cent.), nuts (35 to 60 per cent.). Phosphatides come mostly from the lecithins of egg-yolk, liver, and kidney.

Calorific Value. Fats have energy values as high as 9·3 kilocalories per gram. They are important as concentrated sources of energy and are the chief form in which energy is stored in animals and in the seeds of oil-bearing plants.

Lipid Requirement. The optimum lipid requirement of the human subject is assessed at 0·7 to 1 gm. per kg. body weight per 24 hours, depending on the consumer and the sources of lipid. In addition to providing energy, lipids carry in solution micro-essential nutrients, notably vitamins A, D, and E, the provitamin carotenoids and sterols and the essential polyene acids. The complex lipids also provide choline and other nitrogenous bases of value to the animal. Fat intake requires to be balanced by carbohydrate intake. Although fats and carbohydrates are interconvertible in the organism by means of acetic acid, a metabolite common to both, surplus carbohydrate is much more readily converted into fat than fat is converted into sugar. Consequently, when the diet is deficient in carbohydrate, an excess of fat can evoke a ketosis, or accumulation of ketones (acetoacetic acid and acetone), caused by overload of the products of fat metabolism. Dietary ketosis cannot arise if twice the total carbohydrate intake and half the protein intake together are greater in weight than the total fat intake.

Diets rich in animal fats tend to raise the level of the blood plasma cholesterol, a circumstance implicated in the development of atherosclerosis and coronary thrombosis.

Polyene Acids Essential in Nutrition. Young animals on diets free from fat, but otherwise adequate, fail to grow, and eventually develop a dermatitis. The condition can be cured by addition of a small amount of linoleic, linolenic, or arachidonic acid to the diet, but not by saturated lipid acids or by oleic acid.

Isotope experiments show that the animal can desaturate stearic acid to oleic acid, but is unable to continue the process so as to produce unsaturated acids that are *polyenes*, in that they have more than one unsaturated methyne unit, $=CH-$, in the chain. The animal also is unable to assemble polyene lipid acids from carbohydrate or other sources. The polyene acids are believed to be essential in human nutrition, but their significance and requirement is unknown. They are present in all unprocessed vegetable oils, animal fats, and fatty tissues, and appear to be interconvertible in the organism.

Stearic Acid, $C_{17}H_{35}.COOH$ (Octadecoic).

Oleic Acid, $C_{17}H_{33}.COOH$ (9-Octadecenoic).

Linoleic Acid, $C_{17}H_{31}.COOH$ (9, 12-Octadecadienoic).

Linolenic Acid, $C_{17}H_{29}.COOH$ (9, 12, 15-Octadecatrienoic).

Arachidonic Acid, $C_{19}H_{31}.COOH$

Polyene carboxylic acids.

VITAMINS

Definition. A vitamin is a micro-essential organic nutrient. Unlike the specifically essential amino acids, the daily requirements are of the order of milligrams and not grams. Unlike the micro-essential metals, the vitamins are destructible and are liable to be lost during food processing and preservation.

The term " vitamin " is usually restricted to the needs of animals; corresponding compounds required by plants and micro-organisms are included in the term " growth factors ".

Vitamin requirements differ among different species. They are provided directly by the diet, or, indirectly, by the activity of the micro-flora of the alimentary tract. Like many of the hormones, they are therapeutic agents of great potency.

The Vitamin Theory. The acceptance of the vitamins as an independent class of food constituents is based on evidence from five distinct sources: (1) the clinical recognition of rickets, scurvy, and beri-beri as deficiency diseases; (2) the empirical use of natural products rich in vitamins, such as liver oils, lemon juice, and yeast; (3) the experimental proof that animals are unable to live and grow on dietaries of purified protein, carbohydrate, lipid, and inorganic salts; (4) the production and cure of typical deficiency diseases; (5) isolation of the vitamins and their chemical synthesis.

History. In 1873, Forster, Voit's assistant in Munich, examined the effect of a de-mineralised diet on dogs and pigeons. Using purified protein, fat, and starch, he found that the animals died within a month, and concluded that " food deprived of its inorganic salts causes death more rapidly than total deprivation of food."

In 1881, Bunge repeated these experiments on mice in order to find which salts were necessary for life. He concluded that an additional factor was required, " although animals can live on milk alone, yet if all the constituents of milk which according to the present teaching of physiology are necessary for the maintenance of the organism be mixed together, the animals rapidly die . . . does milk contain in addition to protein, fat, and carbohydrates, other organic substances which are also indispensable to the maintenance of life?" (1902).

Hopkins, in 1906, recognised the association between these unknown food factors and the widespread occurrence of deficiency diseases: " Scurvy and rickets are conditions so severe that they force themselves on our attention; but many other nutritive errors affect the health of individuals to a degree most important to themselves, and some of them depend on unsuspected dietetic factors."

A year later, Fraser and Stanton obtained by the alcoholic extraction of rice bran a product capable of curing beri-beri, and, in 1911, Funk obtained a growth-promoting residue; since it contained basic nitrogen, it was termed a " vitamine ".

Classification

I. Fat-soluble

1. Vitamins A

2. Vitamins D:
   Ergocalciferol,
   Cholecalciferol

3. Vitamins E:
   Tocopherols

4. Vitamins K

(5. Polyene acids)

II. Water-soluble

a) Co-enzyme class

1. Vitamin B_1:
   Thiamine

2. Vitamin B_2:

3. Niacins: Nicotinic acid,
   Nicotinic amide

4. Vitamins B_6: Pyridoxine,
   Pyridoxal, Pyridoxamine

5. Pantothenic acid

6. Biotin

7. Lipoic acid

8. Folacins: Folic acids, Leucovorin

9. Vitamins B_{12}: Cobalamins

(b) Redox class

1. Vitamin C:
   Ascorbic acid

(2. Ubiquinones)

This classification includes the vitamins required by man and many higher animals. The status of the polyene acids, linoleic, linolenic and arachidonic, is uncertain.

In an important paper, published in 1912, Hopkins showed the presence of " accessory food factors " in milk which were essential for the growth of rats. In 1915, these were resolved by McCollum and Davis into a fat-soluble A factor and a water-soluble B factor, and a third, the water-soluble C factor was recognised and identified with the scurvy-preventing factor present in citrus fruits. Factor A, abundant in fish-liver oils, was shown to be distinct from an associated rickets-preventing factor, vitamin D, the existence of which was postulated by Mellanby, in 1919. Factor B was found to be a mixture of several vitamins also present in yeast and bran.

I. FAT-SOLUBLE VITAMINS

Then the angel said unto him, Take out the entrails of this fish and lay up his heart and his gall and his liver for thee, for these are necessary for useful medicines.

Tobit, VI, 5.

(A) **Vitamins A.** Vitamin A was first recognised as a growth-promoting factor in cod-liver oil and in butter (McCollum and Davis, Osborne and Mendel, 1913–5), and subsequently shown to be necessary for the maintenance of epithelial tissue and the visual activity of the retina. It is a derivative of β-ionone and carries a side-chain terminating in a primary alcohol group. Vitamin A does not occur in plants, but can be obtained indirectly by the animal from provitamin carotenoids in the diet. These carotenoids contain the -ionone nucleus, and are represented chiefly by the carotenes, a-, β-, and γ-, and by cryptoxanthin, present in all green plants and many pigmented roots. The formulæ of these compounds are given on pp. 169–170.

Conversion of the provitamins into the vitamin takes place in the mucosa of the small intestine, and the absorbed vitamin is esterified and stored principally in the liver. A related form, A_2, occurs in freshwater fish.

Properties. Vitamin A is a yellow oil, freely soluble in fats and fat-solvents. It is stable to acids and alkalies. Mild oxidation converts it into vitamin A aldehyde, or *retinene*, in which form it occurs in the retina. Stronger oxidation inactivates it, and in this way it can be separated from the more stable vitamins D. Preparations of vitamin A can be preserved by addition of anti-oxidants, such as vitamin E and hydroquinone. Industrial hydrogenation of oils to form solid fats results in the destruction of vitamin A and the provitamins. Vitamin A shows a characteristic absorption band in the ultra-violet, the maximum wavelength of which is 326 mμ, in ethanol, and 332 mμ, in chloroform. This enables the vitamin to be detected and estimated. Because of the double-bonds, *cis-trans* isomers of the vitamin and the provitamin carotenoids exist. Natural vitamin A_1 is chiefly the all-*trans* isomer.

Effects of Vitamin A Deficiency. The vitamin is essential for vertebrates, all of which can convert the provitamin carotenoids into A, but no vertebrate appears to be able to synthesise either the vitamin or the provitamins. The deficiency syndrome, avitaminosis A, is characterised by:

(1) *Failure of Growth.* This is obvious only in young animals. The growth-rate falls off rapidly when the vitamin is withheld and the tissue-reserves have been exhausted. The animal continues to exist at a subnormal weight until secondary disturbances or infections develop.

(2) *Keratinisation of Epithelial Tissue.* The most characteristic sign of avitaminosis A is the change seen in the skin, mucous membranes and conjunctiva. Dryness of the skin is followed by a papular eruption caused by lack of secretion from the sebaceous glands of the hair follicles. This state of *phrynoderma*, or " toad skin ", has been recognised in Africa and in Asia as an early form of deficiency in human subjects.

(i) *Xerophthalmia*, or keratosis and ulceration of the cornea. The lachrymal secretion is diminished, and the conjunctiva becomes dry and inflamed. Secondary infections lead to ulcerations, which, by involving the anterior chamber, may terminate in total blindness.

While the infection is independent of the vitamin, the predisposing syndrome is characteristic of avitaminosis A, and in the early stages yields specifically to treatment.

(ii) *Gastro-enteritis.* The mucosa of the alimentary tract degenerates and the villi become necrosed. Ulceration of the stomach and intestines may set in subsequent to oral infection.

(iii) *Pharyngitis.* Keratinisation of the naso-pharyngeal epithelium predisposing to inflammation of the upper respiratory tract.

(iv) *Bone Abnormality and Nerve Degeneration.* Vitamin A controls the shape and moulding of growing bone, by influencing osteoblast and osteoclast activity. Avitaminosis A leads to malformation and thickening of the bones, which by compressing nerve structures in the vicinity can result in widespread peripheral and central nerve degeneration.

(3) *Nyctalopia* (night blindness) and *Hemeralopia* (day blindness). Before marked clinical signs appear, an early deficiency condition can be inferred from ocular changes leading to loss of vision in dim light, and terminating in degeneration of the retina and optic nerve. The condition was endemic in Newfoundland, and was treated empirically by fish liver, a prescription adopted successfully by Tobit some three thousand years ago.

Metabolism of Vitamin A in the Retina. The rods of the retina contain a lipoprotein, *rhodopsin*, or visual purple, which is photosensitive and takes part in the conversion of light energy into transmissible nerve stimuli. On exposure to light, rhodopsin is bleached by conversion to *lumi-rhodopsins* (*transient orange*, changing by loss of an electron to *indicator yellow*), which break-down to a protein, *scotopsin*, and *retinene*, the aldehyde of *trans*-vitamin A. Retinene is reduced to *trans*-vitamin A by the retinal enzyme retinene reductase. *Trans*-vitamin A is unable to rejoin the cycle until it has been isomerised to *cis*-vitamin A by an isomerase present in the retina and liver. On dehydrogenation, *cis*-vitamin A forms *cis*-retinene, which recombines with scotopsin in absence of light to regenerate rhodopsin.

Rhodopsin is widely distributed, and occurs in the retinas of mammals,

Light
Rhodopsin ─────────────→ Lumi-rhodopsins
   ↑   ↖   ↗   ↓
Cis-Retinene   Scotopsin   *Trans*-Retinene
   ↑   ↓
Cis-Vitamin A ←───────── *Trans*-Vitamin A
                 ↕
             [liver]

Rhodopsin Cycle (Wald, 1935–).

marine fish, amphibians, and crustaceans. Percentage values for dry retinal tissue are: frog, 35; cattle, 14. A corresponding pigment, *porphyropsin*, occurs in the retina of freshwater vertebrates, and is formed from retinene 2, the aldehyde of vitamin A_2.

Iodopsin, or visual violet, a chromoprotein of *cis*-retinine and photopsin, occurs in the cones of the retina, which are the receptors for colour vision and vision in bright light. Iodopsin takes part in a cycle similar to that of rhodopsin but for the difference in the protein component. The specific effect of light in the visual cycles is the isomeric conversion of *cis*-retinene to *trans*-retinene, which releases it from its protein conjugate, to act as an electron donor.

Vitamin A Standard and Requirements. The International Unit, I.U., used for assay and administration is defined as the potency of 0·6 micrograms of crystalline β-carotene, which represents 0·3 μg. of the pure vitamin.

The minimum 24-hour requirement for the prevention of night-blindness in human subjects is of the order of 30 units per kg. body weight. Allowing a 50 per cent. safety margin for inadequate absorption, the adult 24-hour requirement is assessed at 2,500 to 5,000 units; the requirements of pregnant and lactating women and young children are 6,000 to 8,000 units. On an adequate intake, vitamin values for the human liver are about 200 units per gm., and for the blood plasma 120 units per 100 ml. In the body the vitamin circulates and is stored chiefly in the form of esters.

Vitamin A and Provitamin A Values of Food Materials

Source.	Units per Gram.	Daily Need Equivalent.
Fish liver oils	500 to 50,000	60 mg. to 12 gm.
Cod liver oil	600 to 2,000	1 gm. to 10 gm.
Liver, beef	75 to 1,500	1·5 gm. to 112 gm.
Butter	10 to 100	30 gm. to 1 kg.
Milk, cow	0·8 to 2·5	1 litre →
Maize, yellow	20 to 150	15 gm. to 400 gm.
Green leaves	5 to 100	60 gm. to 1 kg.
Carrot	120	20 gm.

185

Potent natural sources of A are halibut-liver oil (1·5 per cent.), tuna-liver oil (4·5 per cent.) and high-grade cod-liver oil. Satisfactory dietary sources are butter, cream, cheese, and liver. The provitamins are well represented in apricot, carrot, lettuce, spinach and other green vegetables, and egg-yolk. As a guide, the chlorophyll content is roughly proportional to the carotene content, hence the green outer leaves of lettuce and cabbage are better sources of provitamins than the pale inner leaves. The vitamin content of animal food materials is dependent on the carotene content of the animal's diet. Milk contains both carotene and vitamin A, depending on species and season of the year.

To yield vitamin A in nutrition, a carotenoid must contain a β-ionone nucleus. Substituted rings, such as occur in zeaxanthin and lutein, render the carotenoid unavailable. This is a defect of the important feeding stuff, Indian corn or maize, which contains more zeaxanthin than carotene or cryptoxanthin. The unsaturated structure of the carotenes renders them liable to oxidative inactivation. Thus the carotene value for fresh pasture grass is 42 mg. to 56 mg. per kg. dry weight, while that for hay is only 0·01 to 0·6 mg.

Hypervitaminosis A. Ingestion of excessive amounts daily of vitamin A (500,000 units, by infants; 2,000,000 units, by adults) induces a syndrome characterised by hepatic dysfunction, nausea, lethargy, dermatitis, and skeletal overgrowth. The condition has been observed among Eskimos on diets rich in polar bear liver, which can contain 15,000 units per gram.

Assay of Vitamin A and Provitamins A. (1) *Biological.* Young animals, usually rats, are kept on standard diets deficient only in the vitamin and provitamins until their weight starts to decline. Known amounts of the test material then are given to one group of animals, and the effect on the growth rate recovery is compared with that of other groups of animals to whose diets have been added known amounts of the vitamin.

(2) *Spectrometric.* Estimation of the extinction coefficient of the absorption band in the ultra-violet.

(3) *Colorimetric.* Measurement of the absorption regions in the antimony trichloride reaction (pp. 171–172).

(4) *Physiological.* Measurement of the time required for dark-adaptation to enable a subject to recognise a dimly-lit diagram provides an index of vitamin deficiency and response to treatment.

VITAMINS D

(B) **Calciferols.** Contemporary records and paintings show that rickets was prevalent in parts of Europe during the sixteenth century. In 1650 Glisson published the first description of the disease as a clinical entity distinct from other bone deformities. During the intervening years cod-liver oil became recognised as a remedy. In 1906 Hopkins suggested that rickets was a deficiency disease, caused by lack of an anti-rachitic factor in the diet. This was found to be present in the unsaponifiable fraction obtained from liver oils and butter, and, unlike vitamin A, was not destroyed by aeration at 120° (Mellanby, 1919; McCollum, 1922).

The value of solar and ultra-violet irradiation in the treatment of rickets had been known for many years, when in 1924 Hess and Steenbock, independently, showed that inert or low-potency food materials could be rendered anti-rachitic by irradiation. This property was shown to reside in the sterol fraction. The first provitamin D to be recognised was ergosterol, obtained from ergot or yeast, and the corresponding vitamin was named D_2, or *calciferol* (Rosenheim and Webster; Pohl and Windaus, 1925-7). The Vitamin in liver oils, D_3, or *cholecalciferol*, is the commonest of the D vitamins, and is derived from 7-dehydrocholesterol. Other provitamins and vitamins D exist, but have not the biological importance of cholecalciferol or the industrial importance of D_2, now renamed *ergocalciferol*, which is the common synthetic form of the vitamin. The structural formulæ of these compounds are given on pp. 141–142.

Properties. D_2, $C_{28}H_{43}.OH$, is isomeric with ergosterol; D_3, $C_{27}H_{43}.OH$, is isomeric with 7-dehydrocholesterol. Both vitamins are colourless, odourless crystalline compounds, soluble in fats and fat-solvents and insoluble in water. Like the other D vitamins, they show a characteristic ultra-violet absorption spectrum with one maximum at 265 mμ, by which they can be detected and estimated.

Effects of Vitamin D Deficiency. The calciferols regulate calcium and phosphate distribution by promoting calcium absorption from the intestine, calcification by the osteoblasts of skeletal tissue, and phosphate retention by the body. Avitaminosis D is characterised by: (1) *Subnormal phosphate level in the plasma.* The plasma inorganic phosphate values of 7·5 to 13·5 mg. PO_4 per 100 ml., or 2·5 to 4·5 mg. P per 100 ml., in human adults, and 12 to 18 mg. PO_4 per 100 ml., or 4 to 6 mg. P per 100 ml., in children may fall below 6 mg. PO_4 per 100 ml., or 2 mg. P per 100 ml. in untreated rickets and osteo-malacia. (2) *Subnormal calcium level in the plasma.* The total calcium value may fall from its normal level of about 10 mg. per 100 ml. to half this amount. Values below 7 mg. induce hypocalcæmic tetany unless the fall has been so gradual that the organism has become adapted to the lower level. (3) *Decrease in the Ca × PO_4 product in plasma.* Rickets cannot occur if the product Ca (in mg. per 100 ml. plasma) × PO_4 (in mg. P per 100 ml.) is above 40. Severity and rapidity of onset depend on the extent to which the product falls below 36. (4) *Decrease in the excretion of phosphate and calcium by the kidney.* (5) *Increase in the excretion of phosphate and calcium by the intestine.* These conditions are ascribed to defective absorption from the alimentary tract, the contents of which tend to become more alkaline in the absence of vitamin D.

Pathological Conditions Associated with Vitamin D Deficiency

(i) *Rickets.* This disease, characterised by defective ossification of the growing skeleton, is determined by five ætiological factors: (1) the calcium content of the dietary; (2) the phosphate content of the dietary, including the phosphoproteins; (3) the supply of vitamin D; (4) the degree of exposure to ultraviolet irradiation; (5) the decalcifying agents in the dietary, the most important of which is *phytic acid*, a constituent of the outer coatings of cereal grain, and present in bran and high-extraction flour. It accounts for the severe form of rickets that follows excessive consumption of cereals, uncompensated by adequate supplies of vitamin D, Ca^{++} and PO_4'''.

(ii) *Osteomalacia*. A disease rare in Europe but common among women in certain parts of China. It is an adult form of rickets, and is characterised by de-calcification of the skeleton developing during the later months of pregnancy, when the resources of the mother are being exhausted to supply the fœtus. The domestic proverb: " For every child, a tooth," is a recognition of this sur-tax imposed by ignorance on maternity.

(iii) *Dental Defects*. Consequent on delayed eruption of the permanent teeth and imperfect calcification, the tendency to caries is increased. There is no evidence, however, that vitamin D has any protective effect on the fully-formed teeth. The target and the mode of action of the calciferols are uncertain. They can maintain blood calcium and phosphate levels in animals on diets deficient in both these nutrients; this may be because the action of the calciferol is localised in the bones, and by promoting the release of inorganic phosphate from phospholipids and other organic sources they direct the calcium and phosphate traffic.

Vitamin D Standard and Requirements. The International Unit is the potency of 0·025 micrograms of crystalline D_2; therefore by definition 1 mg. of D_2 is equivalent to 40,000 I.U. D_3, the natural vitamin, is slightly more potent than D_2 in man and other mammals, and nearly a hundred times more potent in the chick, an important difference in poultry feeding.

The vitamin is required principally during the period of skeletal growth. The 24-hour requirement of human subjects under one year is 400 to 800 units; between the ages of one to twenty it is 400 units. The requirements of the adult are unknown. Provided the diet is adequate as regards calcium and phosphate, and is free from excess of calcium-precipitants, such as phytic acid, the individual appears to be able to meet his own needs for the vitamin by making D_3 while the sun shines. Higher animals in a similar way obtain D_3 by the action of sunlight on the 7-dehydrocholesterol present in the skin or fur oil, whence it is absorbed into the blood or licked-off and ingested.

The vitamin-synthesising region of the spectrum extends from 256 mμ to 313 mμ. Because of atmospheric absorption, the shortest solar radiations reaching the earth are about 290 mμ. For this reason avitaminosis D is a hazard to children living in Northern latitudes and dwellers in city areas where the sunlight available during winter months is insufficient, and the soda glass used in window panes is opaque to rays shorter than 330 mμ. In these circumstances it is necessary to ensure that the diet contains vitamins D.

Sources. Vitamin D_3, like vitamin A, is concentrated in the liver lipids of fishes, the amount varying with species and season. Important dietary sources are butter, cream, and egg-yolk. Vegetables as a class are free from vitamins D, though products, such as oleo-margarine may be fortified by addition of synthetic D_2.

Vitamin D_3 Values of Food Materials

Source.	Units per gram.
Liver oils:	
Tuna	40,000
Halibut	1,200 to 2,000
Cod	40 to 200
Egg-yolk	300
Butter	0·08 to 1·2
Milk:	
Cow	5 to 45 per quart
Human	60 per quart
Colostrum	160 per quart

Hypervitaminosis D. Large doses of ergocalciferol, up to 2 mg. per 24 hours, may be beneficial in treatment of *Lupus vulgaris* and some forms of arthritis. Continued high dosage (3·5 mg. per 24 hours) evokes a rise in the blood calcium level, even when calcium is excluded from the diet, and results in a syndrome characterised by nausea, muscular weakness and, eventually, calcification in the kidneys and blood vessels.

Assay of Vitamins D. (1) *Biological.* The vitamin can be detected and estimated by comparing the anti-rachitic potency of the sample with that of a known standard preparation. Potency can be measured by ability to promote the calcification of the bones of young animals (rats or dogs) on rachitogenic diets, free from vitamin D, poor in phosphate but rich in calcium. Response can be detected radiographically by evidence of calcification in the epiphyses of the long bones, and also by rise in the blood phosphate level. Alternatively, the fixation of phosphate as bone salt can be measured, after injection of radioactive phosphate.

(2) *Spectrometric.* Measurement of the extinction coefficient of the characteristic absorption band at 265 mμ.

Vitamins E

The importance of an anti-sterility factor in nutrition was demonstrated in 1922–3 independently by Evans and by Sure, who found that rats reared on standard diets, supplemented by cod-liver oil and yeast, grew normally but became infertile. Fertility could be restored by inclusion in the diet of lettuce leaves, entire cereals, egg-yolk, or beef liver. The factor concerned was isolated from wheat-germ oil (Evans, 1936), and named tocopherol (Gk. *tokos*, child-

189

birth). Subsequently, three closely-related compounds were obtained from other sources, and included in a class of vitamins E, or tocopherols.

Structure. The tocopherols are derived from a double-ring parent, *tocol*, which is a chromane nucleus with a methyl group and a C_{16} side-chain at 2, and a hydroxyl group at 6.

Chromane.   α-Tocopherol.

$$R = -(CH_2)_3-CH(CH_3)-(CH_2)_3-CH(CH_3)-(CH_2)_3-CH(CH_3)_2$$

α-Tocopherol is 5,7,8-trimethyltocol; β-tocopherol is 5,8-dimethyltocol; γ-tocopherol is 7,8-dimethyltocol; δ-tocopherol is 8-monoethyltocol.

The tocopherols are yellow oils, insoluble in water, but soluble in fats and fat-solvents. On mild oxidation, the oxygen ring is reversibly opened, forming a quinone.

Effects of Vitamin E Deficiency. The popular description of tocopherol as the anti-sterility vitamin is misleading, for, although it is essential for the maintenance of the reproductive process in certain species, it is not any more important in ensuring fertility than vitamin A.

(1) *Reproductive System.* In the female, vitamin E deficiency does not obviously affect the œstrus cycle or the implantation of the ovum, but induces fœtal death at an early stage, consequent on defects in the allantois and yolk sac. Hens fed on diets lacking in vitamin E produce eggs that are infertile because of death of the embryo.

In male animals vitamin E deficiency results in degeneration of the germ-cell tissue during the onset of sexual maturity and causes permanent sterility. These effects on the reproductive system have been demonstrated only in some species (rat, rabbit, guinea pig) and there is no evidence that the human subject requires an external supply of the vitamin, or that it is of specific therapeutic value.

(2) *Muscular System.* An early sign of vitamin E dificiency in many species is degeneration of the uterine and skeletal muscles, accompanied by the excretion of muscle metabolites in the urine: creatine, methylhistidine. The condition resembles the pathological muscular dystrophies, but responds unambiguously to administration of the vitamin.

(3) *Redox Effects.* Vitamins E can act as anti-oxidants and in this way can protect vitamin A and the carotenoids, and also may participate in metabolic systems involving reduction and oxidation. This *redox* property is attributed to the ability of the oxygen bridge in the chromane to open up, forming a hydroquinone.

190

Vitamin E Standard and Requirements. The International Unit is the potency of 1 mg. of α-tocopherol acetate, which is the average daily amount required to maintain fertility in a rat on a tocopherol-free diet. Rich sources, in units per gm., are: wheat germ oil, 2 to 10; wheat germ, 0·15 to 0·8; cotton seed oil, 0·1 to 0·5; fresh lettuce leaf, 0·02 to 0·1. Animal products are poor in the vitamin, and it is absent from the liver oils of fish. The status of vitamin E in human nutrition is obscure. A normal adult human body contains 3 to 8 gm., dissolved in the storage lipid; and, as the average diet provides 10 to 25 mg. daily, deficiency conditions are unlikely to be widespread. A supplementary intake of 10 to 50 mg. daily during the latter half of pregnancy has been advocated.

Assay of Vitamin E. Biological methods are based on the ability of the vitamin to establish fertility in 50 per cent. of colonies of young rats on diets lacking tocopherols but otherwise adequate. Spectrophotometric methods depend on measurement of absorption maximum, 294 mμ.

Vitamins K

In 1934, Dam and Schønheyder described a deficiency disease in chicks, characterised by anæmia, increased blood-coagulation time, pathological changes in the gizzard, and tendency to hæmorrhage. The condition was traced to the lack of a specific fat-soluble, alkali-labile but thermostable factor, vitamin K.

The vitamin was isolated, in 1939, by Dam, Karrer *et al.*, and a related vitamin, K$_2$, was isolated by Doisy *et al.*

Structure of Vitamins K. Both are derivatives of 1,4-*naphthoquinone*, in which there is a methyl group at position 2, and either a *phytyl* group (K$_1$) or a *difarnesyl* group (K$_2$) at position 3. Unlike vitamins E, the long-side chain is not necessary for activity, and can be effectively replaced by H, as in the synthetic K vitamin, 2-*methyl*-1,4-*naphthoquinone*, or *menadione*, which is three times as potent as K$_1$.

1,4-Naphthoquinone.   Vitamins K.

$$K_1, R = -CH_2.CH=C-(CH_2)_3-CH-(CH_2)_3-CH-(CH_2)_3-CH.CH_3$$

with CH$_3$ groups below.

$$K_2, R = -CH_2.CH=C-CH_2-(CH_2-CH=C-CH_2)_4-CH_2-CH=C.CH_3$$

with CH$_3$ groups below.

Effects of Vitamin K Deficiency. In higher animals, the 2-methyl-naphtho-quinone nucleus, present in all forms of vitamin K, is necessary for the production of prothrombin, a factor in blood coagulation, which is made in the liver and circulated in the plasma. When supplies of the vitamin are inadequate, the prothrombin level in the plasma falls and the coagulation time of the blood is prolonged, thereby increasing the potential dangers of hæmorrhage.

Sources. K_1, or phylloquinone, occurs in green leafy vegetables and grasses (spinach, cabbage, alfalfa) and tomato, but not to any important extent in other fruits, tubers, or roots. K_2, which was isolated originally from decaying fish meal, is produced by many species of bacteria, including those of the animal intestine, but not by yeast. Menadione, 2-methyl-1,4-naphtho-quinone the synthetic form of the vitamin, is three times as active as K_1 or K_2. Because of their low solubility, vitamins K require transport by the bile acids for their absorption from the intestine. Consequently, hypoprothrom-binæmia and tendency to hæmorrhage can occur in conditions of obstructive jaundice, and chronic intestinal disorders. It also can arise from prothrombin deficiency in both child and mother at parturition, and is responsible for fatal hæmorrhages. Hypoprothrombinæmia can be remedied by daily doses of 1 to 2 mg. of menadione. As a protection, the maternal diet during the later months of pregnancy should include ample supplies of K_1 in its natural state.

Assay of Vitamin K. Methods are based on the amount of the sample required to shorten the blood-coagulation time to less than 10 minutes in 15-day chicks that have been on diets free from vitamin K since hatching. For this, 0.3 μg. of menadione is sufficient.

α-Lipoic Acid

After complete removal of water-soluble vitamins and other solutes from yeast and liver preparations, extraction of the residual material with fat solvents yields a fraction that can stimulate growth in bacteria and protozoa. The active component is a cyclic disulphide, α-lipoic acid, or thioctic acid, which can be formed by reversible dehydrogenation of 6,8-dithiocaprylic acid, $H_2C(SH).CH_2.CH(SH).CH_2.CH_2.CH_2.CH_2.COOH$ (Gunsalus, 1953; Reed, 1953).

$$\begin{array}{cccc} CH_2 & CH_2 & CH_2 & COOH \\ / \ \ \ \ \backslash & / \ \ \ \ \backslash & / \ \ \ \ \backslash & / \\ H_2C \ \ \ \ \ CH & CH_2 & CH_2 \\ | \ \ \ \ \ \ \ \ \ \ \ | \\ S———S \end{array}$$

α-Lipoic acid.

Lipoic acid is required for the oxidative decarboxylation of pyruvic acid in cells, and for CO_2 fixation during photosynthesis. It acts as a collector of acetyl units, $H_3C.CO$—, generated in decarboxylations, and transfers them to co-enzyme A. Although of fundamental importance in tissue metabolisms, lipoic acid has not been shown to be necessary in the diet of higher animals and hence is not regarded as a typical vitamin.

II. WATER-SOLUBLE VITAMINS

(a) Co-enzyme Class

Industrial yeast, liver, cereal germ and bran contain a mixture of chemically-unrelated, water-soluble vitamins, collectively described as the " B group " the designation B, later B_1, having been applied to the first member to be recognised, the anti-neuritic factor that protects against beri-beri. All or most of these vitamins are components of co-enzymes necessary for the metabolism of carbohydrates, proteins, and lipids. They are of very wide biological significance, and are produced by various micro-organisms, some of which colonise the alimentary tract of man and other animals. They can be detected and estimated by methods of micro-biological assay, by observing the growth-promoting effect on cultures of micro-organisms in media lacking the particular vitamin under investigation.

(1) B_1, Thiamine

Structure. B_1 was isolated as the chloride of a quaternary nitrogen base $(C_{12}H_{17}ON_4S)^+$, from rice bran (Jansen and Donath, 1926), and yeast (Windaus, 1931; Kinnersley, O'Brien, and Peters, 1932). In 1936 Williams showed that it was assembled from 2-methyl-6-aminopyrimidine and a thiazole ring, and, since it contained sulphur, it was named *thiamine*. Salts of B_1 are very soluble in water, and insoluble in fat solvents. The vitamin is stable in acid solutions, but is inactivated by boiling at pH 5·5. Oxidation converts it to *thiochrome*, a yellow pigment with a blue fluorescence.

Thiamine Base.

Significance. Thiamine pyrophosphate, or *co-carboxylase*, in which the hydroxyl group in the thiazole ring side-chain has been replaced by —O—PO(OH)—O—PO(OH)$_2$, is the operative form of the vitamin, and acts as the co-enzyme in the enzyme-catalysed reactions involving release of CO_2 from pyruvic and from a-oxoglutaric acids. These reactions are of two types: (1) *Simple decarboxylation*, as occurs in yeast and other micro-organisms under anaerobic conditions:

$$Pyruvic\ acid\ CH_3.CO.COOH \longrightarrow CO_2 + CH_3.CHO\ Acetaldehyde$$

(2) *Oxidative decarboxylation*, as occurs in animal tissues, and involves the transfer of an unstable radical, such as acetyl, $CH_3.CO$—. These decarboxylations require an additional factor, *co-enzyme* A, derived from the vitamin *pantothenic acid*.

By these decarboxylations, end-products of anaerobic metabolism of glucose and aliphatic acids are made available for complete combustion by aerobic systems. Hence, thiamine deficiency both depresses metabolism by decreasing the supply of fuel, and also results in accumulation of pyruvate or other α-oxo (α-keto) acids in the tissues.

Effects of Vitamin B_1 Deficiency. (i) *Beri-beri*. This disease is endemic among the rice-eating communities of the East, including India, the Malay Peninsula and Japan, where the diet is almost entirely restricted to rice that has been " polished " by removal of the outer husk to improve storage qualities. Beri-beri also appears among wheat-eating communities, such as those of Labrador and Newfoundland, who subsist mainly on refined wheat flour. Infantile beri-beri is a direct consequence of a vitamin deficiency in the diet of the nursing mother, and is responsible for a large part of the enormous infantile mortality of India and the East in general. Beri-beri is a polyneuritis characterised by loss of muscular co-ordination, gradual paralysis of the limbs, alimentary disturbances (indigestion, constipation and colitis), degeneration of the heart muscle, and general emaciation, often associated with dropsy.

(ii) *Avian Polyneuritis*. When birds are fed on an exclusive diet of polished rice and water no ill effects are seen for several weeks. Then signs of acute polyneuritis appear rapidly. The bird is unable to fly, to walk, and, eventually, to stand. Exhaustion and death follow in a few days unless the vitamin be supplied. Recovery is dramatic.

The key observation on the association of polished rice with beri-beri and avian polyneuritis was made by the Dutch physician, Eijkman, when in Java, in 1897. He noticed that domestic fowl fed on the polished rice developed the same type of neuritic disorder as that found among prison inmates on the same dietary, whereas birds fed on unpolished rice were free from the disease. Grijns (1901), his colleague, concluded that the disease was due to a deficiency, a negative factor, and not a positive infection or toxin. Similar and independent conclusions were reached by Frazer and Stanton, working in the Malay Peninsula (1909), and by Chamberlain, in the Philippine Islands (1910). Twenty years later, Peters observed that oxidation of pyruvate and lactate is subnormal in brain tissue from vitamin B_1 deficient pigeons, and thus found the clue to the significance of B_1 in metabolism.

(iii) *Bradycardia*. This is a slowing of the heart-beat owing to sinus changes, and responds rapidly to vitamin therapy. It is a feature of rat beri-beri. The phenomenon has been used by Birch and Harris (1934) for the electrocardiographic assay of vitamin preparations. Rats that have been depleted of vitamin B_1 are fed, under controlled conditions, with graded doses of the test materials, and the resulting cardiac response is observed. In infants and human adults, a tachycardia, or increased heart rate, on slight exertion, is evoked by B_1 deficiency.

(iv) *Gastro-intestinal Dysfunction.* Impairment of appetite, decreased motility of the stomach and loss of tonus, subnormal temperature, anhydræmia, and decreased resistance to fatigue go to constitute a syndrome arising from disturbed co-ordination in the movements of the alimentary tract and, possibly, from changes in the pattern of the intestinal micro-flora.

Vitamin B_1 Standard and Requirements. The International Unit is the potency of 3 μg. of crystalline thiamine chloride hydrochloride. Values for rich sources, in units per gm., are: brewer's yeast, dry, 6 to 23; wheat germ, 6 to 19; wheat, entire, 2·3 to 3·4; rice bran, 5·6 to 7·6; beans, dry, 1·4; egg-yolk, 1·4; kidney and liver, raw, 0·9 to 3·4. As the synthetic vitamin is now available, requirements and supplies are expressed usually in terms of milligrams. The animal need depends chiefly on the quantity of glucose being metabolised, each gram of which requires about 2·4 μg. of thiamine. A properly balanced adult dietary should provide 0·5 mg. B_1 for each 1,000 kilocalories intake daily, with a minimum of 1 mg. For children, the daily requirement ranges from 0·4 mg. for infants, up to 1·2 for children of 12 years. In subjects on an adequate intake, the thiamine level in the blood is about 5 μg. per 100 ml., and the urinary output is 0·1 to 0·3 mg. per 24 hours.

Vitamin B_1 in Plant Growth. Thiamine is essential in plant metabolism. Some green plants and fungi are autotrophic in that they synthesise sufficient for their complete needs. Many bacteria, yeasts and fungi are heterotrophic as regards thiamine, and require an external supply. This apparently universal demand for the vitamin is associated with the universal employment of glucose as a source of energy, and is evidence of the common chemical ancestry of organic life.

Assay of Vitamin B_1. *Biological tests* include: (1) cure of retracted neck in pigeons rendered polyneuritic by a diet of polished rice and water; (2) cure of convulsive paralysis or of bradycardia in rats on deficient diets; (3) stimulation of growth of yeasts and moulds in standard thiamine-free media; (4) Increase in the rate of alcoholic fermentation of glucose by yeast. *Chemical tests* include oxidation by alkaline ferricyanide with production of thiochrome, and measurement of its fluorescence in ultra-violet irradiation.

(2) Riboflavin

The " water-soluble B " factor present in milk possesses growth-promoting and anti-dermatitis properties not displayed by vitamin B_1. These were attributed to a second vitamin, B_2, but closer investigation has shown that they are the combined effects of a group of vitamins, and the designation B_2 is now abandoned, or restricted to one member of the group, **riboflavin.**

Properties. Riboflavin, $C_{17}H_{20}N_4O_6$, is an orange-yellow crystalline compound, insoluble in fat solvents, slightly soluble in water and in ethanol, and freely soluble in alkalies. The aqueous solution is greenish-yellow and displays a vivid yellow-green fluorescence which is discharged by acids. The vitamin is assembled from the cyclic base, *iso*-alloxazine, and the sugar alcohol, ribitol. It is the chief representative of the flavin pigments present in the biosphere. Its structure is described on pp. 172–173.

Functions. Riboflavin-5'-phosphate, free as **flavin mononucleotide**, FMN, or combined with adenosine phosphate as **flavin adenine dinucleotide**, FAD, constitutes two of the principal co-enzymes concerned in the transfer of hydrogen from food metabolites. The reactions are catalysed by a family of dehydrogenases which, when combined in working partnership with FMN or FAD, are described as the flavoproteins, or " yellow enzymes ".

Effects of Riboflavin Deficiency. The operational field of the vitamin is wide-spread, and the effects of deficiency, *ariboflavinosis*, are liable to be obscured. Diagnostic signs are: (1) *Cheilosis*, pallor and fissure of the mucosa in the angle of the lips; (2) abnormal redness and swelling of the tongue (glossitis) and lips; (3) ocular lesions, including capillary invasion of the cornea, conjunctivitis, and hypersensitivity to light (photophobia); (4) scaly desquamation of the skin about the ears and nose.

Sources and Requirements. The flavoprotein enzymes are universally distributed, and are concentrated in yeasts, fermenting bacteria, and in liver. Representative riboflavin values in μg per gm. are: yeast, dry, 20 to 54; liver, kidney, 20 to 30; eggs, 3 to 6; cheese, 5; green vegetables, 0·6 to 2·4; wheat, entire, 0·2 to 1; milk, 1·7.

The human daily requirements are not known precisely; recommended mg. amounts are: children, 0·9 to 1·8 mg., adolescents, 2 to 2·5; adults, 1·5 to 2; pregnant and lactating women, 2·5 to 3.

The availability of the vitamin differs in different sources; free riboflavin, such as occurs in milk, is more rapidly absorbed than flavin nucleotides, from tissues, which require preliminary hydrolysis. The free vitamin is unstable in alkaline solution and is inactivated by exposure to strong light.

Ariboflavinosis is unlikely to arise on an ordinary mixed diet; one pint of milk or three ounces of liver can supply the entire daily need.

Assay of Riboflavin. Biological methods are based on the growth response of young rats or chicks on a riboflavin-free diet, or on the lactic acid production by standard cultures of *Lactobacillus casei*, before and after addition of the sample. Fluorimetric methods are based on the intensity of the fluorescence, which shows a maximum at 565 mμ in solutions at pH 6.

(3) Nicotinic Acid and Nicotinamide

Pellagra-preventing Vitamins. Pellagra (Italian, *rough skin*) is a condition known in Italy, Rumania, South Russia, and the Southern States of America. Described by Aykroyd as " perhaps the most horrible of all food deficiency diseases ", it is characterised by dermatitis, pigmentation and thickening of the skin, inflammation of the tongue and intestinal tract, and nervous disorders leading to atrophic paralysis and dementia. A corresponding condition, known as " black tongue " can occur in dogs. The pioneer work of Goldberger between 1910 and 1930 showed that endemic pellagra is a poverty disease, and can be abolished by diets in which maize, the principal ingredient, was replaced or supplemented by fresh meat and wheat products.

Goldberger attributed the disease to lack of a " pellagra-preventing " factor, which he was able to supply by adding yeast or liver to the diet. The factor was isolated and identified by Elvehjem, in 1937, as nicotinic acid amide; its immediate precursor, nicotinic acid, is equally effective. The names nicotinamide, or niacinamide, are used, popularly, for the vitamin, and niacin, for the provitamin.

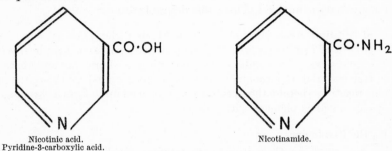

Nicotinic acid.
Pyridine-3-carboxylic acid.

Nicotinamide.

Functions. Nicotinamide is a component of two co-enzymes that are widely distributed in plants and animals: diphosphopyridine nucleotide, DPN, and triphosphopyridine nucleotide, TPN. These pyridine nucleotides act as transporters of hydrogen and electrons in cellular metabolism.

Sources and Requirements. The higher animal appears to have three sources of the vitamin: local synthesis in the liver and possibly other tissues; synthesis by the micro-flora of the alimentary tract; preformed nicotinamide in the diet. The precursor of all these supplies is the amino acid tryptophan, and when tryptophan is deficient in the diet the animal is compelled to rely on external sources of the vitamin. Endemic pellagra is conditioned both by a lack of tryptophan in the diet, in which maize is the chief source of protein, and by the absence of natural foods rich in nicotinamide.

Representative values, in μg. nicotinamide per gm., are: yeast, dry, 500 to 650; liver, 120 to 160; wheat, entire, 50 to 60; meat, kidney, pork, 40 to 60; eggs, milk, 10.

Because of the alternative sources, it is difficult to assess the human requirements of dietary nicotinamide, or to specify precisely the signs of deficiency. The syndrome in pellagra is liable to be complicated by other vitamin deficiencies. On a normal diet the healthy human adult excretes in the urine 0·25 to 1·2 mg. nicotinic acid, 0·5 to 4 mg. nicotinamide, and 3 to 12 mg. of the metabolite, N-methylnicotinic acid amide. This suggests that, independent of the activity of the micro-flora, a daily intake of 4 to 12 mg. for children, and 10 to 18 mg. for adults, ensures an ample supply of nicotinamide. Satisfactory dietary sources are yeast concentrates and extracts, animal tissues, and bread from high-extraction flour. Milk and eggs are poor sources and the synthetic vitamin is available in quantity.

Nicotinic acid is less suitable for clinical administration, as it has an unpleasant vaso-dilator effect not shown by nicotinamide in moderate doses. When both the hydrogen atoms in the —NH_2 group of the amide are replaced by —C_2H_5, nicotinic acid N-diethylamide, or " nikethamide ", is obtained. It is a powerful cardiac and respiratory stimulant. *Nicotine*, the poisonous liquid alkaloid of the tobacco plant, yields nicotinic acid on oxidation, but the human body is unable to effect this desirable decomposition.

Assay of Nicotinic Acid. Microbiological methods include the measurement of the growth of *Proteus vulgaris* and the production of lactic acid by *Lactobacillus arabinosus*, grown under standard conditions in presence and absence of the test material. Colorimetric methods are represented by the cyanogen bromide reaction whereby the pyridine ring is opened up to form a chromogen that yields a yellow pigment with aniline.

(4) B_6, the Pyridoxines

During his search for the anti-pellagra vitamin, Goldberger observed that rats kept on deficient diets developed acrodynia, a symmetrical dermatitis of the extremities. The condition was not relieved by thiamine or riboflavin, but was cured specifically by a residual fraction, B_6, from yeast and rice bran. This fraction was found to owe its activity to three pyridine derivatives: *pyridoxine*, 2-methyl-3-hydroxy-4,5-di(hydroxymethyl) pyridine; *pyridoxamine*, the corresponding amine, in which —$CH_2.OH$ at 4 is replaced by —$CH_2.NH_2$; and *pyridoxal*, the corresponding aldehyde, in which —$CH_2.OH$ at 4 is replaced by —CHO.

These pyridine vitamins are interchangeable in animal nutrition, but not in the nutrition of some B_6-dependent organisms, and thus can be differentiated and assayed.

Significance. The operative form of the vitamins is pyridoxal phosphate, formed by esterification of the —$CH_2.OH$ group at 5, to produce —$CH_2.O.PO(OH)_2$. Pyridoxal phosphate is a co-enzyme concerned in *transamination*, the exchange of amino groups in amino acid metabolism. It is employed also by enzymes concerned in decarboxylations and dehydrations.
Sources and Requirements. Like the other vitamins of the co-enzyme class, B_6 is concentrated in cereal bran and germ, yeast and liver.

Values in mg. per 100 gm. fresh material are: yeast, dry, 4; wheat germ, 1 to 2; wheat, entire, 0·4; molasses, 0·3; liver, 0·2 to 0·7; muscle, green vegetables, milk, 0·1.

B_6 has been shown to be required by the chicken, dog, pig and rat, and, by inference, the human subject, whose daily need is believed to be 1 to 2 mg.

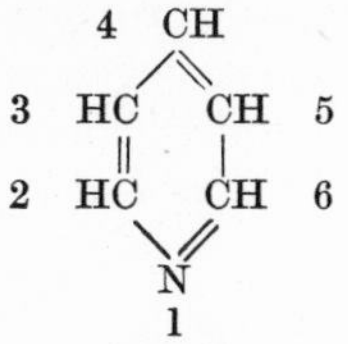

Pyridoxine, $R = -CH_2.OH$

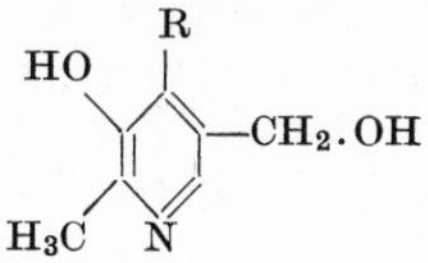

Pyridoxamine, $R = -CH_2.NH_2$

Pyridoxal, $R = -CHO$

Pyridine.   Vitamins B_6.

(5) Pantothenic Acid

Extracts of yeast, liver and bran contain a factor necessary for the growth of young birds and for the prevention of avian dermatitis. This factor had been recognised previously as a powerful stimulant of the growth of microorganisms. It was isolated and identified by Williams and Major in 1940 and, because of its universal distribution, was named pantothenic acid. It is a semi-peptide of *pantoic acid* 3,3-dimethyl-2,4-dihydroxybutyric acid,

$$HO.CH_2.C(CH_3)_2.CH(OH).COOH,$$

and the amino acid β-alanine, $H_2N.CH_2.CH_2.COOH$.

$$HO.CH_2.\overset{\overset{\displaystyle CH_3}{|}}{\underset{\underset{\displaystyle CH_3}{|}}{C}}.CH(OH) \;-CO-NH.CH_2.CH_2.COOH$$

Pantothenic Acid.
(Pantoyl-β-alanine).

Significance. In linkage with an adenosine triphosphate and thioethanol-amine, $HS.CH_2.CH_2.NH_2$, pantothenic acid forms **co-enzyme A,** or coA, one of the essential co-enzymes in animal and plant life. Co-enzyme A collects the acetyl units, $CH_3.CO$, liberated in the break-down of sugars and aliphatic acids, and feeds them to the citric cycle for complete combustion. It also takes part in various acetylating reactions, such as the formation of acetylcholine.

Sources and Requirements. The vitamin, chiefly in the form of co-enzyme A, is widespread in low concentrations. The richest known source is " royal jelly ", the food material that effects the metamorphosis of the queen bee from ordinary larvæ. Less exotic sources in human nutrition are yeast, cereal bran, kidney and liver.

Representative values, in mg. per 100 gm., are: yeast, dried, 20; liver, 5; eggs, 2·7; meat, oatmeal, entire wheat, 1 to 1·5; white bread, potato, tomato, spinach, 0·3 to 0·7.

The human requirement is unknown. In health, 2 to 5 mg. pantothenic acid are excreted in the urine per 24 hours, and daily intakes of 5 to 15 mg. have been recommended.

The signs of pantothenic deficiency are diffuse, and liable to be complicated by other vitamin deficiences. They differ in different species, but include: failure of growth, dermatitis (rat, chick); fur-depigmentation, or achromotricia (rat, fox, monkey); loss of hair, or alopecia (mouse, rat); nerve degeneration, paralysis (mouse, dog, pig). The vitamin is assayed micro-biologically by measuring the growth-effect on standard cultures of *Lactobacillus arabinosis.*

(6) Biotin

Rats on experimental diets in which raw egg-white is the only source of protein develop a severe dermatitis which can be cured by a factor present in yeasts, pollen, seeds, and liver, isolated and identified by Kögl and by du Vigneaud in 1942, and named *biotin.* It is a growth-stimulant for many micro-organisms. The toxic substance in the egg-white is a protein, *avidin,* which has the property of combining with biotin and rendering it unavailable for nutrition. On cooking the egg, this avidin effect is abolished.

Structure. Biotin contains a double-ring nucleus with a valeric acid side-chain, by means of which it is bound to amino acids or peptides, as in *biocytin,* a lysine semi-peptide.

$$
\begin{array}{c}
CO \\
HN \quad\quad NH \\
| \quad\quad\quad | \\
HC\text{---}CH \\
| \quad\quad\quad | \\
H_2C \quad\quad CH\text{---}(CH_2)_4CO.R \\
S
\end{array}
$$

Biotin, $R = -OH$

Biocytin, $R = -NH-(CH_2)_4.CH.COOH$
$\qquad\qquad\qquad\qquad\qquad\quad NH_2$

Significance. Biotin stimulates or is necessary for the growth of many micro-organisms, including the nitrogen-fixing *Rhizobium,* in root nodules. This was formerly described as the " co-enzyme R " effect. It is required in reversible decarboxylation reactions whereby CO_2 is captured or liberated. In higher animals, biotin is necessary for the production of citrulline from ornithine, during the process of urea synthesis, and thus is concerned with the detoxication and elimination of surplus amino nitrogen.

Effects of Biotin Deficiency. (1) *Dermatitis.* In man, extreme pallor of the skin and mucous membranes, followed by a dry dermatitis. A similar dermatitis developing in rats also shows a characteristic " spectacle " zone round the eyes.

(2) *Nitrogen disequilibrium,* accompanied by increased excretion of NH_4^+ in the urine, fall in body weight, lassitude, and somnolence, conditions that are relieved rapidly by injection of biotin.

Sources and Requirements. Biotin occurs free in milk and mostly peptide-bound in animal tissues.

Representative values, in mg. per 100 gm., are: yeast, dried, 0·2; liver, 0·1; egg-yolk, 0·04; entire wheat, milk, meat, 0·005.

Biotin is synthesised by the intestinal bacteria; consequently, its status in the human diet is difficult to define. Signs of deficiency evoked by raw egg-white or by intestinal antiseptics are removed rapidly by daily biotin injections of 0·1 to 0·3 mg. Because of its ability to act as a growth-stimulant for many different species of micro-organisms, a variety of micro-biological methods are available for assay.

(7) Folic Acids

In 1941, Mitchell obtained from extracts of spinach and other leaves a factor that stimulated the growth of *S. lactis* R and *L. casei*, organisms commonly used in micro-biological assay. Because of its source, it was designated " folic acid ". Related growth-stimulants, or " *L. casei* factors ", were found in yeast, liver, and meat extracts, and their structure was elucidated by Angier and others in 1946.

In the meantime these folic acids had been identified with the anti-anæmic factors found in yeast and in liver, and factors necessary for chicken growth and feathering.

Structure. The parent folic acid, *pteroic acid*, is a conjugate of a pteridine (p. 174) and *para*-aminobenzoic acid; the derivatives are linear peptides of pteroic acid or N-formylpteroic acid with one, three, or seven glutamic acid units (p. 109).

Significance. All the folic acids are effective in the treatment of nutritional macrocytic anæmia and other non-pernicious anæmias. The monopeptide, pteroyl glutamic acid, is curative in daily doses of 20 to 100 mg., by mouth or injection.

Para-aminobenzoic acid, $H_2N-C_6H_4.COOH$, (PAB), was recognised as a growth-stimulant for animals and micro-organisms prior to the discovery of the folic acids. How far it functions independently of them is obscure. It is very widely distributed, and is essential for the growth of some bacteria. Yeasts contain about 0·8 mg. per gm. The bacteriostatic effects of the sulphonamide drugs are neutralised by addition of *p*-aminobenzoate and, conversely, the therapeutic effects of sulphonamides in high concentration is attributed to their competition with *p*-aminobenzoate for possession of an intracellular enzyme system necessary for the growth of the infecting organisms.

Significance. The operative form of the vitamins appears to be *iso*-folinic acid, or N^{10}-**folinic acid,** in which the double bonds in the pyrazine part of the nucleus at 5 : 6 and 7 : 8 are hydrogenated, and the bridge nitrogen atom, N^{10}, carries a formyl group. *Iso*-folinic acid acts as a collector of single carbon units, such as *formyl*, —CH : O; *formimino*, —CH : NH; *hydroxymethyl*, —CH_2.OH, and transfers them to meet metabolic requirements in the synthesis of purines and some amino acids.

INTRODUCTION TO BIOCHEMISTRY

N^{10}-Folinic acid.
N^{10}-Formyl-5,6,7,8-tetrahydropteroylglutamic acid).
A = hydrogenated xanthopterin nucleus.
B = para-aminobenzoic radical.
C = glutamic acid radical.

Leucovorin, or N^5— folinic acid, in which the formyl group is attached to the nitrogen atom at position 5 in the pyrazine ring, was discovered independently as a growth factor for *Leuconostoc citrovorum*. It is ineffective as a donor of formyl units until transformed into the active N^{10} isomer.

Sources and Requirements. On ordinary diets the human subject excretes 130 to 550 micrograms of folic acids by the intestines daily, which is about six times as much as that supplied by the food. This indicates that the vitamin is provided chiefly by the activities of the intestinal micro-flora.

Dietary sources, in mg. per 100 gm., are: yeast, dry, 0·7; spinach, 0·1 to 0·2; liver, 0·08; peas, oatmeal, beef, entire wheat, 0·02 to 0·05.

Methods of micro-biological assay for the folic acids include the growth response of *L. casei* and *S. fœcalis*. Organisms differ in their specific demands for the vitamin complex. *Leuconostoc citrovorum* requires the complete folinic acid; *L. casei* is satisfied by pteroylglutamic acid; *S. lactis*, by pteroic acid; and *Clostridium acetobutylicum* demands only *para*-aminobenzoic acid. In consequence, growth-response can be exploited for the identification of the type of the vitamin as well as for its estimation.

(8) B_{12}, Cobalamins

In 1927 Minot and Murphy showed that raw liver contained a heat-stable substance capable of curing the usually fatal disease, pernicious anæmia. Victims of this anæmia tend to be deficient in gastric hydrochloric acid, and often derive benefit from preparations of gastric mucosa. In 1929 Castle postulated that the disease was the result of lack of an *extrinsic factor*, present in beef muscle, egg-yolk, yeast and milk, which required the action of an *intrinsic factor*, present in normal gastric juice, prior to absorption and storage in the liver. In 1948 the extrinsic factor was isolated from liver extracts by Lester Smith and by Folkers as a red, crystalline solid, containing 4 per cent. of cobalt. It was designated B_{12}, or cobalamin. Castle's intrinsic

202

factor is a heat-labile protein, which is some way promotes the absorption of dietary B_{12}. Hence, pernicious anæmia can arise either from lack of the vitamin or from defective gastric secretion.

Cobalamin, $C_{63}H_{90}O_{14}N_{14}P$ Co, has the most complicated structure of all the known vitamins. It contains a cobalt atom held centrally in a tetrapyrrole framework, and several modifications exist. In *cyanocobalamin*, the Co carries a cyanide residue, —CN; in *hydroxocobalamin*, or B_{12a}, the Co carries hydroxyl. Cobalamin is the most potent of all the vitamins. A daily injection of 3 μg. is sufficient to cure pernicious anæmia; given by mouth, the dose must be increased to 300 μg to allow for loss during absorption.

The vitamin is not present in higher plants, but is synthesised by some bacteria and moulds, notably *Streptomyces griseus*, which also produces the antibiotic *streptomycin*. The fact that cobalt is part of the vitamin may explain the need for this metal in the diet of animals, such as sheep, who depend on the activities of their intestinal micro-flora for their supplies of cobalamin.

The functions of the cobalamins are obscure. They are present in the stroma of the red corpuscles, but not in the contents of the corpuscle, and may be concerned in cellular construction. Unlike the folic acids, they are not very effective in the treatment of non-pernicious forms of anæmia, but they are specifically and uniquely effective in the treatment of the pernicious anæmia syndrome, which includes degeneration in the spinal cord, resulting in ataxia and paralysis.

Precise functions attributed to the cobalamins are: maturation of bone marrow megaloblasts, from which the red corpuscles are derived; chain-reactions concerned with the synthesis of pyrimidines, purines and nucleic acids; activation of other vitamins, including the folic acids.

(9) Vitamin C, Ascorbic Acid

The usefulness of fresh vegetables and citrus fruits, lemon, lime and orange in the prevention of scurvy was known to the Dutch sailors in the fifteenth century, and by this means the condition was avoided in the British Navy in the days of Nelson, when disease could be more dangerous than gun-fire. The subsequent replacement of fresh fruits by preserved lime juice, in which the vitamin content had been depleted by storage, led to loss of confidence in the belief that scurvy was a deficiency disease until it was shown that scurvy could be induced in guinea pigs by keeping them for three weeks on a diet of oats and bran, and could be cured by fresh fruits or vegetables (Holst and Frölich, 1907–12). The anti-scorbutic factor, designated vitamin C, was fractionated from lemon juice by Zilva and others (1918–), isolated by Waugh and King (1932), and shown to be identical with the " hexuronic acid " that Szent-Gyorgyi had isolated from adrenal glands, oranges, and cabbage, in 1928. It was synthesised, in 1933 (Hirst and Haworth, Reichstein), and renamed *ascorbic acid*.

Properties. Ascorbic acid, $C_6H_8O_6$, m.p. 192° is a colourless monobasic acid, freely soluble in water. It has an ene-diol structure, which makes it a powerful reducing agent, capable of bleaching indicator dyes and reducing silver salts in cold, acid solutions. It gives all the copper reduction tests of the reducing sugars. In aqueous solution, ascorbic acid undergoes atmospheric oxidation, a change promoted by traces of catalytic metals (Cu, Fe), light, or hydroxyl ions. This can be avoided by anti-oxidants, such as sulphite, or thiourea.

Fresh fruits and vegetables contain an enzyme, *ascorbic oxidase*, which contributes to the disappearance of the vitamin when plant products are macerated.

On oxidation, ascorbic acid loses two hydrogen atoms and is converted into *dehydro-ascorbic acid*, which is still biologically active, and can be reconverted into the vitamin by reducing agents, such as H_2S. In neutral or alkaline solution, dehydro-ascorbic acid is spontaneously hydrolysed to 2 : 3-diketo-L-gulonic acid, a derivative of the sugar L-gulose. This acid has no anti-scorbutic properties and cannot be reconverted into the vitamin by reduction. Since the vitamin is derived from the L-sugar, it is termed L-ascorbic acid. Its lævorotary isomer, D-ascorbic acid, has been synthesised and shown to be biologically inactive.

Vitamin C (L-ascorbic acid).	Dehydro- L-ascorbic acid.	2 : 3-diketo- L-gulonic acid.
Biologically Active.		Biologically Inactive.

Both forms of ascorbic acid are lactone derivatives of the substituted gulonic acid. When the lactone ring had been opened by hydrolysis, the vitamin is irreversibly inactivated, and readily oxidised to oxalic and L-threonic acid.

Sources. The synthetic vitamin is obtainable commercially. Other highly potent sources are concentrates prepared from black-currants and rose hips. Natural food sources are represented by citrus fruits and raw vegetables, especially tomato, celery, onion and rhubarb. The best animal sources are liver and fresh milk.

Root vegetables are poor in C; the potato, however, is important, because of the quantity eaten, which in some European communities is 1 to 2 lb. per person daily.

Representative Ascorbic acid values, in mg. per 100 gm. fresh material

Source.	Ascorbic Acid.	Source.	Ascorbic Acid.
Apple	0·1 to 10	Brussel sprout . . .	90 to 110
Banana. . . .	1 to 15	Cabbage, ...	60 to 140
Citrus juice:		boiled	1 to 9
orange . . .	22 to 89	Cauliflower	60 to 80
grape-fruit . . .	35 to 45	Kale	130
lemon . . .	47 to 73	Spinach, ...	60 to 480
Currants, black . .	200	boiled	2 to 3
Pineapple juice . .	30	Potato	10 to 40
Tomato juice . . .	17 to 70	Liver	10 to 80
Marmalade . . .	6 to 14	Milk, cow	1 to 3
Rose hips . . .	300 to 1,000	human	10 to 15
		Adrenal gland, ox . .	80 to 200

Bacharach and his colleagues, from whose work much of the above data has been taken, report that storage for a month causes a 20 per cent. loss of ascorbic acid in oranges, and a 6 per cent. loss in lemons. The loss, however, was negligible in juices properly concentrated and stored. The vitamin C value of cooked vegetables depends largely on the time and condition of the cooking. Where the sodium bicarbonate added to improve the colour and texture is excessive, and the boiling is prolonged, the ascorbic value drops to zero. Rapid and brief sterilisation of milk by heating to about 65° (pasteurisation) has little effect on the vitamin, boiling for more than ten minutes may complete the inactivation that has been in progress ever since the milk was secreted.

Ascorbic acid is synthesised rapidly in germinating seeds exposed to light, which thus provides an emergency source of the vitamin.

Requirements. Most of the higher animals, with the strange exception of man, apes, monkeys, and the guinea pig, are immune from scurvy, and presumably can synthesise their requirements from glucose, which is a precursor in the plant. The minimum daily requirement to prevent scurvy in man is 10 to 20 mg., the recommended intake is 75 mg. for the adult and 30 to 75 for the child. The animal organism is unable to store the vitamin beyond a tissue saturation limit, and the vitamin excess appears in the urine. The saturation minimum intake for human adults is 25 to 35 mg. per 24 hours; below this, excretion of the vitamin in the urine ceases.

Functions. Because of its ene-diol structure, ascorbic acid may assist in keeping thiol-enzymes and other compounds containing —SH groups in a reduced

205

state in the tissues. Activated by ascorbic oxidase, it can function as a hydrogen donor-acceptor system, and can aid in the transfer of electrons in metabolic chain reactions. Ascorbic acid is required for the construction of collagen fibres both in soft tissues and bone matrix, and therefore promotes repair. It is probably essential for normal hæmopoiesis, possibly because it has a function in the conversion of folic to folinic acid.

Effects of Vitamin C Deficiency. (i) *Infantile Scurvy.* This condition is found in children fed exclusively on sterilised or artificial dietaries, or by mothers whose milk is deficient in ascorbic acid. After a period of anæmia and irregular growth the characteristic syndrome appears: sore gums, subperiosteal hæmorrhages and hæmorrhages into the joints, subcutaneous hæmorrhages and hæmaturia.

(ii) *Adult Scurvy.* This is seen among explorers and others on dietaries deprived of fresh foodstuffs for prolonged periods and is always a potential danger in communities living on artificially modified foods, especially when individual requirements are increased by pregnancy, lactation or disease. The scorbutic syndrome includes hæmorrhages from mucous membranes and into the skin, joints, limbs and bone marrow. Spongy and bleeding gums, pain and swelling in joints and limbs are common clinically. The disease progresses to complete incapacitation, and terminates fatally.

Many of the signs of scurvy are referable to increased capillary permeability and escape of blood into the tissues.

(iii) *Dental Disorders.* Spongy and bleeding gums, decay and loosening of the teeth, pyorrhœa: all have been attributed to avitaminosis C, and have been cured or checked by ascorbic acid. The vitamin appears to be necessary for maintaining the activity of the formative cells, odontoblasts, ameloblasts and osteoblasts.

(iv) *Delayed Wound Repair.* In scorbutic subjects the fibroblasts that normally invade zones of injury are less active and scar tissue may fail to develop.

Assay. Biological methods are based on the response of guinea pigs rendered scorbutic by a deficiency diet. Ascorbic acid gives a typical ene-diol reaction with tetrazolium and with *o*-dinitrobenzene (p. 91). It can be estimated by its power to bleach coloured oxidisers, such as 2,6-dichlorophenol indophenol, used as titration reagents.

Animal tissues contain reducing substances, notably adrenalines, glutathione and cysteine, which may affect the titration. These can be removed by pretreatment with mercuric acetate, which does not precipitate ascorbic acid. After filtration, the filtrate is treated with H_2S to remove excess of mercury and to ensure that all the vitamin is in the reduced state prior to titration.

The oxidised form of the vitamin, dehydroascorbic acid, can be estimated colorimetrically by condensing it with 2,4-dinitrophenylhydrazine, which yields an osazone that forms a red solution when dissolved in sulphuric acid.

Miscellaneous Factors in the Diet

Choline acquired recognition in nutrition when it was found to have both a curative and a preventive action on the excessive accumulation of fat in the mammalian liver. It is a constituent of the ordinary mixed diet, being present in the form of lecithin and other phospholipids in animal foods rich in fat. Lecithin contains about 14 per cent. of choline; its principal sources are egg-yolk, liver, heart and pancreas. Percentage values for milk are: human, 0·02 to 0·08; cow, 0·06 to 0·11. *Betaine*, the onium compound in beetroot and other vegetables, has a similar effect on hepatic liposis as choline. Young rats on diets deficient in choline develop hæmorrhagic enlargement and degeneration of the kidneys, and enlargement of the spleen. This can be averted by doses of methionine, or of choline or betaine, in amounts too small to affect the deposition of liver lipid. The severity of the condition is aggravated by cystine, fats, or cholesterol, and is ascribed to a shortage of methyl groups available for metabolism. Methionine, choline and betaine are potential sources of $-CH_3$, and their inclusion in the diet protects the animal from the effects of methyl-starvation or "amethylosis". The structure of choline and betaine is described in Chapter 21.

Inositol. The cyclohexanol *myo*-inositol, $C_6H_6(OH)_6$ (p. 85), is a member of the *bios* group of compounds that act as growth-stimulants for many micro-organisms. It has a physiological action in higher animals, shown by increased motility of the stomach and small intestine, and it can restrict the accumulation of cholesterol in the liver. Mice and rats on diets free from inositol develop a dermatitis, resulting in baldness (Woolley, 1940); the condition can be cured by including 0·01 per cent. of inositol in the diet. Inositol is a component of some animal and plant phosphatides, such as *lipositol*, from soya bean, which contains 16 per cent. of inositol. It occurs also as the hexaphosphate, phytic acid, in bran. Its status in human nutrition is unknown, though it may operate as an indirect vitamin by promoting the growth of beneficial organisms in the alimentary tracts of higher animals.

Anti-vitamins

Specific vitamin deficiency effects can be induced by two types of agent: *vitamin competitors* and *vitamin inactivators*. Compounds that closely resemble a vitamin in some part of their structure often can displace that vitamin by competition in a reaction. These biochemical imposters are mostly synthetic products, such as: *pyrithiamine*, an anti-thiamine, in which pyridine replaces thiazole; *dichloro-riboflavin*, an anti-riboflavin, in which Cl replaces CH_3; *pyridine-β-sulphonic acid*, an anti-nicotinic acid vitamin, in which $-SO_2.OH$ replaces $-COOH$; *dicoumarol*, a naturally-occurring anti-vitamin K, used therapeutically to depress blood coagulability in thrombosis; *gammexane*, an anti-inositol, used as an insecticide.

Anti-vitamins are used in research as a means of inducing specific vitamin deficiences without the need for employing special deficiency diets. That their

207

effect is the result of competition and not toxicity is shown by its abolition when an excess of the corresponding vitamin is supplied.

Vitamin-inactivators either combine chemically with the vitamin, like avidin, the anti-biotin, or degrade the vitamin.

Vitamin-degrading enzymes, such as *thiaminase*, present in raw fish, and *ascorbic oxidase*, in raw vegetables, are catalysts employed in vitamin metabolism, and only act as anti-vitamins if allowed to attack food materials prior to use.

DIETARY CONSTRUCTION

Knowledge of human dietary requirements has been gained by three methods: (1) Observation and statistical analysis of the diets of civilised and primitive communities; (2) experimental study of the growth-rate and health of individuals and groups on normal and artificial diets; (3) chemical analysis of foodstuffs. The information thus accumulated is vast, and has been augmented by the world-wide, though involuntary, experiences of nations stricken by the methods of total warfare.

The construction of an individual diet involves:—

(1) Calculation of the calorie requirements of the subject, as indicated by his age, condition and occupation.

(2) Calculation of the minimum protein requirement. This is supplemented, as far as circumstances allow, to provide a good safety margin. The daily calorie and protein requirements represent levels which must be reached, however the dietary be planned.

(3) Calculation of the lipid requirement, which is usually assumed to be at least equal in weight to the optimal protein requirement.

(4) Calculation of the carbohydrate intake necessary to supplement the calories provided by the proteins and lipids, so as to bring the total up to the full calorie requirement.

(5) Calculation of the essential micro-nutrients required: the vitamins, provitamins and biological elements. In practice, these are usually taken to be: vitamin A and carotene, B_1, B_2, C, D, the metals Ca and Fe, and the non-metals PO_4 and I. The residual vitamins of the B group, and the elements Na, K, Mg, Cu, Mn, Zn, along with Cl, S and, possibly, F, are sufficiently represented in a good mixed dietary not to require special consideration.

(6) Survey of the subject's normal diet to see how far it conforms to the calculated requirements; with rectifications, where necessary, by inclusion or exclusion of particular nutrients.

The material needs of mankind are reasonably well known, and the difficulties of dietary construction are economic and social rather than biochemical. Dietary inadequacy is usually revealed by subnormal growth in the young child, by subnormal weight in the adult, and by the evidence of diseases caused by lack of specific nutrients. In practice, these conditions are inter-related, as a dietary is rarely deficient in only one essential constituent.

Recommended Daily Allowances
Food and Nutrition Board, National Research Council, U.S.A., 1953

	Kilocal.	Prot.	Ca	Fe	A	B₁	B₂	Nc.	C
Man (70 kg.):									
sedentary	2,500	70	0·8	12	5	1·5	2·2	15	75
moderately active .	3,000	70	0·8	12	5	1·8	2·7	18	75
very active . .	4,500	70	0·8	12	5	2·3	3·3	23	75
Woman (56 kg.):									
sedentary . .	2,100	60	0·8	12	5	1·2	1·8	12	70
moderately active .	2,500	60	0·8	12	5	1·5	2·2	15	70
very active . .	3,000	60	0·8	12	5	1·8	2·7	18	70
pregnant . .	2,500	85	1·5	15	6	1·8	2·5	18	100
lactating . . .	3,000	100	2·0	15	8	2·3	3·0	23	150
Child:									
under 1 year . .	100/kg.	4/kg.	1·0	6	1·5	0·4	0·6	4	30
1 to 3 years . .	1,200	40	1·0	7	2	0·6	0·9	6	35
4 to 6 years . .	1,600	50	1·0	8	2·5	0·8	1·2	8	50
7 to 9 years . .	2,000	60	1·0	10	3·5	1·0	1·5	10	60
10 to 12 years . .	2,500	70	1·2	12	4·5	1·2	1·8	12	75
Adolescent:									
Girl:									
13 to 15 years . .	2,800	80	1·3	15	5	1·4	2·0	14	80
16 to 20 years . .	2,400	75	1·0	15	5	1·2	1·8	12	80
Boy:									
13 to 15 years . .	3,200	85	1·4	15	5	1·6	2·4	16	90
16 to 20 years . .	3,800	100	1·4	15	6	2·0	3·0	20	100

Prot., Protein, in gm. Under one year, the child's need increases month by month, and for the period 6 to 8 months is 3 to 4 gm. per kg. body weight. The quantities of protein and calcium are less if they are obtained from human milk.

Ca, Calcium, in gm.; **Fe,** Iron, in mg.; **A,** Vitamin A, in 1,000 International Units (the need is less if provided entirely as A, and more if provided as carotenoids); **B₁,** Thiamine, in mg.; **B₂,** Riboflavin, in mg.; **Nc.,** Nicotinic acid or amide, in mg.; **C,** Ascorbic acid, in mg.

The vitamin D daily requirements for pregnant or lactating women or for very young children are 400 to 800 International Units. When not available indirectly, from sunlight, it should be supplied to older children and to adults in at least the same amount.

Energy Requirement. The energy needs of the animal are provided by the combustible nutrients: carbohydrates, proteins, lipids, the individual values of which are expressed in terms of kilocalories per gram of dry material as found by combustion in a calorimeter.

For the human adult, living an ordinary life in a temperate climate, and not engaged in manual work, the basic requirement is 2,400 kilocalories per 24 hours. This is supplemented according to work output. Additions required, in terms of kilocalories per hour, are: light work, 75; moderate work, 75 to 100; hard work, 150 to 300, and upwards. The requirements of pregnant or lactating women are 2,500 to 3,000 kilocalories per 24 hours. The special needs of children are calculated by multiplying the basic requirement by an age-coefficient. Children under one year require an intake of about 100 kilocalories per kg. body weight. Above that age, the daily requirement scale is:

Year	1–2	2–3	3–5	5–7	7–9	9–11	11–12	12–15
Kilocals .	840	1,000	1,200	1,440	1,680	1,920	2,160	2,400

The calorie demand for growth is higher than is popularly known, and explains the hunger for sugar, characteristic of healthy childhood.

The percentage contribution of the nutrients to the total calorie input is determined by racial and social circumstances, representative values are: carbohydrates, 55 to 66; proteins, 10 to 15; lipids, 20 to 35. The normal human adult of 65 to 70 kg., spending about 36 kilocalories per kg., in 24 hours, excretes 2,300 to 3,600 gm. of water, and 470 litres of carbon dioxide, equivalent to 250 gm. of carbon consumed during the same period, at least half of which has come from carbohydrates.

General References

Bacharach, A. L. (1945), " Science and Nutrition." London.

" Biochemistry and Physiology of Nutrition." Ed. by G. H. Bourne and G. W. Kidder (1953). New York.

Drummond, J. C., and A. Wilbraham (1939), " The Englishman's Food." London.

Harris, L. J. (1951), " Vitamins." London.

Horder, C. Dodds, and T. Moran (1954), " Bread." London.

Hutchison, R., V. H. Mottram and G. Graham (1956), " Food and the Principles of Dietetics." 11th Ed. London.

Leitch, I. (1942), " Evolution of dietary standards." *Nutrit. Abs. Rev.*, **11,** 509.

McCance, R. A., and E. M. Widdowson (1946), " Chemical Composition of Foods." H.M. Stationery Office, London.

McLester, J. J., and M. J. Darby (1952), " Nutrition and Diet in Health and Disease," 6th Ed. Philadelphia; London.

" Modern Nutrition in Health and Disease." Ed. by M. G. Wohl and R. S. Goodhart (1955). London.

Moore, T. (1957), " Vitamin A." London.

"The Nation's Food." Ed. by A. L. Bacharach and T. Rendle (1946). London.

Rosenberg, H. R. (1942), " Chemistry and Physiology of the Vitamins." New York.

Sherman, H. C. (1943), " The Science of Nutrition." Columbia; London.

Sherman, H. C. (1947), " Calcium and Phosphorus in Foods and Nutrition." New York.

Taylor, C. M., G. Macleod and M. S. Rose (1956), " Foundations of Nutrition." New York; London.

" Vitamina E." *Atti del terzo Congresso Internazionale Venezia*, 1955. (1956), Verona.

Williams, R. J., et al. (1950), " Biochemistry of the B Vitamins." New York.

Part II
Dynamic Biochemistry
Chapter 14 Catalysts

" Catalysis is one of the most significant devices of nature, since it has endowed living systems with their fundamental character as transformers of energy, and all evidence suggests that it must have played an indispensable part in the living universe from the earliest stages of evolution."

F. G. Hopkins.

Organic life is manifest in a continuum of chemical events occurring within the framework of the cell. These events, which include the making, unmaking and distribution of molecules, are organised and promoted by specific agents, the biological catalysts.

Chemical reactions are events involving the reconstruction of molecules and the rearrangement of atoms. They display *direction, order, rate* and *extent*. The direction of a reaction is denoted by the expression:

$$\text{Reactants} \longrightarrow \text{Products.}$$

The order of a reaction describes the number of different species of reactant. In a monomolecular reaction, such as the decomposition of hydrogen peroxide, $2H_2O_2 \rightarrow H_2O + O_2$, only one species of molecule is undergoing change. In a bimolecular reaction there are two different species of reactant, as in the hydrolysis of sucrose to glucose and fructose:

$$C_{12}H_{22}O_{11} + H_2O \longrightarrow C_6H_{12}O_6 + C_6H_{12}O_6$$

The rate of a reaction is expressed as the quantity of material removed or produced in unit time. The extent of a reaction is measurable as the percentage change in the concentration of the reactants. While the direction, order, rate, and extent of a reaction depend primarily on the chemical nature of the reactants, they are subject to modifying conditions.

Chemical Equilibrium. When the products of a reaction are removed as they are formed, either by being caught up in some other reaction or by escaping from the system as a gas or precipitate, the reaction proceeds towards completion. Where the products of the reaction accumulate, a reverse reaction is set up that retards the original reaction and eventually establishes an equilibrium condition in which the composition of the mixture remains constant.

Thus, for a bimolecular reaction, the rate of the primary change,

$$A + B \longrightarrow C + D,$$

decreases with fall in the concentrations of A and B, until it is exactly balanced by the reverse reaction,

$$A + B \longleftarrow C + D,$$

211

which has increased from zero with increasing concentration of C and D. The system is now in a steady state of mobile equilibrium, in which

$$K_c = \frac{[C] \times [D]}{[A] \times [B]}.$$

K_c is the equilibrium constant for the reaction. The symbols in brackets denote the molar concentrations of the constituents when equilibrium has been reached.

For exact work, each concentration value is multiplied by its activity co-efficient (p. 41), but this is usually disregarded for reactions in dilute, aqueous solutions. Where activity values are used instead of molar concentrations, the constant is denoted by K_a.

The value for K_c is determined by the nature of the reactants and the temperature at which the reaction takes place. It is an index of the extent of the reaction; if the primary reaction has proceeded almost to completion, the equilibrium, by convention, is said to lie far to the right and, $[C] \times [D]$ is much greater than $[A] \times [B]$. In order to obtain values of K_c for reference, the reacting system is adjusted to a " standard state " at the start.

Temperature Effect. In a system undergoing chemical change, the rate at which the reaction takes place will depend on the frequency of collision between the reacting molecules and, consequently, on their concentrations. Rise in temperature, by increasing molecular motion, will increase collision frequency and, therefore, will increase reaction rate. It is found experimentally that the rate of a simple chemical reaction is increased approximately two-fold for each rise in temperature of $10°$ C., within critical limits. This increase, however, is far less than that required by the kinetic theory and it is now assumed that, in order to react, molecules must be in an activated *transition* state of relatively higher energy content.

Reactants $\rightleftharpoons$ Transition State $\rightarrow$ Products.

Only a small proportion of the population of reactant molecules are in a transition state, which explains the relatively slow rate of many organic reactions.

Catalysts. Any substance that can promote the activation of a reactant is able to increase the speed at which a reaction can take place; such a substance is a catalyst, and, in the words of Moelwyn-Hughes, " enables certain molecules to undergo chemical changes on receiving critical energy that is less than they would require in the absence of the catalyst."

Characteristics of Catalysts. (1) *Survival.* Unlike the other reactants, the catalyst is not necessarily removed by the reaction, although it may be inhibited by end-products, competitors, or contaminants. (2) *Potency.* Under favourable conditions, a minimum amount of catalyst is able to promote the transformation of an indefinitely large amount of reactant.

At $0°$ C., one molecule of the enzyme catalase can effect the decomposition of

40,000 molecules of H_2O_2 in one second. At 37° C., crystalline rennin can clot a million times its own weight of milk in one minute.

The equilibrium state of a chemical reaction is independent of the way in which it has been attained. Catalysts increase the speed at which equilibrium is reached, but do not alter the composition of the final equilibrium mixture. **Classification.** Catalysts may be divided into inorganic and organic types. Inorganic catalysts are heat-stable, and include: *Hydrogen ions*, which catalyse the hydrolysis of oligosaccharides, polysaccharides, aromatic esters, and many other organic reactions. *Hydroxyl ions*, which catalyse the hydrolysis of aliphatic esters, the oxidation of phenols, the isomerisation of monosaccharides, and other reactions. *Polyvalent ions of* Mn, Fe, Cu, Co, *and other metals*, which catalyse reactions involving electron transfer and molecular fission. Organic catalysts may be divided into a heat-stable group and a heat-labile group. Heat-stable organic catalysts, represented by hæms, hæmatins, and cupro-porphyrins, usually owe their potency to catalytic metals, such as Fe or Cu, included in their structure. Heat-labile catalysts are represented largely, if not exclusively, by the enzymes, the dictators of dynamic biochemistry.

Enzymes. An enzyme is a protein endowed with catalytic properties. In addition to the general properties of all catalysts, namely power of survival and potency of influence, enzymes display a group of properties, including: (1) colloidal characteristics, (2) high selectivity, (3) high sensitivity to temperature, hydrogen ion concentration, electrolytes, and special factors including specific activators, inactivators and poisons.

Colloidal Characteristics. Enzymes occur immobilised in cell structures, aggregated in cell inclusions and dissolved in cytoplasm and in cellular secretions. More than sixty have now been obtained in crystalline form. Molecular weights range from 12,700 (ribonuclease) to more than a million (glutamic dehydrogenase).

Representative molecular weights are: trypsin, chymotrypsin, 23,000; pepsin, carboxypeptidase, 34,400; α-amylase, 45,000; hexokinase, 90,000; arginase, 140,000; glucose oxidase, catalase, 230,000; urease, 480,000.

These values correspond to molecular dimensions of 2 mμ radius upwards, indicating that enzymes belong to the family of colloids.

Selectivity. The substance activated by an enzyme is termed its substrate. A few enzymes, notably urease, are specific in that they act on only one species of substrate. Other enzymes are class-selective in that they act on a particular class of substrates, usually with different intensities. The hydrolysis of esters by lipase is an example. Specificity of reaction path is displayed when the same substrate is acted on in different ways by enzymes that have different points of attack. Thus, when the trisaccharide raffinose is hydrolysed by yeast saccharase, it yields fructose and melibose; when hydrolysed by emulsin, it yields sucrose and galactose.

213

Temperature Effects. Rise in temperature has a double effect on enzyme-catalysed reactions; acceleration and inactivation. Up to about 35° C., the rate increases with rise in temperature like that of an uncatalysed reaction; at higher temperatures, although the rate may continue to increase, it is soon retarded by thermal destruction of the enzyme. At temperatures above 60° C., inactivation proceeds so rapidly that the reaction rate falls to zero. Because of this, every enzyme reaction has an optimum temperature of maximum activity. This is modified by several factors, including the hydrogen-ion concentration, the presence of electrolytes and the amount of substrate present which, when in excess, can protect the enzyme from adverse conditions. Thermal inactivation is a consequence of the fact that enzymes belong to the class of higher proteins, and can undergo irreversible denaturation by heat. Neither the optimum temperature nor the inactivation temperature, by themselves, are sufficiently precise to be of use in identifying a particular enzyme; but the temperature effect is of value in that it enables enzymes to be distinguished from other catalysts. All enzymes are inactivated by being boiled in aqueous solution.

Hydrogen Ion Effect. Enzymes display maximum activity within the region of a particular hydrogen ion concentration, the optimum pH. On either side of this, activities decrease to zero and the enzyme may undergo irreversible denaturation.

Optimum pH values usually are between pH 4·5 and pH 7·5, but range from pH 1·5 (pepsin) to about pH 9 (trypsin, alkaline phosphatase).

Essential Metals and Co-enzymes. Enzymes can be divided into (1) simple proteins, such as pepsin and urease, (2) metallo-proteins, and (3) conjugated proteins.

The metallo-protein enzymes have a metal incorporated into their structure: Fe, in peroxidases and catalases; Cu, in phenol oxidases; Zn, in carbonic anhydrase and carboxypeptidase; Mg, in enolase and carboxylase; Mo, in xanthine oxidase. The occurrence of a metal in these enzymes is one of the factors that determine the need for certain metals in the diet. Conjugated enzymes carry a heat-labile prosthetic group, which can be detached by dialysis. The prosthetic group is termed the **co-enzyme,** the residual protein is the **apo-enzyme.** Neither, by itself, displays catalytic activity until the partnership is restored. At least a dozen co-enzymes are now recognised, most of which are derived from water-soluble vitamins.

The coenzymes act as transporters of hydrogen, acetyl, formyl, or other active units, from one enzyme-catalysed reaction to another. Important examples are: the hydrogen carriers, *co-enzyme I* (diphosphopyridine nucleotide, DPN), *co-enzyme II* (triphosphopyridine nucleotide, TPN), and *flavin adenine dinucleotide*, FAD; the carrier of acyl units, $R.CO$, including acetyl, $CH_3.CO$, *co-enzyme A*; the carrier of amino units, *phosphopyridoxal*; the carrier of formyl, $H.CO$, and hydroxymethyl $HO.CH_2$, units, *co-enzyme F*; the carrier of aldehyde during the decarboxylation of pyruvic and other keto acids, *cocarboxylase*, or pyrophosphothiamine.

Activators and Inhibitors. Many enzymes require ions in low concentration for their activity, such as: Mg^{2+}, for phosphatases; Mn^{2+}, for arginase; Cl^-, for amylase. The significance of many of these ionic activators is obscure; some can be replaced by related ions. Conversely, substances which combine with activating ions or metals in metallo-protein enzymes can inhibit the catalysed reaction. Examples are the inhibition of metallo-enzymes containing Fe or Cu by cyanide and by H_2S. Protein precipitants of the heavy metal type, Ag, Cu, Hg, and Pb, inactivate most enzymes, unlike protein flocculants, such as ammonium sulphate, which, though they drive the enzyme out of solution, do not damage the catalysing properties. Specific anti-enzymes, such as are formed in the organism in response to injections of a foreign enzyme, inhibit by acting as selective protein precipitants.

Free thiol groups, HS—, are required for the activity of many enzymes, including alcohol dehydrogenase, hexokinase, papain, pyruvic oxidase, succinic dehydrogenase, and urease. These thiol-enzymes are selectively inhibited by oxidisers, including free oxygen at high pressure, which convert the thiol groups into disulphide bridges,

$$\text{—SH} + \text{HS—} + O \longrightarrow \text{—S—S—} + H_2O.$$

This effect can be reversed by reducing agents, such as ascorbic acid, cysteine and glutathione. Specific compounds that inactivate thiol enzymes by combining with the thiol groups include iodoacetate and its esters, acrolein and organic derivatives of mercury or arsenic. Several of these compounds are well known, though not popular, as lachrymators and " war gases ", including " Lewisite ". The effect of these thiol immobilisers can be prevented or reversed by thiol-rich compounds, including the " British Anti-Lewisite ", $HS.CH_2.CH(SH)$, $CH_2.OH$, introduced by Peters.

Anti-enzymes. Enzymes, like other higher proteins, when injected into the blood stream of an animal to which they are foreign, can evoke the production of specific flocculants, or anti-enzymes. An anti-serum thus obtained may be used for the detection and separation of a particular enzyme, which may or may not retain its potency in the precipitated form.

Enzyme-catalysed reactions can be inhibited by substances that resemble the substrate and can compete with the substrate for possession of the enzyme, and by substances that can combine with the substrate and render it resistant to the enzyme.

History of Enzyme Chemistry. Four spontaneous natural changes have been known to man ever since he first applied his power of rational observation. They are: (i) the alcoholic fermentation of sugars; (ii) the lactic fermentation, or souring, of milk; (iii) the acetic fermentation of wine; and (iv) the ammoniacal fermentation of urine. Each is due to the growth of a microscopic organism and its attack on a particular substance or *substrate*. The mechanism of these natural fermentations remained completely obscure until the beginning of the last century.

(1) In 1830, Dubrunfaut found that malt extract could convert starch paste

into sugar in a manner comparable to the action of a strong acid, as shown previously by Kirchoff (1815). In 1833, Payen and Persoz separated the active amyloclastic principle from malt extract by addition of excess of alcohol. This precipitate, the first true enzyme isolated in the crude state, they named *diastase*, and compared it to one of the unknown natural " ferments " that brought about the souring of milk or wine. The wide distribution and importance of these ferments was realised, and Berzelius introduced the term *catalysis* to describe the changes that they brought about.

(2) Between 1850 and 1870, Pasteur showed that the natural fermentations were invariably due to the growth of micro-organisms, called by him the " organised ferments." Non-living agents, such as the pepsin of gastric juice or the diastase of malt extract were called the " soluble or unorganised ferments ".

(3) Confusion having arisen as to the meaning of " ferment ", Kühne, in 1870, introduced the term *enzyme* (Gk. *in yeast*) to describe biological catalysts. Though this term indicates the extent to which yeast fermentation was occupying the minds of biological chemists 100 years ago, Kühne emphasised that it was not intended to be applied only to ferments derived from yeast.

(4) In 1896, Ostwald defined a catalyst as the accelerator of a chemical reaction. This stimulated research into the physical chemistry of enzymes, and many equations were obtained connecting speed of zymolysis with concentration of catalyst, substrate, and end-products.

(5) Since 1900, enzyme research has developed to such an extent that each single enzyme or a single property of a class of enzymes has proved sufficient to engage the attention of a group of investigators. Important early dates are: 1926, crystallisation of urease (Sumner); 1932, discovery of flavin enzymes (Warburg); 1933, isolation of the co-enzymes; 1935, isolation of virus protein; 1940, enzyme synthesis of starch and glycogen.

CLASSIFICATION OF ENZYMES

The number of possible enzymes is very large, since every organic compound associated with life requires at least one catalyst for its construction or degradation. The number of known enzymes, listed by Dixon and Webb (1959), is 659. These are classified in terms of the types of reaction they catalyse and the substrates they activate, which are denoted by the suffix ase. A few older names, such as pepsin and trypsin, are retained because of long-established usage.

A. **Hydrolases.** Enzymes catalysing reactions in which substrates are broken-down or built-up by addition or removal of water:

$$AB + H.OH \longleftrightarrow AH + B.OH$$

B. **Transferases.** Enzymes catalysing the transfer of a unit from the substrate to an acceptor:

$$AB + CD \longleftrightarrow AC + BD.$$

If the hydroxyl group of water is regarded as an acceptor, the hydrolases can be included among the transferases; for simplicity in classification they are usually regarded as an independent genus of enzymes.

C. **Adductases.** Enzymes catalysing the non-hydrolytic addition or removal of water, or of ammonia, to or from the substrate:

$$A = B + H.OH \longleftrightarrow AH.B.OH$$
$$A = B + NH_3 \longleftrightarrow AH.B.NH_2.$$

This classification of enzymes is neither exhaustive nor precise, but serves to emphasise the features possessed by catalysts that work in close association in metabolic systems.

A. HYDROLASES

Hydrolysing enzymes are prominent in the digestive secretions of animals and the seeds of plants, where they are concerned in the break-down of food materials prior to utilisation. They are the esterases, glycosidases, peptidases and amidases and hydrolytic deaminases.

A1. Esterases. Enzymes catalysing the hydrolysis of an ester into an acid and an alcohol, sugar, or base.

Representative Esterases

Enzyme.	Substrate.	Products.
Carboxylic esterases: Ali-esterases	Carboxylic esters: Aliphatic esters of low molecular weight.	Aliphatic acid and alcohol.
Lipases	Aliphatic esters of high molecular weight, glycerides.	Aliphatic acid and glycerol or other alcohol.
Cholinesterase Phosphoric esterases: Phosphatases	Phosphoric esters	Phosphate and alcohol, sugar, or base.
Sulphuric esterases: Sulphatases	Sulphuric esters	Sulphate, phenol or carbohydrate.
Thiolesterases: Deacylase	Acetylcoenzyme A	Acetate and co-enzyme A.

Carboxylic esterases catalyse the reaction:

$$R.CH_2.CO.OR + H_2O \longleftrightarrow R.CH_2.COOH + HO.R$$

They are widespread in animal and plant tissues, moulds and bacteria.

Lipases preferentially attack fats, hydrolysing them in stages. Rich sources are the pancreas and the castor oil bean (*Ricinus communis*).

Cholinesterase occurs in nerve and other animal tissue and in snake venoms. By hydrolysing the chemical transmitter, acetylcholine, it stops the effect of tissue stimulation by cholinergic nerves. The enzyme is also termed acetylcholinesterase, or " true " cholinesterase, to distinguish it from the less selective ali-esterases of blood and other tissues, which also hydrolyse acetylcholine, but less effectively.

Lecithinase. The venom of the cobra and other snakes, scorpions and wasps, contains an enzyme, Phospholipase A, that removes on acid radical from the phospholipids lecithin and cephalin, thereby converting these harmless tissue phospholipids into powerful hæmolytic agents, lysolecithin and lysocephalin. *Phosphoric esterases*, or *Phosphatases*, catalyse the reaction:

$$R.O.PO(OH)_2 + H_2O \longleftrightarrow H_3PO_4 + R.OH.$$

Because of the unique position of phosphate esters in metabolism, the phosphatases are universally distributed. Their substrates include glycerophosphates, phospholipids, phosphoproteins, nucleotides, polyphosphates, and phytic acid. The monophosphatases can be subdivided into an alkaline and an acid type.

Alkaline phosphatases, optimum pH 9, occur in kidney, intestinal mucosa, leucocytes, bone, and milk. **Acid phosphatases,** optimum pH 5, occur in prostate, liver, pancreas, rice bran, yeasts and bacteria.

Estimation of these two phosphatases in the serum is of diagnostic significance. Alkaline phosphatase is increased in rickets and in some other bone disorders; acid phosphatase is increased in malignant disease of the prostate particularly when there are secondary tumour deposits in the skeleton.

Polyphosphatases. Enzymes that hydrolyse the acid anhydride links in condensed phosphates, such as diphosphates, $R.O.PO(OH).O.PO(OH)_2$, and triphosphates, $R.O.PO(OH).O.PO(OH).O.PO(OH)_2$.

Adenosine triphosphatase, from muscle and other animal tissues, degrades adenosine triphosphate, ATP, to the diphosphate, ADP. It attacks similarly other triphosphates. The enzyme in muscle has been identified with *myosin*, the chief protein in muscle. It is activated by Ca^{2+}.

Apyrase, present in potato and other plants, hydrolyses adenosine triphosphate to the diphosphate, which it then hydrolyses to adenylic and phosphoric acids.

A2. Glycosidases. Enzymes catalysing the hydrolysis of α- or β-glycoside linkages, such as occur in carbohydrates. They can be divided into *oligoglycosidases*, which attack compounds with only a few (one to four) glycoside links, and *polyglycosidases*, which attack polysaccharides. The end-products of the hydrolysis of a carbohydrate is a simple sugar, or a mixture of simple sugars. Other glycosides yield a sugar and a non-sugar, or aglycone.

Maltase, an α-glucosidase, is present in many fungi, yeasts and bacteria, and as an insoluble precursor in ungerminated cereals, from which it is released during the malting process. Maltose, the sugar substrate, does not occur free in Nature, but is split off from polysaccharides by the amylase that usually accompanies maltase. The optimum pH ranges from 4·1 (malt-extract maltase) to 6·1 (intestinal maltase).

Representative Oligoglycosidases

Enzyme.	Source.	Substrate.	Products.
Maltase	Malt, intestinal mucosa	Maltose	Glucose
Cellobiase	Fungi, bacteria	Cellobiose	Glucose
Sucrase	Yeast, intestinal mucosa	Sucrose	Glucose and fructose
Lactase	Moulds, bacteria, intestinal mucosa	Lactose	Glucose and galactose
Glycuronidase	Moulds, bacteria, liver	Glycuronides	Uronic acid and sugar or aglycone
Nucleosidase	Fish muscle, yeast, bacteria	Nucleosides	Pentose and purine or pyrimidine

Maltase, cellobiase, sucrase and lactase are examples of disaccharidases in that they hydrolyse disaccharides.

Cellobiase, a β-glycosidase in plants, animals, and micro-organisms. Its substrate, cellobiose, comes from the hydrolysis of cellulose.

Sucrase, a fructofuranosidase, occurs in the intestinal secretions of many animals, including the bee and the snail. It is present in all plants, notably sugar beet, and in bacteria, fungi, and yeasts, with the exception of the " wine " yeasts. Sucrase, or saccharase, or invertase, hydrolyses sucrose into " invert sugar ", an equimolecular mixture of fructose and glucose.

Lactase, a β-galactosidase, occurs in the intestinal secretion of all young mammals, although it may disappear in later life if milk is excluded from the diet. It occurs in plants, especially almond seeds, in moulds, including *Aspergillus oryzæ*, and in the milk-sugar yeasts, but not in " top-fermentation " brewer's yeast.

Representative Polyglycosidases

Enzyme.	Source.	Substrate.	Products.
Amylase	Pancreas, plants, moulds, bacteria	Starch, glycogen, and dextrins	Maltose
Cellulase	Fungi, bacteria	Cellulose	Cellobiose
Inulase	Yeasts	Inulin	Fructose
Pectinase	Snail, fungi, bacteria	Pectin	Pectic acid and sugar
Lysozyme	Egg-white, spleen, nasal mucosa	Mucopolysaccharides	Amino sugar aglycone
Hyaluronidase	Testicle, snake venoms	Hyaluronic acid	Amino sugar

Amylases, or diastases. A family of enzymes long known because of their ability to convert starches into sugar. They occur in the digestive secretions of animals, in the roots, seeds and shoots of higher plants, and in fungi, moulds and bacteria. Rich sources are the pancreas, germinating barley (malt), and the mould *Aspergillus oryzæ*, from which the enzyme has been isolated in crystalline form. The saliva of man, the pig, the rat, and some other mammals contains an amylase, ptyalin, that is absent from the saliva of dogs and carnivora.

The substrates for the amylases, are starches (amylose and amylopectin), glycogen, and dextrins. Because of their complex structure, different types of amylase are required. These include: (1) Endo-amylase, or α-amylase, which preferentially attacks central 1,4-glycosidic linkages in starch and glycogen, liberating dextrins, which are eventually hydrolysed to maltose and iso-maltose. (2) Exo-amylase, or β-amylase, which splits off maltose units, which attacks the penultimate 1,4-glycosidic links in polysaccharide chain or branch, splitting-off maltose units one by one until a resistant 1,6-linkage is encountered at the point where the branch starts. The end-products are a mixture of maltose and resistant or " limit " dextrins.

Hydrolysis is completed by enzymes that usually accompany the amylases, namely maltase and 1,6-glucosidases. The final product is glucose.

The 1,6-glucosidases include iso-maltase and a " debranching ", or " R " enzyme, which unlocks the resistant dextrins, and exposes them to attack by amylase.

Cellulase is secreted by bacteria, soil organisms, wood-destroying fungi and insects, and some marine worms. It is a necessary agent for all organisms that attack the natural cellulose of plants, leaf-mould and timber. Cellulase hydrolyses cellulose into the disaccharide cellobiose, a 1,4-β-glucoside, which is then converted into glucose by the enzyme cellobiase.

Cellulase is absent from higher animals, apart from that secreted by the micro-flora of the digestive tract, which are necessary partners in the nutrition of herbivora.

The overall reaction catalysed by the amylases and cellulase is,

$$(C_6H_{10}O_5)_n + n/2 \ H_2O \rightarrow n/2 \ C_{12}H_{22}O_{11}.$$

Lysozyme, a mucopolysaccharidase, is one of the defence factors of the higher animal in that it confers on nasal and lachrymal secretions their ability to effect the lysis, or dissolution, of Gram-negative bacteria. Lysozyme attacks the mucopolysaccharide of cell walls. This is achieved by breaking-down the mucopolysaccharide of the cell wall, and releasing acetylamino sugars, N-acetyl glucosamine.

Hyaluronidase, present in spermatozoa, testicle, snake and other venoms, and some bacteria, hydrolyses the mucopolysaccharide, hyaluronic acid, of skin and other tissues, with production of derivatives of glucuronic acid and glucosamine. Hyaluronidase acts as a " spreading factor " in promoting the diffusion of venoms and bacterial toxins penetrating the skin.

In mammals and some other animals, the unfertilised ovum is protected by a coating of cells cemented with hyaluronic acid. This is dissolved by the hyaluronidase carried in the attacking fleet of spermatozoa, which thus makes it possible for fertilisation to be accomplished by a single sperm. Hyaluronidase-deficiency may be responsible for some types of male-sterility.

Hyaluronidase is unusual among enzymes, in that after inactivation by heating to 100° C., it regains activity when kept at 0° C.

A3. Peptidases. Enzymes catalysing the hydrolysis of the peptide linkage, —CO—NH—, such as occur in proteins.

They can be divided into extracellular peptidases, which occur in digestive secretions; and intracellular peptidases, which operate within the cell.

Representative Extracellular Peptidases

Enzyme.	Source.	Substrate.	Products.
Pepsin	Gastric juice	Proteins and some peptides	Peptides
Rennin	Gastric juice	Casein.	Paracasein
		Other proteins	Peptides
Trypsin	Pancreatic juice	Proteins and some peptides	Peptides and amino acids
Chymotrypsin	Pancreatic juice	Proteins and some peptides	Peptides and amino acids
Carboxy-peptidase	Pancreatic juice	Some peptides	Amino acids
Amino-peptidase	Pancreatic juice	Some peptides	Amino acids
Enterokinase	Intestinal juice	Trypsinogen	Trypsin

Pepsin. The digestive power of gastric juice on meat protein was demonstrated by Spallanzani, in 1784; the agent, pepsin, was isolated in crystalline form by Northrop, in 1931.

Pepsin is a linear peptide of molecular weight 36,000. In the cells of the gastric mucosa, and as freshly secreted, it occurs as an inactive precursor, pepsinogen, from which it is released by the acid in the gastric juice.

Pepsin preferentially attacks a peptide bond between a glutamic acid unit and an aromatic amino acid unit (phenylalanine or tyrosine) in proteins, and thus splits them into peptides. It is the only mammalian enzyme that acts in strongly acid solutions, optimum pH 1·5 to 2. In less acid media, as the pH rises above 4, the activity of pepsin falls to zero.

Rennin, or chymase, occurs in the gastric juice of young mammals. Working in an optimum range of pH 6·0 to 6·5, it converts the casein (caseinogen) of the milk diet into paracasein, which, by forming an insoluble compound with calcium, produces a clot. Under the name of " rennet ", extracts of the gastric mucosa of the calf are used for the curdling of milk required in cookery.

In the pH range of 3 to 4, rennin attacks some other proteins.

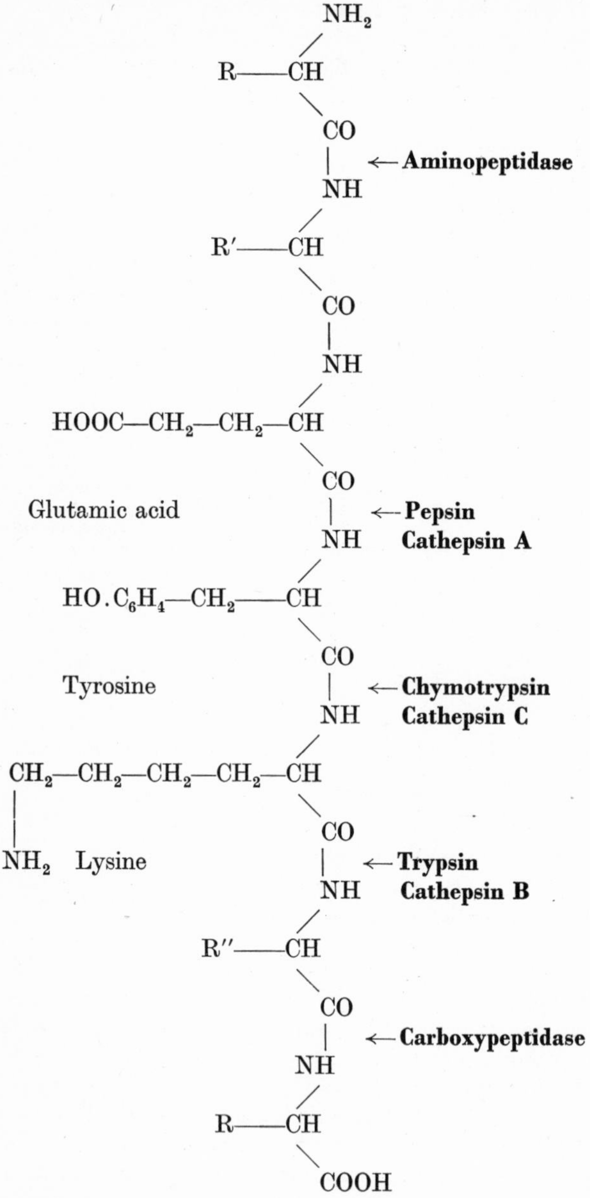

$$
\begin{array}{l}
\quad\quad\quad\quad NH_2 \\
\quad\quad\quad\quad / \\
R\text{——}CH \\
\quad\quad\quad\quad \backslash \\
\quad\quad\quad\quad CO \\
\quad\quad\quad\quad | \quad \leftarrow \textbf{Aminopeptidase} \\
\quad\quad\quad\quad NH \\
\quad\quad\quad\quad / \\
R'\text{——}CH \\
\quad\quad\quad\quad \backslash \\
\quad\quad\quad\quad CO \\
\quad\quad\quad\quad | \\
\quad\quad\quad\quad NH \\
\quad\quad\quad\quad / \\
HOOC\text{—}CH_2\text{—}CH_2\text{—}CH \\
\quad\quad\quad\quad \backslash \\
\quad\quad\quad\quad CO \\
\text{Glutamic acid} \quad | \quad \leftarrow \textbf{Pepsin} \\
\quad\quad\quad\quad NH \quad \textbf{Cathepsin A} \\
\quad\quad\quad\quad / \\
HO.C_6H_4\text{—}CH_2\text{——}CH \\
\quad\quad\quad\quad \backslash \\
\quad\quad\quad\quad CO \\
\text{Tyrosine} \quad | \quad \leftarrow \textbf{Chymotrypsin} \\
\quad\quad\quad\quad NH \quad \textbf{Cathepsin C} \\
\quad\quad\quad\quad / \\
CH_2\text{—}CH_2\text{—}CH_2\text{—}CH_2\text{—}CH \\
| \quad\quad\quad\quad \backslash \\
| \quad\quad\quad\quad CO \\
NH_2 \; \text{Lysine} \quad | \quad \leftarrow \textbf{Trypsin} \\
\quad\quad\quad\quad NH \quad \textbf{Cathepsin B} \\
\quad\quad\quad\quad / \\
R''\text{——}CH \\
\quad\quad\quad\quad \backslash \\
\quad\quad\quad\quad CO \\
\quad\quad\quad\quad | \quad \leftarrow \textbf{Carboxypeptidase} \\
\quad\quad\quad\quad NH \\
\quad\quad\quad\quad / \\
R\text{——}CH \\
\quad\quad\quad\quad \backslash \\
\quad\quad\quad\quad COOH
\end{array}
$$

Trypsin, the proteinase in pancreatic juice, attacks peptide links involving the carboxyl of arginine or lysine units. It acts in alkaline solutions within the range pH 8 to 11.

Chymotrypsin, which accompanies trypsin, attacks peptide links involving the carboxyl of a tyrosine or phenylalanine unit.

Carboxypeptidase and **aminopeptidase,** also present in pancreatic juice, are representatives of the oligopeptidases that preferentially hydrolyse short-chain peptides, such as are released by the other peptidases. Carboxypeptidase attacks the end of the chain, and removes the amino acid unit that carries the free carboxyl group. It is inhibited by a free amino group in the adjacent unit. Aminopeptidase attacks the other end of the chain, and removes the amino acid unit carrying the free amino group. It is inhibited by adjacent carboxyl groups.

Because of these restrictions, neither peptidase is able to hydrolyse a dipeptide; this is accomplished by another type of enzyme, the **dipeptidases.** The iminodipeptidases, *prolinase* and *prolidase*, attack dipeptides containing a prolyl or a proline unit, such as prolyl-glycine and glycyl-proline.

Trypsin and chymotrypsin are secreted as inactive zymogens. In acid solution, pH5 to 6, the conversion of trypsinogen to trypsin is catalysed by the intestinal enzyme, **enterokinase**; in alkaline solutions, the change proceeds spontaneously. Chymotrypsinogen is activated by trypsin, but not by enterokinase. An anti-trypsin occurs in blood plasma and in the secretion of intestinal parasites.

Plasmin, or fibrolysin, is present as an inactive plasminogen in blood plasma, and serves to dissolve fibrin clots and protect the animal from thrombosis. It is a typical peptidase.

Intracellular Peptidases. From homogenates of spleen, kidney and other tissues, a family of peptidases has been obtained, designated the **cathepsins,** I, II, III, and IV. Cathepsin I, or A, resembles pepsin in its target; cathepsin II, or B, resembles trypsin; cathepsins III and IV are identical with leucine-aminopeptidase and carboxypeptidase respectively. An additional enzyme, cathepsin C, resembles chymotrypsin. Unlike the extracellular peptidases, the cathepsins are concerned chiefly with the construction and modification of proteins. This they do by transpeptidation, the collection and transfer of amino acid units or short peptide chains.

The cathepsins are activated by thiol compounds, including cysteine and glutathione, and in this respect differ from pepsin, trypsin, and chymotrypsin.

Plant peptidases are represented by papain, from *Carica papaya* latex; bromelin, from pineapples; and ficin, from figs.

Target points of the Peptidases

(1) Amino acid units must belong to the L series. Peptides synthesised from D-amino acids are not attacked by animal or plant peptidases.

(2) Aminopeptidase is inhibited by an adjacent free carboxyl group in residue R'.

(3) Pepsin requires a free carboxyl group in the glutamic residue. It is inhibited by adjacent amino groups.

(4) The tyrosine unit can be replaced by phenylalanine without altering the sensitivity to pepsin or chymotrypsin.

(5) The lysine unit can be replaced by arginine without altering the sensitivity to trypsin.

(6) Carboxypeptidase is inhibited by an adjacent free amino group in residue R''.

A4. Amidases, Desimidases and Hydrolytic Deaminases. A miscellaneous group of enzymes capable of hydrolysing the —C—N— linkage in amines, $R—NH_2$, and amides, $R—CO—NH_2$, the nitrogen being eliminated as ammonia, and the amino group being replaced by hydroxyl.

Representative Amidases and Aminases

Enzyme.	Substrate.	Product.
Adenase	Adenine	Hypoxanthine + NH_3
Guanase	Guanine	Xanthine + NH_3
Allantoinase	Allantoin	Allantoic acid + NH_3
Allantoicase	Allantoic acid	Urea + NH_3
Urease	Urea	Carbonic acid + NH_3
Glutaminase	Glutamine	Glutamic acid + NH_3

Adenase and **Guanase** occur in bacteria and in the tissues of invertebrates and vertebrates, especially liver and spleen. They deaminate the amino purines, adenine and guanine, respectively.

Adenine.
6-amino purine.

Hypoxanthine.
6-hydroxy purine.

Guanine.
2-amino-6-hydroxy purine.

Xanthine.
2,6-dihydroxy purine.

Other purine deaminases include *adenosine deaminase, cytosine deaminase,* and *cytidine deaminase.*

Allantoinase and **Allantoicase,** present in amphibia, some invertebrates, green plants and yeast, catalyse the final stages in purine metabolism by degrading allantoin, the product of uric acid oxidation, to urea and glyoxylic acid.

Allantoin.

Allantoic acid.

Glyoxylic acid.

Urease, in moulds, bacteria and plants, notably the root nodules and seeds of the *Leguminosæ*, catalyses the conversion of urea to carbamic acid, which breaks down to carbon dioxide and ammonia. It is responsible for the alkaline fermentation that takes place in urine that has become infected. Urease is one of the few specific enzymes. It is employed analytically in the detection and estimation of urea in blood and tissues. Rich sources are the soya bean, the sword bean and the jack bean, from which the enzyme was isolated in crystalline form by Sumner in 1925.

$$H_2N—CO—NH_2 + H_2O \rightarrow NH_3 + H_2N—COOH \rightarrow NH_3 + CO_2$$

Glutaminase, in bacteria, protozoa, and animal tissues, including brain cortex, retina and kidney, converts glutamine into glutamic acid and ammonia.

$$
\begin{array}{ccc}
\begin{array}{l}
CH_2.CO.NH_2 \\
| \\
CH_2.CH.COOH \\
| \\
NH_2
\end{array}
&
\begin{array}{c}
+\ H_2O \\
\longrightarrow
\end{array}
&
\begin{array}{l}
CH_2.COOH \\
| \\
CH_2.CH.COOH \\
| \\
NH_2
\end{array}
\quad +\ NH_3
\end{array}
$$

Glutamine.　　　　　　Glutamic acid.
α-Amino glutaric acid.

Enzymes attacking substituted amides and amines include hippuricase and arginase.

Hippuricase, an aminoacylase, occurs in liver and kidney. It activates hippuric acid and other N-acylamino acids.

$$
\begin{array}{ccc}
\begin{array}{l}
CH_2.COOH \\
| \\
C_6H_5.CO—NH
\end{array}
& +\ H_2O \rightleftharpoons &
\begin{array}{l}
CH_2.COOH \\
| \\
NH_2
\end{array}
\quad +\ C_6H_5.COOH
\end{array}
$$

Hippuric acid.　　　　　Glycine.　　　　　Benzoic acid.
N-benzoylglycine.

Hippuric acid is a form in which foreign metabolites, such as benzoic acid, are inactivated and excreted in the urine.

B. TRANSFERASES

Enzymes that operate by transferring part of their substrate to an acceptor constitute an increasingly large family that eventually may be found to

Representative Transferases

Class.	Unit transferred.	Symbol.
1. Phosphatases	Phosphate	Φ
2. Oxidoreductases	Atomic hydrogen, or hydride ion	H:
3. Transaminases	Amino	$NH_2—$
4. Transacylases	Acetyl	$CH_3.CO—$
5. Transmethylases	Methyl	$CH_3—$
6. Transglycosylases	Glycosyl	Gl
7. Transpeptidases	Amino acid or peptide	

include members previously described as esterases, peptidases and other hydrolases.

B1. Phosphate Transferases

Phosphate is employed by all known forms of life for the construction of energy-accumulators within the cell and for the sensitising of sugars and other prospective metabolites.

Adenosine triphosphate, ATP, is the most popular of the energy-accumulators. It is assembled from the amino purine, adenine and the pentose sugar, D-ribose, the fifth carbon atom of which carries a chain of three phosphate radicles.

Adenosine: $R = -OH$
Adenosine monophosphate: $R = -O-PO(OH)_2$
Adenosine diphosphate, ADP: $R = -O-PO(OH)-O-PO(OH)_2$
Adenosine triphosphate, ATP: $R = -O-PO(OH)-O-PO(OH)-$
$O-PO(OH)_2$

The Adenosine Phosphates. Adenosine is formed by condensation between NH at 9 in adenine and HO at 1 in ribose. It belongs to the class of nucleosides. The polyphosphates are energy-rich compounds; hydrolysis of ATP to ADP and phosphate ions yields 7,700 calories of free energy per mole, at pH 7, and 30° C. Expressed otherwise, $F = -7,700$. Adenosine monophosphate, or adenylic acid, is more stable and resembles the ordinary monophosphate esters in having a low energy yield on hydrolysis, $F = -2,000$ calories. Although the concentration of ATP in the tissues is small, it is continuously being charged and discharged, like the battery in a motor car. Charging is effected by energy transferred from phosphate-sensitised oxidations, or oxidative phosphorylations. Discharge is effected by release of the chain-terminal phosphono group.

Phosphate transferases catalyse reactions of the type:

$$A-O-PO(OH)_2 + HB \rightleftharpoons A-OH + B-PO(OH)_2.$$

Dixon and Webb (1959) specify 76 different enzymes in this class, where HB is a phosphate acceptor. If the hydroxyl group of water is regarded as an acceptor, the phosphatases can be included with the transferases.

Phosphokinases. These enzymes transfer a high-energy phosphono unit from adenosine triphosphate to a sugar or other acceptor. The acceptor is phosphorylated and made more reactive; the donor is degraded to the diphosphate, ADP.

ATP + Glucose → ADP + Glucose-6-phosphate
(hexokinase).

ATP + Fructose-6-phosphate → ADP + Fructose-1,6-diphosphate
(6-phosphofructokinase).

ATP + Creatine → ADP + Phosphocreatine

Phosphomutases catalyse the mutation or exchange of phosphate groups in the molecule.

Glucose-1-phosphate + Glucose-1,6-diphosphate
→ Glucose-1,6-diphosphate + Glucose-6-phosphate
(phosphoglucomutase).

Phosphorylases. In the plant and the animal, starch and glycogen are synthesised by condensation of glucose-1-phosphate molecules; a reverse reaction releases the sugar from storage.

$$n \text{ Glucose-1-phosphate} \rightleftharpoons (C_6H_{10}O_5)_n + n\ H_3PO_4 + n\ H_2O.$$

Enzymes catalysing the reaction occur in liver, muscle, tubers, and other polysaccharide-storing tissues and cells. Originally termed phosphorylases, in the belief that they were concerned in phosphate transfer, they are now recognised as transglycosylases, which operate by adding or removing sugar units to or from the polysaccharide chains.

When a phosphate ester labelled with ^{18}O is attacked by a phosphate transferase the isotope remains attached to the organic residue, showing that link-fission has taken place between the P atom and the O.

$$R\text{—}'O\text{—}P'O(OH)_2 + H_2O \rightarrow R\text{—}'OH + HO\text{—}PO(OH)_2$$

This indicates that the enzyme has removed a $PO(OH)_2$ unit, and not a phosphate radical, $\text{—}O\text{—}PO(OH)_2$.

B2. Hydrogen Transferases

Biological oxidations are mostly indirect processes in which hydrogen atoms are removed and transferred to a chain of hydrogen carriers. It is only in the last stage of an aerobic sequence that the transferred hydrogen encounters and reacts with molecular oxygen, and forms water or hydrogen peroxide. Where oxygen actually enters a substrate that is being oxidised it is derived from a preliminary hydration followed by removal of hydrogen.

$$R.CHO + H_2O \rightarrow R.CH(OH)_2 \rightarrow R.COOH + 2H.$$

Enzymes that transfer hydrogen from the substrate to a carrier other than molecular oxygen are termed dehydrogenases; when working in reverse they are described as reductases. Enzymes that transfer hydrogen directly to molecular oxygen are termed oxidases. Both these types of hydrogen-transferring enzymes are collectively described as oxido-reductases.

Dehydrogenases are highly selective enzymes present in all cells. As every organic metabolite is the target of at least one enzyme, the number of different dehydrogenases is very large. Dixon and Webb list more than 120. The carriers mostly employed are co-enzyme I (DPN), co-enzyme II (TPN), and, for a small group of flavo-enzymes, a cytochrome.

Representative Dehydrogenases

Substrate.	Carrier.	Product.
Alcohol	DPN or TPN	Aldehyde
α-Glycerophosphate	DPN	Dihydroxyacetone phosphate
Lactate	Cytochrome c	Pyruvate
Malate	DPN or TPN	Oxaloacetate
iso-Citrate	DPN or TPN	Oxoglutarate
Succinate	Cytochrome c	Fumarate
Glucose	DPN or TPN	Gluconic acid, via lactone

The dehydrogenases are specified by prefixing the name of the substrate. Reactions catalysed by them are described in Chapter 19.

The Hydrogen Carriers

Co-enzyme I, diphosphopyridine nucleotide, or DPN, and **co-enzyme** II, triphosphopyridine nucleotide, TPN, function as prosthetic groups conjugated to the particular enzymes that employ them.

Each carrier is assembled from a molecule of the nucleoside, adenosine, and a corresponding nucleoside formed by condensation between N1 of nicotinamide and HO— of C1 in β-D-ribose. The nucleosides are linked by a pyrophosphate chain, —O—PO(OH)—O—PO(OH)—, between the C5 in each of

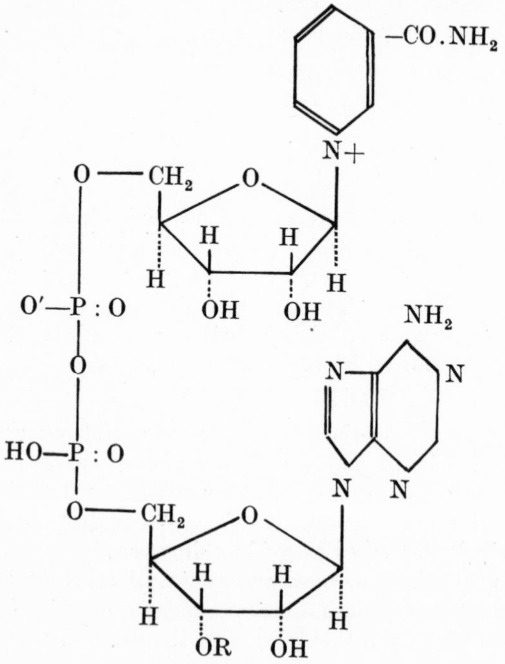

Co-enzymes I and II.
The pyridine nucleotides.

the ribose molecules. Co-enzyme II, in addition, has a phosphate radical attached to C3 in its adenine ribose unit.

The co-enzymes function as reversible hydrogen carriers by the ability of the nicotinamide radical to react with two hydrogen atoms released by the dehydrogenase. One of these hydrogen atoms becomes attached to the pyridine ring, the other loses its electron and becomes a hydrogen ion, thereby compensating for the loss of positive charge on the N atom in the ring.

Unreduced co-enzyme.
DPN+, TPN+.

Reduced co-enzyme.
DPNH, TPNH.

Alternatively, the two hydrogen atoms may react with the production of a negative hydride ion and a positive proton, or the hydrogen may be transferred from the substrate as a hydride ion.

$$2H. \rightarrow H :' + H^+$$

Flavins. The flavoprotein enzymes, or " yellow enzymes " owe their colour and catalytic efficiency to the presence of a riboflavin prosthetic group. These include riboflavin-5-phosphate (flavin-mononucleotide, FM), the structure of which is shown on p. 310, and flavin-adenine-dinucleotide (FAD), in which adenosine is linked to flavin mononucleotide by a pyrophosphate chain joining the C5 carbon of the adenine ribose unit with the C5 carbon of the ribotyl side-chain in the riboflavin.

Hydrogen transport is effected by the reversible addition of two hydrogen atoms to the isoalloxazine nucleus in the flavin.

Flavin.
(yellow).

Leuco-flavin.
(colourless).

Important flavoprotein dehydrogenases are the diaphorases I and II, the cytochrome reductases, lactate dehydrogenase, succinate dehydrogenase, and acyl-co-enzyme A dehydrogenase. These enzymes contain FAD as their prosthetic group.

229

Diaphorases I and **II** transfer hydrogen from reduced co-enzyme I (DPNH) and II (TPNH), respectively, and restore the active form.
Cytochrome reductase catalyses hydrogen exchanges involving co-enzymes I and II co-enzymes I or II and cytochrome c.
Oxidases catalyse reactions involving transfer of hydrogen to molecular oxygen, which is reduced to H_2O_2 or H_2O.

Representative Oxidases

Enzyme.	Substrate.	Products.
D- or L-amino acid oxidase, F	D- or L-amino acid	α-keto acids, $NH_3 + H_2O_2$
Glycine oxidase, F	Glycine	Glyoxalate, $NH_3 + H_2O_2$
Monoamine oxidases, F	Monoamines	Aldehydes, $NH_3 + H_2O_2$
Glucose oxidase, F (notatin)	D-glucose	Gluconolactone $+ H_2O_2$
Xanthine oxidase, F, Fe	Hypoxanthine, Xanthine Aldehydes	Urate $+ H_2O_2$ Acids $+ H_2O_2$
Urate oxidase, Cu	Uric acid	?
o-Diphenol oxidases, Cu	Monophenols, o-diphenols	o-quinones $+ H_2O$
Cytochrome oxidase, Fe	Reduced cytochrome c	Oxidised cytochrome $c + H_2O$

Flavoprotein enzymes are denoted by F, copper-containing enzymes by Cu, iron-containing enzymes by Fe.

Hydrogen peroxide is a dangerous reagent and is kept from accumulating in tissues by being employed by peroxidases or destroyed by catalases.

Amino acid Oxidases, or α-deaminases, convert α-amino acids into the corresponding keto acids,

$$R.CH(NH_2).COOH + \tfrac{1}{2}O_2 = R.CO.COOH + NH_3.$$

The process is aerobic, and employs molecular oxygen, here denoted by $\tfrac{1}{2}O_2$, to simplify the equation.
The enzymes were discovered in liver and kidney by Krebs (1935), they occur also in moulds and bacteria. Two types exist: L-deaminases, which attack the common amino acids, and D-deaminases, which attack the very rare D-series of amino acids. As these acids are foreign to animal tissues and are not present in food proteins, though they occur in some antibiotics, the significance of the D-deaminases is obscure, unless it be to protect the organism from evolutionary errors or extravagances in antibiotic therapy.
Glucose oxidase, or notatin, from *Penicillium notatum* and other moulds, was first recognised by its bacteriocidal effect, later shown to depend on the production of hydrogen peroxide during the oxidation of its substrate glucose. The enzyme is specific for β-D-glucose, which it oxidises to the 1,5-lactone.

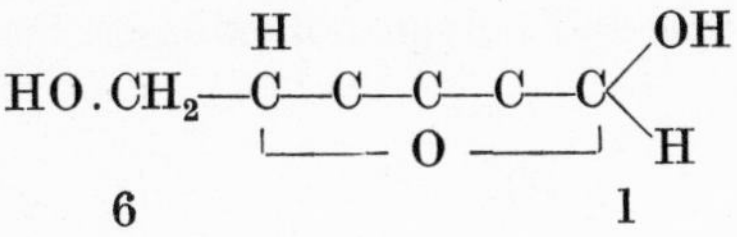

$$\text{HO.CH}_2\!-\!\underset{\underset{\displaystyle 6}{\rule{0pt}{1.2em}}}{\overset{\displaystyle H}{C}}\!-\!C\!-\!C\!-\!C\!-\!C\!\overset{\displaystyle OH}{\underset{\displaystyle H}{\diagdown}}$$

β-D-Glucose skeleton

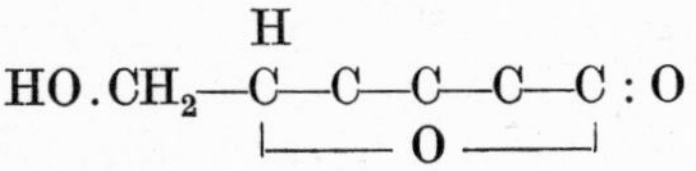

$$\text{HO.CH}_2\!-\!\overset{\displaystyle H}{C}\!-\!C\!-\!C\!-\!C\!-\!C:O$$

1,5-Gluconolactone

On alkaline hydrolysis, the lactone ring is opened, forming gluconic acid. Because of its specificity, the enzyme is used in the detection and estimation of glucose (p. 94).

Xanthine oxydase, which occurs in animal tissues, milk, and bacteria, oxidises the purines hypoxanthine and xanthine to uric acid.

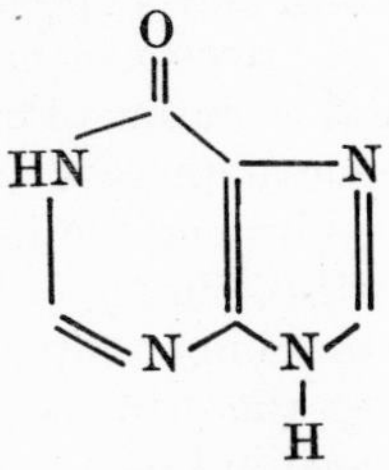

Hypoxanthine.
6-oxypurine.

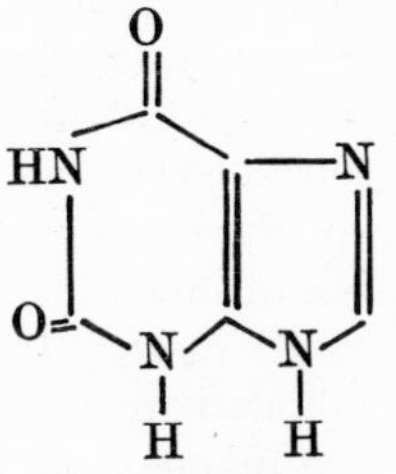

Xanthine.
2,6-dioxypurine.

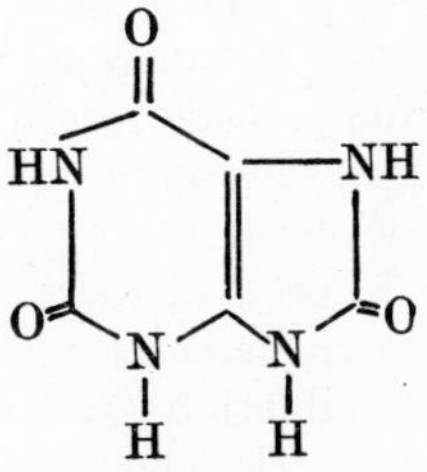

Uric acid.
2,6,8-trioxypurine.

The substrates are depicted in their alternative oxo-form.

Xanthine oxidase is remarkably unselective. It can catalyse the oxidation of the reduced form of co-enzyme I (DPNH), and the oxidation of aldehydes to acids.

In 1902 Schardinger observed that some samples of milk had the property of bleaching the dye methylene blue. After boiling, the property was lost, and hence could be attributed to a catalyst, the *Schardinger enzyme.*

The substrate was found to be formaldehyde, which had been added to the milk as a preservative. The enzyme was separated twenty years later by Dixon, and shown to be a versatile oxidase capable of employing reducible dyes as hydrogen-acceptors.

Uricase, or urate oxidase, occurs in the livers of mammals, and in the kidneys of oxen, pigs, dogs, rats and frogs. It is absent from the tissues of animals, such as man and higher apes, that are uricotelic in that they excrete purine nitrogen in the form of uric acid. Uricase oxidises uric acid into a precursor of allantoin, preparatory to excretion.

Phenol oxidases catalyse the oxidation of monophenols to o-dihydroxy compounds, and then to o-quinones. They can be classified in terms of substrate preference into monophenol and polyphenol oxidases, but the distinction is not precise.

$$+ \tfrac{1}{2}O_2 \qquad\qquad + \tfrac{1}{2}O_2$$

Phenol. → o-Quinone. $+ H_2O$

Phenol oxidases are common among plants, but, with the exception of tyrosinase, are rarely found in animals.

Tyrosinase occurs in most animals and plants, notably clover, potato and higher fungi. It functions in the formation of red and brown melanoid pigments from tyrosine, and is responsible for the natural colouring of hair, fur and skin. In the condition of albinism (recessive whiteness), there is complete failure to inherit the enzyme; in dominant whiteness an enzyme inhibitor operates to prevent the formation of melanin; in parti-colouring, either the enzyme or the substrate is unequally distributed in the skin or cuticle.

Melanin production has been exploited for defence by the octopus and the squid, Sepia. The chemistry of the pigments is discussed in Chapter 12.

Polyphenol oxidases, including catechol oxidase, or laccase, are responsible for the discoloration of cut or over-ripe fruit and tubers. The quinones produced are very reactive compounds and can enter into oxidation-reduction sequences, or undergo polymerisation, as in the production of melanins. The guaiacum colour reaction given by fresh plant tissues is attributed to a preliminary oxidation of the plant phenols by local oxidases, with production of o-quinones, which oxidise the guaiacum chromogen to a blue pigment.

Phenol oxidases are copper-containing enzymes, and are inhibited by cyanide, sulphide, and other copper immobilisers.

Cytochrome oxidase is an outpost enzyme, the last in the aerobic respiratory chain. It transfers metabolically discarded atomic hydrogen to molecular oxygen, and thereby restores it to the environment in the form of water. The enzyme is an essential part of the equipment of all aerobic organisms.

In 1885, Ehrlich showed that animals, after injection of a mixture of p-phenylenediamine and α-naphthol, developed a blue colour in their tissues, which was caused by the local formation of an indophenol pigment. Batelli and Stern in 1912 found that this property was displayed by almost all mammalian tissues, and ascribed it to an enzyme, *indophenol oxidase*. Keilin, in 1929, discovered the significance of this enzyme when he showed that it was able to reoxidise cytochrome and thus form an essential part of the respiratory chain.

Peroxidases, or hydroperoxidases, catalyse reactions involving the decomposition of hydrogen peroxide:

$$AH_2 + H_2O_2 \rightarrow A + 2H_2O; \quad H_2O_2 + H_2O_2 \rightarrow O_2 + 2H_2O.$$

Where the reaction involves two molecules of hydrogen peroxide, with release of molecular oxygen, the enzyme is termed a *catalase*. Peroxidases occur chiefly in plants, horse radish and potato tuber being rich sources. Animal peroxidases include cytochrome *c* peroxidase, lactoperoxidase in milk, and verdoperoxidase in leucocytes. Peroxidases, apart from the highly selective cytochrome peroxidase, catalyse the oxidation of diphenols, aminophenols, urate, and some other reductants. They can be detected by the pigments they produce from chromogens such as benzidine, amidopyrine, pyrogallol, and guaiacum resin, in presence of hydrogen peroxide.

The peroxidases are hæmo-proteins, containing iron held in a porphyrin framework. Other hæm compounds, including hæmoglobin, display similar but less powerful catalytic properties, which are made use of in clinical and forensic tests for blood. Because of their heat-stability, these non-enzymes can be described as pseudo-peroxidases.

Catalases are present in all aerobic tissues, including red corpuscles and liver, from which one has been isolated in crystalline form (Sumner, 1937). The catalytic destruction of hydrogen peroxide is very vigorous, at least 1,000 molecules of H_2O_2 per second at ordinary temperatures, which gives little opportunity for the demonstration of other peroxidase effects.

Cytochrome *c* peroxidase, like cytochrome *c* oxidase, catalyses the dehydrogenation of reduced cytochrome *c*, but, differs from the oxidase in that it employs H_2O_2 instead of O_2. All the peroxidases, being iron-containing enzymes, like some other dehydrogenases are completely inhibited by cyanide, carbon monoxide, or sodium azide, NaN_3, in concentrations as low as 0.01 M to 0.001 M. Cyanide and carbon monoxide effects are of more than academic interest, since, by inhibition of one single enzyme, cytochrome oxidase, they can stop the entire traffic of aerobic respiration in the vital centres, with fatal results that are frequently demonstrated, unintentionally or intentionally.

The inhibition effect of CO on iron-containing, but not copper-containing enzymes, is reversed by exposure to strong light, a phenomenon of analytical value in the identification of cytochrome oxidase in tissues.

The catalytic property of the metallo-enzymes resides in the ability of the multi-valent metal to alternate between two states of oxidation by losing or gaining electrons.

$$Fe^{2+} \rightleftharpoons Fe^{3+} + e'; \quad Cu^{2+} + e' \rightleftharpoons Cu^+.$$

B3. Transaminases

Transaminases catalyse the reversible exchange of an amino group between a donor α-amino acid and an acceptor α-oxo acid, or α-keto acid.

$$R_1.CH.COOH \quad R_2.C.COOH \quad R_1.C.COOH \quad R_2.CH.COOH$$
$$\underset{NH_2}{|} \quad + \quad \underset{O}{\|} \quad \rightharpoonup \quad \underset{O}{\|} \quad + \quad \underset{NH_2}{|}$$

Any one of the biological amino acids can act as donor, those in most general use being glutamic acid, $HOOC.CH_2.CH_2.CH(NH_2).COOH$, in animal tissues, and aspartic acid, $HOOC.CH_2.CH(NH_2).COOH$, in plants. Acceptors include pyruvic acid, α-oxoglutaric acid, (or α-ketoglutaric acid), and oxaloacetic acid.

Oxaloacetic acid.

$\rightarrow HOOC.CH_2.CO.COOH$
$+$
$HOOC.CH_2.CH_2.CH(NH_2).COOH$
$+$
$\rightarrow CH_3.CO.COOH$
Pyruvic acid.

Aspartic acid.

$\rightharpoonup HOOC.CH_2.CH(NH_2).COOH \leftarrow$
$+$
$HOOC.CH_2.CH_2.CO.COOH \leftarrow$
$+$
$CH_3.CH(NH_2).COOH \leftarrow$
Alanine.

Glutamic Transamination

The transamination mechanism enables the organism to deaminate amino acids, store amino units as glutamic or aspartic acids, and provide amino groups for the construction of new amino acids. Surplus amino nitrogen is disposed of as urea, uric acid, or urinary ammonium ions.

The co-enzyme of the transaminases is phosphopyridoxal, derived from the pyridoxine vitamins. By means of its aldehyde group it combines with, and removes, the amino group of the donor acid. Then, in the form of phosphopyridoxamine, it transfers the amino group to the accepting oxo-acid.

$$\begin{array}{c} R \\ | \\ HO-\!\!\!\diagup\!\!\!\diagdown\!\!\!-CH_2.O-\!\!-PO(OH)_2 \\ H_3C-\!\!\!\diagdown\!\!\!\diagup \\ N \end{array}$$
Pyridoxine.

Phosphopyridoxal: $R = -CHO$

Intermediate compounds:
$R = CH=N-CHX.COOH$,
$R = -CH_2-N=CX.COOH$
Phosphopyridoxamine: $R = -CH_2-NH_2$

B4. Transacylases

The transfer of acetyl units, $CH_3.CO$, is the chief linking process between anaerobic and aerobic departments of metabolism. The units are provided by pyruvate, the end-product in glycolysis, the anaerobic degradation of glucose, and by cleavage products formed during the degradation of long-chain aliphatic acids. From a carrier, acetyl-co-enzyme A, or acetyl-co A, the units are fed to the citric cycle for complete combustion to CO_2 and H_2O. The process is operated by a class of enzymes, the **transacylases,** present in all aerobic organisms, and capable of transferring other two-carbon units, including hydroxyacetyl, $HO.CH_2.CO$, and imino acetyl, $HN:CH.CO$. Alternatively, transferred units can be employed for the construction of acetylcholine and for acetylation reactions, such as the construction of citrate from oxaloacetate, and formation of acetylcholine.

Co-enzyme A, CoA, the acetyl carrier, is a derivative of adenosine diphosphate (p. 199), in which the terminal hydroxyl of the diphosphate chain has been condensed with the terminal hydroxyl of *pantotheine*, the operative form of the vitamin pantothenic acid (p. 226). The ribose unit, in addition, carries a phosphate group replacing the hydroxyl at C3 in the sugar ring.

$$\overset{\displaystyle \text{Pantotheine, R = HO—}}{\underset{\displaystyle \underset{\text{Pantothenic acid}}{\underset{\text{R = HO—}}{}}}{\text{R—CH}_2\text{—C(CH}_3)_2\text{—CH(OH)—CO—NH—CH}_2\text{—CH}_2\text{—CO——NH—CH}_2\text{—CH}_2\text{—SH}}}$$

Acetyl uptake and transfer is effected by addition of the acetyl unit to the terminal thiol group of the co-enzyme.

$$\underset{\text{CoA.}}{\text{R—SH}} + \text{CO.CH}_3 \rightleftharpoons \underset{\text{Acetyl-CoA.}}{\text{R—S—CO.CH}_3.}$$

B5. Transmethylases

Transmethylases, prominent in liver and in some plants, transfer methyl groups required for the construction of sarcosine from glycine, anserine from carnosine, creatine from guanidinoacetate, choline from ethanolamine, and adrenaline from noradrenaline. The methyl carrier is S-adenosyl methionine, a derivative of adenosine (p. 326), in which the hydroxyl of the —CH₂.OH side-chain has been replaced by the amino acid methionine in such a way as to form a sulphonium link carrying a high-energy transferable methyl unit.

$$\underset{\text{S-Adenosyl-methionine.}}{\text{R——CH}_2\text{—}\overset{+}{\text{S}}\text{—CH}_2.\text{CH}_2.\text{CH.COO}^-}$$
$$\underset{\text{CH}_3 \qquad\qquad \text{NH}_2}{}$$

By demethylation, the methionine radical is degraded and released as homocysteine, $HS—CH_2.CH_2CH(NH_2).COOH$, which can be used as a collector of methyl groups from betaines.

B6. Transglycosylases

These enzymes transfer whole glycosyl units, i.e. simple sugar groupings, from one carbohydrate molecule to another, from one part of a large molecule to another part of the same molecule or from a carbohydrate to a noncarbohydrate combination. In many instances the glucosyl group is transferred to phosphate and in these cases the enzymes are, of course, phosphorylases.

Many of these enzymes play an important role in the synthesis of carbohydrate and in building up large carbohydrate molecules. Only a small number of the total of thirty or more occur in animals; the majority are found in plants or bacteria.

From their nature some enzymes in this class have similar actions to those of the glycosidases.

Transketolases and transaldolases are also concerned in the photosynthesis of sugars but transfer much smaller units.

Transketolases reversibly transfer hydroxyacetyl units, $HO.CH_2.CO$, from the ends of ketose molecules to aldehyde acceptors.

$$R_1.CO.CH_2.OH \qquad R_1.CHO$$
$$+ \qquad\overline{\qquad\qquad}\qquad +$$
$$R_2.CHO \qquad R_2.CO.CH_2.OH$$

In this way, sugar chains are elongated or curtailed, as in the production of sedoheptulose, $C_7H_{14}O_7$, from ribose, or 4- and 5-carbon sugars from fructose. Transketolases differ from transacetylases, which also effect the transfer of hydroxyacetyl, in that they employ pyrophosphothiamine as co-enzyme, and not co-enzyme A.

Transaldolases catalyse comparable reactions involving transfer of dihydroxy-acetone residues, $HO.CH_2.CO.CH(OH)$—, to aldehydes.

Both these classes of enzymes are prominent in the photosynthesis of sugars, and in special departments of sugar metabolism.

B7. Transpeptidases

In addition to their hydrolytic activity certain of the peptidases also catalyse the transfer of amino acids and peptides. The glutamyl radical is often involved in these transfers.

C. MISCELLANEOUS ENZYMES

The remaining two or three hundred members of the enzyme population are not amenable to simple general classifications. Many of them can be described as Adductases or Deductases, in that they catalyse the addition or removal of an intact molecule, without involving hydrolysis or group-transfer. Others are desmolases, capable of breaking carbon-to-carbon bonds.

Dehydrases remove or add H_2O. They are universally distributed, and operate in the glycolytic and lipolytic processes, and in the citric cycle.

Enolase, a magnesium-containing enzyme, catalyses the dehydration of the low-energy substrate, 2-phosphoglycerate, to the high-energy phospho*enol*-pyruvate:

$$\begin{array}{ccc} CH_2.OH & & CH_2 \\ | & & || \\ H.C.O\text{—}o & \rightarrow & C.O\text{—}o \quad o = \text{—}PO(OH)_2 \\ | & & | \\ COOH & & COOH \end{array}$$

The enzyme is inhibited by fluoride, which immobilises the Mg as a fluoro-phosphate.

Crotonase, or lipid ene-acyl-CoA hydrase, belongs to a class of enzymes which add groups to double bonds. It operates on lipid-acid-co-enzyme A complexes formed during the metabolism of the lipid acids:

$$R.CH = CH.CO\text{—}CoA + H_2O \text{———} R.CH_2.CH(OH).CO\text{——}CoA.$$

Aconitase, a component of the citric cycle, catalyses the interconversion of citric and *iso*-citric acid, by successive dehydration to *cis*-aconitic acid, and hydration to the substrate isomer:

$$
\begin{array}{ccc}
\underset{\text{Citric acid.}}{\begin{array}{l} CH_2.COOH \\ | \\ C(OH).COOH \\ | \\ CH_2.COOH \end{array}} \quad \overset{\rightharpoonup}{H_2O} \quad
\begin{array}{l} CH_2.COOH \\ | \\ C.COOH \\ || \\ CH.COOH \end{array} \quad \overset{\rightharpoonup}{H_2O} \quad
\underset{\text{Iso-Citric acid.}}{\begin{array}{l} CH_2.COOH \\ | \\ CH.COOH \\ | \\ CH(OH).COOH \end{array}}
\end{array}
$$

Fumarase, a component of the citric cycle, powerfully catalyses the reversible hydration of fumaric to malic acid:

$$HOOC.CH{=}CH.COOH + H_2O \rightleftharpoons HOOC.CH_2.CH(OH).COOH$$

Fumaric acid.   Malic acid.

Decarboxylases are desmolases catalysing the release of carbon dioxide, by breaking the carbon-to-carbon linkage. Pyruvic decarboxylase, present in yeasts and bacteria, but not in animal tissues, decarboxylates pyruvic and other -oxo acids to the corresponding aldehydes:

$$CH_3.CO.COOH \text{———} CH_3.CHO + CO_2$$

Pyruvic acid.   Acetaldehyde.

Pyruvic decarboxylase operates in the penultimate stage in the production of alcohol from sugars by yeast fermentation. Amino acid decarboxylases catalyse the non-oxidative decarboxylation of α-amino acids into the corresponding amines. They are highly-selective enzymes, and can be employed analytically for the identification of amino acids. These decarboxylases mostly employ phosphopyridoxal as amino carrier. The general reaction is:

$$
\underset{\text{α-Amino acid.}}{\begin{array}{l} R.CH.COOH \\ | \\ NH_2 \end{array}} \quad \text{———} \quad
\underset{\text{Amine.}}{\begin{array}{l} R.CH_2 \\ | \\ NH_2 \end{array}} + CO_2
$$

The end-products of these decarboxylations are strong bases with special physiological properties; 5-hydroxytryptamine, or serotonin, is a hormone; histamine is a factor in " shock " and allergic responses. Carbonic anhydrase, a non-desmolase, catalyses the reversible hydration of carbon dioxide to carbonic acid: $CO_2 + H_2O \rightleftharpoons H_2CO_3$. It is a zinc-containing enzyme present in plants and animal tissues, including red corpuscles, brain cortex, gastric

Representative Amino Acid Decarboxylases

Source.	Substrate.	Product.
Bacteria	Arginine	Agmatine
Bacteria	Aspartic acid	Alanine
Brain, plants, yeast, bacteria	Glutamic acid	Aminobutyric acid
Animal tissues, bacteria	Histidine	Histamine
Bacteria	Lysine	Cadaverine
Bacteria	Ornithine	Putrescine
Animal tissues, bacteria	Tyrosine	Tyramine
Animal tissues	5-hydroxy tryptophan	5-hydroxy tryptamine

mucosa, pancreas and liver, and operates in the transport of CO_2 by the blood, the secretion of H^+ by the stomach and kidney, and the calcification of egg shells.

Aldolase, or zymohexase, a universally-distributed desmolase, catalyses the reversible fission of fructose-1,6-diphosphate into glyceraldehyde-3-phosphate and dihydroxyacetone phosphate, and thus effects the resolution of a 6-carbon sugar into two trioses, a necessary stage in glycolysis.

KINETICS OF ENZYME ACTION

An enzyme is where it acts. Enzymes were discovered first by their ability to alter particular substances, later defined as their substrates. In this property their powers range from the absolute specificity displayed by urease and D-glucose oxidase to the class-selectivity of the esterases and amylases. When the catalytic character of enzyme activity was recognised it became necessary to measure the speed at which they worked, with the object of finding the conditions that determined their activity and the mechanisms they employed. By estimating the amount of substrate transformed in a given time, under standard conditions, by a known weight of the enzyme preparation, an arbitrary unit of activity is obtained which is used in measuring the potency of the successive fractions obtained during the purification of the enzyme.

Progress Curves. When the activity of an enzyme is measured over a period of time, in terms of the amount of substrate removed or product formed, a progress curve is obtained, characterised by a fall in rate as the reaction proceeds. This may be because the chemical reaction catalysed by the enzyme is approaching its steady-state of equilibrium, or because the fall in substrate concentration is such that the enzyme is no longer saturated to a point of maximum activity, or because the enzyme is being inhibited by accumulated products, or is undergoing spontaneous denaturation.

Velocity Curves. By measuring the amount of substrate transformed at the start of a reaction, when the rate is at a maximum, curves can be drawn showing the relationship of the initial velocity to any one of the other variables: (1) substrate concentration, (2) enzyme concentration, (3) temperature, (4) pH, (5) activators, (6) inhibitors.

(1) Velocity/Substrate curves show an increase in velocity with substrate concentration until a value is reached when the enzyme is completely saturated. The velocity is then at its maximum, and is not increased by increase in substrate concentration.

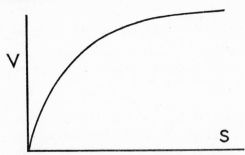

Typical velocity/substrate concentration curve.

(2) Velocity/Enzyme curves show a linear increase in velocity with enzyme concentration.

(3) Velocity/Temperature. The speed of the reaction reaches a maximum with rise in temperature, and then falls, as the progressive thermal inactivation of the enzyme overtakes the accelerating effect of temperature increase. This maximum, the optimal temperature, is not sharply defined and depends on the rate of heating and the concentrations of enzyme and of substrate, which when present in excess can protect the enzyme from inactivation. The temperature coefficient, or change in rate per unit change in temperature, can be found by working with systems within the safety region below 35° C. Under such conditions, for a rise in temperature of 10°, say from 20° to 30°, the coefficient, Q_{10}, is 2 to 3, which denotes that the rate of the reaction has been increased two- to threefold.

(4) Velocity/pH. The speed of an enzyme-catalysed reaction rises and falls with change in hydrogen ion concentration, and shows a maximum in a narrow range, the optimum pH. On either side of this the enzyme is progressively less effective and may undergo irreversible inactivation at extremes of pH.

The optimum pH response is a characteristic of all enzymes and is a consequence of their protein structure, the ionic state of which is determined by the hydrogen ion concentration of the surroundings.

$$\text{Enzyme} \quad H_3N^+.E.COOH \underset{+H^+}{\overset{+OH'}{\rightleftarrows}} H_3N^+.E.COO' \underset{+H^+}{\overset{+OH'}{\rightleftarrows}} H_2N.E.COO' \quad \text{Enzyme}$$
Enzyme cation   Enzyme anion

Substrate electrolytes are also affected by change in pH, and the optimum conditions for the reaction are not necessarily those for the iso-electric point of the enzyme.

Representative optimum pH values are: lipase, pancreatic, 8; castor oil bean, 4·7; trypsin, 7·8 to 8·7; urease, catalase, 6; amylase, pancreatic, 6·9; malt, 4·6 to 5·2; maltase, 6·5; sucrase, 4·5; pepsin, 1·5 to 2·5.

Kinetic Characterisation of Enzymes

The Michaelis Constant. A process catalysed by an enzyme can be represented as a chain-reaction:

Enzyme + Substrate —— Enzyme-Substrate —— Enzyme + Products

The concentration of the unstable enzyme-substrate complex, ES, determines the speed of the reaction, and can be related to its precursors by the equation:

$$E \times S = K_s \, ES,$$

where E and S denote the respective concentrations of unbound enzyme and free substrate, and K_s is the dissociation constant. Its reciprocal, $1/K_s$, is an index of the affinity of an enzyme for a particular substrate.

In order to obtain a method for calculating K_s, Michaelis and Menten (1913), by making simplifying assumptions obtained the equation:

$$V(S + K_m) = V_{max} \, S,$$

where V is the velocity of the reaction for a given concentration of substrate, S; V_{max} is the maximum velocity attainable; and K_m is the Michaelis constant, which under ordinary working conditions is assumed to be equal to K_s. When the substrate concentration is such that the velocity is half that of the maximum, the equation is $V(S' + K_m) = 2VS'$, and K_m is numerically equal to S'. By this means, the constant can be calculated from the rate-substrate curves, in the absence of other data regarding the molecular weight and concentration of the enzyme.

The Michaelis equation can be rearranged to give a straight-line equation,

$$\frac{1}{V} = \frac{K_m}{S V_{max}} + \frac{1}{V_{max}}$$

In this form of the equation, popularised by Lineweaver and Burk (1934), $1/V$ is plotted against $1/S$ in the velocity-concentration curve.

The " Lineweaver-Burk plot " is convenient. It gives a straight line, cutting the vertical axis at the point where x (or $1/S$) $= 0$, and $y = 1/V_{max}$. If the line is produced backwards it will cut the horizontal axis at the point giving $-1/K_m$. In this way, both V_{max} and K_m can be obtained by inspection from the Lineweaver-Burk plot.

Michaelis constants have been calculated for a number of purified enzymes acting under specified conditions. Thus, for urease at pH 7·1 and 20·8° C., K_m is 0·004. As K_m is a dissociation constant, the greater the affinity of the enzyme for the substrate, the lower the value of K_m.

Inhibition Effects. A competitive inhibitor is one that competes with the substrate for possession of the enzyme, and thus retards the formation of the enzyme-substrate complex. K_m, which is inversely proportional to *ES*, is increased in value. The maximum velocity of the reaction is unchanged, provided sufficient substrate is present to swamp the inhibitor. Conversely, a non-competitive inhibitor by combining with the enzyme lessens the amount available, and the maximum attainable velocity of the reaction is lowered. K_m is unaffected, as it is independent of the amount of enzyme present. These differences can be seen by inspection of the Lineweaver-Burk plot.

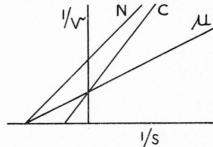

U, Uninhibited reaction.
C, Competitively-inhibited reaction.
N, Non-competitively-inhibited
    reaction.

In both types of inhibition the slope of the curve is raised. In C, the line cuts the vertical axis at the same point as in the uninhibited reaction, showing that $1/V_{max}$, and therefore V_{max}, is unchanged. When extended, it cuts the horizontal axis at a point nearer 0, showing that $1/K_m$ is decreased and therefore K_m is increased.

In N, the line cuts the vertical axis at a higher level, showing that $1/V_{max}$ is increased, and therefore V_{max} is decreased. When extended, it cuts the horizontal axis at the same point as in the uninhibited reaction, showing that $1/K_m$ and K_m are unchanged.

Turn-over Number. This may be defined as the number of substrate molecules transformed in unit time by one active centre in an enzyme, working under standard favourable conditions. As the number of active centres per enzyme are known only for a few catalysts, turn-over numbers are expressed provisionally in term of enzyme molecules, or other equivalent. Turn-over values per minute, per molecule, at 20° C., include: alcohol dehydrogenase, 2×10^4; polyphenol oxidase, 7×10^4. The speed record is held by catalase, which can decompose over 2 million molecules of hydrogen peroxide per minute, at 0° C. As catalase has four active hæm groups per molecule, the turn-over number, at 0°, is $1 \cdot 25 \times 10^6$.

EXTRACTION AND PURIFICATION OF ENZYMES

Enzymes are harvested from rich sources that were discovered accidentally or by systematic exploration of tissues. The invention of a delicate analytical method, such as Thunberg's vacuum tube, Barcroft's manometer, or Conway's diffusion unit, has stimulated the investigation of particular classes of enzymes.

Rich sources, such as seeds and glands, may be extracted directly after grinding or mincing; tissues and cell suspensions, in general, require special treatment. The material is disintegrated at low temperature by grinding with a neutral solvent, such as 0·44 M sucrose. The resulting homogenate is fractionated by being centrifuged at a series of increasing speeds. In this way five fractions can be separated in order of particle diameter (mμ): intact cells and tissue debris (10,000 to 20,000); nuclei (6,000); mitochondria (300 to 750); microsomes (60 to 250); supernatant liquid.

The solid fractions are purified by being resuspended and recentrifuged. When these fractions are tested it is found that cytochrome oxidase, the dehydrogenases of glutamate, iso-citrate and succinate, and the co-enzymes, are exclusively or largely concentrated in the mitochondria; the esterases and phosphatases are in the microsomes; and most of the remaining enzymes are soluble and remain in the supernatant fluid.

After extraction with water or a dilute buffer, the extract is purified by dialysis, which removes small molecule solutes, and then is submitted to systematic fractionation. The methods include:

(1) Flocculation by alcohols or acetone at low temperature. Urease, the first enzyme to be crystallised, was isolated by the simple process of extracting fat-free jack bean flour with 31·6 per cent. acetone and allowing the filtrate to remain at 0° C. (Sumner, 1926). Crystalline catalase was obtained, similarly, by dioxan treatment of liver extract.

(2) Fractional salting-out by ammonium sulphate. This method was used by Northrop in the isolation of the enzymes of the stomach and pancreas.

(3) Fractional adsorption at pH 5 to 6 by calcium phosphate gel, or activated alumina gel. In this way, irrelevant material is removed, or the required enzyme is adsorbed, and can be eluted by another solvent. Alumina adsorbs acid dyes, such as eosin, and enzyme anions, including lipases, peptidases and peroxidases. Kaolin, an aluminium silicate, adsorbs basic dyes, such as methylene blue, and enzyme cations, including trypsin.

The separation of enzymes is complicated by the fact, that, apart from those in the digestive secretions, very few enzymes operate as individuals. They are members of closely-organised teams within the cell, incessantly active, yet obedient to control by hormones and other directors. Although working conditions provide neither optimum temperature, optimum pH, nor optimum substrate concentration, it can be calculated than an intra-cellular enzyme molecule may be transforming a hundred or more substrate molecules per second.

"As a very active cell, such as baker's yeast, metabolises 10^{-6} of a gram molecule of O_2 per gram dry weight per second, we can get some idea of the possible complexity of the transformation undergone in it. If 5 per cent. of the dry weight of the cell consists of enzymes of an average molecular weight of 50,000, then 1 gm. dry weight contains 10^{-6} gm. molecule of such enzymes, and less than 1 per cent. of this would be required for any particular process, e.g. the activation of O_2. In other words, the average atom on its metabolic path through the cell may be dealt with by more than 100 catalysts in succession."

Haldane, 1930.

Enzyme Induction

Every cell has an endowment of constitutive enzymes, so called because they are part of its natural equipment. In response to the stimulus of a specific foreign agent, cells can construct induced, or adaptive enzymes, that enable them to attack the stranger, and exploit it for nutrition. This property is displayed prominently by micro-organisms in the course of their survival and evolution; a single bacterial species may be trained to catalyse several hundred different chemical reactions.

Higher organisms do not show the ability to manufacture useful induced enzymes to any considerable extent, apart from what may be implied in man's zealously-acquired tolerance for alcohol.

The enzyme inducer is usually the prospective substrate of the new enzyme, or a closely related compound. The effect may be transitory, and eventually disappear when the cell or culture is kept deprived of the new substrate. Alternatively, it may involve a permanent change in the genetic mechanism and produce a new strain or species.

A false-induction effect may be shown when a cell population contains a few individuals naturally capable of attacking the foreign substrate, but held in check by lack of sufficient nutrient. When the inducer is supplied the growth of these cells is promoted by improved economic conditions. True induction can be distinguished from false induction by the fact that it can be demonstrated in conditions when increase in cell population is halted, as when cell division is prevented completely by β-dichlorodiethyl sulphide.

Examples of enzyme induction are the production of β-galactosidase and lysine decarboxylase when *Esch. coli* is grown in presence of galactose and lysine, respectively.

Mechanism of Enzyme Action

An enzyme-catalysed reaction can be regarded as a three-stage process: adsorption of the substrate by the enzyme, activation of the substrate while in the enzyme field, and generation of the products.

Substrate Adsorption. The evidence for the preliminary formation of an unstable enzyme-substrate complex is partly inferential, from the success of kinetic predictions based on the Michaelis-Menton hypothesis, and partly experimental, such as the spectroscopic recognition of intermediate complexes formed during the decomposition of H_2O_2 by peroxidases (Chance, 1943–). The fact that for a given concentration of enzyme there is a limiting concentration of substrate beyond which the reaction rate is not increased, suggests

243

that enzyme potency resides in a surface and is maximum when this surface is saturated. The adsorbed substrate is held at two or more points by effector groups on the enzyme surface. The pattern of these groups is precise, and requires a corresponding pattern in the substrate, which must approximate in such a way that the two binding-planes are less than one millimicron apart. In this way, the high degree of enzyme selectivity is explained, especially as regards choice between optical isomers of amino acids and sugars. It also explains the ability of compounds resembling the substrate to inhibit the catalysis by competing for effector groups belonging to the enzyme.

Thus, malonic acid, $HOOC.CH_2.COOH$, inhibits the dehydrogenation of succinic acid, $HOOC.CH_2.CH_2.COOH$, by succinic dehydrogenase; compounds containing quaternary nitrogen, R_3N^+—, inhibit the hydrolysis of acetylcholine by esterases.

Substrate Activation. The nature and causes of the changes undergone by the substrate while in the enzyme field are obscure. Dixon and Webb (1959), after consideration of more than a dozen different theories, find none of them free from objection, and all of them lacking experimental proof.

A simple example is the " Strain Theory " (Haldane, 1930), according to which the substrate molecule, A–B, is stretched by the pull of the effector groups until the bond becomes sufficiently weak to be attacked by water or other molecules.

Since the majority of enzymes can be regarded as transferases, it may be that substrate activation consists in splitting off a free radical, which reacts with water or some other acceptor. A mechanism of this kind has been suggested to explain the activity of the iron-containing peroxidases.

Illustrative Reactions

Oxidations Catalysed by Iron. *Tartrate Dehydrogenation.* Mix a few drops of 2 per cent. ferrous sulphate with 5 ml. of a dilute (1 to 5 per cent.) solution of tartaric acid. Add 5 drops of 3 per cent. (or " 10 volume ") hydrogen peroxide. Mix, and let remain for a couple of minutes. Make alkaline with 20 per cent. sodium hydroxide. A deep violet colour develops, which may be intensified by ferric ions.
The test depends on the dehydrogenation of tartaric acid,

$$HOOC.CH(OH).CH(OH).COOH,$$

to dihydroxymaleic acid,

$$HOOC.C(OH)=C(OH).COOH,$$

which as an ene-diol gives a colour with ferric ions, also formed in the reaction. Glyceric acid,

$$HO.CH_2.CH(OH).COOH,$$

gives a similar colour. Malic acid,

$$HOOC.CH(OH).CH_2.COOH,$$

is dehydrogenated to oxaloacetic acid,

$$HOOC.CO.CH_2.COOH,$$

which gives a red colour with ferric ions, prior to addition of alkali. The applications of the test are discussed by its discoverer (Fenton, 1906). If a chromogen such as guaiacum resin or pyramidon is used instead of the tartrate, a colour develops rapidly in the neutral mixture.

Mechanism. Ferrous ions, Fe^{2+}, by liberating an electron bring about the fission of hydrogen peroxide into a hydroxyl ion, OH', or : OH, and a neutral hydroxyl radical, .OH, which is a highly active free radical. The ferrous ion is oxidised, or de-electronated to the ferric state, Fe^{3+}, the gain in positive charge being balanced by the OH'.

$$Fe^{2+} + HO..OH \longrightarrow Fe^{3+} + : OH' + .OH$$

The hydroxyl free radical attacks and removes hydrogen atoms, especially from adjacent carbon atoms that also carry hydroxyl groups.

$$-CH(OH)-CH(OH)- + 2.OH \longrightarrow -C(OH) = C(OH)- + 2H_2O.$$

Under these conditions, the iron is not acting as a true catalyst, because it is eventually converted to the ferric state, in which it is unable to effect the fission.

Pseudo-peroxidase Effect of Hæm Pigments. Mix 5 ml. of very dilute blood (1 in 5,000) with 5 drops of the chromogen reagent (3 per cent. alcoholic guaiacum resin). Add 3 per cent. hydrogen peroxide, slowly, drop by drop, shaking between each addition. A blue colour develops. Repeat the test using (i) benzidine in glacial acetic acid, and (ii) pyramidon in alcohol as chromogens instead of guaiacum (p. 357). Repeat the tests, having previously boiled and cooled the blood. The results are positive, showing that the catalyst is heat-stable, and not an enzyme.

True Peroxidase Effect of Milk Peroxidase. Dilute 2 ml. of fresh milk with 5 ml. of water. Add 5 drops of the guaiacum reagent, and about 10 drops of turpentine that has become activated by exposure to light and moisture. Shake the mixture. A blue colour develops. Previously boiled and cooled milk no longer gives the reaction, which is caused by an enzyme, and not a heat-stable catalyst. Hydrogen peroxide may be used instead of oxidised turpentine, but is liable to destroy the milk enzyme. These reactions depend on the reversible oxidation and reduction of an iron atom. These reactions differ from those initiated by ferrous ions in that they are catalytic, a mechanism operating to restore the iron continuously to the ferrous form.

Oxidase Reactions of Potato. Suspensions in water of fresh scrapings of potato and other tubers give an immediate blue colour with the guaiacum reagent, in absence of added peroxide. The system is heat-labile and enzymatic. Tyrosinase in the tuber, in presence of free oxygen, converts tyrosine to a quinone, 3,4-dioxyphenylalanine, that can oxidise the guaiacum.

Pseudo-catalase Effects. Ferrous ions do not release oxygen from hydrogen peroxide, unless the solution is made alkaline, when they undergo atmospheric oxidation to the ferric state. Ferric ions react directly in alkaline solution:

$$4Fe^{3+} + 2H_2O_2 \longrightarrow 4Fe^{2+} + 4H^+ + 2O_2 \longrightarrow 4Fe^{3+} + 2H_2O + O_2$$

Hæmatin, or ferric hæm, which forms spontaneously in shed blood, has a powerful effect, as shown by the rapid liberation of oxygen gas when 10 drops of 3 per cent. H_2O_2 are added to 5 ml. of a 1 in 1,000 dilution of blood. The reaction is catalytic and heat-stable. True catalase effects are displayed by aqueous suspensions of potato scrapings, and adipose and other animal tissues.

General References

"Advances in Enzymology," Vol. I. Ed. by F. F. Nord (1940). New York; London.

Baldwin, E. (1952), " Dynamic Aspects of Biochemistry." 2nd Ed. Cambridge.

Bergmann, M. (1942), " Classification of proteolytic enzymes." *Adv. Enzymol.*, **2**, 49.

Bray, H. G., and K. White (1957), " Kinetics and Thermodynamics in Biochemistry." London.

Colowick, S. P., and N. O. Kaplan (1955), " Methods in Enzymology," Vol. I. New York.

Dawes, E. A. (1956), " Quantitative Problems in Biochemistry." Edinburgh; London.

Dixon, M. (1949), " Multi-Enzyme Systems." Cambridge.

Dixon, M., and E. C. Webb (1959), " Enzymes." London; New York.

Gale, E. F. (1947), " Chemical Activities of Bacteria." London.

" Enzymes," Ed. by H. O. Gaebler (1956). New York; London.

Haldane, J. B. S. (1930), " Enzymes." London.

Lardy, H., *et al.* (1948), " Respiratory Enzymes." Minneapolis.

Nielands, J. B., and P. K. Stumpf (1955), " Outlines of Enzyme Chemistry." New York; London.

Northrop, J. H., *et al.* (1948), " Crystalline Enzymes." Columbia.

Sumner, J. B., and K. Myrbäck (1950–52), " The Enzymes," Vols. I to IV. New York.

Sumner, J. B., and G. F. Somers (1947), " Chemistry and Methods of Enzymes." New York.

" Symposium on the Mechanism of Enzyme Action " (1953). Ed. by B. Glass. Baltimore.

" Some aspects of enzyme research." *British med. Bull.*, 1953, **9**, No. 2.

Chapter 15 Digestion

Digestion is the chemical procedure whereby food materials are made available for the nutrition of cells and tissues. In general, it comprises a series of enzyme-catalysed hydrolyses that resolve the insoluble or colloidal lipids, starches and proteins into assimilable units. Green plants and other autotrophic organisms absorb nutrients in the simplest form, and do not need a digestive mechanism. Animals, parasitic plants and other heterotrophs derive their organic nutrients from food materials that require to be digested. Among monocellular types, this is done by liberation of enzymes into the culture medium. Higher animals have attained mobility and independence by the employment of a digestive tract, which forms a mobile alimentary environment that is kept replenished with food, irrigated by digestive secretions, and, in its lower part, occupied by beneficent or innocuous bacteria.

The Human Digestive System

The digestive system in man includes oral, gastric, and intestinal departments, each with its characteristic structure, secretions, and movements. This involves an elaborate mechanism of control, which is entrusted to the autonomic nervous system, the apparatus of the unconscious self. Psychosomatic and other factors operate in determining the volume and composition of the digestive secretions, with the result that data for the human subject is apt to be inconsistent. Each digestive juice appears to be formed from a solvent secretion, isotonic with the blood plasma, and qualitatively similar in composition, except in that it is free from plasma colloids and glucose. This solvent is enriched by addition of the enzymes and other characteristic solutes of the digestive secretion, depending on the rate at which the gland is working. The more rapidly the gland is compelled to work, the more closely does its secretion conform to the composition of the solvent.

Oral Digestion.

Saliva, the mixed product of three pairs of glands, acts as a lubricant for the mouth cavity, a solvent and adhesive for food materials, and has a hydrolytic action on starch, which may persist for some time after the food has reached the stomach. The pH ranges from 6·3 to 7·8, and rises after secretion because of escape of CO_2. The electrolytes, in m.equiv. per litre are: Na^+, up to 90 (parotid), 33 (mixed); K^+, 20; Cl^-, up to 50 (parotid), 34 (mixed); HCO_3^-, up to 60 (parotid), 15 (mixed); $H_2PO_4^-$, 3 to 7.

Composition of human mixed saliva, in mg. per 100 ml.: total protein, 320 (mucoproteins, 250; ptyalin, +; albumins and globulins, +); steroids, 8;

thiocyanate, 0 to 15; urea, 10 to 20; uric acid, 1·5; inorganic solutes, 200 to 350. Contaminants, of local bacterial origin are: NH_4^+, 6 to 30; NO_2^-, 0 to 1. Micro-constituents of diagnostic interest include: blood-group substances, androgens, and œstrogens.

Constituents of Saliva. (1) **Mucoproteins** separate on acidification with dilute acetic acid, and can be removed by filtration. They include the blood-group substances, which can be typed serologically, amino sugar polymers, and sialic acid. Mucoproteins give the copper peptide and general carbohydrate test.

(2) **Ptyalin,** or salivary amylase, is detected by incubating saliva with a dilute starch substrate at pH 7 and 40° C. Samples withdrawn at intervals on testing show: (i) the progressive change of the iodine reaction from blue, through red-brown (dextrin stage), to no colour change (final stages); (ii) production of maltose, as shown by the methylamine and the copper reduction tests.

Ptyalin acts on starches, glycogen, and dextrins, converting them to the disaccharide *maltose*. Carbohydrates are not kept sufficiently long in the mouth for this change to take place, but it will continue in the stomach until inhibited by the acid of the gastric juice. Ptyalin is not necessary for the digestive process, and is absent from the saliva of many animals, including dogs, cats, and herbivora.

(3) **Thiocyanate,** NCS^-, a curiosity of unknown significance, is responsible for the red colour developed when a drop of dilute ferric chloride is added to saliva.

(4) **Nitrite** is revealed by appearance of a yellow colour when a few drops of benzidine reagent (2 per cent. in glacial acetic acid) are mixed with saliva. It arises, like ammonia, from the bacterial decomposition of food residues, and is an indication of oral infection.

Other salivary constituents include calcium, 4 to 11 mg. per 100 ml., chiefly in submaxillary and sublingual saliva. It contributes to the formation of " tartar " deposits on the teeth of the lower jaw.

The adult output of saliva is about 1,500 ml. per 24 hours.

Gastric Digestion

The organic solutes of gastric juice, including the enzymes, are provided by the tubular glands lining the greater part of the stomach; the inorganic solutes, notably the free hydrochloric acid, are contributed by the eosin-staining parietal cells in the glandular epithelium.

Parietal secretion is, essentially, an isotonic solution of hydrochloric acid of about N/7, 150 millimolar, or 0·547 per cent. concentration, though higher values have been recorded. The secretion is evoked by histamine injection. The non-parietal secretion, evoked by pilocarpine injection, is rich in proteins and Cl^-, but neutral or slightly alkaline in reaction.

Because of the varying amounts of these two components, gastric juice as collected by fistula or tube may have a concentration of 0·05 to 0·10 N HCl. The pH values range from 1·1 to 1·8, in adults and are about 5 in the infant. **Composition of Gastric Juice.** This varies greatly with rate and circumstances of secretion, and must be evoked under specified conditions, if required for clinical tests.

Representative values for human juice, in mg. per 100 ml., are: inorganic solutes, 600 (total chloride, 300 to 500; H^+, as HCl, 200 to 400; Na^+, 50 to 70; K^+, $+$; Ca^{2+}, 3; Mg^{2+}, $+$; HPO_4^{2-} $+$); organic solutes, 40 to 150 (pepsinogen, pepsin, rennin, gastrin, esterase, mucoproteins, intrinsic antianæmic factor).

Constituents of Gastric Juice. (1) **Hydrochloric Acid.** The low pH value of the juice, implying the presence of a strong acid, is shown by indicators that change colour below pH 3: crystal violet, blue to green; thymol blue, orange to red; tropæolin 00, orange to red. Precise data are obtained by means of the glass electrode.

Gunzburg's Test (1887). Evaporate to dryness in a dish, or, with precautions, on a filter paper, a mixture of 2 to 4 drops of gastric juice and 2 to 4 drops of Gunzburg's reagent. Avoid charring. The presence of HCl in the juice is shown by the development of a carmine patch in the dry residue. The colour disappears on cooling, and reappears on heating. A similar colour is given by other strong acids, such as H_2SO_4, but these are absent from the juice. Weak acids, such as lactic, butyric and citric, give no colour with the reagent.

Congo Red Test (Gamgee, 1893). Congo red indicator, used in solution or as test paper, gives a dark blue, with strong mineral acids, including HCl, and violet, with organic acids, other than oxalic.

Its high concentration of acid distinguishes gastric juice from all other secretions. The acid has several functions: antiseptic, activation of pepsin, hydrolysis of sucrose, maltose, and lactose. When the concentration is low, as in conditions of hypochlorhydria, the antiseptic action is insufficient to check bacterial activity of organisms accompanying the food. Resulting fermentation products include CO_2, H_2S, and lactic acid, a contributor to the " heart-burn " effect.

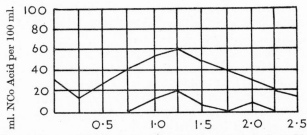

Normal Range of Hcl Secretion after Standard Carbohydrate Meal.

The Redox Pump. Energy is required for the secretion of hydrogen ions. This can be explained on the assumption that they are derived from hydrogen atoms generated by tissue oxidation, and subsequently de-electronated: H. $\longrightarrow$ H$^+$ + e^-, the electron being removed by an acceptor. Conway and others have postulated a metabolic pump, which operates during active secretion to remove cations from the blood plasma and eject hydrogen ions into the gastric secretion.

(2) **Proteinases.** Prominent among the higher peptidases in gastric juice is pepsin, which, by splitting the peptide chains at the links between glutamic acid and phenylalanine or tyrosine units, fragments the proteins. Pepsin only works in an acid medium, below pH 4. It is identified by incubation with an insoluble protein substrate (fibrin, coagulated egg-white) at pH 1·5 to 2. Zymolysis is shown by dissolution of the substrate, which may be demonstrated more easily by using insoluble proteins stained with congo red or eosin, or a strip of developed photograph film. Rennin is detected by its coagulating effect on neutral milk, which can be converted into a clot of paracasein when 5 ml. are incubated with 5 drops of neutralised juice, at 45° C.

The juice must be neutral, otherwise the free acid will flocculate the casein, simulating a clot, and the pepsin will dissolve the flocculate.

CLINICAL ANALYSIS OF GASTRIC CONTENTS

This is undertaken to find the nature and amount of acid present, the secretion of acid in response to stimuli, the activity of the enzymes, and the presence of abnormal constituents, such as blood. Many different techniques are available.

Gastric material for analysis is obtained by giving a standard " test meal ", followed by aspiration of stomach contents at intervals, by means of a tube that can be retained in the œsophagus and stomach during the experiment. Secretion of juice is encouraged by alcohol in the test meal or by subcutaneous injection of 0·25 mg. of histamine hydrochloride.

Titration Acidity. Successive samples, 5 or 10 ml., of contents are titrated with N/10 NaOH, using thymol blue as indicator. The volume of alkali required to raise the pH to 3 (from red or orange to yellow) is an index of the HCl content; the subsequent amount of alkali to raise the pH from 3 to 9 (yellow to blue) is an index of the non-ionised, or weak, available acid. Total acidity is the sum of both titration values.

Representative values for free (F) and total acid (T), expressed in ml. N/10 NaOH per 100 ml. sample, are: resting, F, 0 to 20, T, F + 10; 30 minutes after test meal, F, 5, T, 15; 45 minutes, F, 20, T, 30; 60 minutes, F, 30, T, 42; 75 to 90 minutes, F, 35, T, 50; 120 minutes, F, 15, T, 28. The acid maximum is reached within an hour and a half after taking the meal. The fall in acidity during the first half hour is a dilution effect.

Hyperacidity caused by high secretion of HCl (hyperchlorhydria) is shown by maximum free acid values in the region of 70 to 80, or by a " climbing " secretion curve, in which the free acid is still increasing at the end of the first two hours. The difference between total and free acid titration values is usually not greater than the normal value of about 10 ml. NaOH.

Hyperacidity is associated with tendency to gastric ulceration, the climbing type of curve is characteristic of delayed emptying of the stomach, which may be due to pyloric dysfunction consequent on duodenal ulceration.

In *hypoacidity*, or *hypochlorhydria*, because of lack of HCl, free acid values range from zero to about 10. Because of bacterial fermentations, total acid values may rise to 20 or more. The difference in the titration values, T — F, is an index of the amount of organic acids present.

Achlorhydria is the absence of HCl from all the specimens. It is associated with pernicious anæmia and malignant conditions, and its unequivocal diagnosis is important.

An ingenious method for detecting hypochlorhydria consists in administering in powder form an insoluble anion-binding resin carrying a dye-stuff, which is liberated by the free acid in the stomach. After absorption the dye is excreted by the kidney and can be estimated colorimetrically in the urine. This method avoids the inconvenience associated with intubation.

Alternative indicators used in the titration of gastric contents are *methyl orange*, which is red at pH 3·1, and yellow at pH 4·4; *N-dimethylamino azobenzene (Topfer's reagent)*, (red at pH 2·9, yellow at pH 4·4); and *tropæolin 00* (pink at pH 2, yellow at pH 3). As these are single change indicators, *phenolphthalein* (colourless at pH 8·3, red at pH 10) is added where total acidity values are required.

Detection of Organic Acids in Gastric Contents

Volatile Aliphatic Acids. Butyric, valeric, and caproic acids can be recognised by their sour smell. They are not necessarily fermentation products, as they arise during the hydrolysis of butter fat, but they are suggestive when present in excess.

Test. Carefully neutralise a few ml. of gastric contents with N/10 NaOH, using phenolphthalein as indicator. Add 2 per cent. $CuSO_4$, drop by drop, till the red colour of the indicator is bleached. Then add an equal volume of benzene, and shake the tube gently. The copper salts of valeric and caproic acid are soluble in benzene, and impart a blue colour to the solvent. If there is no extraction of colour, decant off the benzene, and replace by ether. Repeat the extraction. The ether layer will be coloured blue if butyric acid is present.

Lactic acid, $CH_3.CH(OH).COOH$, is non-volatile, and therefore has no smell. It arises from the fermentation of lactose in milk, which is inhibited

251

by the acidity of normal stomach contents. Lactates form a yellow complex with Fe^{3+}. This is bleached by stronger acids, hence, samples of gastric contents must be neutralised before testing for lactate.

Test. Neutralise the sample to phenolphthalein, as previously described. Add 1 per cent. $FeCl_3$, drop by drop, till the red colour of the indicator is discharged. If lactic acid is present the solution will acquire a bright yellow colour. Excess of $FeCl_3$ must be avoided so as not to obscure the colour. Small amounts of lactate can be detected by comparison with a control. A fallacy may arise from thiocyanate in swallowed saliva. HSCN gives an orange-red colour with Fe^{3+}, but, unlike the lactate pigment, it is bleached by a few drops of 5 per cent. $HgCl_2$.

DUODENAL DIGESTION

The first stage in intestinal digestion involves three secretions: pancreatic juice, bile, and intestinal juice. Digestive activity is greatest in the duodenum, and continues throughout the small intestine.

Pancreatic Juice

The pancreatic gland has two external secretions: an alkaline secretion rich in carbonate and isotonic with the blood plasma. It is poor in enzymes and is evoked by the duodenal hormone, secretin. There is also a viscid secretion, rich in enzymes and evoked by vagal stimulation or by the hormone pancreozymin. As a result, the quality of the mixed juice varies. The output of pancreatic juice in the adult is assessed at 2 litres in 24 hours.

Representative values for human pancreatic juice as obtained by duodenal intubation, in mg. per 100 ml., are: inorganic solutes, 800 (Na^+, 250; HCO_3^-, 500); organic solutes, 700 (trypsinogen, trypsin, chymotrypsinogen, chymotrypsin, carboxypeptidase, amylase, lipase, nuclease).

The pH of the human juice is about 8, and the titration alkalinity approximates to that of $N/10\ Na_2CO_3$, hence one volume of gastric juice is neutralised by about the same amount of pancreatic juice.

Enzymes of Pancreatic Juice. (1) **Peptidases.** The protein-hydrolysing power of pancreatic juice is demonstrated by incubation with an insoluble protein substrate at pH 8. Suitable substrates are fibrin, coagulated egg-white, or developed photographic film. Proteins stained with congo red or eosin are unsuitable, because the dye anion is removed by the alkali. The proteolytic effect thus demonstrated is commonly referred to as *trypsin*, but is the result of several enzymes that can only be distinguished by use of special substrates. *Trypsin*, the chief of these, splits peptide chains at linkages involving the carboxyl group of an arginine or a lysine unit; *chymotrypsin* attacks linkages involving the carboxyl of a phenylalanine, tyrosine or tryptophan unit.

(2) **Amylase** hydrolyses starches, glycogen, and dextrins to maltose, accom-

panied by small amounts of *iso*-maltose, the 1,6-linked isomer, derived from the branching points in the polysaccharide chains. Amylase, like ptyalin, is identified by its action on a 1 per cent. starch substrate.

(3) **Lipase** is an esterase that preferentially attacks glycerides. The long-chain acid residues are removed with increasing difficulty, one at a time. The enzyme is attacked by the proteinases, and can best be demonstrated in fresh extracts of the gland, or recently secreted juice, by incubation at pH 8 with an emulsion of olive oil or butter fat, such as milk. By including an indicator in the mixture the progressive increase of acidity can be demonstrated.

(4) **Nucleases** attack and depolymerise ribonucleic acid and deoxyribonucleic acids, with liberation of mononucleotides, which are attacked subsequently by enzymes in the intestinal secretion.

Bile

Unlike the stomach and the pancreas, the liver is continually eliminating its secretion, which is accumulated in the gall bladder between the intervals of active digestion. For this reason, two types of bile are recognised; *hepatic*, or *fistula* bile, the fresh secretion, and *bladder* bile, the composition of which depends on the duration of storage. In general, bladder bile is 4 to 6 times as concentrated as fresh bile.

Representative human values for fresh (F) and bladder bile (B) in gm. per 100 ml., are: total solids, 1 to 3·5 (F), 4 to 17 (B); bile cholates, 0·2 to 2 (F), 1·5 to 10 (B); bile pigments, 0·05 to 0·1 (F), 0·2 to 1·5 (B); cholesterol, 0·05 to 0·16 (F), 0·1 to 0·9 (B); higher aliphatic acids, 0·1 + (B); mucins, 0·5 (F), 2 + (B). The pH ranges are: 7·5 to 8 (F), 6·5 to 7 (B).

Although bile is secreted by all animals endowed with a liver and digestive tract, the gall bladder is absent from several higher species, including the horse, and the composition of the secretion varies. Human bile is notably rich in cholesterol, fatty acids and soaps.

Composition of Bile. (1) **Cholates**, or " bile salts ". These semi-peptides of glycine or taurine and a cholic acid are the digestive agents. They are chiefly glycocholic acid, from condensation of cholic acid and glycine.

$$C_{23}H_{36}(OH)_3.COOH + H_2N.CH_2.COOH \rightarrow$$
$$C_{23}H_{36}(OH)_3.CO.NH.CH_2.COOH,$$

and taurocholic acid, in which the glycine is replaced by a residue derived from taurine, $H_2N.CH_2.CH_2.SO_2.OH$.

Human fistula bile contains 1 to 1·5 per cent. of glycocholates, and 0·3 to 0·5 per cent. of taurocholates. The relative proportion of steroid acids present being: cholic, 3; deoxycholic, 1; cheno-deoxycholic, 1; lithocholic, 1.

253

The bile cholates lower surface tension and thus promote emulsification of food colloids and intestinal absorption of lipids. Acting as solubilising carriers of fatty acids and glycerides, they are absorbed into the lymphatic and portal systems, and after discharge are collected and re-secreted by the liver, and thus are kept in continual circulation. In the resting state before meals, up to 95 per cent. of the total cholates in the animal may have been mobilised in the gall bladder. Administered by the mouth, they act as powerful natural cholagogues, or expellers of bile. In conditions of obstructive jaundice, the absence of cholates from the intestine results in digestive disturbances arising from inability to absorb lipids.

Sugar Test (Pettenkofer, 1844). Dissolve a drop of undiluted bile in 5 ml. of 60 per cent. v/v H_2SO_4. Add a small particle of fructose. Mix well, and incubate at 50 to 60° C. The solution gradually acquires a deep purple colour and a characteristic spectrum, with a broad band in the green (500 to 530 mμ) and a narrow band in the yellow (575 mμ). The test is not given by deoxycholates or lithocholates, but only by steroids such as cholic acid, which have a hydroxyl group at carbon 7 in the sterane nucleus (p. 138). Many other substances, including phenols give colours with fructose under the same conditions (p. 89), so the test must be controlled spectroscopically.

Sulphur Sedimentation Test. This test, which depends on the lowering of surface tension, is described in Chapter 22.

The cholates are elaborated and condensed in the liver; their precursor is cholesterol.

(2) **Bile Pigments.** The characteristic colour of bile is caused by the presence of water-soluble glucuronides of the pigments biliverdin, bilirubin, and meso-bilirubin, the proportions of which differ in different species. Human bile is rich in the golden-brown bilirubin; ox bile is green because of biliverdin and phylloerythrin, a related pigment from the chlorophyll in the diet.

$$M = -CH_3$$
$$P = -CH_2.CH_2.COOH$$
$$R = -CH : CH_2$$

Bilirubin and Mesobilirubin

Both are orange coloured, and are derived from biliverdin by successive additions of 2H atoms. In bilirubin, R is a vinyl group, $-CH = CH_2$, V, which

254

in mesobilirubin is further reduced to an ethyl group, E, —$CH_2.CH_3$. The glucuronides are formed by conjugation between the carboxyl of the propionic acid group, P, and the hydroxyl group on C′ of glucuronic acid (p. 86). Their formation precedes excretion of pigment in the bile. On reoxidation, bilirubin and mesobilirubin are reconverted to biliverdin, from which, in turn a series of pigments are obtained, as oxidation continues. This is the basis of a series of tests for bile pigment.

Solubility. Dilute a few drops of pig's bile with 10 ml. of water. The golden yellow colour persists because of the high tinctorial value of the bilirubin. On shaking, a transient yellow colour is imparted to the froth. Extract with a few ml. of toluene or chloroform. If the bile is fresh no pigment will be removed, because it is present as mono- and di-glucuronides, which, unlike free bilirubin, do not dissolve in these solvents.

Oxidation Tests. (i) *Gmelin's Test* (1826). Add carefully by pipette 3 to 5 ml. of dilute bile so as to form a layer above 2 ml. of concentrated, yellow HNO_3 in a tube. At the liquid junction, a spectrum of pigments develops as oxidation proceeds upwards, ranging from green (biliverdin) through blue and violet (biliviolin) to pale yellow (choletelin). A similar colour phenomenon is observed during the degradation of extravasated blood in the tissues. (ii) *Mercuric Test.* Add a few drops of 5 per cent. $HgCl_2$ to 5 ml. of dilute bile. A similar series of colour changes is obtained. The test is delicate, but not applicable to the detection of bile in urine.

Diazo Test (Ehrlich, 1883). Add recently-prepared " diazo reagent " (diazotised sulphanilic acid) drop by drop to 5 ml. of dilute bile. A red colour develops, that changes to violet on acidification with glacial acetic or hydrochloric acid. The reaction is selective for bilirubin and mesobilirubin, and is not given by biliverdin, or by bilinogens. Because of their low solubility in water, free bilirubin and mesobilirubin require the addition of a solvent, alcohol or glacial acetic acid, before they give the diazo reaction. In this way van den Bergh has been able to distinguish between the directly-acting, soluble glucuronides, which react promptly, and the " indirect ", sparingly soluble and slowly-acting free pigments in the diagnosis of different types of jaundice. The colour is only developed by the latter when they are brought into solution by the addition of alcohol.

By colorimetry, using a standard containing 0·5 mg. bilirubin per 100 ml., values for blood plasma and other liquids can be found. These values were formerly expressed in units equivalent to 1 part of bilirubin in 200,000, but are now usually given in mg. per 100 ml. Results thus obtained are: fistula bile, 50 units, or 25 mg. per 100 ml.; normal blood plasma, 0·2 to 0·5 units per 100 ml., increased in obstructive jaundice, and conditions of increased destruction of the red corpuscles.

Metabolism of the Bile Pigments. The pigments represent the final stages in the excretion of the hæm-containing proteins. Their chief sources, expressed as percentages, are: corpuscular hæmoglobin, 70; cytochromes, catalase, peroxidases, 15 to 20. They may arise, also as by-products during the construction of hæmoglobin in bone marrow.

Evidence for this is obtained by feeding men and other animals for a few days on diets containing glycine labelled with ^{15}N. Glycine is used in the synthesis of hæm, and when incorporated into the young red corpuscles the nitrogen isotope remains localised there for the rest of the 18 weeks life-time of the labelled cells, after which it appears in the pigments of the bile and in the intestine.

As unsaturated compounds, the bile pigments can act as hydrogen acceptors. In the intestine, bilirubin is hydrogenated, via mesobilirubin, to mesobilirubinogen, a colourless tetrapyrrole, which is designated a bilinogen, because on oxidation it forms a bile pigment. As a result of bacterial activity, mesobilinogen is further hydrogenated to stercobilinogen, originally discovered in the urine and termed urobilinogen.

Oxidation of stercobilinogen forms stercobilin, or lævorotatory urobilin, the characteristic pigment of the intestinal contents.

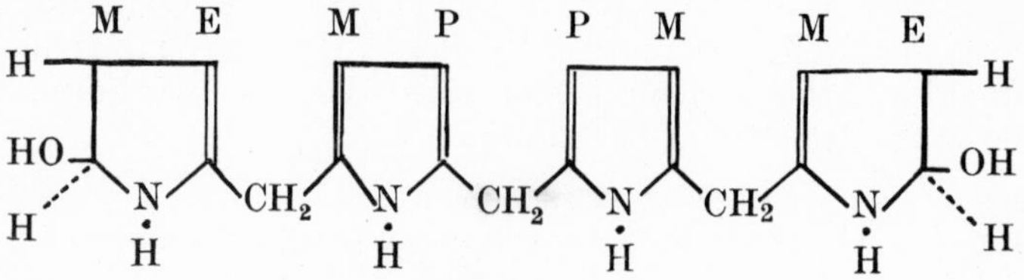

$$M = —CH_3$$
$$E = —CH_2.CH_3$$
$$P = —CH_2.CH_2.COOH$$

Stercobilinogen.
((—) Urobilinogen).

In stercobilinogen, the pigment precursor, the central methyne bridge, —CH<, is hydrogenated to methylene, —CH_2—, and the N in the adjacent ring carries a hydrogen atom.

Mesobilinogen, which differs from stercobilinogen in not having the two additional hydrogen atoms in each of the terminal rings, can give rise to oxidation derivatives.

Bilirubin, via mesobilirubin, can give rise to at least two other bilin pigments: dextrorotatory urobilin, formed in the liver, and excreted both in the bile and in the urine; and inactive urobilin IXa, formed in the intestine.

About 250 mg. of bile pigment, chiefly as stercobilin, are excreted intestinally by the adult, in 24 hours; about 2 mg. are reabsorbed as stercobilinogen, and excreted in the urine.

Metabolism of the Bile Pigments

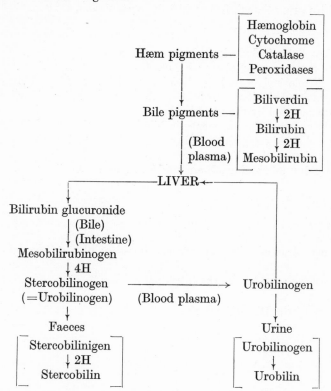

Degradation of the hæm pigments, which may begin in the aging red corpuscles, is effected in the liver and involves removal of the iron and protein, and opening up of the porphyrin nucleus by cleavage of the methyne bridge between pyrrole rings I and II.

(3) **Cholesterol.** Bile, unlike all other digestive secretions, is rich in cholesterol, values of 0·2 to 0·9 per cent. have been reported for bladder bile. The average 24-hour output of the sterol is 0·3 to 0·4 gm. It is synthesised in the liver, and the biliary output of 0·3 to 0·4 gm. per 24 hours may represent the surplus after the requirements of other tissues and systems are satisfied. Cholesterol is insoluble in water and is kept solubilised in bile by the soaps and muco-proteins. When these are inadequate, there is a tendency to the formation of sterol calculi, the commonest type of " gall stones ".

Cholestanol, or dihydrocholesterol, formed by reduction of cholesterol in the liver and other tissues, accompanies biliary cholesterol. A *cis*-isomer, coprostanol, is formed by bacterial reduction of cholesterol in the intestine and is excreted along with cholestanol and unchanged cholesterol.

Biliary cholesterol can be obtained from calculi, or from dried bile, by extraction with warm ethanol, from which it crystallises in characteristic notched plates.

(4) **Biliary lipids** include lecithins, soaps, lipid and lipid acids. When bile is acidified they separate, along with mucins, as a dense precipitate. The lipid fraction is relatively soluble in glacial acetic acid, and thus can be separated. The nature and significance of these substances await investigation, some of them are secreted by the gall bladder.

The only enzyme of consequence in bile is an alkaline phosphatase, derived from the skeletal osteoblasts and transported to the liver by the blood.

Bile is a channel for the excretion of heavy metals and contains Fe, up to 7 mg. per 100 ml., and small amounts of Zn and Cu.

INTESTINAL JUICE

The mixed secretion of the small glands of the duodenum, jejunum and ileum constitutes the intestinal juice, or succus entericus. As obtained from experimental fistulæ, it is an alkaline liquid of pH 7·1 (duodenum) to 7·6 (ileum), and contains a great variety of enzymes, mostly derived from the break-down of the cells of the intestinal mucosa.

Summary of the Digestive Process

Region.	Secretion.	Reaction.	Enzymes.	Substrates.	End-products.
Mouth .	Saliva.	Slightly acid or neutral ; pH 5·8–7·0.	Ptyalin (amylase). Maltase.	Starch. Dextrin. Glycogen. Maltose.	Maltose. Glucose.
Stomach .	Gastric juice.	Acid ; pH 1·7.	Pepsin. Rennin. Lipase.	Proteins. Caseinogen. Fats.	Peptides. Casein. Aliphatic acid + glycerol.
Intestine	Pancreatic juice.	Alkaline ; pH 8–10.	Trypsin. Peptidases. Amylase. Maltase. Lipase.	Proteins. Peptides. Starch, etc. Maltose. Fats.	Peptides. Amino acids. Maltose. Glucose. Acid + glycerol.
	Bile.	Alkaline ; pH 8.	Phosphatase	Organic phosphates	H_3PO_4.
	Intestinal juice.	Alkaline ; pH 7–8.	Peptidases. Sucrase. Lactase. Nucleinase. Nucleotidase. Lipase. Enterokinase.	Peptides. Sucrose. Lactose. Nucleic acids. Nucleotides. Fats. Trypsinogen.	Amino acids. Glucose + fructose. Glucose + galactose. Nucleotide. Nucleoside. Trypsin.
Intestinal mucosa.	—	—	Nucleosidase. Phosphatase.	Nucleosides. Hexoses.	Purines + sugar. Hexose phosphate.

Composition. Intestinal juice, as obtained by intubation, or by short-circuit fistula, varies in composition in different regions of the tract. The pH ranges from 7·1 (duodenum) and 7·6 (ileum) to 8 (colon). The total solutes are 1·2 ± 0·2 per cent., and includes a mixture of peptide-hydrolysing enzymes, or peptidases, grouped as *erepsin*; enzymes that hydrolyse disaccharides (sucrase and lactase); and *enterokinase*, the activator of pancreatic trypsin. The intestinal mucosa contains important *phosphokinases*, which phosphorylate the hexoses prior to their absorption, and *nucleosidases*, which hydrolyse the nucleosides derived from the nucleoproteins (p. 321).

Intestinal Absorption

Intestinal absorption is characterised by high, preferential efficiency. Galactose and glucose are absorbed much more rapidly than the smaller molecules of pentoses; amino acids of L-series are accepted, those of the D-series are excluded. Hypertonic solutions of low-priority solutes, such as xylose, or magnesium sulphate, can act as cathartics by abstracting water from the plasma and thus diluting the intestinal contents.

The absorption process is administered by a frontier of active mucosal cells lining the small and large intestines, and covering the projecting villi. These cells operate special conveyor systems, which enable them to select and collect nutrients and discharge them into the portal blood or lacteals against unfavourable concentration gradients.

Conveyor absorption is an aerobic process and is inhibited by cyanide, iodoacetate and phloridzin, which indicates that it obtains its necessary energy from a generator such as the citric cycle and the cytochrome chain.

Carbohydrate Absorption. Carbohydrates are absorbed in the form of monosaccharides. Phosphate-transfer enzymes occur in the cells of the mucosa, and it was believed that sugar absorption was effected by the formation and hydrolysis of phosphate esters. This explanation is inadequate, because galactose, a sugar more rapidly absorbed than glucose, is not phosphorylated by the enzymes of the mucosa. Transport, possibly, may be by a glycoside, formed in the free boundary of the cell.

Proteins are absorbed chiefly if not entirely in the form of amino acids, as shown by the rise in the amino acid content of the portal blood after a protein meal. In some circumstances absorption of higher peptides may take place. This is shown in the absorption of immunity proteins, in the form of milk colostrum, by new born animals, including calves, lambs, kittens, puppies, but not infants. In this way the young animal is provided with a ready-made defence equipment.

Peptide absorption is also observed in subjects who display allergy to particular food proteins, such as casein of cow's milk.

Lipid Absorption. In the duodenum, the pancreatic lipase, a mixture of esterases, progressively removes acid radicals from the terminal groups of glyceride tri-esters and, finally, from the remaining central carbon, thus releasing glycerol. As a result, the duodenal contents contain a mixture of the tri-, di-, and mono-esters, together with free fatty acids and their anions. Furthermore, lipases are acyl-transferring enzymes, and bring about the exchange of acid radicals among the glycerides. This is shown by means of fatty acids labelled with ^{14}C.

At an early stage in the process the bile cholates come into action, and, by forming water-soluble complexes, promote the absorption of glycerides and fatty acids by the intestinal villi. Within the mucosal cells a partition effect is observed, postulated by Munk (1891), popularised by Frazer (1938–), and still being explored. The effect is shown in the segregation of the long-chain fatty acids, and their combination with partially hydrolysed glycerides or locally produced glycerol to form chylomicrons, or microscopic particles of neutral fat, which, stabilised by phospholipids, are absorbed by the lacteals, travel in the lymph stream and eventually enter the blood. This roundabout path enables the bulk of the absorbed fat to by-pass the liver on its way to entering the general circulation.

Glycerides of short-chain fatty acids, containing less than 11 carbon atoms, are more rapidly hydrolysed, the acids being preferentially absorbed into the portal blood. At the same time, special " clearing factors " in the blood tend to dissolve the chylomicrons in circulation.

Inorganic Solutes. Sodium and potassium cations, and chloride anions circulate freely between the blood plasma and the intestinal contents. During the 24 hours, at least 14 gm. Na^+ (over 600 millimoles), and 3 gm. K^+ (77 millimoles) are discharged by the digestive secretions into the adult human digestive tract, and mostly reabsorbed. Because of this, by administration of insoluble cation-binding resins, which are excreted by the intestine, it is possible to withdraw considerable quantities of sodium and potassium from the living animal.

Calcium. The mechanism of calcium absorption is obscure, and it is doubtful if conclusions drawn from studies on lower animals can be applied directly to the human subject. In the average pH range of 6 to 7, the contents of the human intestine are insufficiently acid to keep calcium from being precipitated as phosphate or soap, although some free Ca^{2+} may exist in the acid zones of the jejunum, and be absorbed as such. Calcium absorption may depend on the production of a diffusible non-ionised complex, such as is formed with citric acid, which explains why citrus fruits, although free from vitamin D, promote calcium uptake. A soluble complex is also formed by bile acids and calcium soaps. Vitamins of the D group promote the absorption of calcium, but the action is indirectly effected through phosphate-balance control. After absorption, about 0·5 to 1 gm. of Ca^{2+} returns to the intestine daily in the digestive secretions, but this is reabsorbed again. Calcium absorption is retarded by calcium precipitants present in the ordinary mixed diet, and promoted by proteins or amino acids.

Precipitants include *fatty acids*, when the fat eaten is in excess; *phosphates*; *phytic acid*, from bran and entire cereals; *oxalic acid*, from fruits (strawberry, gooseberry) and vegetables (rhubarb, sorrel), or from fermentation of carbohydrate in the stomach. As a result, even under favourable conditions, about three-quarters of the total calcium of the dietary may escape absorption; while, if the calcium precipitants are in excess or if the diet be poor in calcium or vitamin D, not only will no calcium be absorbed, but the calcium in the digestive secretions may also be lost, resulting in a state of negative calcium balance, and decalcification of the body.

FACTORS REGULATING CALCIUM ABSORPTION

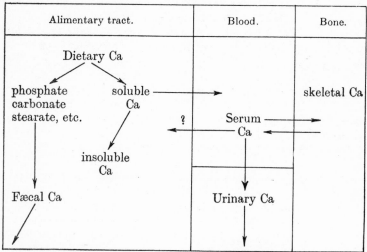

Alimentary tract.	Blood.	Bone.

Intestinal Ca Output increased by:
(1) Excess Ca in diet.
(2) Excess of P in diet.
(3) Alkaline dietaries.
(4) Excess of fat in diet.
(5) Phytic acid in diet.
(6) Lack of vitamin D.

Renal Ca Output increased by:
(1) Excess Ca in diet.
(2) Deficit of P in diet.
(3) Acid Dietaries.
(4) Starvation.
(5) Parathyrin injection.
(6) Any other condition tending to raise the serum Ca level.

Seasonal variations in calcium absorption and excretion have been demonstrated in human subjects; minimum uptake occurs in February and March, maximum in July and August (McCance et al., 1943). This may be a sunlight effect.

Phosphate. Tracer studies, using PO_4^{3-} labelled by the radioactive isotope, ^{32}P, show that about two-thirds of the daily phosphate intake of 1 to 1·5 gm. P are absorbed, the rest being excreted as calcium and magnesium phosphate. Once absorbed or injected, very little phosphate is re-excreted by the intestine. Phosphate present in the diet as phytic acid or phytates, the chief phosphorus compounds of cereals, is almost unavailable for human nutrition,

261

what is released comes from the action of phosphatases present in the intestinal micro-organisms, or in the yeast used in bread-making, or already present in the cereal.

Iron. Gastric HCl releases iron from the foodstuffs and it is reduced to the ferrous form, Fe^{2+}, in which it is absorbed in the duodenum. Reduction is probably by cysteine or thiol groups liberated during digestion of proteins, though ascorbic acid also may act. Iron absorption is determined by the iron needs of the organism, and is increased in conditions of anæmia. Absorption is effected by an iron-collector in the cells of the intestinal mucosa, *ferritin*, which is in equilibrium with an iron-transporter, *ferri-globulin* (transferrin), in the plasma. Thus, iron is brought to the storage depots: liver, spleen, and red marrow; and stored as ferritin until required for hæmoglobin manufacture of hæm compounds.

Ferritin is a variable complex of a protein, apoferritin, and ferric iron in hydroxide and phosphate form. Fully loaded, it contains about 25 gm. Fe^{3+} per 100 gm. dry weight.

In this way the uptake of iron is regulated by alternate reduction and oxidation of the iron atom, which provides an absorption gradient.

Uptake of iron from the alimentary tract is retarded by precipitants, such as phosphate, sulphide, and excess unabsorbed fatty acids. Food iron in the form of hæmoglobin and the hæm pigments of muscle is poorly absorbed, and a practical distinction is drawn between sources of *available* iron, such as liver, kidney, entire cereals, and green vegetables, and sources, such as lean meat, that in spite of their reputation and appearance, contain iron chiefly in a *non-available* form. Once absorbed, iron is not excreted to any significant extent either by the intestine or the kidneys, consequently the requirement of the adult human male is very small; the loss occasioned by menstruation in the female must be made good if anaemia is to be avoided.

Intestinal Excretion.

The waste material eliminated by the human intestine varies greatly in composition and amount; the daily output of 100 gm., being raised to 200 gm., or more, by consumption of foodstuffs rich in cellulose and fibre, such as leafy vegetables and high-extraction cereals, or brown bread. Taking 100 gm. as an average output, this represents about 20 to 40 gm. of total solids, which contain 2 to 3 gm. of nitrogen and are derived from: (1) epithelium mucin and other secretions of the alimentary tract; (2) unabsorbed food residues, chiefly cellulose and soaps of Mg and Ca; (3) steroids, chiefly from bile; (4) bacteria and other micro-organisms, most of which are dead. Fæcal lipoids, representing some 10 per cent. of the total solids, are defined as the ether-soluble fraction, and include coprosterol and other steroids derived from bile cholesterol, as well as unabsorbed steroids from the diet. Fæcal pigment is chiefly stercobilin, formed by bacterial reduction of bilirubin. Volatile constituents include indole, scatole, H_2S and thiols, and traces of lower fatty acids, such as valeric.

Micro-organisms make up 10 to 20 per cent. of the fæcal solids, and are represented by: (1) acid-forming types, such as *Lactobacillus acidophilus, L. bifidus, E. coli* and *Bact. aerogenes*, all of which ferment sugars, forming lactic and other acids, and gases, such as CO_2, H_2 and CH_4; (2) proteoclastic or putrefactive types, chiefly *Streptococcus fœcalis* and *Clostridium welchii*, which decarboxylate and dehydrogenate amino compounds. The metabolic activities of these organisms are determined by the composition and pH of the intestinal contents, which, in turn, depend on the dietary. Thus, a preponderance of carbohydrate, especially the slowly assimilated sugar lactose, favours the growth of acid-forming types and, by increasing the acidity of the intestinal contents, retards the growth of putrefactive types and members of the colon group, including *Escherichia coli*, the dominant organism.

The small intestine is not colonised by a resident flora; its organisms are tourists that have escaped the antiseptic action of the gastric juice, and are more closely associated with the mouth than with the large intestine. Obviously, an independent anti-bacterial mechanism is operating in the small intestine, but this ceases to be effective at the ileo-cæcal sphincter, beyond which a profuse fæcal-type of flora exists (Cregan and Haywood, 1953).

The hydrogen-ion concentration of the alimentary tract is important in regulating the growth of intestinal flora as well as determining the uptake of nutrients. A gradient exists both longitudinally, down the length of the tract and, transversely, in the contents. This is shown by values obtained by insertion of a glass electrode into the alimentary tract of the pig.

Results expressed as pH of (*a*) peripheral liquid layer, and (*b*) central food mass, are: stomach, 0·95 to 3·66 (*a*), 1·3 to 5·3 (*b*); duodenum, 2·34 to 6·15 (*a*), 3·0 to 6·0 (*b*); middle jejunum, 5·14 to 7·68 (*a*), 5·0 to 6·5 (*b*); lower ileum, 6·63 to 7·97 (*a*), 6·5 to 7·5 (*b*). (Møllgaard, 1946.)

Biological Value of the Intestinal Flora. Unexpected results from the use of drugs that sterilise the alimentary tract, such as the poorly-absorbed sulphaguanidine, have shown that the long-term resident flora contribute to the vitamin requirements of the animal, by synthesising biotin, folic acids, inositol, nicotinamide, pantothenic acid and, sometimes, thiamine.

Selective sterilisation, obtained in pigs, by including certain antibiotics in the diet, can result in a growth-promoting effect attributable to changes in the activity of the intestinal flora.

Indole Derivatives. Tryptophan from the dietary proteins is the source of the indole derivatives constantly present in the large intestine.

Indolyl-3-Acetic Acid (Indole-β-acetic acid) which is odourless, is absorbed into the blood, and is excreted in the urine as the chromogen of the pigment, *urorosein*. Indolyl-3-acetic acid is a powerful plant-growth factor.

$$CH_2$$

CH . COOH

$$NH_2$$

H

Tryptophan.

$$CH_2$$

COOH

H

Indolyl-
3-acetic acid.

$$CH_3$$

H

3-Methyl indole.
(Scatole).

H

Indole.
C_8H_7N.

About 50 mg. of indole are excreted daily by the human intestine, depending on protein intake and activity of the intestinal flora; and about 8 to 10 mg. are absorbed into the blood, and excreted in detoxified form as indoxyl compounds, the indigo chromogens of the urine. Indole-production is increased in conditions of intestinal stasis and putrefaction. Indole occurs in some forms of pus, and is responsible for the odour associated with pyorrhœa. Scatole has an odour even more unpleasant than that of indole.
Both indole and scatole can be removed from alkaline solutions by steam-distillation. They are sparingly soluble in water.

Natural sources of indole include oil of jasmine and oil of orange blossom; many putrefactive organisms, including *E. coli*, and *V. cholerœ*, produce it abundantly from tryptophan. Scatole is formed by decarboxylation of indolyl-3-acetic acid; it occurs naturally in civet, a secretion of the male civet-cat. In very dilute concentration, both indole and scatole are ingredients of several celebrated perfumes.

Tests for Indole. (1) *Nitroso Reaction.* Add a drop of very dilute (0·1 per cent.) $NaNO_2$ to a few ml. of the solution and acidify with 2 or 3 drops of concentrated H_2SO_4. A red colour is given by indole in concentrations down to about 1 in 50,000. Scatole gives no colour, but may yield a white precipitate. Some organisms, notably *V. cholerœ*, produce nitrite as well as indole, and their culture media, or urine from an infected subject, gives the test directly on acidification. Thus obtained, it is described as the " cholera red " reaction, and is of diagnostic value.
(2) *Aldehyde Reactions.* In dilute acids (N/10 to N HCl), indole gives a bright cerise red with Ehrlich's aldehyde. Scatole will not react unless an excess of acid be present, when, like tryptophan and other 3-substituted indoles, it will give a violet to blue colour (p. 447).
(3) *Naphthoquinone Reaction* (Herter, 1906). Make 4 ml. of solution alkaline with 4 drops of 10 per cent. NaOH, and add a few drops of fresh, aqueous 2 per cent. 1 : 2-naphthoquinone-4-sulphonate (Folin's amino acid reagent). A blue pigment forms, and can be extracted as a red solution in chloroform. Scatole similarly treated, develops an orange colour, not extractable by chloroform.

Biological Significance of the Intestinal Flora. While it is popularly believed that the micro-organisms that colonise the lower alimentary tract of man and other animals are only to be tolerated as undesirable but permanent aliens, evidence from nutritional studies shows that some of these parasites may contribute to the welfare of their hosts by synthesising useful vitamins. Conversely, when the alimentary tract is sterilised by administration of drugs such as sulphaguanidine, which is not absorbed from the intestine, signs of multiple vitamin deficiency have been found to develop.

Vitamins provided by the activity of the intestinal flora are believed to include: inositol, pantothenic acid, biotin, folic acid, p-aminobenzoic acid and, under certain conditions, thiamine.

Micro-organisms also supply the enzyme *cellulase*, or *cytase*, necessary for the digestion of the cellulose that makes up the bulk carbohydrate in the diet of cows, horses and other graminivora.

Barcroft has calculated that in this way large amounts of acetate, propionate and other lower aliphatic acids are made available for animal nutrition. Conversely, when urea, an end-product of animal metabolism, is included in the ruminant diet, it can supply nitrogen for the synthesis of bacterial proteins, and thus, indirectly, provide amino acids for the animal. In this way urea, and, to a less extent, ammonium salts, can act as food substitutes.

General References

Alvarez, W. (1940), " Introduction to Gastro-Enterology." New York.

Babkin, B. P. (1951), " Secretory Mechanism of the Digestive Glands." 2nd Ed. New York.

Conway, E. J. (1953), " Biochemistry of Gastric Acid Secretion." Springfield.

Florey, H. W., *et al.* (1941), " Secretions of the intestine." *Physiol. Rev.*, **21,** 36.

Frazer, A. C. (1946), " Fat absorption and fat metabolism." *Physiol. Rev.*, **26,** 103.

Ivy, A. C. (1934), " Physiology of the gall bladder." *Physiol. Rev.*, **14,** 1.

Ivy, A. C. (1941), " Internal secretions of the gastro-intestinal tract." *J. Amer. med. Ass.*, **117,** 1013.

James, A. H. (1957), " Physiology of Gastric Digestion." London.

Jenkins, G. N. (1954), " Physiology of the Mouth." Oxford.

Josephson, B. (1941), " Circulation of the bile acids." *Physiol. Rev.*, **21, 463.**

Krasnow, F. (1936), " Composition of Saliva." Dental Cosmos, **78, 301.**

" Modern Trends in Gastro-Enterology." Ed. by F. A. Jones. London.

Sobotka, H. (1937), " Physiological Chemistry of the Bile." London.

Verzár, F., and E. J. McDougall (1936), "Absorption from the Intestine." London.

Wolf, S., and H. G. Wolff (1947), " Human Gastric Function." 2nd Ed. Oxford University Press.

Younge, C. M. (1937), " Evolution and adaptation in the digestive system of the metazoa." *Biol. Rev.*, **12, 87.** Cambridge.

Chapter 16 Carbohydrate Metabolism

Metabolism denotes the continuum of chemical changes whereby an organism maintains and asserts its existence. These changes occur as highly-organised sequences, catalysed by enzymes, and, in higher organisms, regulated by hormones.
A metabolic process is a chain of events, which may be linear, starting from a primary source, or may be cyclical, maintained by a reactant. Substrates involved in the chain are described as **intermediate metabolites.** The concentration of an individual substance in a cell or tissue is not an index of its significance. It may be a short-term metabolite, present in very small amounts, but forming a link in a process necessary for life; it may be a storage product, of secondary importance; or it may be inert material awaiting excretion.
Metabolic sequences are described by the name of a primary or prominent reactant, such as the *glycolytic process*, whereby glucose is degraded to pyruvic acid, the *lipoclastic process*, whereby aliphatic acids are fragmented into acetyl units, and the *citric cycle*, wherein the end-products of other processes are combusted.
Events taking place in the digestive tract are not described as metabolic; they are physiologically outside the organism. It is only after absorption from the alimentary environment that the nutrients enter into the working life of the cells.

Carbohydrate Distribution. Dietary carbohydrate enters the animal chiefly as glucose. Passing into the portal blood, it reaches the liver and is built up into glycogen. Sugar present above the storage capacity of the liver goes into the glucose-pool in the blood and extra-cellular fluid, whence it contributes to cell requirements and muscle glycogen maintenance. Sugar in excess of all these demands is converted into aliphatic acids and stored as fat; only in pathological states does it overflow from the organism and escape in the urine.

Galactose and fructose form a relatively small part of the sugar provided by the diet. Like glucose, they are used in the construction of glycogen by the liver, which both transforms and stores carbohydrate.

Glucose-6-phosphate dominates sugar metabolism, and is the primary reactant in the metabolic transformations of glucose. It is formed by transfer of a phosphate unit from the high energy donor, adenosine triphosphate, ATP, which is thereby degraded to the diphosphate, ADP. The exchange is catalysed by a phosphokinase, such as hexokinase, present in cells capable of utilising glucose.

$$HO.CH_2.R + ATP \rightarrow (HO)_2.PO.O.CH_2.R + ADP$$

Interconversion of the hexoses is effected by formation and rearrangement of phosphate esters, generated by ATP:

Glucose		**Glycogen**	
I $\downarrow$	II	$\downarrow$ III ·	
Glucose-6-phosphate	$\rightleftharpoons$	Glucose-1-phosphate	
IV $\uparrow$		$\uparrow$	V
Fructose-6-phosphate		Galactose-1-phosphate	
VI $\uparrow$		$\uparrow$	VII
Fructose		Galactose	

The enzymes operating each individual change are: I, Hexokinase; II, Phosphoglucomutase; III, Phosphorylase; IV, Phosphoglucose isomerase; V, Uridyl transferase; VI, Fructokinase; VII, Galactokinase.

Hepatic Function

(1) **Glycogenesis,** the construction of glycogen from glucose, occurs chiefly in liver and muscle, and also in placenta, and to a slight extent in brain. Glycogen, because of its multi-branched structure, can be grown and pruned rapidly and provides a quickly-accessible glucose store.

The starting material is glucose-1-phosphate, obtained from glucose, via the 6-phosphate. Activated by a phosphorylase (glucosan phosphorylase, or P-enzyme), glycosyl units, transferred from the phosphate, are added one by one to the limbs of the glycogen tree, until branches of about 14 units long are formed. These branches are of the amylose type, each glucose unit being in α-1,4'-linkage. From time to time a second enzyme intervenes, glucosan transglycolase, Q-enzyme, or " branching factor ", which transfers part of a 1,4-glucosan chain from a 4- to a 6-position on the limb, thus exposing a new growth-point for the start of a fresh branch. In presence of sufficient sugar, glycogenesis continues until a stage of cell overcrowding is reached.

Animals on carbohydrate-free diets, such as carnivora, can manufacture glycogen, the operation being described as **glyconeogenesis,** to indicate that the polysaccharide is being newly made from compounds other than sugars. The term is misleading; the precursors, derived from proteins and lipids, must be converted into glucose phosphate before they can contribute to glycogenesis.

(2) **Glycogenolysis.** The breaking-down of glycogen to glucose is reversibly catalysed by phosphorylase, which in presence of phosphate ions effects the release of glucose units, as the 1-phosphate, from the ends of the amylose

267

branches. An accompanying phosphatase hydrolyses the ester into phosphate and free glucose.

The phosphorylase-resistant 1,6-linkages at the starting points of each branch are split off as glucose by a " debranching factor ", amylo-1,6-α-glucosidase, or R-enzyme.

The glycogen content of the human liver varies with circumstances, an average value is 3 gm. per 100 gm. fresh tissue, rising to 5 or 6 gm. after a meal very rich in sugar. The total glycogen content of the adult human body is between 300 and 400 gm., more than 250 gm. of which is in the muscles.

The Blood Sugar. The venous or capillary concentration of glucose in the post-absorptive state, 12 hours after a meal, is usually within the limits 70 to 120 mg. per 100 ml. After ingestion of 50 to 100 gm. of glucose, the blood level rises rapidly, and reaches a maximum within 20 to 40 minutes.

For venous blood this is between 130 and 150 mg. per 100 ml.; and is about 40 mg. lower than the corresponding capillary, or arterial maximum, because of continuous transfer of sugar from blood to tissues. The values return to the normal range after two hours. The rise in blood sugar levels is not proportional to the quantity of sugar ingested, but depends on several factors. Thus, when the blood sugar level falls below 60 ± 5 mg. per 100 ml., hepatic glycogenolysis is stimulated to raise the level. When the level rises above 100 ± 16 mg. per 100 ml., sugar is withdrawn by the liver and stored as glycogen.

Glucose is an essential metabolite and has a high renal threshold. In the normal subject it must exceed 180 to 210 mg. per 100 ml., in the blood, before it can " overflow " into the urine. This condition of " alimentary glycosuria " is hard to evoke in the ordinary subject, who will fatten rather than excrete such a valuable nutrient.

Under ordinary dietary conditions the renal mechanism is so efficient that only traces of glucose appear in the urine, although the glomerular filtrate, which has a sugar content presumably equal to that of the plasma, has been concentrated at least fiftyfold during its passage through the kidney. The glucose is retained by being reabsorbed by the cells of the renal tubules. Tubular reabsorption can be abolished by injection of phloridzin, which inhibits cell metabolism by obstructing the citric cycle. This evokes a phloridzin diabetes, in which the renal glucose threshold approaches zero, and the resulting glycosuria can deplete the carbohydrate reserves of the animal and cause severe hypoglycæmia.

Blood Sugar Curves. Rise in blood sugar level, as a result of ingestion of carbohydrate or injection of glucose, by stimulating the pancreas evokes a compensatory secretion of the hormone insulin. Insulin lowers the amount of sugar in circulation by a multiple effect, which includes: (1) increased glycogenesis in liver and muscles; (2) increased peripheral utilisation of glucose; (3) increased synthesis of fat and protein; (4) inhibition of gluconeogenesis.

The extent and duration of the hyperglycæmia following glucose administration is a valuable clinical index of the insulin output and efficiency of the pancreas, provided that the subject has been on a uniform diet.

Representative Blood Sugar Values
(Expressed in mg. glucose per 100 ml.)

Subject.	Time in minutes after ingestion of 50 gm. glucose.				
	0	30	60	90	120
Normal Adult :					
Diet A .	100	120	130	110	100
Diet B .	100	118	118	110	120
Diet C .	100	170	200	160	145
" Lag " type .	100	150	230	140	80
Diabetic :					
Mild . .	170	187	198	190	182
Severe .	240	270	294	300	314
Renal glycosuric	98	100	94	96	98

Diet A included 300 gm. carbohydrate daily during the previous week; diet B included 500 gm. carbohydrate and 40 gm. fat; diet C included 50 gm. carbohydrate and 240 gm. fat. These observations by Himsworth (1935) show that a high-fat low-carbohydrate diet can repress the pancreatic response in the normal subject and produce a sugar-tolerance curve resembling in rise and prolongation that of the diabetic. Hence, for accurate assessment of clinical states the subject should have been on a diet containing at least 300 gm. of carbohydrate for not less than three days before the sugar-tolerance test. The " lag " type of curve is usually accompanied by alimentary glycosuria, and denotes that the subject's capacity for sugar storage is sub-normal in relation to his sugar-absorption rate.

The average true glucose value for human blood obtained after a night's rest is 80 ± 20 mg. per 100 ml. The total reducing value, as obtained by the older analytical methods, is much higher and gives glucose equivalents of about 120 mg. per 100 ml.

Glycosuria may be the result of a low renal threshold, either congenital (renal diabetes) or experimental (phloridzin diabetes) in origin. It may result also from metabolic conditions causing hyperglycæmia: (1) insulin deficiency, removal or disease of the pancreas (pancreatic diabetes), or poisoning of the gland by alloxan (alloxan diabetes); (2) excessive hepatic glycogenolysis, following injection of adrenaline, adrenal cortex hormones, glucagon, thyroxine, or the growth hormone of the pituitary gland, or may arise from the release of these hormones in conditions of asphyxia, general anæsthesia, emotional stress, toxic goitre, acromegaly, and experimental injury to the floor of the fourth cerebral ventricle (puncture diabetes).

Glucose tolerance expresses either (a) the total amount of carbohydrate that

269

can be consumed daily without evoking glycosuria, or, more exactly (b) the dosage of glucose necessary to raise the blood sugar above the renal threshold. Alimentary glycosuria from carbohydrate over-feeding is very unusual, as the resources of the organism for carbohydrate storage and conversion are considerable.

In some pathological conditions, notably *diabetes mellitus*, glucose tolerance is low, and excess of carbohydrate in the diet readily evokes glycosuria.

Hypoglycæmia. When the glucose content of the blood falls below a critical value, 0.07 to 0.03 per cent. in man, a characteristic hypoglycæmic syndrome sets in, the signs and symptoms of which are: (i) extreme hunger, (ii) fatigue and prostration, (iii) motiveless anxiety, (iv) tremors, (v) vaso-motor unbalance with flushing or pallor, (vi) delirium, coma, loss of deep reflexes. Hypoglycæmia has little effect on the contraction or irritability of the denervated muscle, and it is inferred that the motor disturbances arise centrally from glucose starvation of the nervous system. Hypoglycæmia may be evoked by injection of insulin and abolished by injection of glucose, insulin antagonists, or agents promoting hepatic glycogenolysis.

Experimental removal of the liver results in a rapid fall in blood sugar. Hepatectomised dogs require glucose infusion at the rate of 250 mg. per kg. body weight per hour, if hypoglycæmia is to be averted. This indicates that the liver of a 10 kg. dog during carbohydrate starvation is producing about 64 gm. glucose in 24 hours. If the human body is comparable in efficiency, the adult liver is secreting up to 400 gm. daily, or a little less than the carbohydrate content of the ordinary diet.

Sources of Blood Sugar

(1) *Carbohydrates.* While it is believed that all, or almost all, of the blood sugar normally comes from hepatic glycogen, substances other than the simple hexoses can contribute either to glycogen or to sugar formation. The simplest of these are (+)-lactic acid, and glycerol. Lactic acid is the characteristic end-product in muscle metabolism and may be produced in other tissues during glycolysis. Glycerol is a constituent of all fats and complex lipids, and is liberated during digestion. The relative efficiency of these substrates has been computed by the Coris, who measured the glycogen increase in the livers of rats, previously starved for 24 to 48 hours, until the hepatic glycogen had fallen to 0.1 to 0.2 per cent.

Food Material.	Absorption Time.	Amount absorbed per 100-gm. Body Weight.	Liver Glycogen.
Glucose . .	4 hours.	1·06 gm.	5·3 per cent.
Fructose . .	4 ,,	0·54 ,,	5·7 ,,
Galactose . .	4 ,,	1·10 ,,	1·2 ,,
(+)-Lactic acid .	3 ,,	0·11 ,,	1·2 ,,
Glycerol . .	4 ,,	—	2·4

(2) *Proteins.* Animals on a carbohydrate-free diet continue to store liver glycogen, showing that it can be obtained from sources other than food saccharides. Of these, the most obvious are the surplus amino acid residues after removal of the nitrogen. In diabetic animals unable to utilise sugar, the food or tissue proteins are diverted to the manufacture of the glucose which appears in the urine. In these conditions the " dextrose " : nitrogen output in the urine, or D/N ratio, is about 2·8 : 1. In animals unable to retain sugar owing to phloridzin injections, the D/N ratio in the urine is as high as 3·6 : 1. Since 100 gm. of food protein yield about 16 gm. of urinary nitrogen, the value of the D/N ratio indicates that, in favourable circumstances, up to 58 per cent. of protein can be transformed into glycogen or glucose. By individual feeding experiments on phloridzin-treated animals it has been shown that the glucogenic amino acids are arginine, proline, hydroxyproline, cystine, serine, alanine, glycine, glutamic acid, hydroxyglutamic acid and aspartic acid.

(3) *Fats.* Addition of fat to the diet of a depancreatised or otherwise diabetic animal neither increases liver glycogen nor sugar excretion, and it was formerly assumed that carbohydrate cannot arise from fat in the animal body, apart from 10 per cent. of the molecule, which is released as glycerol. In pancreatic diabetes, however, the respiratory quotient may fall as low as 0·7, which indicates that fat alone is being oxidised.

Oxidation of sugars and of fatty acids in the animal is competitive, the preference being for the sugars. After a meal rich in carbohydrate, sugar oxidation dominates metabolism for several hours.

In conditions of carbohydrate scarcity, lipid metabolism predominates. The long-chain fatty acids are fragmented in the liver into 2-carbon units which are used as fuel for the citric cycle, or condensed to acetoacetic acid, circulated, and metabolised by the peripheral tissues. If the carbohydrate shortage is sufficiently severe, as in starvation or if the blood sugar is unavailable because of lack of insulin, the tissues may become swamped by acetoacetate, which accumulates in the blood, accompanied by a precursor and reduction product, β-hydroxybutyric acid, and a decarboxylation derivative, acetone.

$$CH_3.CH(OH).CH_2.COOH \xrightleftharpoons{\pm 2H} CH_3.CO.CH_2.COOH \rightarrow CH_3.CO.CH_3 + CO_2$$

Acetone is relatively stable in the animal, and is eliminated by the kidneys and the lungs.

The accumulation of these metabolites leads to acidosis, or acid poisoning, and ketonæmia, terminating in ketosis, or ketone poisoning, characterised by drowsiness, coma, and death. The condition is rapidly abolished by glucose and insulin, which repress the excessive lipid break-down.

GLYCOTROPIC HORMONES

The blood sugar level is regulated in accordance with the varying requirements of the animal by means of sugar-regulating, or glycotropic hormones, the structure of which is described in Chapter 24.

(1) **Insulin,** the chief hormone of the pancreas, is secreted by the β-cells of the insular tissue. Its activities are manifold.

(a) *Glucose Transfer.* Insulin in some way promotes transfer of glucose and at least one other sugar, arabinose, from the blood to the tissue cells, possibly by acting on the sugar carrier mechanism or by increasing cell permeability.

(b) *Glucose Phosphorylation.* In order to be metabolised, cellular glucose must be phosphorylated to glucose 6-phosphate by transfer from ATP. The reaction is catalysed by hexokinase. It is claimed that hexokinase is inhibited by pituitary and adrenocortical hormones, and that this inhibition is cancelled by insulin, but the evidence is incomplete. Alternatively, lack of insulin, by starving the citric cycle, may decrease the production of ATP.

The effects of insulin injection vary with the size of the dose and the condition of the subject. In normal animals, insulin, in small doses, can increase the storage of sugar as glycogen. Larger doses evoke a rapid fall in blood sugar and a compensating decrease in liver glycogen. In the diabetic animal, insulin injection (0·5 mg.) promotes general utilisation of sugar by the tissues and storage as hepatic and muscular glycogen. The nature of the insulin response is complicated by the operation of extra-hepatic factors, including the hormones of the adrenal and pituitary glands.

Insulin is a peptide, and is destroyed by the enzyme *insulinase* of the pancreatic juice. For this reason, the hormone is ineffective when given by mouth.

(2) **Glucagon,** a peptide hormone, is secreted by the α-cells of the pancreatic insular tissue. By activating hepatic phosphorylase, it promotes glycogenolysis, and thereby raises the level of the blood sugar.

Early preparations of insulin were apt to be contaminated by the then unknown glucagon, which contributed to the confusing versatility of the product.

(3) **Cortisol** and **Cortisone,** steroid hormones from the adrenal cortex, promote hyperglycæmia and glucose-retention, consequent on gluconeogenesis. The effect is attributed to inhibition of protein synthesis, and the resulting increase in the supply of amino acids available for conversion into sugar. Removal or lesions of the adrenal cortex, as seen in Addison's disease, result in hypoglycæmia, depletion of liver glycogen and diversion of sugar metabolites from the path of glycogenesis.

(4) **Adrenaline,** or epinephrine, from the adrenal medulla, activates phosphorylases both in liver and muscle; injection of 0·1 to 0·5 mg., subcutaneously, promotes: (a) conversion of liver glycogen to glucose; (b) conversion of muscle glycogen to lactate; (c) hyperglycæmia, usually leading to a temporary glucosuria. Adrenaline is not essential for carbohydrate metabolism; its sudden release by the gland provides an emergency supply of

glucose for the brain and lactate for the heart. The related hormone, *noradrenaline*, has very little effect on carbohydrates.

(5) **Pituitary Hormones.** In 1930 Houssay showed that removal of the anterior pituitary gland led to a decrease in the output of glucose and ketones in the urine of depancreatised dogs. These " Houssay animals " were able to survive for months, without special treatment, although precariously poised between fatal hypoglycæmia and diabetic coma, showing that animals can utilise carbohydrate even in the complete absence of insulin. If the anterior pituitary is removed, while the pancreas is left intact, the animals will tend to develop hypoglycæmia, and become hypersensitive to carbohydrate starvation and insulin injection. In 1937 Young showed that extracts of the anterior pituitary, or adenohypophysis, contains a *diabetogenic factor*, capable of evoking permanent diabetes when injected into cats or dogs. This factor, one of the effects of which is stimulation and ultimate destruction of pancreatic islet cells, has been identified with the *growth hormone* of the pituitary.

Associated with its effects are those of the anterior pituitary hormone, *adrenocorticotropin*, or ACTH, which stimulates secretion of hormones by the adrenal cortex.

(6) **Thyroid hormones.** Hyperthyroidism and thyrotoxic states often display hyperglycæmia, and in severe conditions the glycogen content of the liver may fall to zero. This is attributed to the general intensification of metabolic processes by the hormones.

Carbohydrate Circulation in the Animal

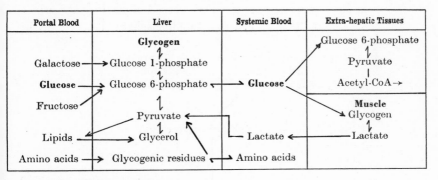

GLUCOSE METABOLISM

Glucose is the chief source of energy in all organisms, other than green plants and some peculiar bacteria. Its status depends on its ability to generate energy in absence of oxygen, by rearrangement into compounds of lower energy content, such as pyruvate or lactate, and, incidentally, to provide intermediate metabolites of biological value.

Glycolysis denotes the anaerobic fission of glucose into two molecules of pyruvic

273

acid, irrespective of the subsequent changes undergone by the pyruvate. It is a primitive and fundamental activity of all living cells, and is exploited by yeasts and other sugar-fermenting organisms. In higher plants and animals, glycolysis is used to provide fuel for the more efficient aerobic processes, notably the citric cycle. Muscle tissue also employs a glycolytic system to convert glycogen reversibly into lactate to meet special demands for energy. Malignant cells exploit glycolysis in order to grow rapidly in circumstances of restricted oxygen supply.

In addition to generating energy, glycolysis provides an essential metabolite, pyruvic acid, which can be decarboxylated and transported as acetyl-co-enzyme A, to feed the citric cycle or to provide units for synthesis of aliphatic and amino acids. Alternatively, it can be hydrogenated to lactic acid, as in lactic fermentations and muscle metabolism; or decarboxylated to acetalde-hyde and then hydrogenated to ethanol, as in the alcoholic fermentations. Glycolysis can be described as the glucose-pyruvate sequence. It is known also as the EMP process, in recognition of the pioneer investigators, Embden, Myerhof, and Parnas.

In outline, glycolysis is a nine-stage process, each step of which is reversible, and is controlled by a special enzyme. At stages 1 and 3, energy is invested in the process by degradation of adenosine triphosphate, ATP, and at stage

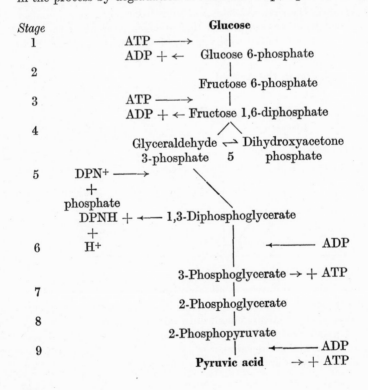

5, by co-enzyme I (DPN+). Energy is returned two-fold in stages 7 and 9, by the regeneration of two molecules of ATP per molecule of sugar glycolysed.

Stages in the Glycolytic Process

(1) **Glucose to Glucose 6-Phosphate.** The energy and phosphate for this phosphorylation are provided by the degradation of ATP to ADP. The reaction is catalysed by a hexokinase, the enzyme in liver and muscle (glucokinase) being more selective than that in yeast or brain. An alternative source of glucose 6-phosphate is starch in the plant and glycogen in the animal, from which units of glucose 1-phosphate can be removed by a phosphorylase and then transformed to glucose 6-phosphate

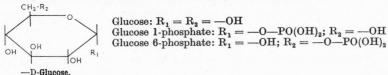

Glucose: $R_1 = R_2 = $ —OH
Glucose 1-phosphate: $R_1 = $ —O—PO(OH)$_2$; $R_2 = $ —OH
Glucose 6-phosphate: $R_1 = $ —OH; $R_2 = $ —O—PO(OH)$_2$

—D-Glucose.

(2) **Glucose 6-Phosphate to Fructose 6-Phosphate.** An isomerisation involving the opening and closing of the sugar ring.

(3) **Fructose 6-Phosphate to Fructose 1,6-Diphosphate.** A phosphorylation effected, as in stage 1, by ATP

Fructose 6-phosphate: $R_1 = $ —OH; $R_2 = $ —O—PO(OH)$_2$
Fructose 1,6-diphosphate: $R_1 = R_2 = $ —O—PO(OH)$_2$

D Fructofuranose.

(4) **Fructose 1,6-Diphosphate to Glyceraldehyde 3-Phosphate and Dihydroxyacetone Phosphate.** The sugar ring splits into two triose phosphates, which form an equilibrium mixture (Stage 4):

$(HO)_2PO.O.CH_2.CH(OH).CHO$ 3-Phosphoglyceraldehyde

$(HO)_2PO.O.CH_2.CO.CH_2.OH$ Dihydroxyacetone phosphate

Fission is catalysed by *aldolase*. Equilibration is catalysed by *phosphotriose isomerase*.

(5) **Glyceraldehyde 3-Phosphate to 1,3-Diphosphoglycerate.** In this complex change, the aldehyde is oxidised and phosphorylated forming a high-energy phosphate. The reaction is catalysed by *phosphoglyceraldehyde dehydrogenase*, a thiol-containing enzyme that is inhibited by iodoacetate. Stage 5 is the first stage in glycolysis in which the actual dehydrogenation, or indirect oxidation of the sugar substrate takes place. The hydrogen atoms removed are, in part, H+ and DPNH, the reduced form of accompanying co-enzyme.

(6) **1,3-Diphosphoglycerate to 3-Phosphoglycerate.** The 1,3-diphosphate, a high energy compound, is able to transfer a phosphate unit to ADP, thereby exalting it to ATP. This is the first stage in glycolysis which the energy generated is diverted to recharge an energy accumulator.

$$\underset{\substack{\text{Glyceraldehyde}\\\text{3-phosphate.}}}{\overset{\displaystyle\text{CHO}}{\underset{\displaystyle\text{H}_2\text{C.}\text{—O—PO(OH)}_2}{|\;\;\overset{\displaystyle\text{HC.OH}}{|}}}} +\text{H}_3\text{PO}_4 \quad \underset{\substack{\text{1,3-Diphospho-}\\\text{glyceric acid.}}}{\overset{\displaystyle\text{O : C—O—PO(OH)}_2}{\underset{\displaystyle\text{H}_2\text{C—O—PO(OH)}_2}{|\;\;\overset{\displaystyle\text{HC.OH}}{|}}}} + \text{ADP} \rightarrow \underset{\substack{\text{3-Phospho-}\\\text{glyceric acid.}}}{\overset{\displaystyle\text{O : C.OH}}{\underset{\displaystyle\text{H}_2\text{C—O—PO(OH)}_2}{|\;\;\overset{\displaystyle\text{HC.OH}}{|}}}} + \text{ATP}$$

(7) **3-Phosphoglycerate to 2-Phosphoglycerate.** The intra-molecular transfer of the phosphate radical involves the intermediate formation of a 2,3-diphosphate.

(8) **2-Phosphoglycerate to 2-Phosphopyruvate.** This dehydration produces a high-energy ester derived from the *enol* form of pyruvic acid. The reaction, catalysed by *enolase*, requires Mg^{2+}, and is inhibited by F^-, which immobilises the magnesium as a fluorophosphate.

(9) **Phosphopyruvate to Pyruvate.** The phosphate radical is transferred to ADP, thereby generating ATP, and storing the second moiety of energy obtained from glycolysis.

$$\underset{\substack{\text{2-Phospho-}\\\text{glyceric}\\\text{acid.}}}{\overset{\displaystyle\text{COOH}}{\underset{\displaystyle\text{CH}_2\text{.OH}}{|\;\;\overset{\displaystyle\text{HC—O—PO(OH)}_2}{|}}}} \underset{\longrightarrow}{-\text{H}_2\text{O}} \underset{\substack{\text{2-Phospho-}\\\text{pyruvic}\\\text{acid.}}}{\overset{\displaystyle\text{COOH}}{\underset{\displaystyle\text{CH}_2}{|\;\;\overset{\displaystyle\text{C—O—PO(OH)}_2}{||}}}} + \text{ADP} \rightarrow \text{ATP} + \underset{\substack{\text{Pyruvic acid.}\\\text{(enol) (keto)}}}{\overset{\displaystyle\text{COOH COOH}}{\underset{\displaystyle\text{CH}_2 \leftrightarrows \text{CH}_3}{|\;\;\;\;|\;\;\overset{\displaystyle\text{C—OH CO}}{||\;\;\;\;|}}}}$$

The overall reaction in glycolysis is:

$$C_6H_{12}O_6 \rightarrow 2\ CH_3.CO.COOH\ (+\ 4H).$$

Extensions of the Glycolytic Process

(10) **Pyruvate to L-(+)-Lactate.** The hydrogen atoms removed in Stage 5 can be used to hydrogenate pyruvic to lactic acid, $CH_3.CH(OH).COOH$. Equilibrium is catalysed by *lactic dehydrogenase*, working with reduced co-enzyme DPNH as hydrogen donor. Lactate-extension of glycolysis is prominent in muscle and can occur in leucocytes and in brain tissue deprived of oxygen. It is employed by many sugar-fermenting organisms, some of which, such as yeast, require no co-enzyme. The dehydrogenase of *Bacillus delbrückii* is of interest in that it is selective for the isomer, D-(−)-lactic acid, and can form it from pyruvate.

(10a) **Pyruvate to Ethyl Alcohol.** This involves decarboxylation to acetaldehyde, and subsequent hydrogenation, the hydrogen atoms for which can be provided by Stage 5 of the glycolytic process.

$$CH_3.CO.COOH \rightarrow CO_2 + CH_3.CHO\ (+\ 2H) \rightarrow CH_3.CH_2.OH.$$

The first stage is catalysed by *carboxylase*, a magnesium-containing enzyme present in yeasts and some plants, but not in animals. Thiamine pyrophosphate is the co-enzyme. Equilibrium in the second stage is catalysed by *alcohol dehydrogenase*, a zinc-containing enzyme present in yeasts and in liver, where its activities are responsible for the production of the aldehyde that participates in the downfall of the drunkard.

Enzymes of the Glycolytic Process. These enzymes, many of which have been crystallised, are usually designated by the name of one of their substrates. In stage order, the enzymes are: 1, hexokinase; 2, phosphohexose isomerase; 3, phosphofructokinase; 4, aldolase; 5, phosphotriose isomerase; 6, phosphoglyceraldehyde dehydrogenase; 7, phosphoglyceric kinase; 8, phosphoglyceromutase; 9, enolase; 10, pyruvic kinase. Enzymes 1, 3, 7, 8, 9 and 10, are activated by Mg^{2+}. Enzyme 6 contains thiol, or —SH, groups, and is inactivated by iodoacetate.

Energy Output of the Glycolytic Process

Glycolysis is a very extravagant way of obtaining energy. When glucose is completely combusted to CO_2 and H_2O, under biological conditions, the maximum free energy yield, ΔF is 691 kilocals per mole. When degraded as far as lactic acid the yield is only about 47·5 kilocals per mole. The free energy change ($+ \Delta F = $ input; $-\Delta F = $ output) for each stage in glycolysis can be calculated from equations derived from the relationship: $\Delta F = -RT \log_e K$, where R is the gas constant, T is the absolute temperature, and K is the equilibrium constant of the particular reaction.

When this is done, it is found that the total output of free energy in the glycolytic conversion of glucose to lactate, at pH 7, is 31·3 kilocals per mole. The difference, 47·5—31·3, or 16·2 kilocals, represents the energy that has been saved by being invested in ATP. The remaining 31·3 kilocals, unless diverted, is lost as heat.

Alternative Pathways of Glucose Metabolism

Intermediate metabolites can be removed from or put into the glycolytic process at different stages, and used in construction or degradation of 4-, 5-, and 7-carbon sugars. In this way are obtained the pentoses, D-ribose and 2-deoxy-D-ribose, which are in continual employment in the manufacture of the nucleic acids necessary for cell division and protein synthesis.

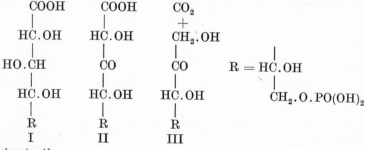

I. 6-Phosphogluconic acid.
II. 3-Oxo-6-phosphogluconic acid.
III. D-Ribulose 5-phosphate.

(1) **6-Phosphogluconic Acid to Pentoses.** Oxidation of glucose 6-phosphate forms a lactone that on hydrolysis yields the corresponding **gluconic acid,** in which the —CHO of the glucose has become —COOH. This, on oxidative decarboxylation is degraded to the ketopentose, ribulose 5-phosphate.

By this process, known as the hexose monophosphate shunt, glucose can be diverted from the glycolytic sequence. The successive enzymes concerned are glucose 6-phosphate dehydrogenase, lactonase and 6-phosphogluconate dehydrogenase, in conjunction with co-enzyme II (TPN) as hydrogen acceptor.

(2) **Pentose Interconversion.** D-Ribulose 5-phosphate (II) can rearrange into an equilibrium mixture with its two isomers, D-ribose 5-phosphate (I) and D-xylulose 5-phosphate (III).

<pre>
  ·   CHO   CH₂.OH   CH₂.OH
           | | |
          HC.OH   CO   CO
           | | |
          HC.OH   HC.OH   HO.CH
           | | |
           R   R   R
           I   II   III
</pre>

$$
\begin{array}{ccc}
\text{CHO} & \text{CH}_2\text{.OH} & \text{CH}_2\text{.OH} \\
| & | & | \\
\text{HC.OH} & \text{CO} & \text{CO} \\
| & | & | \\
\text{HC.OH} & \text{HC.OH} & \text{HO.CH} \\
| & | & | \\
\text{R} & \text{R} & \text{R} \\
\text{I} & \text{II} & \text{III}
\end{array}
$$

(3) **Transketolation.** Transfer of a unit of hydroxyacetyl, or " active glycolaldehyde ", $HO.CH_2.CO$— from a ketose donor to carbon 1 of an aldehyde acceptor. The reaction is reversible. Donors include D-xylulose, D-fructose, and D-sedoheptulose; acceptors include D-glyceraldehyde, D-ribose, and D-erythrose. The sugars react while in the form of phosphate esters.

(4) **Transaldolation.** Transfer of a unit of hydroxyacetone,

$$HO.CH_2.CO.CH(OH)—,$$

from a ketose to an aldose acceptor. Examples of transketolation are the construction of a triose, glyceraldehyde 3-phosphate (III), and a heptose, sedoheptulose 7-phosphate (IV), by transketolation from xylulose 5-phosphate (I) to ribose 5-phosphate (II).

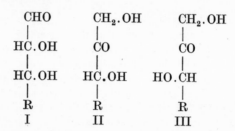

$$
\begin{array}{ccccccc}
 & & & & & & \text{CH}_2\text{.OH} \\
 & & & & & & | \\
 & & & & & & \text{CO} \\
 & & & & & & | \\
\text{CH}_2\text{.OH} & & \text{CHO} & & & & \text{HO.CH} \\
| & & | & & & & | \\
\text{CO} & & \text{HC.OH} & & & & \text{HC.OH} \\
\cdots|\cdots & & | & & & & | \\
\text{HO.CH} & + & \text{HC.OH} & \rightleftharpoons & \text{CHO} & + & \text{HC.OH} \\
| & & | & & | & & | \\
\text{R} & & \text{R} & & \text{R} & & \text{R} \\
\text{I} & & \text{II} & & \text{III} & & \text{IV}
\end{array}
$$

Similarly, fructose 6-phosphate by transketolation to glyceraldehyde 3-phosphate can produce xylulose 5-phosphate and erythrose 4-phosphate. Transaldolation from fructose 6-phosphate (I) to erythrose 4-phosphate (II) produces glyceraldehyde 3-phosphate (III) and sedoheptulose 7-phosphate.

$$
\begin{array}{ccccc}
& & & & CH_2.OH \\
& & & & | \\
CH_2.OH & & & & CO \\
| & & & & | \\
CO & & & & HO.CH \\
| & & & & | \\
HO.CH & & CHO & & HC.OH \\
\cdots|\cdots & & | & & | \\
HC.OH & + & HC.OH \rightleftharpoons CHO & + & HC.OH \\
| & & | \quad\quad | & & | \\
R & & R \quad\quad R & & R \\
I & & II \quad\quad III & & IV
\end{array}
$$

By transketolation and transaldolation, pentoses are built-up or degraded, and intermediates in the glycolytic process are borrowed and returned. These operations are concerned in the photosynthesis of carbohydrates, and explain the occurrence of 4-carbon and 7-carbon sugars in plant tissues. Sugars diverted from the glycolysis to pentose formation can be regarded as entering a subsidiary cycle, from which they can, in part, be restored to the glycolytic process.

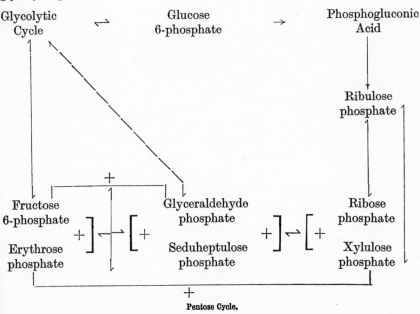

Pentose Cycle.

If the pentoses and derived sugars are not required, the glucose metabolites can be restored to the glycolytic process.

However, each operation of the cycle involves the loss of a (CH_2O) equivalent. Consequently, one glucose molecule can be regarded as being oxidised completely by six revolutions of the pentose epicycle, which thus provides an alternative means for the metabolism of the sugar.

All active cells require ribose and deoxyribose, and the pentose cycle probably is in general operation.

The Uridine Transformations. Uridine is a widely-distributed nucleoside, occurring as a mono-, di-, and triphosphate, denoted, respectively as UP, UDP, and UTP. These nucleotides, or nucleoside phosphates, resemble the adenosine phosphates, but for the replacement of the adenine by a uracil radical. The type pattern of uridine diphosphate, UDP, is:

$$\text{Uracil—ribose—O—PO(OH)—O—PO(OH)}_2.$$

Uridine triphosphate can take part in an exchange reaction with glucose 1-phosphate, to yield uridine diphosphoglucoside and pyrophosphoric acid.

Uridine diphosphoglucoside, or UDP-glucoside, is a key metabolite in many reactions. It is formed by condensation between a terminal hydroxyl in the phosphate side-chain of UDP and the hydroxyl on carbon 1 of glucose.

Catalysed by an enzyme, *UDP- glucoside epimerase,* the glucose radical can be rearranged to galactose and released as galactose 1-phosphate. The system is reversible and is the means whereby galactose is converted to glucose preparatory to being used in hepatic glycogenesis. Failure to inherit the enzyme results in the condition of congenital galactosæmia, characterised by galactosuria.

Catalysed by an enzyme, *UDP-glucoside dehydrogenase,* present in liver, the terminal $—CH_2.OH$ group in UDP-glucoside is oxidised to —COOH, forming a uronic acid radical, held as UDP-glucuronide, which is the universal donor of the glucuronic acid units required in the construction of mucoproteins and the detoxication of some metabolites.

The primary oxidation product of glucose is either gluconic acid or glucuronic acid. Gluconic acid is an aldonic acid formed by oxidation of the —CHO group involving carbon 1; glucuronic acid is a uronic acid formed by oxidation—$CH_2.OH$ group involving carbon 6. Both acids can exist in ring-form, the gluconic as a lactone. In simplified linear formulation they are:

$$HO.CH_2.(CH.OH)_4.COOH \qquad \text{Gluconic acid}$$
$$HOOC.(CH.OH)_4.CHO \qquad \text{Glucuronic acid}$$

Gluconic acid is non-reducing and participates in the inception of the pentose cycle. Glucuronic acid is a reducing sugar acid, and gives rise to a great variety of glucuronides and polymers.

The Pasteur Effect. Glycolysis is characterised by a high rate of carbohydrate destruction and an accumulation of incompletely oxidised products. The use of alternative methods of sugar utilisation is encouraged by a glycolysis-inhibiting effect displayed by free oxygen. This was discovered by Pasteur, who showed that the ratio weight of sugar removed/weight of yeast produced, during alcoholic fermentation, varied from 176 (in complete absence of air) to 4 (in excess of oxygen). The Pasteur effect is observable in most animal and plant tissues, but is weak in those that have great ability for using sugars, notably brain cortex, retina, and embryonic and tumour tissue. Some organisms, the obligatory anaerobes, fail to grow when the oxygen content of their environment has reached a value sufficient to inhibit their glycolytic activity. A few fungi, including brewer's yeast, are able to maintain glycolysis in presence of oxygen. A converse phenomenon is shown when cyanide and other respiratory poisons induce or reveal glycolysis in tissues by preventing the entry of free oxygen into the respiratory machine.

Carbohydrate Employment

In the animal, carbohydrate traffic is organised to meet the needs of four specialised tissues: (1) Skeletal muscle, (2) Cardiac muscle, (3) Brain cortex, (4) Mammary gland.

(1) **Skeletal Muscle.** Muscle is an apparatus for the conversion of chemical energy into mechanical work. As regards rate and continuity, this proceeds more or less uniformly in cardiac and unstriated muscle, but striated skeletal muscle is under voluntary control and subject to abrupt and irregular demands. In consequence, it requires a store of energy that can be released rapidly under anaerobic conditions and replenished during the aerobic resting state. The sources of this energy, in order of employment are adenosine triphosphate, phosphocreatine, and glycogen. Resting human muscle contains about 1 per cent. of glycogen, which in prolonged or violent contraction is glycolysed down to L-(+)-lactic acid, some of which enters the blood stream and contributes to hepatic glyconeogenesis. During the resting phase, the glycolytic process is reversed; lactate is built up into glycogen with the aid of energy obtained from aerobic processes.

These changes were first elucidated by Hopkins and Fletcher (1907), who taught subsequent workers to " respect the biological qualities " of living tissues. By disintegrating fresh muscle in ice-cold alcohol they were able to obtain extracts unchanged by the action of catalysts during analytical treatment.

(2) **Cardiac Muscle.** From some time before the birth of the animal until its death, the heart is constantly active, its brief recovery period being limited to the diastolic phase between each beat. It has a respiratory quotient between 0·8 and 0·9, which indicates that it derives its energy by oxidising fatty acids rather than glucose. Conditions of oxygen shortage, such as asphyxia, evoke a glycogen-lactate process, similar to that in skeletal muscle. The heart is very sensitive to lactic acid, and responds by a protective dilatation of the coronary arteries, but can continue to work as long as the pH

of the blood is kept above pH 7·4, and its scanty supply of glycogen (0·1 to 0·2 per cent.) remains.

(3) **Brain.** Glucose is not merely the food of thought, it is required continually for the maintenance of the functional integrity of the nervous system. Acute anoxæmia can result in loss of consciousness in less than a minute, and if prolonged for three or four minutes may be fatal.

Under conditions of average flow, 10 mg. of glucose are removed from every 100 ml. of blood passing through the human brain, about one-sixth of which is returned as lactate to the venous blood. The importance of glucose is disclosed by the cerebral disturbances, anxiety, confusion, delirium and convulsions which form the hypoglycæmia syndrome evoked by insulin injection. Although brain is endowed with the various enzymes required by the glycolytic process and the pentose and citric cycles, as shown by tissue slice experiments, of all the recognised substrates, only glucose can relieve immediately the hypoglycæmic syndrome when injected into the depleted animal. This may be because of obstructions raised by the blood-brain barrier against the danger of imported intermediate metabolites. Brain contains about 0·1 per cent. of glycogen, which is rapidly glycolysed to lactate in conditions of asphyxia.

In conditions of thiamine deficiency, or avitaminosis B_1, pyruvate is restricted from entering the citric cycle, and by its accumulation, along with lactate, in the lower parts of the brain, evokes the characteristic train of nervous disorders well-displayed by birds. Avitaminous brain tissue has a lowered rate of oxygen consumption, which, as Peters has shown (1936), may be restored to the normal value by addition of thiamine.

(4) **Mammary Gland.** During the 6 to 9 months of normal human lactation, the output of milk increases with the growth of the child, and maintains a value of 850 to 950 ml. per 24 hours for about 20 weeks, representing a daily output of about 60 gm. of lactose. Lactose is a foreign sugar within the organism, and when injected is excreted by the kidney, a phenomenon seen in the overflow lactosuria that accompanies lactation. This indicates that the sugar is constructed locally in the gland and secreted directly into the milk. Tissue-slice and isotope tracer studies indicate that the lactose is formed from glucose 1-phosphate by transfer of a galactosyl radical. The carrier appears to be uridine diphosphate.

As a nutrient, lactose is of special value in that it provides the young animal with a source of galactose for the rapid construction of complex lipids. Lactose, being a β-glycoside, does not undergo alcoholic fermentation by the commoner yeasts and bacteria; otherwise the consumption of stale milk might be socially hazardous.

Sugar Fermentation by Yeast

Natural sugars are liable to attack by yeasts and bacteria, and undergo either aerobic oxidation or anaerobic fermentation, according to circumstances, which led Pasteur to describe fermentation as " life without air ". Brewer's yeast (a culture yeast of the species *Saccharomyces cerivisiæ*) and some facultatively anaerobic bacteria (the lactic and propionic bacilli), however, are able to ferment sugars when oxygen is present, and for this reason are employed industrially in the production of alcohol and lactic acid.

The term *fermentation* (L. *fervere*, to boil) was originally applied to the breakdown of sugar by yeast, on account of the liberation of gaseous carbon dioxide, which caused the mixture to froth. Subsequently, the term was applied to any non-putrefactive change brought about by the growth of living organisms. Other common fermentations include: the *lactic fermentation*, or souring of milk, in which lactic acid is formed from lactose; the *acetic fermentation*, or souring of wine, owing to conversion of ethyl alcohol into acetic acid; and the *ammoniacal fermentation* of urine, in which urea is converted into ammonium carbonate. Yeasts are found naturally wherever sugar is available. They grow less rapidly than bacteria, but can flourish in material preserved from bacterial attack by its high acidity or high osmotic value. By forming alcohol, yeasts can sterilise their media to moulds and bacteria. " Top " fermentation yeasts tend to cluster and to produce CO_2 vigorously. Bread-making yeast is a " top " strain.

Alcoholic fermentation is represented by the overall reaction

$$C_6H_{12}O_6 \rightarrow 2C_2H_5.OH + 2CO_2,$$

in which the monosaccharide is one of the yeast-fermentable sugars: D-glucose, D-fructose, or D-mannose. Conditioned by being cultivated in a medium containing D-galactose, yeasts can acquire the power of fermenting this sugar.

Stages in the Early History of Glycolysis. Between 1857 and 1870, Pasteur founded the science of microbiology by demonstrating that fermentations are initiated and maintained by living organisms.

Between 1897 and 1903 Buchner found that cell-free extracts of yeast were capable of fermenting sugar. This was attributed to a non-living ferment, zymase, now known to be a team of enzymes.

In 1906 Harden and Young separated zymase into a heat-labile enzyme fraction, and a dialysable heat-stable co-enzyme fraction, now known to include co-carboxylase (thiamine pyrophosphate), co-enzyme I (DPN), ATP, Mg^{2+} and PO_4^-. They showed also that the PO_4^- is necessary for fermentation, and isolated a fermentable ester, fructose 1,6-diphosphate. Its precursors, glucose 6-phosphate (Robison, 1932), and fructose 6-phosphate (Neuberg, 1912), were later identified, indicating that phosphorylation is a preliminary event in glycolysis. By interrupting the process at different stages by inhibitors, intermediate products accumulate, and can be identified.

Muscle during contraction anaerobically converts glycogen to lactate (Fletcher and Hopkins, 1907). Cell-free extracts have a similar property (Embden, 1912), and, on fractionation, yield enzymes, co-enzymes, and activators, similar to those obtained from yeast (Myerhof, 1920–; Lohmann, 1928).

283

Lohmann's identification of the phosphate-carrier, adenosine triphosphate, in muscle extracts was of special significance, as was the isolation by Dixon and by the Coris (1939) of triose phosphate dehydrogenase, a key enzyme in glycolytic research because of its sensitivity to iodoacetate. It was subsequently shown (Taylor, 1948) to be a conjugated protein containing DPN. The recognition of the fundamental identity of the glycolytic process in different organisms and tissues (Parnass, 1934) led to the synthesis of much prior work and provided a stimulus to subsequent effort—brain (von Euler, 1936), heart (Ocnoa, 1937), kidney (Jost, 1943).

The optimum pH range for sugar fermentation by living yeast is 5 to 6. If $NaHSO_3$ is added to the mixture, production of alcohol will be replaced by acetaldehyde, trapped by the bisulphite. If the mixture, in the absence of $NaHSO_3$, is kept on the alkaline side of pH 7, production of alcohol and CO_2 will be suppressed, and pyruvate will replace the alcohol. As pyruvate can be decarboxylated to acetaldehyde by yeast carboxylase, and as both pyruvate and acetaldehyde can be converted into alcohol by ordinary yeast, it was concluded that these substances represent the penultimate and the final events in alcoholic fermentation.

$$C_6H_{12}O_6 \rightarrow 2\ CH_3.CO.COOH + 4\ H$$
$$2\ CO_2 + 2\ CH_3.CHO \rightarrow 2\ CH_3.CH_2.OH$$

When alcoholic fermentation is restrained by addition of sulphite, glycerol accumulates in the mixture. It arises from reduction of glyceraldehyde, formed in Stage 4 (p. 274), by hydrogen atoms released in Stage 6, and no longer able to hydrogenate the trapped aldehyde.

This modified fermentation is one of the industrial sources of glycerol, and was exploited as a secret process in Germany during the 1914–18 war.

Carbohydrate Metabolism in Lower Organisms

In addition to operating the glycolytic and related processes, many lower organisms, including yeasts, moulds, and bacteria, synthesise polysaccharides for use as protective material or food reserves, or for extracellular secretions.

Dextrans. Viscid polysaccharides of high molecular weight and optical rotation ($[\alpha]_D + 180°$ to $+ 210°$). The sugar units being in 1 : 6-linkage, dextrans are not hydrolysed by the amylases of pancreatic juice or blood. Partial acid hydrolysis yields dextrans of molecular weight 70,000 to 90,000, which are used clinically for clinical infusion as " plasma expanders " in maintaining blood volume and pressure.

Levans. Polyfructosides produced when *Bac. subtilis*, *Bac. mesentericus*, and some other organisms, are grown in presence of sucrose, which provides the fructose. Like the dextrans, the sugar units are in 1 : 6-linkage. Similar fructosans occur as storage products in higher plants, including the inulins of tubers and the levans of grasses. They are unavailable as nutrients in the human dietary. Inulin is used in renal clearance tests.

Heterosaccharide Haptens. A hapten is a specific compound that, in combination with a protein, forms an antigen.
Antigens are substances that when injected or released into the animal body evoke the production of a specific antidote, inelegantly termed the " antibody ". The capsular material of bacteria usually is rich in heterosaccharides, which, by functioning as haptens, provide immunological tests for the identification of the parent organism. Thus, *pneumococcus* can be subdivided into 32 types, each with its characteristic capsular heterosaccharide, which enables a specific anti-pneumococcal serum to be prepared for therapeutic use against each type.
Heterosaccharide haptens in higher animals are responsible for the iso-agglutins A and B in the red corpuscles, which are inherited as recessive characteristics, and by their presence or absence determine the particular blood-group to which an individual belongs.

CARBOHYDRATE SYNTHESIS IN PLANTS

All green plants and some pigmented bacteria have the power of trapping solar energy for the photosynthesis of organic compounds from carbon dioxide and water, in accordance with the outline reaction:

$$n \; CO_2 + n \; H_2O \rightarrow (CH_2O)_n + nO_2$$

As a result of this process, in continuous and universal operation, about 150×10^{12} kg. of C and 25×10^{12} kg. of H are captured, and 400×10^{12} kg. of O released, every year.

" Perhaps as much as 90 per cent. of the giant chemical industry is carried on under the surface of the ocean by microscopic algæ. Only 10 per cent. of it is conducted on land by our familiar green plants."

Rabinowitch, 1955.

The photosynthetic process, as shown by Blackman in 1905, combines a light-dependent and a light-independent train of events. In 1937 R. Hill showed that an aqueous suspension of chloroplasts, in presence of an electron-acceptor, such as Fe^{3+}, liberated free oxygen on exposure to light. No carbon dioxide was absorbed, and no sugar was synthesised.
This suggested that the primary event in the light-dependent reaction was the photocatalytic fission of water into molecular oxygen and atomic hydrogen, which, when converted to hydrogen ions, could no longer recombine.

$$2 \; H..O..H \rightarrow O :: O + 4 \; H.$$
$$H. + Fe^{3+} \rightarrow H^+ + Fe^{2+}$$

The Dark Reaction. Using an atmosphere containing CO_2 labelled with radio-carbon, ^{14}C, it has been confirmed (Ruben) that CO_2 fixation by plants can

285

occur in darkness. Other tracer studies have shown that the oxygen liberated in photosynthesis comes entirely from the water molecules.

By means of chromatographic analysis of radio-active fractions, several intermediate metabolites in carbon assimilation have been identified. According to Calvin the key reaction is

$$CO_2 + \text{Ribulose 1,5-diphosphate} + H_2O$$
$$\rightarrow \text{3-phosphoglycerate} + \text{3-phosphoglycerate}$$

One molecule of the phosphoglycerate is taken up by the glycolytic process, the other is used in the reconstruction of ribulose diphosphate, and helps to maintain the cycle. Calvin's elaborate theory is summarised and developed by Dixon and Webb (1959).

General References

"Advances in Carbohydrate Chemistry," Vol. I. Ed. by W. W. Pigman and M. L. Wolfram. (1945–). New York.

Baldwin, E. (1952), " Dynamic Aspects of Biochemistry," 2nd Ed. Cambridge.

Bouckaert, J. P. (1947), "Action of insulin." *Physiol. Rev.*, **27**, 39.

Bray, H. G. (1953), " D-Glucuronic acid in Metabolism." *Advanc. Carbohyd. Chem.*, **8**, 251.

Buchtal, F., *et al.* (1956), " Mechanical and Chemical Events in Muscle Contraction." *Physiol. Rev.*, **36**, 503.

" Chemical Pathways of Metabolism," Vol. I. Ed. by D. M. Greenberg. (1954). New York.

Harden, A. (1932), "Alcoholic Fermentation." London.

Hill, R., and C. P. Whittingham (1955), " Photosynthesis." London.

Krebs, H. A. (1954), " The Tricarboxylic Acid Cycle." " Chemical Pathways of Metabolism," Vol. I, Chapter 4.

Ochoa, S., and J. R. Stern (1952), " Carbohydrate Metabolism." *Ann. Rev. Biochem.*, **21**, 547.

Soskin, S., and R. Levine (1952), " Carbohydrate Metabolism." Chicago.

Szent-Györgyi, A. (1947), " Chemistry of Muscular Contraction," 2nd Ed. New York.

Young, F. G. (1948), " Mechanism of the Action of Insulin." *Sci. Progr.*, **36**, 13.

Young, F. G. (1957), " Claude Bernard and the Discovery of Glycogen." *British med. J.*, (June 22) **1**, 1431.

Chapter 17 Protein Metabolism

During alimentary digestion, amino acids are absorbed into the portal blood directly they are liberated from the peptides. Absorption takes place in the small intestine, where the effective area is greatly increased by the projecting villi, and may amount to 8 to 10 square metres in the human adult. Absorption proceeds at the rate of about one gm. per kg. body weight per hour, and is determined by the rate of hydrolysis of the food proteins. The mechanism of amino acid absorption is obscure, but may involve temporary synthesis into peptides by the cells of the intestinal mucosa, as the peptide as well as the amino acid content of the blood rises during protein digestion. The amino nitrogen, or $-NH_2$ content of the plasma in the resting subject is about 3 mg. per 100 ml., values for entire blood being in the range 5 to 8 mg. The values rise within 2 hours after ingestion of proteins, and reach a maximum about 4 hours after the beginning of a meal. Circulating amino acids may be withdrawn and stored temporarily in the tissues during the absorption peak. Individual amino acids in blood plasma can be separated and identified chromatographically, and estimated by micro-biological assay.

Representative values for human plasma, in mg. per 100 ml., are: alanine, 3·3; α-amino butyric, 0·3; arginine, 1·5; asparagine, 0·6; cysteine and cystine, 1·2; glutamine, 0·4 to 1·2; glutamic, 5 to 12; glycine, 1·5; histidine, 1·1; isoleucine, 1; leucine, 1·8; lysine, 2·8; methionine, 0·3; ornithine, 0·7; phenylalanine, 0·9; proline, 2·5; serine, 1·1; threonine, 1·5; tryptophan, 1·1; tyrosine, 1·2; valine, 2·8; total, 35 to 65. In general, the value-pattern resembles those of the proteins of blood plasma, liver and muscle, which are presumed to be in mobile equilibrium with the free amino acids of the plasma.

GENERAL HISTORY OF THE AMINO ACIDS

The fate of the individual amino acids can be traced by feeding or injection experiments, using acids labelled with the isotopes D, ^{14}C, or ^{15}N, and observing the subsequent distribution of the isotope among tissue constituents. Thus, the final concentration of ^{15}N in a tissue protein is an index of the power of the tissue to take up a labelled amino acid. This is greatest in liver and intestinal mucosa, where protein metabolism is very active. About half the total protein N in the liver is exchanged with that in other proteins within a week. Skin and connective tissue proteins are less labile.

After entry into the circulation, amino acids may undergo:

(1) Elaboration into tissue proteins.

287

(2) Transamination, or deamination by transfer of the amino group to a receptor.

(3) Transfer of a specific radical, such as CH_3— (transmethylation) or $H_2N.CO$— (transamidation), to a receptor.

(4) Conversion to related nitrogenous compounds.

(5) Degradation to non-nitrogenous metabolites.

The Amino Acid Pool. After entry into the circulation, the amino acids form part of a metabolic pool, represented by the blood plasma, lymph, and other extra-cellular fluids. This pool forms the mobile nitrogen reserve of the organism, and is being continually drawn upon, or added to, by the tissues. In a 70-kg. subject, the pool has a volume of about 17 litres, and contains 5 to 6 gm. of non-protein nitrogen, about half of which is in the unavailable form of urea.

On leaving the pool, amino acids may undergo:

(1) Transamination, or deamination by transfer of the amino group to an α-oxo or α-keto acid.

(2) Katabolic changes leading to nitrogenous and non-nitrogenous metabolites.

(3) Anabolic changes elaborating peptides and tissue proteins.

(1) **Transamination.** The α-amino acid is deaminated to the corresponding α-oxo acid by transfer of the amino group to an acceptor α-oxo acid, which is thereby converted into an α-amino acid. By this operation, different species of amino acids are constructed as required. The acceptor oxo acid can be provided by the glycolytic process or by one of the metabolic cycles. With the exception of glycine, all or most of the common dietary amino acids can undergo transamination. It is a reversible process, catalysed by a selective transaminase, and uses phosphopyridoxal as the carrier of the amino group.

$$R'—CH(NH_2).COOH \quad R''—CH(NH_2).COOH$$
$$+ \qquad \rightleftharpoons \qquad +$$
$$R''—CO.COOH \qquad R'—CO.COOH$$

Specially prominent in transamination reactions are the amino acids: glutamic, glutamine, aspartic, and asparagine.

$$HOOC.CH_2.CH_2.CH(NH_2).COOH \qquad H_2N.CO.CH_2.CH_2.CH(NH_2).COOH$$
Glutamic acid.   Glutamine.

$$HOOC.CH_2.CH(NH_2).COOH \qquad H_2N.CO.CH_2.CH(NH_2).COOH$$
Aspartic acid.   Asparagine.

Prominent receptors associated with these donors are the α-oxo acids: α-oxoglutaric, and oxaloacetic.

$$HOOC.CH_2.CH_2.CO.COOH \qquad\qquad HOOC.CH_2.CO.COOH$$
α-Oxoglutaric acid.   Oxaloacetic acid.

In addition, pyruvic acid, $CH_3.CO.COOH$, and glyoxylic acid, $HCO.COOH$, are employed.

The transfers are catalysed by highly selective glutamate transaminases, widely distributed in animal and plant tissues.

Transamination Exchanges

Amino acid.		Oxo acid.		Amino acid.		Oxo acid.
L-Glutamic	+	Oxaloacetic	⇌	L-Aspartic	+	α-Oxoglutaric
L-Glutamic	+	Pyruvic	⇌	L-Alanine	+	α-Oxoglutaric
L-Glutamic	+	Glyoxylic	⇌	Glycine	+	α-Oxoglutaric

In this way, reserves of glutamic acid in the animal, and aspartic acid in the plant, can be accumulated. The acids are important both as sources of amino groups in transaminations and in the synthesis of urea and uric acid. Both glutamic acid and aspartic acid can combine with NH_3 to form the respective amides, glutamine and asparagine. The reaction, which is reversible, is catalysed by a synthetase, in conjunction with ATP. Worked in reverse, glutamine provides a source of NH_3 for the animal, and asparagine provides a source for the plant.

Glutamine on transamination yields the unstable α-oxoglutaric amide

$$H_2N.CO.CH_2.CH_2.CH(NH_2).COOH ⇌ H_2N.CO.CH_2.CH_2.CO.COOH$$

Asparagine on transamination yields α-oxosuccinic amide,

$$H_2N.CO.CH_2.CH(NH_2).COOH ⇌ H_2N.CO.CH_2.CO.COOH$$

Oxidative Deamination. Both D- and L-series amino acids can be degraded to oxo acids and free ammonia by oxidases present in liver, kidney, moulds, and bacteria (Krebs, 1933). D-Amino acids are very rare, and the presence of D-oxidases in liver is hard to explain. The importance of oxidative deamination in protein metabolism is not established. Transamination is the popular method for amino transfer, as it avoids the liberation of the potentially toxic metabolite, NH_3.

(2 and 3) Metabolism of Individual Amino Acids in the Higher Animal
A. **Aliphatic Amino Acids Non-Essential in Nutrition.** These units can be synthesised to meet the needs of the organism.

(1) Serine, 3-hydroxyalanine, $HO.CH_2.CH(NH_2).COOH$.
Origin. 3-phosphoglyceric acid, an intermediate in glycolysis, on oxidation yields 3-phosphohydroxypyruvic acid, $(HO)_2.PO—O—CH_2.CO.COOH$, which on transamination forms phosphoserine. Phosphoserine occurs as a structural unit in phosphoproteins. On enzyme or acid hydrolysis, it yields serine.

The terminal $HO.CH_2$— radical in serine is labile and can be transferred to the folic acid apparatus, which provides a pool of 1-carbon units available for metabolism. The serine residue is released as glycine.

Exchange of the terminal HO— group with HS—, supplied by homocysteine, converts serine into cysteine, from which cystine, taurine and glutathione are derived.

Decarboxylation of serine produces ethanolamine, the base, from which choline is derived.

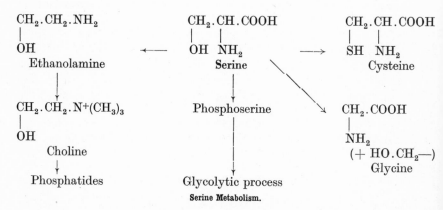

Serine Metabolism.

(2) **Glycine,** aminoacetic acid, the simplest and most versatile of the amino acids. By condensation with succinic acid, $HOOC.CH_2.CH_2.COOH$, followed by decarboxylation, it yields aminolaevulinic acid,

$$H_2N.CH_2.CO.CH_2.CH_2.COOH,$$

from which are constructed the pyrroles necessary for the manufacture of porphyrins, cytochromes, and hæmoglobin. By combining with 1-amino ribose 5-phosphate, glycine contributes an $=N—C=C=$ link required in the synthesis of pyrimidines and purines. On deamination, glycine yields glyoxylic acid, from which are derived oxalic and formic acids. Methylation of the

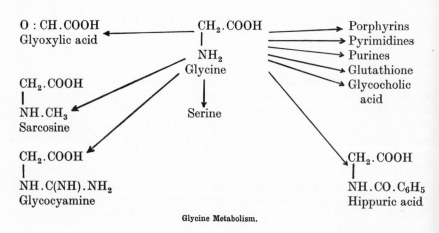

Glycine Metabolism.

amino group produces sarcosine; amidation of the amino group produces glycocyamine, from which is derived creatine.

Glycine is being drawn continually from the amino acid pool for other purposes, such as the production of hippuric acid, or N-benzoyl glycine, the form in which benzoic acid is solubilised and eliminated in the urine.

(3) **Alanine,** α-amino propionic acid, $CH_3.CH(NH_2).COOH$, is readily obtained from and converted into pyruvic acid by transamination and has no special metabolic features of interest. The alanine side-chain occurring in tryptophan and other cyclic amino acids can arise by condensation involving the hydroxyl group of serine.

(4) β-**Alanine,** $H_2N.CH_2.CH_2.COOH$, is unusual in being the only known natural β-amino acid. Its origin in bacteria is from aspartic acid decarboxylation; in mammals, it can come from propionic acid, via β-hydroxypropionate, and from a pyrimidine, dihydrouracil, by chain-opening. β-Alanine is a component of the muscle dipeptides, carnosine and anserine, and forms part of pantothenic acid and the universally essential co-enzyme A.

(5) **Cysteine** and **Cystine.** Cysteine, β-thiol (or sulphydryl) alanine, either free or in compounds that leave its —SH group exposed, is easily and reversibly oxidised to the disulphide, thus linking up two units as cystine, or by a cystine bridge, as in proteins. Dehydrogenation of cysteine to cystine readily occurs in alkaline solutions exposed to air, and can be catalysed by Fe^{3+}, Cu^{2+}, and cytochrome c. Hydrogenation of cystine to cysteine can be effected by H_2S, reduced glutathione, and some reductases.

Cysteine is formed from serine by sulphur transfer from the nutritionally-essential amino acid methionine, and when present in the diet exercises a " sparing-effect " by lessening the need for methionine. Oxidation of the —SH to the sulphonic radical, —$SO_2(OH)$, converts cysteine to cysteic acid, which on decarboxylation yields taurine, or aminoethyl (or ethylamine) -sulphonic acid, a component of the bile acids. Cysteine is a component of the tripeptide, glutathione.

Cystine, unlike cysteine, is sparingly soluble in water.

(6) **Aspartic Acid;** (7) **Glutamic Acid.** In addition to their prominence in transaminations, these dicarboxylic amino acids have special functions. Both are concerned in the synthesis of urea and of the purines. Glutamic acid on reduction forms glutamic semialdehyde, $OCH.CH_2.CH_2.CH(NH_2).COOH$, a metabolite in two important processes: (1) ring-closure, followed by hydrogenation, yields the cyclic imino acid, proline; (2) transamination involving the terminal aldehyde function yields the diamino acid, ornithine, precursor of arginine. Glutamic acid, in turn, can be regenerated from proline. In this way a cycle is formed involving several important amino acids. Other derivatives of glutamic acid include the folic acid vitamins and glutathione.

In the form of its amide, asparagine, aspartic acid stores and supplies ammonia units in plant metabolism. Glutamine serves a similar purpose in the animal, and, because of its easy passage across cell membranes and the blood-brain barrier, acts as a carrier of glutamic acid to the cell.

L 2

Representative glutamine values, in mg. per 100 gm. fresh tissue, are: muscle, heart, 200 to 250; diaphragm, 175 to 200; skeletal, 100 to 150; brain, 45 to 95; liver, 40 to 100; kidney, 10 to 20. Blood plasma contains 10 to 15 mg. per 100 ml.

(8) **Arginine,** α-amino-δ-guanidino valeric acid.

(9) **Ornithine,** α,δ-diamino valeric acid.

(10) **Citrulline,** α-amino-δ-carbamido valeric acid.

These three acids constitute the ornithine cycle, whereby amino nitrogen is converted into urea, preparatory to excretion. The process is described in Chapter 21. Ornithine is derived from glutamic acid, and by successive stages is built up into citrulline and then into arginine, which is hydrolysed by the liver enzyme, arginase, into urea and ornithine and thus returned to the cycle. By a transamidination reaction, the amidino group, —C(NH)—NH₂, can be transferred from arginine to glycine for the construction of guanidoacetic acid. Arginine is widely distributed as a protein component. Along with ornithine, lysine, and histidine it constitutes the group of basic amino acids.

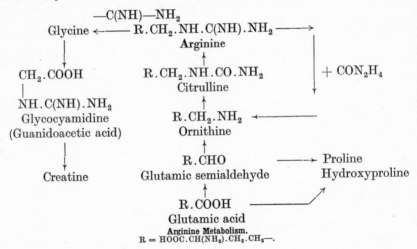

Arginine Metabolism.
$R = HOOC.CH(NH_2).CH_2.CH_2—.$

B. Aliphatic Amino Acids Essential in Nutrition

(1) **Methionine,** α-amino-γ-(methylthio)butyric acid, is the S-methyl ether of homocysteine, the next higher homologue of cysteine. Methionine is the collector and carrier of methyl groups in metabolism. It is activated by adenosine, which combines with the sulphur to form a sulphonium cation carrying a very labile methyl group. On transfer of the methyl group, the methionine complex is degraded to adenosyl-S-homocysteine, which can act as a methyl group collector from donors such as choline. In this way, a methylation cycle is operated.

Homocysteine, escaping from the cycle, reacts with serine, to form cysteine and homoserine, $HO.CH_2.CH_2.CH(NH_2).COOH.$ The cysteine joins the cysteine–cystine pool; the homoserine is deaminated and degraded to pyruvate, via succinate.

Methyl acceptors

Methyl donors

$$R—CH_2S^+\diagdown{CH_3 \atop A^-} \xrightarrow[\text{S—Adenosyl carrier}]{} R—CH_2—S—A^- + CH_4$$

$$+A \uparrow \qquad\qquad\qquad\qquad\qquad\qquad \downarrow -A$$

$$R—CH_2—S—CH_3 \qquad R—CH_2—SH \quad | \quad \text{Homocysteine}$$

Methionine

$$\qquad\qquad\qquad\qquad\qquad\qquad\qquad \downarrow + \text{Serine}$$

R = HOOC.CH(NH₂).CH₂—

$$R—CH_2—OH + R—SH$$

A = Adenosine

Homoserine   Cysteine

Methionine Metabolism.

The inability of the higher animal to construct homocysteine and combine it with the adenosine carrier is the reason why methionine must be supplied ready-made in the diet.

(2) **Lysine,** α-ϵ-diamino caproic acid,

$$H_2N.CH_2.CH_2.CH_2.CH_2.CH(NH_2).COOH.$$

The terminal amino group in lysine remains unbound when it is incorporated as a unit into proteins, thus conferring basic properties on them. It also, through its carbonyl linkage, provides the point of attack for the hydrolysis of peptides by trypsin. Otherwise, the significance of lysine is obscure. It does not take part in transaminations.

(3) **Isoleucine,** α-amino-β-methylvaleric acid,

$$CH_3.CH_2.CH(CH_3).CH(NH_2).COOH.$$

(4) **Leucine,** α-amino-isocaproic acid,

$$CH_3.CH(CH_3).CH_2.CH(NH_2).COOH.$$

(5) **Valine,** α-amino-isovaleric acid,

$$CH_3.CH(CH_3).CH(NH_2).COOH.$$

The significance of these branched-chain amino acids is not yet known.

(6) **Threonine,** α-amino-β-hydroxybutyric acid,

$$CH_3.CH(OH).CH(NH_2).COOH.$$

Threonine aldolase, an enzyme in liver and kidney, reversibly catalyses the fission of threonine into glycine and acetaldehyde, neither of which is an essential nutrient, which suggests that it is the inability of the animal to provide the aldehyde that is the reason why threonine is an essential nutrient. It does not take part in transamination, but can be irreversibly deaminated. The further significance of threonine is obscure.

C. Aromatic Amino Acids.

(1) **Phenylalanine,** α-amino-β-phenyl propionic acid.

(2) **Tyrosine,** para-hydroxy (or 4-hydroxy)-phenylalanine.
Man, like other higher animals, is unable to synthesise compounds containing the benzene ring, and is compelled to import them as phenylalanine and tyrosine. Phenylalanine is an essential nutrient. It is converted by the liver enzyme system, phenylalanine-4-hydroxylase, irreversibly into tyrosine, parent of several necessary metabolites. Hence, tyrosine in the diet can decrease the need for phenylalanine, though it cannot replace it entirely. Apart from being the source of tyrosine, the specific functions of phenylalanine are unknown. As a protein unit, it forms peptide linkages that are susceptible to attack by pepsin and by chymotrypsin. Within the organism, it is deaminated to *phenylpyruvic acid*, $C_6H_5.CH_2.CO.COOH$, which is degraded to *phenylacetic acid*, $C_6H_5.CH_2.COOH$, some of which is excreted as a glutamine peptide in the urine.

Tyrosine yields at least four classes of metabolite.

(*a*) *Melanins*. Oxidation in the aromatic ring produces, *dopa*, or 3,4-dihydroxyphenylalanine, an amino acid found free in plants. Dopa, on further oxidation, yields dopa quinone, from which by ring closure of the side-chain is formed a series of red and brown melanins (Chapter 12). The process is catalysed by a phenol oxidase system widespread in plants and animals, and collectively described as " tyrosinase "; it is the means whereby tyrosine provides the natural pigments of the hair, skin, and eye.

(*b*) *Adrenalines*. On decarboxylation, dopa forms 3,4-dihydroxytyramine, source of noradrenaline and adrenaline in the adrenal gland and sympathetic nerve endings.

(*c*) *Thyronines*. On iodination, tyrosine forms 3,5-diiodotyrosine, from which are derived the thyroid hormones, triiodothyronine and thyroxine.

(*d*) *Homogentisic Acid*. On deamination, tyrosine forms *p*-hydroxyphenylpyruvic acid. By the action of a liver enzyme system employing ascorbic acid, the pyruvic side-chain is degraded and transferred to an adjacent carbon atom in the benzene ring, its place being taken by a hydroxyl group. This remarkable reaction results in the production of *homogentisic acid*, or hydroquinone 2-acetic acid, which can be fragmented to fumaric acid and acetoacetic acid, and thus metabolised.

Failure of tyrosine deamination causes *tyrosinosis*, an abnormal urinary output of tyrosine.

Inborn Errors of Phenylalanine and Tyrosine Metabolism

I. **Phenylketonuria.** The condition is characterised by an abnormally high output of phenylpyruvate in the urine. Values, which depend on the diet, may exceed 2 gm. per 24 hours. Associated with the condition is an imbecility, phenylpyruvic oligophrenia, first recognised by Fölling (1934).

The condition is incurable, and is inherited as a recessive mendelian character, affecting at least 1 in 25,000 individuals in the British Isles.

Phenylketonuria arises from the absence of one of the enzyme systems in the liver that converts phenylalanine into tyrosine. As a result, phenylalanine and its metabolites accumulate and overflow into the urine. The chemical defect underlying the insanity is obscure. If the condition is recognised at birth by the colour which develops when $FeCl_3$ is added to the urine, and the intake of phenylalanine is restricted to 5 mg. per day, mental development may proceed normally.

II. **Alcaptonuria.** The existence of urines that turned almost black in exposure to air was recognised in the Middle Ages, and, like the red urines of porphyria, was attributed to supernatural agencies. The chromogen is the hydroquinone, homogentisic acid, or 2,5-dihydroxyphenylacetic acid, which, in alkaline solution spontaneously oxidises to a series of dark brown pigments. Homogentisic acid is an intermediate in the normal degradation of tyrosine. Under normal conditions, its ring is broken by an enzyme system containing Fe^{2+}, and activated by ascorbic acid. In the alcaptonuric, the enzyme, homogentisic oxidase, is absent. The condition can be evoked temporarily in guinea pigs by administration of 2-2'-dipyridyl, which binds ferrous iron. It can arise also in states of ascorbic deficiency, and is remedied promptly by administration of the vitamin, which, however, is of no value in the treatment of the congenital disorder. Alcaptonuria is inherited as a recessive mendelian character. It does not affect the general health of the subject.

Urines containing homogentisic acid give the hydroquinone reactions described in Chapter 22.

(3) **Tryptophan,** β-(3-indolyl)-alanine, a nutritionally essential unit, enters at least four different metabolic paths in the higher animal.

(*a*) *Serotonin Production.* On oxidation, tryptophan forms 5-hydroxytryptophan, an amino acid reported to occur naturally; subsequent decarboxylation yields 5-hydroxytryptamine, or serotonin, a powerful vaso-constrictor present in brain, intestinal mucosa, blood platelets and in some venoms. Serotonin is associated with brain activity and may be released by tranquilisers, such as reserpine, and antagonised by hallucinogens, such as mescaline and lysergic diethylamide. Serotonin is excreted as 5-hydroxyindolyl acetic acid, the normal urinary output of which is about 7 mg. per 24 hours which represents about 3 per cent. of the dietary tryptophan intake. The output can rise to 0·4 gm. per 24 hours in subjects with malignant carcinoid disease, and is of diagnostic value.

(*b*) *Tryptamine production,* by decarboxylation of tryptophan, is effected by the micro-flora of the large intestine. It is a powerful vaso-constrictor, and may have some functional properties.

(*c*) *Indolylacetic Acid.* On deamination, tryptophan yields indolylpyruvic acid, which is degraded to indolylacetic acid and excreted in the urine, conjugated with glycine. It is one of the plant growth factors, or phytohormones.

(*d*) *Nicotinic Acid.* This vitamin is formed from tryptophan by a 5-stage process, which includes kynurenine, 3-hydroxyanthranilic acid, and quinolinic acid, each of which can give rise to secondary metabolites of interest in comparative biochemistry.

(4) **Histidine,** β-(2-imidazolyl)-alanine, is essential in the diet of rapidly-growing animals, such as the rat, but is not required by the human adult, as far as may be judged.

Histamine, a powerful vaso-dilator, and a factor in vascular shock, is formed from histamine by decarboxylation, which may be effected by histidine decarboxylases in lung, liver, gastric mucosa and muscle, and in many of the micro-flora of the large intestine. Histamine, or imidazole ethylamine, is removed by being converted to imidazole pyruvic acid, degraded to imidazole acetic acid, and excreted in the urine. The enzyme system concerned includes a diamine oxidase, *histaminase*.

Histidine derivatives of obscure significance include ergothioneine, carnosine and anserine.

Histidine is metabolised by deamination to urocanic acid, by histidine deaminase, a liver enzyme; subsequent fragmentation yields glutamic and formic acids.

End-Products of Amino Acid Metabolism

In the animal, the carbohydrates and fats are oxidised completely to carbon dioxide and water; the proteins contain 14 to 16 per cent. of nitrogen, which requires to be eliminated. This is effected in the forms of NH^+_4, urea, and uric acid, the emphasis being determined by the living conditions of the animal. Aquatic species are ammoniotelic, in that ammonia is the chief end-product of their nitrogen metabolism and is rapidly removed by their liquid environment. Within the organism, ammonia is toxic. It is trapped as glutamine and used to construct non-toxic urea and uric acid by terrestrial animals, who retain and circulate waste products prior to excreting them in the urine.

According to Needham, the choice of excreta is determined by the circumstances in which embryonic development takes place. Oviparous vertebrates, such as birds and snakes, are uricotelic, in that uric acid, a sparingly soluble purine containing 30 per cent. of nitrogen, is the form in which waste nitrogen is collected. Otherwise, the embryo, encased in its shell, would be exposed to the chemical and osmotic effects of accumulating ammonia or urea.

Viviparous terrestrial vertebrates are ureotelic and convert waste nitrogen into neutral urea, which is concentrated by the kidney, prior to excretion. Both purinogenesis and ureogenesis take place chiefly or exclusively in the liver, and are described subsequently in Chapters 20 and 21.

Protein Construction in the Animal

The microsomes of the cell are the active centres for the construction of fats, sterols, and proteins, and act as collectors of structural units, including activated acetate and amino acids. Fatty acids and sterols resemble glycogen in that they are built up from similar types of unit; proteins are unique in that they are assembled from a selection of more than twenty different species of unit, which are arranged exactly in accordance with a predetermined pattern, specific for each protein. These patterns are imposed by templates or moulds of ribonucleic acid, concentrated in the cell inclusions and nuclei. Like the chromosomes, these galaxies have the power of self-reproduction, so that when a cell divides, each offspring inherits the necessary apparatus for the manufacture of its enzymes and other proteins.

General References

Bach, S. J. (1952), " Metabolism of Protein Constituents in the Mammalian Body," Oxford.

Baldwin, E. (1952), "Dynamic Aspects of Biochemistry." 2nd Ed. Cambridge.

Borsook, H. (1950), " Protein Turnover." *Physiol. Rev.*, **30**, 206.

" Chemical Pathways of Metabolism." Ed. by D. M. Greenberg (1954). New York.

Dalgliesh, C. E. (1955), "Metabolism of Aromatic Amino Acids." *Advanc. Protein Chem.*, **10**, 31.

Dunn, M. S. (1949), " Microbiological Assay of Amino Acids." *Physiol. Rev.*, **29**, 219.

Fisher, R. B. (1954), " Protein Metabolism." London; New York.

Fry, B. A. (1955), " Nitrogen Metabolism of Micro-Organisms." London; New York.

Lerner, A. B. (1953), " Metabolism of Phenylalanine and Tyrosine." *Advanc. Enzymol.*, **14**, 73.

Schoenheimer, R. (1946), " Dynamic State of Body Constituents." Harvard.

" Symposium on Amino Acid Metabolism." Ed. by W. D. McElroy and B. Glass (1955). Baltimore.

du Vigneaud, V. (1952), " Research in Sulfur Chemistry and Metabolism." Cornell.

Chapter 18 Lipid Metabolism

In describing metabolic inter-relationships, the term " lipid " is extended so as to include fatty acids and their esters, phospholipids, glycolipids, sterols and some associated hydrocarbons. Several mechanisms are concerned in the absorption of lipids by the higher animal, and glycerides do not require to be hydrolysed completely in order to be transferred from the alimentary tract, although molecular structure may be of special importance in the absorption of sterols and carotenoids.

Because of the partition effect, glycerides of short-chain acids appear in the portal blood, while those of the long-chain acids travel in the lymphatic duct, and thus enter the venous circulation. Lipid travels mostly as neutral fat particles, or chylomicrons, ranging in diameter from $0\cdot5\mu$ to 1μ.

These particles are stabilised by an envelope of lipoprotein containing phospholipid. They can be enumerated by the aid of " dark-ground " microscopy.

Plasma lipids. In the resting state, human blood plasma contains about 550 mg. lipid per 100 ml., about one-quarter of which is neutral fat, and one-third free or esterified cholesterol. After ingestion of an average meal containing about 30 gm. of fat, the lipid content of the systemic blood reaches a maximum within 2 to 3 hours, and subsides to the resting level within 5 hours. When at its maximum, approaching 2 per cent. total lipid, plasma has a milky appearance, caused by the great increase in the chylomicron population.

Representative values, in mg. per 100 ml., for the lipid distribution in human blood plasma are: total lipid, 385 to 675; neutral fat, 80 to 240; phospholipids, 110 to 250 (lecithin, 100 to 200; cephalin, 0 to 30; sphingomyelin, 10 to 50); cholesterol, 150 to 250 (esters, 90 to 200); total fatty acids, 150 to 500.

Dissolution of the chylomicrons in the plasma is effected by a lipoprotein lipase present in the blood, and activated by " clearing factors " released from adipose tissue, and by heparin. The liberated fatty acids are captured and carried by the plasma proteins, and eventually are taken up by the tissues.

Structural Lipids and Storage Lipids. According to McCance and Widdowson fat is the greatest variable in the human body. A person of standard weight and height contains 15 to 20 per cent.; thin people may have as little as 7 per cent.; the obese may achieve 50 per cent.

The distribution of body lipid differs according to structure and function. Storage lipid, as neutral fats and phospholipids, accumulates as depot fat in adipose tissue, liver and bone marrow. Structural lipid, including phospho-lipids, glycolipids and sterols, occurs in all tissues, being concentrated in cell membranes and inclusions, such as mitochondria, microsomes and Golgi structures. The type of storage fat depends on the species of the animal, glycerides of oleic, palmitic, and stearic acids being the most popular. Human fat is rich in oleic glycerides, and for this reason is liquid at body-tempera-ture. Storage fat can be hardened or softened to some extent by the type of fat predominating in the diet. Tracer experiments on lower animals, using fatty acids labelled with deuterium, show that depot fats are continually being broken-down and reconstructed, and that fatty acids are being de-saturated or resaturated, and shortened or extended, by the enzymes of the lipoclastic cycle.

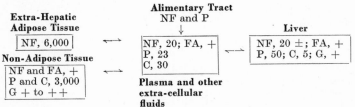

Lipid distribution, in gm., in average 65- to 70-kg. human body: NF, neutral fat; FA fatty acids; P, phospholipids; C, cholesterol, free and esterified; G, glycolipids.

The Lipoclastic Cycle

Fatty acids are metabolised by a process of progressive oxidations involving the carbon atom in the penultimate, or β-position, as regards the terminal carboxyl group. This was first demonstrated by Knoop, in 1904, and has now been confirmed by tracer analysis. The oxidation is effected by a 4-stage spiral process operated in the liver and elsewhere, by enzymes associated with the microsomes of the cells. Preparatory to entering the cycle, the fatty acid is activated by being condensed with co-enzyme A, so as to form a thiol ester.

$$\begin{array}{ccc} \gamma & \beta & \alpha \\ R-CH_2-CH_2-CH_2-COOH + HS.CoA \\ R-CH_2-CH_2-CH_2-CO\text{---}S.CoA + H_2O \end{array}$$

$R = H_3C.(CH_2)_x-$
The co-enzyme is formulated so as to show its free thiol group.

The product is designated acyl-co-enzyme A, and briefly formulated acyl-CoA, the S atom being implied. Condensation is catalysed by a liver enzyme, acyl-CoA synthetase, energy being provided by ATP (page 300).

Fission is catalysed by acetyl-CoA transacylase, or β-ketoacyl thiolase. The degraded acyl-co-enzyme A rejoins the cycle at stage 1, and the process continues. Each time a molecule of a fatty acid circulates it loses two —CH_2— links in its chain, by transfer as " active acetate " to co-enzyme A. Fatty acids containing an even number of total carbon atoms eventually are degraded to acetoacetic acid:

$$CH_3.(CH_2)_{2n}.COOH \rightarrow CH_3.CO.CH_2.COOH + (n-1)CH_3.COOH.$$

Stage 1. Acyl-CoA undergoes α,β-dehydrogenation:

$$R\text{—}CH_2\text{—}CH\text{=}CH\text{—}CO\text{——}S.CoA$$

The enzyme is acyl-CoA dehydrogenase; cytochrome c is the hydrogen acceptor.

Stage 2. The $\alpha : \beta$-double-bond is hydrated, forming a β-hydroxy acid radical:

$$R\text{—}CH_2\text{—}CH(OH)\text{—}CH_2\text{—}CO\text{——}S.CoA$$

Equilibrium is catalysed by crotonase, or enoyl-CoA hydrase.

Stage 3. The hydroxy acid radical is dehydrogenated, forming a β-oxo (or β-keto) acid:

$$R\text{—}CH_2\text{—}CO\text{—}CH_2\text{—}CO\text{——}S.CoA$$

The enzyme is hydroxyacyl-CoA dehydrogenase; DPN^+ is the hydrogen acceptor.

Stage 4. The oxo group of the acid radical is attacked by a second molecule of co-enzyme A, which splits off a unit of acetyl-co-enzyme A, $CH_3.CO\text{—}S.CoA$, and combines with the residue to form an acyl-co-enzyme ester that has two carbons less than the original fatty acid:

$$R\text{—}CH_2\text{—}CO\text{—}S.CoA$$

Fatty acids with an odd number of carbon atoms eventually are degraded to propionic acid: $CH_3.CH_2.COOH$, which can be oxidised to lactic acid, and pyruvic acid, and thus contribute to glycogen production.

Acetyl co-enzyme A, which may be formulated as $CH_3.CO\text{—}CoA$, or as $CH_3.CO\text{—}S.CoA$, is a universal donor of the highly active acetyl unit and supplies many important biological processes, notably: maintenance of the citric cycle and acetyl transfer reactions, as in the formation of citrate from oxaloacetate.

$$CH_3.CO\text{—}SCoA + \begin{array}{c} CH_2.COOH \\ | \\ CO.COOH \end{array} \rightarrow \begin{array}{c} CH_2.COOH \\ | \\ C(OH).COOH \\ | \\ CH_2.COOH \end{array} + HS.CoA$$

The widely-distributed catalyst in this reaction is known as the citrate-condensing enzyme, or oxaloacetate transacetase. The chief sources of acetyl-co-enzyme A are the lipoclastic cycle, in which it is being continually produced, and the glycolytic process, which provides pyruvic acid, capable of oxidative decarboxylation to acetyl units. Acetic acid can be activated by condensation with co-enzyme A in a manner similar to that of the higher fatty acids.

Acetoacetate Metabolism. Acetoacetic acid is produced in the last rotation of the lipoclastic cycle, and can arise also from condensation between two molecules of acetyl-co-enzyme A. The concentration tends to increase when no other demands are being made for acetyl units, and the acetoacetate escapes into the general circulation. The normal range for human blood plasma is 0·8 to 2·8 mg. acetoacetate per 100 ml. Extra-hepatic tissues can use aceto-acetate for the production of acetyl-co-enzyme A, and the maintenance of the citric cycle. In this way, it can be combusted completely to CO_2 and H_2O. In conditions of untreated diabetes or hypoglycæmia caused by starvation or toxic states, lipid metabolism is stimulated to meet demands for energy and specific metabolites. If the output of acetyl-co-enzyme A exceeds the consumption rate, acetoacetate production increases, and is accompanied by its precursor and reduction product, β-hydroxybutyric acid, and its de-carboxylation product, acetone. This is partly because the extra-hepatic tissues, which normally remove acetoacetate from the blood, become swamped.

As a result, depletion of the alkaline reserve of the blood, or acidosis develops, caused by the two acids, and ketonæmia and ketonuria occur, caused by the two ketones. The condition eventuates in a general ketosis, in which the organism is poisoned by the products of its own activity.

That ketosis was not uncommon in former times may be inferred from records, such as Malory's account of the death of Launcelot: " They found him stark dead, and the sweetest savour about him that ever they had smelled."

Synthesis of Fat in the Organism

That tissue fat can arise from carbohydrate was proved experimentally by Lawes and Gilbert (1852), who showed that pigs fed exclusively on barley acquired more body fat than could have come from the fat and protein in the barley. A similar transformation is demonstrated, often unwillingly, in the human subject, and a restriction in carbohydrate intake is a routine procedure in treatment of obesity. Fat can arise also from protein, as shown by the effects of feeding lean meat to dogs whose glycogen and lipid stores had been depleted by starvation.

Fat production requires fatty acids and glycerol. Tracer isotope analysis shows that fatty acids can be assembled from acetyl-co-enzyme A, by a reversal of the lipoclastic cycle; and both the necessary acetyl units and the glycerol can be provided by glycolysis. The use of 2-carbon units in fat con-struction explains why the fatty acids found in animal and plant fats contain an even number of carbon atoms.

For the same reason, milk fat from the lactating gland, wherein fat synthesis is very active, contains a selection of even-number short-chain acids. Values, expressed as percentages of total fatty acid, for human and cow milk fat respectively, are: butyric, 0·4, 3·0; caproic (hexanoic), 0·1, 1·4; caprylic (octanoic), 0·3, 1·5; capric (decanoic), 2·2, 2·7; palmitic (hexadeconoic), 23, 25; stearic (octadecanoic), 7, 9; oleic (octadecenoic) 36, 30. The relatively high concentration of the short-chain acids in cow's milk may be of nutritional significance. However, unlike human milk, it is a poor source of the polyene acids necessary for the health of the skin.

Complex Lipids

a-Phosphatidic acids are formed when a terminal fatty acid radical in a glyceride is replaced by a phosphoric radical. They can be synthesised in the organism from glycerol, *via* a-glycerophosphate. Condensation between the phosphoric side-chain and a base, ethanolamine, serine, or choline, yields a phospholipid, or phosphatide, of which phosphatidyl choline, or lecithin, is the most familiar.

The carrier of the base is cytidine diphosphate, a nucleotide similar to uridine diphosphate, but for the replacement of the uracil residue by cytosine (p. 326).

Phosphatides occur chiefly in the cellular lipids of the liver and other glands and in the blood plasma, the nervous system, and in egg-yolk and leguminous seeds. Cell membranes and inclusions are rich in phospholipid.

Because of their polar structure, phospholipids are soluble both in water and in organic solvents. They regulate the size and stability of the chylomicrons, and thus aid in the transport of fat.

Phospholipids are an important source of choline and ethanolamine in the diet, which have a lipotropic action in preventing excessive accumulation of fat in the liver. Tracer studies, using phosphate labelled with the radio-active isotope, ^{32}P, show that phospholipid formation and resolution is continually taking place, and is specially active during the absorption of lipids.

Sterols

Sterols are universally employed by animals and plants in cell architecture. Cholesterol is the characteristic sterol of the higher animal. It is synthesised abundantly in the human body, the surplus being excreted in the bile. The structure and position of the methyl groups suggests that cholesterol, like other natural hydrocarbons: carotenoids, terpenes, sesquiterpenes, rubber, and balata, is assembled from units of **isoprene,** $H_2C : C(CH_3)$—$CH : CH_2$. Isoprene does not occur as such in Nature, but related C_5 compounds can be constructed from acetyl units.

Tracer studies with ^{14}C-labelled acids show that cholesterol can be assembled from acetate and acetoacetate. By using the two isomers, $^{14}CH_3 . COOH$ and CH_3—$^{14}COOH$, it is possible to locate the individual contributions of the 2-carbon units to the sterol skeleton.

Mevalonic acid, 3-methyl-3,5-dihydroxy valeric acid,

$$HO . CH_2 . CH_2 . C(OH)(CH_3) . CH_2 . COOH,$$

first recognised as a growth factor for bacteria, is readily converted into cholesterol by liver homogenates. Mevalonate, which occurs in distillery waste (dried solubles), can be regarded as an isoprene derivative formed by condensation between acetic and acetoacetic acid, followed by reduction. It can act as a precursor of β-carotene in fungi.

Squalene, $C_{30}H_{50}$, a triterpene present in fish oils, is the most prominent intermediary in the synthesis of cholesterol. Mevalonic acid can be converted anaerobically to squalene by liver extracts (Popjak, 1958), and squalene, labelled with ^{14}C, is converted into labelled cholesterol in the animal body (Bloch, 1953–).

From cholesterol, or a pro-cholesterol, are derived the chief steroids of the animal: bile acids and hormones of the adrenal cortex, ovary, and testicle. Human blood serum contains 200 ± 50 mg. cholesterol per 100 ml., more than half of which is esterified. The serum cholesterol level is affected by the dietary fat intake, being raised by milk fat, beef tallow, cocoa butter, palm oil, lard, and egg-yolk; and lowered by less saturated fats, including the oils: olive, peanut, cotton seed, soya bean, linseed and sardine.

Serum cholesterol is raised in diabetes, some forms of renal disease, hypothyroidism, and obstructive jaundice.

Blood Lipids and Cardiac Disease. Coronary, or ischæmic heart disease is a major cause of death in many civilised countries, and is believed to be related to the type and quantity of lipids in the diet. In atherosclerosis, a fatty degeneration of the arterial wall, the serum cholesterol and lipoproteins are increased. Although the evidence of a dietary implication is circumstantial, and the disease is " both difficult to measure in its prevalence and to predict in its mode of progression " . . ." few problems merit closer attention at the present time " (Bronte-Stewart, 1958).

Summary of Fat Metabolism in the Higher Animal

Alimentary tract	Glycerides	Fatty acids	Glycerol	Phosphatides
Intestinal mucosa		Glycerides	Phospholipids	

Lymphatic system	Long-chain glycerides	Portal system	Short-chain glycerides

General circulation	Fatty acids	*Liver*		
		Fatty acids	Fats	Phospholipids

Extra-hepatic tissues		*Lipoclastic cycle*	
Lipoclastic cycle		Acetyl-CoA	
Citric cycle	Storage fat	Acetoacetate	Pyruvate
		Mevalonic acid	*Glycolytic process*
Glycolytic process		Squalene	
	$CO_2 + H_2O$	Cholesterol	*Citric cycle*
			$CO_2 + H_2O$

General References

" Biochemical Problems of Lipids." Ed. by G. Popjak and E. Le Breton (1956). New York; London.

Bloor, W. R. (1943), " Biochemistry of the Fatty Acids." Oxford.

Duel, H. J. (1951, 1955), " The Lipids." Vols. I and II. New York.

" Lipid metabolism." *Biochemical Society Symposia.* Cambridge University Press.

Lynen, F. (1955), " Metabolism of fatty acids." *Annu. Rev. Biochem.*, **24,** 653.

Smedley-Maclean, I. (1943), " The Metabolism of Fat." London.

Wittcoff, H. (1951), " The Phosphatides." New York.

Chapter 19 Tissue Respiration

" Life is a pure flame, and we live by an invisible sun within us."

Thomas Browne, 1605–82.

Respiration. As originally used in physiology, the term *respiration* was applied to the uptake and output of air by the lungs, and the resulting changes in oxygen and carbon dioxide content. This was later described as *pulmonary respiration.* Aerobic tissues under appropriate conditions take up O_2 and release CO_2, and these activities were described as respiratory. Other activities, such as the fermentation of sugars by yeast, result in the release of CO_2, without any corresponding uptake of O_2; these were paradoxically described as *anaerobic respirations.* As now employed, the term tissue or cellular respiration denotes any process whereby the energy of an organic substrate is made available for tissues or for individual cells.

Tissue respiration involves the catalysed transfer of hydrogen from primary substrates to carriers. In the anaerobic respirations, the final hydrogen acceptor is an organic compound, such as pyruvic acid or acetaldehyde. In the aerobic respirations, the final acceptor is molecular oxygen. Anaerobic respirations, or fermentations, such as glycolysis, are extravagant, though they must have been the chief sources of energy for many primitive organisms during the ages before the activities of the photosynthetic bacteria and algæ had begun to enrich the earth's atmosphere with free oxygen.

" The development of more complicated, and hence more pretentious forms of life became possible only after Nature discovered oxidation by molecular oxygen. This course of events is still reflected in our cells, in which we find oxidation and fermentation intimately mixed and woven into one energy-producing pattern."

Szent-Györgyi, 1937.

Aerobic Respiration

Activation of Acetate. Aerobic respiration is concerned chiefly with the disposal of the end-products of the glycolytic process, I, and the lipoclastic spiral, II.

I. $C_6H_{12}O_6 \rightarrow 2\ CH_3.CO.COOH + 4\ H.$

II. $CH_3.(CH_2)_{2n}.COOH + 2n\ H_2O \rightarrow (n + 1)CH_3.COOH + 4n\ H.$

In order to enter the citric cycle for final metabolism, both the carbon end-products must be in the reactive form of acetyl units, $CH_3.CO—$, or " active acetate ", $(CH_3.COOH)$, carried by co-enzyme A, as the thio-ester,

305

$CH_3.CO$—S—CoA. In this form they emerge from the lipoclastic spiral, and further activation is unnecessary. Pyruvic acid, from the glycolytic process, is converted into " active acetate " by a double process involving decarboxylation and oxidation, followed by transfer. This oxidative-decarboxylation is effected by lipoic acid in combination with thiamine pyrophosphate, or *cocarboxylase*, and is catalysed by *pyruvate dehydrogenase*.

$$CH_3.CO.COOH + \begin{array}{c} S—CH_2 \\ | \qquad\qquad CH_2 \\ S—CH \\ \qquad (CH_2)_4.COOH \end{array} \longrightarrow \begin{array}{c} CH_3.CO.S—CH_2 + CO_2 \\ CH_2 \\ HS—CH \\ \qquad (CH_2)_4.COOH \end{array}$$

Lipoic acid.   Acetyl-lipoic acid.

The acetyl-lipoic acid reacts with co-enzyme A, forming acetyl-co-enzyme A and reduced lipoic acid, $HS.CH_2.CH_2.CH(SH).(CH_2)_4.COOH$, from which the oxidised or cyclic form is regenerated by transfer of hydrogen to co-enzyme I.

The Citric Cycle. The complete combustion of acetate is effected by the citric, or tricarboxylic acid cycle, an 8-stage process, anchored in the cell mitochondria. Acetate, fed in active form to the cycle by *acetyl-co-enzyme A*, combines with a 4-carbon acid, oxaloacetic, to form the first of a series of 6-carbon acids, from which, by decarboxylation, a series of 4-carbon acids is formed, terminating in oxaloacetic, which, by accepting another acetic unit, continues the cycle.

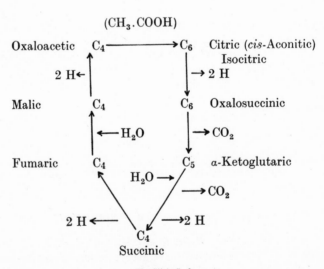

The Citric Cycle.

306

Stage 1. *Oxaloacetate into Citrate.* Acetyl-co-enzyme A transfers its acetyl unit to oxaloacetate, thereby building up a 6-carbon acid:

$$\text{HOOC.CO.CH}_2.\text{COOH} + \text{CH}_3.\text{CO—S—CoA} + \text{H}_2\text{O} \rightarrow \overset{\displaystyle \text{CH}_2.\text{COOH}}{\underset{\displaystyle \text{CH}_2.\text{COOH}}{\overset{|}{\underset{|}{\text{C(OH).COOH}}}}} + \text{HSCoA}$$

The reaction is catalysed by *oxaloacetate transacetase,* the citrate condensing enzyme.

Stage 2. *Citrate into Isocitrate.* This may be effected by dehydration to *cis*-aconitate, $\text{HOOC.CH}_2.\text{C(COOH)} : \text{CH.COOH}$, followed by hydration to isocitrate. Equilibrium is catalysed by *aconitase.*

Stage 3. *Isocitrate to Oxalosuccinate,* by transfer of hydrogen to co-enzyme II (TPN+):

$$\underset{\text{Isocitric acid.}}{\overset{\displaystyle \text{CH(OH)COOH}}{\underset{\displaystyle \text{CH}_2.\text{COOH}}{\overset{|}{\underset{|}{\text{CH.COOH}}}}}} + \text{TPN}^+ \rightarrow \underset{\text{Oxalosuccinic acid.}}{\overset{\displaystyle \text{CO.COOH}}{\underset{\displaystyle \text{CH}_2.\text{COOH}}{\overset{|}{\underset{|}{\text{CH.COOH}}}}}} + \text{TPNH} + \text{H}^+$$

Equilibrium is catalysed by *isocitric dehydrogenase.*

Stage 4. *Oxalosuccinic to α-ketoglutaric.* Decarboxylation to

$$\text{HOOC.CO.CH}_2.\text{CH}_2.\text{COOH}$$

is catalysed by *oxalosuccinic decarboxylase,* in presence of Mn^{2+}.

Stage 5. *α-Ketoglutaric to Succinic,* $\text{HOOC.CH}_2.\text{CH}_2.\text{COOH}$. This complex reaction involves lipoic acid, co-enzyme A, and phosphate, and is comparable to the oxidative decarboxylation of pyruvic acid. Energy released can be used for the generation of adenosine triphosphate.

Stage 6. *Succinic to Fumaric Acid,* $\text{HOOC.CH} : \text{CH.COOH}$. Dehydrogenation is effected by *succinic dehydrogenase.*

Stage 7. *Fumaric to Malic Acid,* $\text{HOOC.CH}_2.\text{CH(OH).COOH}$. Hydration is catalysed by *fumarase.*

Stage 8. *Malic to Oxaloacetic Acid.* The dehydrogenation is catalysed by *malic dehydrogenase.*

Significance of the Citric Cycle. The overall reaction is:

$$\text{CH}_3.\text{COOH} + 2\ \text{H}_2\text{O} \rightarrow 2\ \text{CO}_2 + 8\ \text{H}.$$

Because of the multi-stage nature of the cycle, energy is released gradually, thereby avoiding over-heating of the cell. Each stage is controlled by a feed-back mechanism, whereby the various intermediate metabolites can be diverted to other reacting systems.

The Glyoxylic Cycle. In this extension of the citric cycle, which has been found in moulds and bacteria, isocitrate is diverted from the cycle, and resolved

307

into succinic and glyoxylic acids, each of which can enter separate metabolic paths. Glyoxalate, by condensation with acetate, can form malate, and thus re-enter the main cycle, or enable the cell to open up another citric cycle.

History of the Citric Cycle

In 1909, Thunberg, while studying the ability of various substrates to promote tissue respiration, discovered the powerful enzyme succinic dehydrogenase in animal tissues, yeast, and bacteria. As the substrate, succinic acid, is not a prominent constituent of the diet or the tissues, the status of the enzyme remained obscure. In 1928, Quastel showed that malonic acid,

$$HOOC.CH_2.COOH,$$

inhibits the dehydrogenation by competing with succinate for possession of the enzyme. Addition of malate can lead to an almost complete suppression of the respiratory activity of many tissues, which suggests that succinic dehydrogenase is implicated in some general process. Respiratory activity can be restored to the tissues by addition of fumarate, the dehydrogenation product of succinate. Comparable results were obtained by addition of the related acids, malic and oxaloacetic. As their respective dehydrogenases accompany succinic dehydrogenase in tissues, Szent-Györgyi, in 1937, postulated the existence of a 4-membered chain of dicarboxylic acids in the general respiratory process. Meanwhile, pyruvic acid had been shown to be the end-product of glycolysis, and citric acid had been found to be a universal constituent of animal tissues, where it can be formed by condensation between oxaloacetate and pyruvate, followed by reduction. In 1937–8, Krebbs assembled the facts into a theory of respiration by a cyclical process, fed by 2-carbon units.

Hydrogen Transport in Respiration

Aerobic respiration involves the transport and disposal of the hydrogen that has been released by the various dehydrogenases. This hydrogen is in the form of the atomic unit, H., or its equivalent, a proton and an electron, $H^+ + e'$. Because of their highly reactive nature, neither atomic hydrogen nor free electrons exist as such in biological systems, but are taken up by a sequence of carriers, leading to the final hydrogen acceptor, molecular oxygen.

Hydrogen Carriers. The carriers of atomic hydrogen commonly employed are the co-enzymes I and II and the flavoproteins.

The co-enzymes are primary carriers and work in conjunction with the dehydrogenating enzymes; the flavoproteins are enzymes in which the carrier forms the prosthetic group, and is less easily detached than the co-enzyme associated with its dehydrogenase. Two types of flavoprotein operate: primary flavoprotein dehydrogenases, which release and carry hydrogen from primary metabolites; and secondary flavoprotein dehydrogenases, which transfer hydrogen from the co-enzymes. The third component of the respiratory sequence is the cytochrome chain, a series of porphyro-proteins containing iron, which, by undergoing alternate reduction and oxidation of the type $Fe^{3+} + e' \rightarrow Fe^{2+} \rightarrow Fe^{3+} + e'$, transmits electrons accompanied by H^+ from the reduced flavoproteins.

The Respiratory Sequence

While the entire sequence is operated in the dehydrogenation of a large number of metabolites, some stages are by-passed or modified in accordance with enzyme requirements.

Thus, the oxidases, or aerobic dehydrogenases, such as glucose oxidase, transfer H directly from the metabolite to molecular oxygen, with production of H_2O_2. Succinic dehydrogenase transfers H directly from succinate to the cytochrome chain. The dehydrogenases of the lipoclastic process require an additional flavoprotein in the sequence.

Structure of the Hydrogen-Transporting Co-enzymes

These nicotinamide co-enzymes, or phosphopyridine nucleotides, are chain compounds assembled from adenine + D-ribose + pyrophosphate + D-ribose + nicotinamide. The adenine-ribose-phosphate, or adenylic acid

Co-enzymes I and II.

309

moiety occurs also in the adenosine polyphosphates, co-enzyme A, and one of the flavin nucleotides; it acts, presumably, as a protein-attachment group. The actual hydrogen-carrier is the nicotinamide radical.

In co-enzyme I, or diphosphopyridine nucleotide, DPN, R = H. In co-enzyme II, or triphosphopyridine nucleotide, TPN, R = —PO(OH)$_2$. The second carbon in the ribose unit attached to adenine carries a phosphoric radical.

In the reduced form of the carrier, an electron and a hydrogen atom have been added to the pyridine ring. The reversible reaction is formulated briefly,

$$DPN^+ + 2\,H \rightleftharpoons DPNH + H^+.$$

In the process, the quaternary nitrogen loses its positive charge, and one of the transferred hydrogen atoms is de-electronated to H$^+$, thus preserving the anion-cation balance of the system.

Structure of the Hydrogen-Transporting Flavins

The flavoprotein enzymes have as prosthetic group either flavin mononucleo tide or flavin-adenine dinucleotide, sometimes accompanied by an activating metal.

Flavin Mononucleotide, or FMN, is riboflavin 5'-phosphate, a derivative of vitamin B$_2$, in which the terminal —CH$_2$.OH of the ribityl chain has been condensed with phosphoric acid.

Flavin-adenine Dinucleotide, or FAD, is assembled from riboflavin + pyro phosphate + D-ribose + adenine. It can be regarded as formed by conden-sation of the terminal phosphate groups in FMN and adenylic acid.

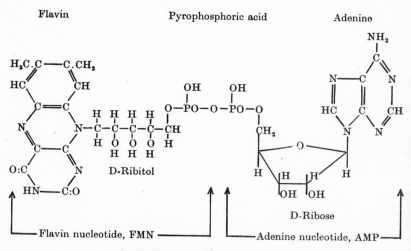

Flavin-Adenine Dinucleotide, FAD.

By undergoing reversible addition of H at positions 1 and 10 in the iso-alloxazine nucleus (p. 173), the flavins act as carriers of hydrogen in the respiratory sequence.

The Cytochromes

The term *cytochrome* was applied by Keilin to intracellular hæmoproteins other than the hæmoglobins and myoglobins, and the enzymes peroxidase and catalase. Hæmoproteins are characterised by porphyrin prosthetic groups holding an iron atom, which can undergo reversible oxidative de-electronation:

$$Fe^{2+} - e' \rightleftharpoons Fe^{3+}.$$

Twenty-five different cytochromes have been identified. If the associated protein has catalytic properties, the cytochrome is an enzyme, such as lactic dehydrogenase and cytochrome c oxidase; otherwise, it is merely a carrier in the respiratory sequence.

History. From work begun in 1913, Warburg concluded that organic iron compounds, present as micro-constituents of tissues, are essential factors in aerobic respirations, and operate by making atmospheric oxygen available for metabolism.

In support of his theory, he showed that iron is present in concentrations of $10 \, \mu g.$ to $100 \, \mu g.$ per gm. of cell substance in all active tissues, and that agents reacting with iron, such as HCN, CO, and H_2S, are powerful inhibitors of tissue respiration. Cyanide in $M/1,000$ concentration inhibits about 90 per cent. of the total respiration of most tissues. The residual 10 per cent. is cyanide-stable, and is now attributed to the existence of cytochrome-independent systems.

Warburg postulated that his respiratory factors were iron porphyrins, because tissues inactivated by exposure to CO displayed a spectrum resembling a carbon monoxide hæm, and could be reactivated by exposure to strong light, under conditions similar to those causing the photo-dissociation of carbon monoxide hæmoglobin.

In 1925, Keilin showed that hæmoproteins were present in all aerobic tissues, and had the characteristics of Warburg's respiratory enzyme, or *atmungsferment*.

According to the nature of the porphyrin, cytochromes can be typed as a, b, and c; and recognised and further subdivided by the position of their absorption bands. Thus, in the reduced state, cytochrome a_3 has an α-band at 603, no β-band, and a γ-band at 445 mμ; cytochrome b has an α-band at 563, a β-band at 530, and a γ-band at 432 mμ. On oxidation, the bands disappear. Functionally, the cytochromes form part of a conveyor network converging on cytochromes c and a_3. Cytochrome c is the penultimate electron-carrier in the chain; a_3 is an enzyme, a *cytochrome oxidase*, the form in which Warburg's respiratory catalyst occurs in animal tissues. Cytochrome a_3 catalyses the transfer of electrons from c, to enable molecular oxygen to be reduced to water by metabolic hydrogen. It might be regarded as the activator of oxygen. Cytochrome c can be fed with hydrogen (as $H^+ + e'$) from several sources some of which await investigation. They include reduced flavoproteins and cytochrome c_1 and cytochromes c_1 and b_5. Co-enzyme I–cytochrome reductase catalyses the transfer of hydrogen directly from reduced Co I to cytochrome c. Co-enzyme I–quinone reductase catalyses transfer of hydrogen from reduced Co I to a quinone, such as vitamin K, from which it is taken up by cytochrome c.

Succinic dehydrogenase transfers hydrogen from the metabolite, succinic acid, to cytochrome c_1. The path involves at least one other cytochrome, and an agent " the Slater factor ", which may be a derivative of vitamin E.

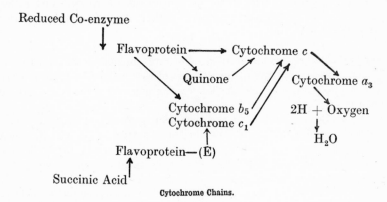

Cytochrome Chains.

Supplementary Oxidation-Reduction Systems

(1) **Lipoic Acid.** This linear 8-carbon acid can exist in oxidised state in which the sulphur atoms form a —S—S— bridge between carbons 6 and 8, and in the reduced state as $HS—CH_2.CH_2.CH(SH).(CH_2)_4.COOH$. Its participation in the oxidative decarboxylation of pyruvic acid has been described on p. 306. The oxidised form of the acid has a characteristic spectrum, with a band about 335 mμ, and becomes sensitised to reducing agents on exposure to light. It is believed to be an acceptor of hydrogen liberated in photosynthesis.

(2) **Glutathione** is a natural tripeptide derived from glutamic acid, cysteine and glycine. It is very widely distributed in animal tissues and forms part of the oxidation-reduction equipment.

$$HOOC.CH.CH_2.CH_2.CO——HN.CH \qquad CH_2.COOH$$

with the substituents NH_2 (below first CH), $CH_2.SH$ (above HN.CH), and $CO——NH$ (below).

Glutathione
(α-glutamyl-cysteinyl-glycine)

312

Sources. Glutathione was isolated in 1921 from yeast, muscle, and mammalian liver by Hopkins, and identified as the compound responsible for Mörner's cysteine reaction—the development of a violet colour when the tissue is treated with sodium nitroprusside and ammonium hydroxide, a reaction given by muscle and other animal tissues, yeasts, fungi, and bacteria, and selective for compounds containing free thiol groups.

Glutathione percentage values for fresh material are: yeast, 0·15; rabbit liver, 0·3; muscle, 0·04; kidney, 0·15; entire blood, 0·04; blood plasma, 0·00.

The outstanding biochemical property of glutathione is its ability to assume either of two forms under conditions that obtain in living tissues:—

$$
\begin{array}{ccc}
\text{G—SH} & & \text{G——S} \\
& + \text{B} \longrightarrow & \quad\ \ | \qquad\qquad + \text{BH}_2 \\
\text{G—SH} & & \text{G——S}
\end{array}
$$

Reduced   Hydrogen   Oxidised
glutathione.   acceptor.   glutathione.

Animal tissues contain systems that vigorously reduce the oxidised glutathione, and systems that vigorously oxidise the reduced glutathione by means of molecular oxygen; hence the tripeptide is capable of acting as an oxygen carrier.

Tissue glutathione is chiefly in the reduced form, as shown by the positive nitroprusside test.

Glutathione is the prosthetic group in glyceraldehyde 3-phosphate dehydrogenase, and is the co-enzyme for glyoxalase. It functions by means of its thiol group, which by combining with aldehyde,

$$R.CHO + HS.R' \rightarrow R.CH(OH)\text{—}S.R',$$

forms a thioacetal that can be dehydrogenated to a thiol ester, $R.CO.S.R'$.

(3) **Ascorbic acid** is a powerful reducing agent and is a potential hydrogen donor in metabolic processes. It serves to keep biological quinones in the reduced state and thus retards melanin formation. Conversely, in presence of Fe^{3+}, it activates the metabolism of homogentisic acid. It aids, also, in the absorption of iron from the alimentary tract, and in the maintenance of the ferrous state. In plants, ascorbic acid is dehydrogenated by ascorbic oxidase to dehydroascorbic acid, which, by accepting hydrogen from reduced co-enzyme I, participates in tissue respiration.

Cellular Location of Respiratory Systems

Micro-chemical tests and analysis of cell inclusions, fractionally separated by centrifuging tissue homogenates, show that individual metabolic systems are anchored to intracellular structures. Thus, the cytochrome chain with its accessories is centred in the intramitochondrial particles of 50 to 100 mμ in diameter; several enzymes of the citric cycle are restricted to the mitochondria; enzymes of the lipoclastic spiral reside in the microsomes. In contrast,

313

the enzymes of the glycolytic process occur as solutes in the cytoplasm, which explains their early discovery in extracts.

Respiratory Inhibitors. The overall respiratory process can be inhibited by agents acting at various stages. Narcotics, such as urethane, in relatively high concentrations, inhibit primary dehydrogenases, without affecting the cytochrome system.

Narcosis and inhibition of respiration are distinct but not necessarily unrelated events; narcosis can be induced in anaerobic cells, and narcotics do not inhibit the oxidation of various metabolites by brain-cortex, with the important exceptions of glucose, lactate, and pyruvate, from which the brain derives the energy for most of its functional activity.

Iron-immobilisers, such as cyanide, hydrogen sulphide, and carbon monoxide inhibit the cytochrome system, without affecting the primary dehydrogenases. The antibiotic, *antimycin* A, stops transport along the cytochrome chain by inhibiting the reduction of cytochrome c. The critical application of selective inhibitors has aided in the recognition of different stages in metabolic processes, and has disclosed the existence of subsidiary or emergency mechanisms.

Assessment of Respiratory Activity

(1) **Anaerobic Respiration.** Many tissues and tissue extracts, including muscle, have the power of bleaching easily-reduced pigments, such as methylene blue, MB, in the absence of free oxygen. This property, discovered by Ehrlich in 1885, was developed by Thunberg (1920–), as a method for exploring anaerobic respiration. The phenomenon depends on the ability of the pigment to act as an acceptor of hydrogen atoms transferred from a substrate activated by a dehydrogenase.

$$XH_2 + MB \to X + MBH_2.$$

Atmospheric oxygen, which would compete with the pigment for possession of the transferred hydrogen, is excluded by carrying out the test in a special tube that can be exhausted of air, or filled with an inert gas. While not applicable to all respiratory processes, the method is of value in the detection of dehydrogenases and the identification of their substrates and inhibitors.

(2) **Aerobic Respiration.** Freshly-cut tissue sections, about 0·3 mm. thick, allow of access to cell surfaces, are suspended in warm, isotonic saline, in equilibrium with an atmosphere containing O_2 and CO_2. Various substrates or inhibitors are added, and the effect on the rate of oxygen absorption measured by means of a respirometer of the Barcroft-Warburg type. Under favourable conditions the structure of the tissue is preserved and the cells remain active for several hours. Results are expressed in terms of oxygen uptake per unit mass of fresh tissue or dry tissue weight, as found at the end of the experiment. The method is applicable to tissue homogenates, particle suspensions, cultures, and cell-free extracts.

Representative values, in microlitres of O_2 absorbed per mg. dry weight per hour, for rat tissues in glucose saline at body temperature: retina, 22 to 33; kidney cortex, 21 to 24; brain cortex, 10 to 16; spleen, testis, 11 to 12; liver, 8 to 17; diaphragm, lung, 7 to 8; pancreas, 4; skeletal muscle, resting, 6, active, 40; entire animal, resting, 4·6 to 6 (Krebs and Johnson, 1948).

The Tissue Respiration Quotient. Tissue respiration is expressed in terms of a special quotient, Q, which represents the quantity of substance produced or consumed per mg. dry weight of tissue per hour. Q is measured in cubic milli-metres of gas (O_2, CO_2, NH_3) at n.t.p., and when negative indicates con-sumption or absorption by the tissue. Q is also qualified by the addition of suffixes, the lower of which specifies the substance transformed, and the upper denotes whether the conditions are aerobic (O_2) or anaerobic (N_2). Thus, $Q_{O_2} = -7$ indicates that the system is consuming 7 μl (microlitres) or cu. mm. of oxygen per mg. dry weight of tissue per hour. Similarly, $Q_{CO_2}^{N_2} = +20$ indicates that the tissue is liberating 20 μl of carbon dioxide per mg. dry weight per hour, in absence of oxygen. A microlitre, μl, is the millionth part of a litre, or the thousandth part of a millilitre (ml.). Representative Q_{O_2} values for rat tissues at body temperature are: liver, -7; kidney cortex, -25; brain cortex, -15; skeletal muscle, resting, -6; skeletal muscle, active, -40. Holmes, from whose work these data are taken, observes that the reason for the high oxygen consumption on the part of some tissues is obviously that they have to do physical work. " The one exception is the grey matter of the central nervous system which, while it does no work which can be measured in terms of osmotic or mechanical energy, consumes a very considerable amount of oxygen." The human kidneys in concentrating 1·5 litres of urine in the 24 hours perform about 3,225 kilogram-metres of work, and have an oxygen consumption representing nearly 9 per cent. of that required by the entire body when at rest.

Oxidation-Reduction Potentials

Oxidation is a term with several meanings:

(1) *Direct addition of oxygen* to the substance oxidised, as in the rusting of iron. When atmospheric or molecular oxygen is involved it is denoted by O_2, or $\frac{1}{2} O_2$, to simplify equations, as in the oxidation of an aldehyde to an acid, $R.CHO + \frac{1}{2} O_2 \rightarrow R.COOH$.

(2) *Dehydrogenation*, or removal of hydrogen from the substance oxidised, as in the oxidation of a primary alcohol to an aldehyde,

$$R.CH_2.OH \rightarrow R.CHO + 2H.$$

Dehydrogenations are classed as oxidations because they can be effected by oxidising agents, which remove the hydrogen as water. However, they can be accomplished in the absence of oxygen or oxidisers, by the use of hydrogen-trappers, such as platinum black. This type of indirect oxidation was investi-

315

gated by Wieland (1912–), who demonstrated the wide distribution and importance of dehydrogenation processes in biological systems, and showed that reactions involving the addition of oxygen could be included among the dehydrogenations, if water molecules took part in a preliminary hydration:

$$R.CHO + H_2O \rightarrow R.CH(OH)_2 \rightarrow R.COOH + 2 H.$$

(3) *Electron transfer* from the substance oxidised. Halogens and ions of poly-valent metals, such as Cu^{2+} and Fe^{3+}, can effect dehydrogenations without combining with hydrogen, by de-electronating the labile hydrogen atoms and thus promoting their release as hydrogen ions. During the process, the oxidant takes up an electron, and is thereby reduced in valency, or acquires a negative charge.

Examples are: (*a*) oxidation of alcohol by chlorine,

$$CH_3.CH_2.OH + Cl_2 \rightarrow CH_3.CHO + 2H. + Cl_2 \rightarrow CH_3.CHO + 2H^+ + 2Cl^-$$

(*b*) oxidation of hydroquinone by ferric ions.

$$HO.C_6H_4.OH + 2Fe^{3+} \rightarrow O : C_6H_4 : O + 2H. + 2Fe^{3+} \rightarrow 2H^+ + 2Fe^{2+} + O : C_6H_4 : O$$

In these reactions the hydrogen atom is formulated with its single electron H., when this is removed it becomes a hydrogen ion, H^+, and serves to maintain the cation concentration of the system.

The rH Scale. When a system containing both oxidising and reducing agent is in equilibrium an electrical potential, the **redox potential,** is developed, the magnitude of which depends on the pH and temperature. It can be measured in terms of the hydrogen electrode potential, Eh. Clark and Cohen (1923) suggested that the redox intensity of such a system could be expressed in rH units in a manner analogous to that in which pH units express reaction. Thus rH = $-\log H_2$, H_2 being the partial pressure of hydrogen gas in equilibrium with the system, by analogy with pH = $-\log H^+$, in which H^+ is the concentration of H ions.

This had the advantage that the single expression rH could take into account both Eh and pH, and a simple relationship between the three could be worked out

$$rH = 2\left(\frac{Eh + pH}{0.06}\right)$$

where 0.06 is the value of $\dfrac{2.303\,RT}{F}$ at body temperature, R is the gas constant (8.315 joules per degree per mole), T is the absolute temperature, F is the faraday—the amount of electricity carried by 1 g.equiv. of an ion with a single charge, 2.303 is the ratio of the logarithm of any number to the base 10 to the logarithm of the same number to the base e.

When there is only hydrogen present at a pressure of 1 atmosphere

$$rH = -\log 1 = 0.$$

In an atmosphere of oxygen, without hydrogen, at pH 7, Eh is found to b

0·83 volts and when these quantities are substituted in the equation, rH = 41. These are the extreme limits of rH at atmospheric pressure and a scale can be constructed within this range. This convenient method of expressing data has been applied to multienzyme systems by Dixon (1949) and it has been used by other biologists.

Representative rH values at pH 7 are: cytochrome c, 22; methylene blue, 14; riboflavin, 7; co-enzyme I, 4; xanthine-uric acid, 2.

Unfortunately the early interest in this approach has been reduced by doubts cast on its soundness by some workers, including Clark. It is pointed out that we know too little about conditions in biological material to justify the simplifications that have to be made. On this account the term rH is not commonly encountered, though it is still discussed by some authors (e.g. Dawes, 1956).

ENERGY EXCHANGE IN BIOLOGICAL SYSTEMS

A chemical change can be formulated thermodynamically as:

$$\text{Reactants} \rightarrow \text{Products}; \quad F = \pm\, x,$$

where F is the change in free energy associated with the reaction. If the reaction releases energy it is described as exergonic and F has a negative value, as energy leaves the system and can be stored, utilised for the performance of work, or dissipated as heat. If energy is absorbed the reaction is endergonic, and F has a positive value. Exergonic reactions proceed spontaneously, though they may require a catalyst; endergonic reactions require a supply of energy from an external source to provide the F gained by the process.

F, alternatively denoted G, or Gibbs function, is not identical with the heat-change accompanying a reaction, only part of which is available for work. Values for F are obtained by calculation, based on the relationship

$$F = -RT \log_e K,$$

where R is the gas constant, T is the absolute temperature, and K is the equilibrium constant for the reaction, under specified *standard* conditions. Values for F for important biochemical reactions, such as those involved in the glycolytic process and the citric cycle, are available (Krebs and Kornberg, 1957).

The living animal represents an open system continually taking in potential energy in the form of nutrients, and ejecting energy as heat and as waste-material. In this way the organism maintains and asserts its existence and, when mature, persists in a steady state in which energy-input balances energy-output.

The affairs of life are characterised by the unique way in which exergonic reactions, such as tissue respirations, are employed to provide the energy necessary to drive endergonic reactions, such as synthesis of proteins.

The coupling of endergonic with exergonic reactions is effected by drawing off energy from particular stages in the three great energy-generating processes of life: glycolysis, fat-combustion, and the citric cycle, which act as "trickle-chargers" to feed the energy-accumulators of the cells.

Energy Storage in the Organism

Potential energy is stored in bulk in the form of combustible carbon compounds: polysaccharides, lipids, and proteins. Directly-available energy is accumulated in labile phosphate units, present in hydrogen-carriers, such as the co-enzymes and flavins, and phosphate carriers, such as the nucleoside polyphosphates.

Coupled phosphorylation, or oxidative phosphorylation. The dehydrogenation of succinate, malate and other citric cycle components, by tissues, is accompanied by conversion of adenosine diphosphate to adenosine triphosphate. The energy is derived, not from the immediate dehydrogenation of the metabolite, but from the subsequent oxidation of the hydrogen carriers by the enzymes in the mitochondria. In this way, three units of ATP can be constructed for each pair of hydrogen atoms metabolised by the respiratory sequence.

(1) Reduced co-enzyme + Flavin + ADP + HPO_4^{2-}
$$\rightarrow \text{Co-enzyme} + \text{Reduced flavin} + \text{ATP}$$

(2) Reduced flavin + Cytochrome + ADP + HPO_4^{2-}
$$\rightarrow \text{Flavin} + \text{Reduced cytochrome} + \text{ATP}$$

(3) Reduced cytochrome + $\frac{1}{2} O_2$ + ADP + HPO_4^{2-}
$$\rightarrow \text{Cytochrome} + H_2O + \text{ATP}$$

Expressed otherwise, three units of ATP are constructed per atom of oxygen consumed, which is equivalent to a phosphate/oxygen ratio of 3.

Coupled phosphorylations can be uncoupled, without necessarily affecting the accompanying respiratory process, by 2,4-dinitrophenol, thyroxine, methylene blue, arsenious acid, and the antibiotics, aureomycin, gramicidin and bacitracin. Under these conditions the free energy is not accumulated as ATP, but escapes as heat.

Energy Accumulators. The hydrogen carriers are concerned with the generation of energy; the phosphate carriers accumulate and transfer energy from exergonic to endergonic reactions.

The chief phosphate carriers are the nucleoside polyphosphate ATP, and, in muscle, phosphocreatine.

Less familiar carriers are the polyphosphates of the four nucleosides: inosine, guanosine, cytidine, and uridine, carbamyl phosphate, employed in urea synthesis, and phosphoarginine, which replaces phosphocreatine in the muscles of invertebrates.

318

The ATP content of a tissue depends on the intensity of activity; mammalian muscle values range from 0·01 to 0·02 per cent. of fresh tissue, or about 0·2 millimoles per 100 gm., in cardiac and unstriated, up to 0·5 millimoles per 100 gm., in skeletal muscle. Surplus ATP is hydrolysed by tissue triphosphatases.

Energy Requirements of the Organism

(1) *Maintenance of Cell Integrity and Volume.* Apart from specialised types, cell membranes are not selectively impermeable to ions less than 0·8 mμ in diameter, and a system of active transport is continuously in operation across them to keep the intracellular level of Na^+ below that of the environment, to maintain compensatory accumulation of K^+, and to preserve anion-cation equilibrium during metabolic activity. Nervous tissue, in particular, demands incessant expenditure of energy to keep the circuits flowing, even in the absence of conscious mental activity.

(2) *Exercise of specialised functions*, such as secretion, contraction, and conduction.

(3) *Growth and cell-division.*

(4) *Synthesis of special metabolites* and storage products.

General References

Baldwin, E. (1952), " Dynamic Aspects of Biochemistry." 2nd ed. Cambridge.

Bray, H. G., and K. White (1957), " Kinetics and Thermodynamics in Biochemistry." London.

" Chemical Pathways of Metabolism." Ed. by D. M. Greenberg. Vol. I (1954–). New York.

Dawes, E. A. (1956), " Quantitative Problems in Biochemistry." Edinburgh and London.

Dixon, M. (1949), " Multi-enzyme Systems." Cambridge.

Dixon, M. (1951), " Manometric Methods." Cambridge; Philadelphia.

Du Bois, E. F. (1936), " Basal Metabolism in Health and Disease."

Giese, A. C. (1957), " Cell Physiology." Philadelphia; London.

Green, D. E. (1956), " Currents in Biochemical Research." New York.

Hewitt, L. F. (1950), " Oxidation-Reduction Potentials in Bacteriology and Biochemistry." 6th Ed. London.

" Isotopes in Biochemistry." (1951), *Ciba Foundation Symposium.*

Mahler, H. R. (1957), " Biological Oxidations." *Annu. Rev. Biochem.*, **26,** 17.

Stephenson, M. (1949), " Bacterial Metabolism," 3rd Ed. London.

Umbreit, W. W., *et al.* (1949), " Manometric Techniques and Tissue Metabolism." Minneapolis.

" Metabolic Functions of the Vitamins " (1953). *Physiol. Rev.*, **33.**

    Snell, E. E., " Nicotinic Acid, Riboflavin, B_6." p. 509.

    Novelli, G. D., " Pantothenic Acid," p. 525.

    Reed, L. J., " Thiamine, Lipoic Acid," p. 544.

    Lardy, H., and R. Peanasky, " Biotin," p. 560.

Chapter 20 Nucleic Acid Metabolism

"A hen is only the way in which an egg makes another egg."

Samuel Butler, 1835–190█

Nucleoproteins are separated from material rich in cell nuclei by extractic with dilute alkali. Good sources are: thymus, pancreas, liver, fish sperm, an yeast. Digestion with trypsin or alkali removes the protein, leaving **nucle█ acid,** which, on further hydrolysis is resolved into a mixture of four differe█ **nucleotides,** each assembled from a pentose sugar unit, a purine or pyrimidir base, and phosphoric acid. Continued hydrolysis removes the phosphat leaving **nucleosides,** or glycosides of the purine or pyrimidine.

Nucleic acids are polynucleotides containing at least four different species █ nucleotide. They are classified according to the type of sugar unit in t█ nucleotides, which in ribonucleic acids, or RNA, is D-ribose, $C_5H_{10}O_5$, and █ deoxyribonucleic acids, or DNA, is 2-deoxy-D-ribose, $C_5H_{10}O_4$.

Deoxyribonucleic acid is restricted to nuclei, where, conjugated with a bas█ protein, such as histone or protamine, it forms the chromosome substance █ animal and plant cells. It also occurs in micro-organisms and viruses.

Ribonucleic acid is located chiefly in extranuclear cell inclusions, such █ mitochondria. Within the nucleus, it is concentrated in the nucleolus.

Test for Deoxypentoses (Feulgen, 1924). The section or film is warmed wi█ dilute HCl for 4 minutes at 60° C., to expose the —CHO groups in the sugar. T█ slide is treated with Schiff's aldehyde reagent (1 per cent. rosaniline bleach█ by SO_2), which will develop a purple colour in regions where deoxypentos█ occur. DNA gives the reaction; the more stable RNA does not. Feulgen's te█ shows that the nucleoproteins of chromatin are of the DNA type.

Deoxyribonucleic acid is a gel-forming colloid, with a molecular weig█ ranging from 500,000 to 8×10^6, indicating the presence of 1,500 to 24,0█ mononucleotide units in the macro-molecule. Ribonucleic acid is obtainable █ a mixture of short-chain polynucleotides.

Stages in Nucleic Acid Hydrolysis

By the action of alkali, or the pancreatic enzyme *nucleogelase*, colloid nucleic acids are resolved into short-chain polynucleotides, which can █ hydrolysed to nucleotides by intestinal nucleotidases, and ultimately resolv█ into their components by the enzymes of the intestinal mucosa.

320

Ribonucleic acid   Deoxyribonucleic acid

Nucleotides

H_3PO_4 H_3PO_4

Nucleosides

Ribose	Deoxyribose
Two purines:	Two purines:
Adenine	Adenine
Guanine	Guanine
Two pyrimidines:	Two pyrimidines:
Cytosine	Cytosine
Uracil	Thymine

PURINES

The biological purines are simple amino or hydroxy derivatives of a parent purine, $C_5H_4N_4$, that does not occur as such in Nature.

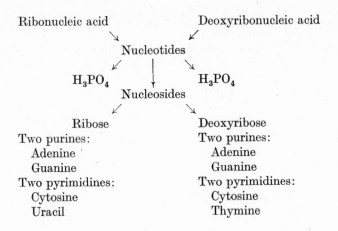

Adenine: 6-aminopurine, $C_5H_3N_4(NH_2)$
Hypoxanthine: 6-hydroxypurine, $C_5H_3N_4(OH)$
Guanine: 2-amino-6-hydroxypurine,
        $C_5H_2N_4(NH_2)(OH)$
Xanthine: 2,6-dihydroxypurine, $C_5H_2N_4(OH)_2$
Uric acid: 2,6,8-trihydroxypurine, $C_5HN_4(OH)_3$.

Purine

History. The first purine to be discovered was uric acid, found by Scheele (1776) in urinary calculi and sediments, and as the chief nitrogen compound in the excreta of birds and snakes. Subsequently, xanthine was found in urine; guanine, in guano; hypoxanthine, in meat extracts; and adenine, the most important of the purines, was obtained from pancreas and other glands. The inter-relationship of the compounds was established by Emil Fischer, who, in 1898, synthesised the parent purine. Meanwhile, the characteristic alkaloids of tea and coffee had been shown to be methyl derivatives of xanthine.

Tissue purines occur chiefly combined as nucleosides, or N-linked glycosides, formed by condensation of a sugar unit with the nitrogen atom in position 9 in the purine.

Amino Purines

Adenine is widely distributed as the nucleoside; *adenosine* the monophosphates, or *adenylic acids*; the high-energy phosphates, *adenosine di-* and

triphosphate; *co-enzymes* I and II (DPN, TPN); *co-enzymes* A; and in bo
types of nucleic acid.

By deamination, adenine is converted into hypoxanthine.

Guanine occurs free in some plant tissues, notably leguminous seeds and be
root; in guano deposits, fish scales, and the excreta of spiders. In high
animals, guanine occurs chiefly as the nucleotide, *guanylic acid*, both free a
bound as nucleic acids. On drastic oxidation, guanine yields *guanidi*
NH_2—$C(NH)$—NH_2, which distinguishes it from adenine and other purin
By deamination, guanine is converted into the corresponding dehydro
purine, xanthine.

Hydroxy Purines

These compounds can be regarded also as oxypurines, since they exist in en
and keto form: —N:$C(OH)$— $\rightleftharpoons$ —$NH.CO$—. Alkali promotes enolisati
and ionisation of the hydroxyl.

Hypoxanthine and **Xanthine** occur as minor solutes in urine and in tissu
as deamination products of amino purines; as metabolites in the oxidati
of purines to uric acid; and as intermediaries in the synthesis of the puri
ring.

Hypoxanthine is converted into xanthine, and then into uric acid, by t
xanthine oxidase system, present in liver and in milk.

Methyl Purines

The chief natural methyl purines are derivatives of xanthine, which can
represented in keto form.

Xanthine.

Paraxanthine: 1,7-dimethyl xanthine
Theophylline: 1,3-dimethyl xanthine
Theobromine: 3,7-dimethyl xanthine
Caffeine: 1,3,7-trimethyl xanthine.

Paraxanthine occurs in small amounts in urine. It acts as an inhibitor of t
thyroid hormones. Theophylline occurs in tea leaves; theobromine, in coc
seeds and cola nuts; caffeine, in coffee beans and leaves, cocoa seeds, co
nuts, and tea leaves, where it may reach a value of 3 gm. per 100 gm. dry lea
These methyl xanthines act as cerebral stimulants and diuretics.

Uric acid, 2,6,8-trioxy purine, is the characteristic end-product of prote
metabolism in uricotelic animals: insects, snakes, and birds. It is the en
product of purine metabolism in man and the anthropoid apes. Other mar
mals are endowed with a liver enzyme, urate oxidase, or uricase, whi
degrades uric acid to the much more soluble allantoin by opening the py
midine ring in the purine nucleus. In the Dalmatian dog, the rate of excretio

of uric acid by the kidney exceeds the rate of its destruction by the liver, and this animal resembles man and the anthropoids in eliminating purine nitrogen chiefly as uric acid.

Uric acid is sparingly soluble in water: 1 in 15,500 at 37° C. Alkali converts it into the soluble, monobasic and dibasic urates, $C_5H_3N_4O_3'$ and $C_5H_2N_4O_3''$. In tissue fluids and urine, it occurs as monobasic urate and as free acid, solubilised by colloids.

Representative values in mg. uric acid per 100 ml., for the human subject: urine, 100 $\pm$ 50; entire blood, 3·0 $\pm$ 1; blood plasma, 4·0 $\pm$ 1; cerebro-spinal fluid, 0·9 $\pm$ 0·6. Saliva and milk can contain about 1 mg. per 100 ml.

Analytical Reactions of the Purines

The purines as a family are precipitated by Ag^+ in acid or alkaline solution, and by Cu^{2+}, in presence of HSO_3^-, and thus may be fractionated.

(1) **Purpurate, or Murexide Test.** Evaporate at 100° C., a little of the solid purine and a few drops of concentrated HNO_3, in a porcelain dish on a water bath. When dry, uric acid, theophylline, and caffeine yield rose or orange-red residues; guanine and xanthine yield bright yellow residues. On moistening with NH_4OH, the colour will become violet. This reaction was described as the murexide test, because of the resemblance of the final shade to that of the natural dye, Tyrian purple, obtained from gastropods of the genus *Murex*. Xanthine was first recognised by the yellow colour it gives in the primary stage of the test.

(2) **Tests for Uric Acid.** Unlike the other purines, urate is a reducing agent in alkaline solution, and forms a black precipitate with Ag^+, and a deep blue colour with phosphotungstate or phosphomolybdate, which has been adapted for colorimetry, by Folin. These tests are given by other reducing agents, including ascorbic acid.

Zinc Test. Suspend a little powdered uric acid in 3 ml. of water, and dissolve by addition of a few drops of 20 per cent. NaOH. Add 3 drops of 5 per cent. zinc acetate or sulphate and mix so as to obtain a suspension of $Zn(OH)_2$. Add 1 per cent. iodine drop by drop. If urate is present, a dark blue colour will develop, and persist when sufficient iodine has been added. This test is specific both for uric acid and for zinc.

Sources of the Purines

The purines excreted as uric acid by man and other non-uricotelic animals, are derived partly from synthesised purine, and partly from purines in the food. On a purine-free diet, the human adult excretes 0·1 to 0·3 gm. of uric acid in 24 hours. The ordinary mixed diet raises the daily output to about 0·7 gm., diets rich in nucleoproteins can raise to 1·5 or 2 gm.

M 2

Values for food materials, in gm. purine $N/100$ gm. fresh tissue: pancreas, thymus, 0·4; sardine, 0·2; herring, kidney, liver, 0·15; fish roe, 0·1; meat, fish, 0·02 to 0·1; beans, lentils, mushroom, spinach, 0·01 to 0·05; other vegetables and fruits, 0·00 to 0·01; fresh eggs, milk, 0·001. Dietary purines are chiefly nucleic acids, the uric acid equivalent of which can be found by multiplying the purine N value by 3.

Inosinic acid on hydrolysis yields hypoxanthine, from which adenine is formed by amination, and xanthine by oxidation. This complicated process which involves a team of carriers to supply NH_3, CO_2, and $H.COOH$, is in outline the method whereby surplus protein nitrogen is collected and excreted by uricotelic animals.

Degradation of Uric Acid

The purine nucleus can be regarded as formed by fusion of a 6-member pyrimidine ring, and a 5-member imidazole ring, such as occurs in the amine acid, histidine. Oxidation of uric acid by HNO_3, or other oxidisers in acid solution, destroys the imidazole structure, leaving *alloxan*, an intermediary in the murexide test. Oxidation of urate in alkaline solution, or oxidative hydrolysis by urate oxidase, opens the pyrimidine ring, forming *allantoin*.

Alloxan.   ←   Uric acid.   →   Allantoin.

Allantoin represents the end-product of purine metabolism in many animals It occurs in plants and in the allantoic fluid of herbivora, and the urine of herbivora and carnivora in the following average concentrations; expressed i grams per litre: calf, 5 to 6; cow, 2 to 2·5; sheep, horse, pig, rabbit, 0·7 to 1·8 dog, 1·9 to 2·6. The amount excreted daily by the cow is 20 to 30 gm. Onl small and variable traces are found in human urine; its place being taken b its precursor uric acid.

Allantoin is much more soluble than uric acid, the solubility in water bein 1 : 160 at 20° C. It is much more desirable as an end-product of purine meta bolism, since it does not form calculi.

Hydrolysed by acids, or the enzyme allantoinase, allantoin is converted int allantoic acid, the end-product of purine metabolism in some teleosts (bon fish). Further hydrolysis by acid, or the enzyme allantoicase, yields glyoxyl acid and urea, end-products of purine metabolism in amphibia, fresh-wat lamellibranchs, and most fishes.

Allantoin → $HOOC.CH(NH.CO.NH_2)_2$ → $HOOC.CHO + 2 H_2N.CO.NH$

324

PYRIMIDINES

The biological pyrimidines are derivatives of a parent 6-membered ring, pyrimidine, or 1,3-diazine, which does not occur free in Nature.

```
    CH 6
   /  \
1  N    CH  5
   |    ||
2  CH   CH  4
   \  /
    N
    3
Pyrimidine.
```

Cytosine: 2-hydroxy-6-amino pyrimidine
5-Methylcytosine
Uracil: 2,6-dihydroxy pyrimidine
Thymine: 5-methyluracil
Orotic Acid: uracil 4-carboxylic acid
Barbituric Acid: 2,4,6-trioxy pyrimidine
Alloxan: 2,4,5,6-tetraoxy pyrimidine.

The amino pyrimidines were originally discovered among the products of nucleic acid hydrolysis. Like the purines, they exist in tautomeric form.
Cytosine combined with ribose occurs as a nucleoside, *cytidine,* in both types of nucleic acid, and as a series of nucleotide phosphates.
5-Methylcytosine occurs in bacterial deoxyribonucleic acids.
Uracil occurs as the ribose nucleoside, *uridine,* in ribonucleic acid, and as uridine polyphosphates.
Thymine occurs in deoxynucleic acids as the nucleoside, *thymidine,* and as nucleotide phosphates.
Orotic acid is an intermediate in purine synthesis. It is a minor constituent of milk. On decarboxylation, it yields uracil.

Barbituric acid has not been found to occur naturally, but is of pharmacological interest; by substitution of hydrogen at position 5 in the ring, many hypnotics and tranquillisers are obtained.
Alloxan, a product of uric acid oxidation, not known to occur naturally. It has a destructive effect on the β-cells of pancreatic islet tissue, and can evoke diabetes when injected into animals.

The amino pyrimidines are colourless, basic compounds, moderately soluble in water. Unlike purines, they are not precipitated by Ag^+ in acid solution, but require a slight degree of alkalinity. On boiling with aqueous bromine, cytosine and uracil are oxidised to dialuric acid, 5-hydroxybarbituric acid, which develops a purple colour on neutralisation with $Ba(OH)_2$ (Wheeler and Johnson Test, 1907).

NUCLEOSIDES AND NUCLEOTIDES

Nucleosides are glycosides in which the nitrogen atom at position 9 in a purine, or at position 3 in a pyrimidine, is joined to carbon 1 of a sugar, D-ribose or 2-deoxy-D-ribose, in a β-glycosidic linkage.
Nucleotides are phosphoric esters of nucleosides, containing one, two, or three phosphoric radicals. The ester attachments are at positions 2′, 3′, or 5′, in the pentose ring.

325

Purine Nucleoside.
Adenosine.

Pyrimidine Nucleoside.
Cytidine.

Base.	Nucleoside.	Nucleotide.
Adenine	Adenosine (9-ribosyl adenine)	Adenylic acids: adenosine 5'-phosphate adenosine 3'-phosphate
Guanine	Guanosine (9-ribosyl guanine)	Guanylic acids: guanosine 5'-phosphate guanosine 3'-phosphate
Hypoxanthine	Inosine (9-ribosyl hypoxanthine)	Inosinic acid: inosine 5'-phosphate.
Xanthine	Xanthosine (9-ribosyl xanthine)	Xanthylic acid: xanthosine 5-phosphate
Cytosine	Cytidine (3-ribosyl cytosine)	Cytidylic acid: cytidine 3'-phosphate
Uracil	Uridine (3-ribosyl uracil)	Uridylic acid: uridine 3'-phosphate

Corresponding compounds containing deoxyribose units are denoted by the prefix *deoxy*. Thus, deoxyadenosine is 9-deoxyribosyl adenine; the OH at 2' in the pentose ring being replaced by H.

Functions of the Nucleosides

(1) **Nucleic Acid Construction.** The nucleosides, held in a phosphate scaffolding, are the characteristic units in the nucleic acids.

(2) **Phosphate Transfer and Energy Exchange.** The nucleoside diphosphates, in which pyrophosphoric acid, $HO—O—PO(OH)—O—PO(OH)_2$, is attached to carbon 5' in the pentose, have the special property of being able to take up and release a third phosphate radical, forming a high-energy triphosphate chain, $R—O—PO(OH)—O—PO—(OH)—O—PO(OH)_2$, and thus can accumulate energy, and transfer it from one process to another. Adenosine diphosphate is the chief of these carriers; the other diphosphates operate some less general transfers.

326

Reactions Involving Nucleoside Triphosphates

(1) **Adenosine Triphosphate.** Phosphorylations in sugar metabolism and polysaccharide synthesis; activation of amino acids in peptide synthesis; activation of fatty acids; construction of co-enzymes I, II, and A; construction of flavinadenine dinucleotide; formation of carbamyl phosphate, glutamine, and glutathione.

(2) **Guanosine Triphosphate.** Activation of succinic acid and mannose.

(3) **Cytosine Triphosphate.** Choline synthesis.

(4) **Uridine Triphosphate.** Activation of sugars in synthesis of glucuronic acid, hexosamines and mucopolysaccharides.

NUCLEIC ACIDS

The Mendelian genes that determine inheritance have as their physical carriers the chromosomes, or chromatin threads, contained within the cell nuclei. These chromosomes consist of basic protein conjugated with deoxyribose nucleic acid.

Analytical methods applicable to tissues, separated nuclei, cell inclusions and extracts are represented by: (1) Selective staining by basic dyes, such as toluidine blue, pyronine and methyl green, in which the pigment is a cation, and forms a coloured salt with the nucleic acid. (2) Feulgen's reaction, the precise nature of which is obscure, but which serves to identify and locate deoxyribose nucleic acid. (3) Microspectrophotometry, based on the presence of an absorption band in the ultra-violet, maximum 260 mμ, caused by the purine and pyrimidine rings. (4) Selective hydrolysis by the enzyme *ribonuclease*, from pancreas, and *deoxyribonuclease*, from pancreas or streptococci. (5) Chromatographic separation and identification of hydrolytic products of hydrolysis at different levels. (6) Estimation of phosphate, and of individual purines and pyrimidines. (7) X-ray diffraction.

A representative liver cell, diameter 20,000 mμ, has a nucleus of diameter 6,000 mμ, of which deoxyribonucleate forms 12 to 40 per cent. of the dry weight.

Deoxyribonucleic acid is a filament of about 2 mμ in diameter. Molecular weight values range from 0·5 $\times$ 10^6 to 8 $\times$ 10^6, depending on the length of the filament, which exceeds 3,000 mμ, and contains 1,500 to 24,000 nucleotide units. The structure plan is a chain of alternating phosphoric and pentose radicals, the sugar units being in 3' and 5' linkage with the phosphate, and spaced out at intervals of 3·34 Å along the chain. Each pentose unit is in 1' linkage alternately with a purine or pyrimidine base, which projects at right-angles to the axis of the chain.

```
        purine                  pyrimidine                  purine
          |                         |                         |
—O—PO(OH)—O—pentose—O—PO(OH)—O—pentose—O—PO(OH)—O—pentose
```

327

The purine residues in DNA are adenine and guanine; the pyrimidines are thymine and cytosine, which may be replaced by 5-methylcytosine or hydroxymethylcytosine, in DNA of bacteria.

Complete hydrolysis of DNA from different sources yields purines and pyrimidines in varying amounts, but the adenine and thymine are in equivalent amounts, as also are the guanine and cytosine, indicating that they occur in pairs.

The diameter of the DNA filament suggests that it is formed of two parallel chains held in cross-linkage by union between the purine and pyrimidine residues:

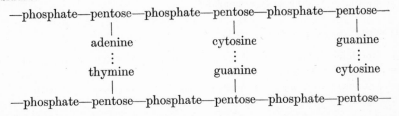

The purines and pyrimidines are held in the cross-linkages by hydrogen bonding between neighbouring —NH₂ and HO— groups, —NH₂...H—O—. Hence, only amino purines and pyrimidines are employed. The order in which the purines and pyrimidines occur along the chain can vary, but each must have its appropriate partner: adenine...thymine; guanine...cytosine, forming the rungs of a molecular ladder. The properties of the molecule are such that it cannot be an extended linear filament. According to the theory of Watson and Crick (1953–), the double strand has the conformation of a helix, comparable to a circular staircase, in which the hand-rails are the pentose–phosphate chains and the steps are the purine–pyrimidine pairs.

Ribonucleic acid, RNA, which occurs chiefly as extra-nuclear nucleic acid, and is only represented in the nucleus as a component of the nucleolus, is similar in structure to DNA, but the filaments are shorter, and occur as single strands as well as in helical conformation.

Significance of the Nucleic Acids

The outstanding property of the nucleic acids is their ability to reproduce themselves indefinitely, in favourable circumstances. This is shown by the deoxyribonucleic acid of the nucleus, which, starting from the fertilised ovum, reproduces itself in every cell of the adult body. Similarly, the cytoplasmic ribonucleic acid reproduces itself in every dividing cell and also carries the power of synthesising the specific proteins that characterise the individual tissues and constitute the enormous equipment of enzymes required for life. Unlike the proteins, which can be assembled from their 20 to 25 different amino acids in several million different ways, the nucleic acids have to prepare and transmit their directives in a code that contains only 4 or 5 different symbols: 2 purines and 2 or 3 pyrimidines. This, apparently, can be done by varying the order of arrangement of units on a very long filament, just as the history of the human race might be stored for posterity, in Morse code on a tape-recorder.

According to Watson and Crick, self-duplication (replication) is an endowment of the double-strand helix. Part of the filament unwinds and the bonds holding the purine-pyrimidine cross-linkages are broken. As a result, two complementary single-chain strands are exposed. Each chain then begins to collect appropriate nucleotides from the environment, and, by attaching them to corresponding residues along the axis, constructs a new chain which is twisted into helical formation as it is built up. In this way two exact copies of the original parent molecule are obtained.

Mutations, the abrupt transmissible changes that may occur spontaneously but very rarely in gene structure and can be promoted by ultra-violet irradiation, are referred to local alterations in the nucleic acid chains.

Viruses and **Bacteriophages** are nucleoprotein entities capable of causing diseases in animals, plants, and bacteria. They are not living organisms, as they can neither grow nor reproduce themselves in the absence of a host, and, when isolated, they are inert and do not engage in respiratory activity or other energy transformations.

A typical bacteriophage consists of a core of deoxyribonucleic acid, and a protein coating, by which it adheres to the organism attacked. The bacterial wall dissolves at the place of attachment, and the nucleoprotein enters the cell. Reduplication is rapid. Within 25 minutes, the infected cell explodes, releasing about 200 particles, each identical with the original invader.

Viruses are responsible for yellow-fever, smallpox, influenza, foot-and-mouth disease, and many other animal and plant infections. The first to be isolated in crystalline form was the virus of tobacco mosaic disease (Stanley, 1935). Rickettsia, the group of viruses carried by lice, and responsible for typhus, differ from the smaller and simpler viruses in that its members have a primitive enzyme equipment that enables them to metabolise glutamate, pyruvate, and succinate, and to produce the toxin that causes the rash and fever of typhus.

Diameters of representative viruses in $m\mu$, as calculated from sedimentation data: foot-and-mouth disease, 10; tobacco mosaic, 33; bacteriophage, 30 to 100; herpes, 100 to 150; vaccinia, 175; rickettsia, 300; chicken-pox, 220 to 250; mumps, 140; influenza, 100.

Protein Synthesis. Nucleic acids provide the framework required in the cellular synthesis of proteins.

The evidence, at present circumstantial, is derived mostly from microbiological data. Purines and pyrimidines are required for protein synthesis by *Esch. coli*, and some other organisms. Dissolution of nucleic acids by ribonuclease inhibits protein synthesis in bacteria, protozoa, and liver homogenates. Ribonucleic acid is most abundant in cells actively engaged in protein construction.

Although proteins are resolved into amino acids by fragmentation and erosion of peptides, they do not appear to be assembled in the animal by successive addition of amino acid units to a growing peptide chain. This is inferred from the absence of short-chain peptides from tissue extracts. Short-chain peptides, apart from glutathione, are almost absent from animal tissues. Furthermore, the construction of such highly specialised molecules as the proteins, link by link, implies both the activity of a specific enzyme for each individual amino acid and the presence of a specific organiser for each individual protein.

According to the alternative hypothesis, the nucleic acid filament can extend its activities to protein replication, by combining with a pre-formed peptide chain and employing it as a template, or working pattern, on which are assembled the amino acids in proper selection and order. As they come into alignment, the carboxyl groups of the amino acids are activated by reaction with adenosine triphosphate:

$$H_2N.CH(R).COOH + ATP \rightarrow H_2N.CH(R).CO—O—PO(OH)—adenosine + 2H_3PO_4$$

The activated amino acid can condense with the amino group of another amino acid, forming a peptide, and releasing adenosine monophosphate. In this way, long-chain peptide replicas can be assembled, and wound-off as fibrous or globular proteins during the process (Dalgliesh, 1953).

Biosynthesis of Purines and Pyrimidines

Growing tissues rapidly synthesise purines and pyrimidines in accordance with their requirements for intracellular nucleic acids. Tracer studies, using compounds labelled with radio-active carbon, ^{14}C, and chromatographic analysis, have disclosed the stages in each process.

Purines. Purine synthesis starts with the easily-obtained amino acid glycine, and hypoxanthine is the first purine obtained.

(*a*) Glycine combines with 1-amino ribose 5-phosphate, H_2N—RP, to form glycinamide ribosyl phosphate, $H_2N.CH_2.CO$—NH—RP; which takes up a formyl unit, —CHO, from a folic acid carrier, yielding:

(*b*) N-formyl glycinamide ribosyl phosphate, OCH—$NH.CH_2.CO.NH$—RP.

(*c*) Transfer of NH_3 from glutamine, followed by ring-closure, produces the 5-amino imidazole derivative. This provides the 5-membered ring of the purine.

(*d*) For the remaining part of the molecule, three agents co-operate: aspartic acid provides nitrogen 1 of the purine skeleton, formate provides carbon 2, and CO_2 provides carbon 6. The result is inosinic acid, the hypoxanthine nucleotide, from which hypoxanthine is released by hydrolytic removal of the ribose phosphate side-chain.

| 5-amino imidazole. | Inosinic acid. | Purine skeleton. |

Sources of the Atoms in the Purine Skeleton. N at 1 from aspartate; C at 2 from formate, *via* folic acid; N at 3 and 9 from glutamine; C at 4 and 5, and N at 7 from glycine; C at 6 from CO_2.

Pyrimidines. Synthesis starts with aspartic acid,

$$HOOC.CH(NH_2).CH_2.COOH,$$

which, by condensation with carbamyl phosphate,

$$H_2N.CO.O.PO(OH)_2,$$

yields ureidosuccinic acid, or carbamylaspartic acid,

$$H_2N.CO.NH—CH(COOH).CH_2.COOH,$$

from which, by ring-closure and dehydrogenation, orotic acid, the parent pyrimidine is obtained.

END-PRODUCTS OF PURINE METABOLISM

Dietary nucleic acids or their components do not contribute any important nutrients to the higher animal, whose nuclear requirements are met entirely by synthesis. Unabsorbed purines and pyrimidines are broken down by the bacteria of the large intestine, some of which require adenine or uracil as growth-factors.

Absorbed purines are degraded mostly to uric acid and allantoin, and excreted in the urine, along with similar end-products of endogenous nucleic acid metabolism.

Accumulation of purines and pyrimidines in the tissues is prevented by the action of deaminating and oxidising enzymes. Adenine and guanine are deaminated to xanthine and hypoxanthine, respectively, by deaminases present in tissues other than muscle. Xanthine oxidase, present in liver and kidney, oxidises hypoxanthine and xanthine to uric acid, which is excreted as such by man and the anthropoids, and degraded to allantoin prior to excretion, by animals whose tissues contain urate oxidase.

From the extent to which a known amount of labelled urate is diluted after injection, it can be calculated that the adult human body contains about 1·1 gm. of uric acid, about half of which is eliminated and replaced every 24 hours. In conditions of gout, the rate of purine synthesis is increased, and blood urate exceeds its normal range of 2 to 6 mg. per 100 ml., and may reac 15 mg. per 100 ml.

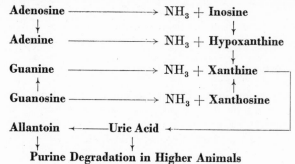

Purine Degradation in Higher Animals

General References

Carter, C. E. (1956), "Metabolism of Purines and Pyrimidines." *Ann. Re* *Biochem.*, **25**, 125.

"Chemistry and Biology of Purines" (1957). *Ciba Foundation Symposium.*

Darlington, C. D. (1949), "Genetic Particles." *Endeavour*, **8**, 51.

Davidson, J. N. (1953), "Biochemistry of the Nucleic Acids." London.

Johnson, T. B. (1942), "Pyrimidines, Purines and Nucleic Acids." *Organi* *Chemistry*. Ed. by H. Gilman. 2nd ed. London.

Lythgoe, B. (1945), "Chemistry of Nucleosides and Nucleotides." *Chem. Soc* *Ann. Rep.*, **41**, 200.

Markham, R., and J. D. Smith (1954), "Nucleoproteins and Viruses." *Th* *Proteins*. Ed. by H. Neurath and K. Bailey. Vol. II, Part A.

"The Nucleic Acids." Ed. by E. Chargaff and J. N. Davidson, (1955) New York.

"Viruses" (1955). *Ciba Foundation Symposium.*

Chapter 21 Amines and Amides

In its association with life, nitrogen forms three classes of compounds: the amino acids, and their condensation products, the proteins; the amines, or nitrogen bases; and the amides. Cyclic structures, such as the pyrimidines, purines, pteridines, and imidazoles, can be regarded as cyclic amine or amide types.

Amines

By definition, a *base* is a compound capable of accepting a hydrogen ion, and forming a cation:

$$B + H^+ \rightleftharpoons BH^+.$$

Apart from the ubiquitous hydroxyl radical, HO', the majority of biological bases are primary, secondary, or tertiary amines, from which by addition of H^+ are derived the corresponding cations:

$$R\text{—}NH_2 + H^+ \rightarrow R\text{—}NH_3^+; \quad R{=}NH \text{ or } R\text{—}NH\text{—}R + H^+$$
$$\rightarrow R{=}NH_2^+, R\text{—}NH_2^+\text{—}R; \quad \text{—}N{=} + H^+ \rightarrow \text{—}N^+H{=}$$

Also, there are the stable nitrogen cations, or *onium* ions, R_4N^+, in which the nitrogen atom is in quaternary union with radicals other than hydrogen. These cations, termed *onium* by analogy with *ammonium*, NH^+_4, are not bases as now defined, but resemble the sodium and potassium cations in many ways, and like them form stable salts.

Complex amines and onium compounds include the plant alkaloids and betaines, and bacterial products, many of which have powerful physiological effects.

Because of the diversity of biological and pharmacological interests, a comprehensive classification of the amines and onium compounds is not yet achieved. Functionally, the target may be a tissue, such as muscle, or a nerve terminus in a ganglion, a muscle, or a gland, and the result of application or injection may be a motor or an inhibitor response. Prominent among mixed responses are the pressor effects, including: (1) vascular constriction, with accompanying rise in blood pressure; (2) increased force of cardiac contraction; (3) inhibition of the peristaltic movements of the intestine; (4) dilation of the pupil of the eye; (5) contraction of the uterus. These pressor effects provide a basis for classification, they are described as sympathomimetic, because they resemble some of the effects obtained when sympathetic nerves are stimulated.

333

Pressor Amines. Every amino acid on decarboxylation yields the corresponding amine: $R.CH(NH_2).COOH \rightarrow R.CH_2.NH_2 + CO_2$. Selective decarboxylases for all the known amino acids are found among the microorganisms, and, to a very limited extent, in the animal, for whom the principal pressor amines are the hormones tyramine, noradrenaline, and adrenaline, derived from tyrosine, and 5-hydroxytryptamine, derived from tryptophan.

These compounds are described along with the other hormones in Chapter 24.

Depressor Amines. In the higher animal, these are histamine and acetyl choline.

Histamine, or imidazolyl ethylamine, the amine derived from histidine, is widely distributed as an inert precursor in animal tissues, notably lung, spleen, and intestinal mucosa, from which it can be released rapidly by tissue enzymes. It can arise, also, from histidine, by the action of histidine decarboxylase, present in liver, and kidney, and in many micro-organisms.

$$
\begin{array}{cc}
\underset{\substack{\text{Histidine.}}}{\underset{\displaystyle\underset{\text{CH}}{HN\diagdown\diagup N}}{HC\!=\!\!=\!\!C-CH_2.\underset{\substack{| \\ NH_2}}{CH}.COOH}}
&
\underset{\substack{\textbf{Histamine.}}}{\underset{\displaystyle\underset{\text{CH}}{HN\diagdown\diagup N}}{HC\!=\!\!=\!\!C-CH_2.\underset{\substack{| \\ NH_2}}{CH_2}}} + CO_2
\end{array}
$$

Properties of Histamine. Unlike the amines derived from other amino acids histamine is a powerful depressor. Release or intravenous injection is followed by a rapid fall in blood pressure, caused by capillary loss of tone, with passive dilatation, and escape of fluid into the tissues. A state of histamine shock results, which may be compensated by reflex stimulation of the adrenal glands, or which may lead to vascular failure, collapse and death. Local or general histamine release is implicated in conditions of asthma, hay-fever, skin and other alergic responses in skin, and shock evoked by burns and other injuries.

Histamine stimulates unstriated muscle of the intestinal tract, uterus, bronchioles, and arterioles. The response varies with animal species; young guinea pigs, whose muscles will react to concentrations of histamine as low as 1 in 10^7, may develop bronchospasm and fatal asphyxia. Histamine has no direct effect on the heart.

Histamine is a powerful secretagogue; injected subcutaneously, so that it is absorbed slowly, it evokes salivary, gastric, pancreatic, and lachryma secretion. The sweat glands are not affected.

Significance. Histamine may be a factor in the local control of the circulation as in the vaso-dilation observed when the activity of a tissue is increased or its blood supply is obstructed. It is set free during the disintegration of blood platelets. Normally, the histamine level in human blood is kept below 5 μg. per 100 ml. by the action of diamine oxidiase, or histaminase, present in kidney, intestinal mucosa, as well as in plants and bacteria. The placenta is the source of the blood histaminase observed in pregnancy. Liberation of histamine, or a histaminoid in the tissue is responsible for allergic and anaphylactic reactions: nasal congestion in " hay fever ", bronchiole spasm in asthma, itch in pruritis, and eruptions in urticaria. Such conditions can be relieved by adrenaline, the physiological antagonist of histamine, and by the synthetic antihistamines, such as benadryl and neoantergan. These drugs are structurally related to histamine, and may act as competitors for particular types of target tissue (Gaddum, 1948–).

Miscellaneous amines of no obvious function include putrescine or tetramethylene diamine,

$$H_2N.CH_2.CH_2.CH_2.CH_2.NH_2,$$

from ornithine and cadaverine, or pentamethylene diamine, from lysine. Formerly regarded as typical " ptomaines ", or poisonous bases produced by putrefaction of proteins, they are not highly toxic compounds, and may occur in urine, notably in conditions of cystinuria.
Spermine,

$$H_2N.(CH_2)_3.NH.(CH_2)_4.NH.(CH_2)_3.NH_2$$

and spermidine,

$$H_2N.(CH_2)_3.NH.(CH_2)_4.NH_2,$$

are polyamines manufactured or concentrated in the testicle and prostate, which, in man, contains about 150 mg. spermine per 100 gm. fresh tissue.

Onium Compounds

Choline, N-trimethyl ethanolamine, $(CH_3)_3N^+.CH_2.CH_2.OH$, is widely distributed in plants and animals as a component of the lecithins.

Values for combined choline, in mg. per 100 gm. fresh material: egg-yolk, 1,100 to 1,700; liver, 470 to 700; wheat germ, 400; hepatic bile, 180 to 450; blood plasma, 26 to 35; brain and nerve, 200 to 600; milk, 4 to 48.

Choline is a strongly electro-positive cation, comparable with Na^+. It is the precursor of the hormone acetyl choline and also provides a source of methyl groups for biological methylation. The ordinary choline requirements of the animal are met by synthesis from serine, which by decarboxylation provides ethanolamine, $HO.CH_2.CH_2.NH_2$, from which choline is formed by methylation. When the diet is very rich in fats, additional supplies of choline or methionine are required to provide enough methyl groups for phospholipid construction and transportation, and the avoidance of hepatic liposis.

Acetyl choline, discovered in ergot (Ewins, 1914) and in animal tissue (Dale and Dudley, 1929), is 100,000 times more powerful than choline as a depressor base. It constitutes the chemical mediator in transmission of impulses both

335

by the voluntary motor nerves and the *cholinergic* nerves of the autonomic system: sympathetic (including splanchnic) preganglionic and parasym pathetic preganglionic and postganglionic fibres.

Liberated at the nerve terminals, acetyl choline is rapidly hydrolysed to choline by a local enzyme **choline esterase.**

$$CH_3.CO.O.CH_2.CH_2.\overset{+}{N}(CH_3)_3 \xrightarrow{+ H_2O} HO.CH_2.CH_2.\overset{+}{N}(CH_3)_3 + CH_3.COOH$$

Acetyl choline.   Choline.

These compounds are discussed along with the other hormones in Chapter 24 **Betaines** are dipolar onium compounds derived from amino acids by full methylation of the amino nitrogen. Examples are: betaine, or trimethyl glycine, from beet; myokinine, or trimethylarginine, and carnitine, or tri methylglutamic acid, both of which occur in muscle.

$$\begin{array}{ccc}
CH_2.COO^- & HC\!\!=\!\!C\!\!-\!\!-CH_2.CH.COO^- \\
| & | \quad | \qquad\qquad | + \\
N(CH_3)_3 & N\quad NH \qquad\quad N(CH_3)_3 \\
+ & HS\!\!-\!\!C
\end{array}$$

Betaine   Thioneine (Ergothioneine)
(dipolar form).   (dipolar form).

Betaines are widely represented in plants. Because of their dipolar structure, they are neutral solutes. Their chief function appears to be the storage and provision of methyl groups.

Guanidines

These bases contain the guanidino function, $—NH.C(NH)—NH_2$. The chief examples are the amino acid, arginine, the phosphate-carrier, creatine, and its precursor glycocyamine.

Creatine, methylguanidino acetic acid, or methyl glycocyamine, was discovered in meat extracts by Chevreul in 1835. Since then, it has been shown to be a constant constituent of vertebrate muscle. Values in mg. per 100 gm. fresh muscle range from about 300, in fish, up to 500, in rabbit.

Representative values in mg. per 100 gm. fresh muscle: rabbit, 520; pigeon, cat, 450; ox, 430; man, dog, horse, 390; fish, 300. The adult human body has 90 to 130 gm. of creatine, about 98 per cent. of which is in muscle, and 1·5 per cent. in nerve.

Creatine is obtainable commercially as a by-product in the manufacture of meat extracts. It is a colourless, neutral compound, soluble in water to the extent of 1 in 74 at 18° C., and freely soluble at 100° C. In solution it undergoes ring-closure to its anhydride, creatinine, a change greatly accelerated by boiling with acids.

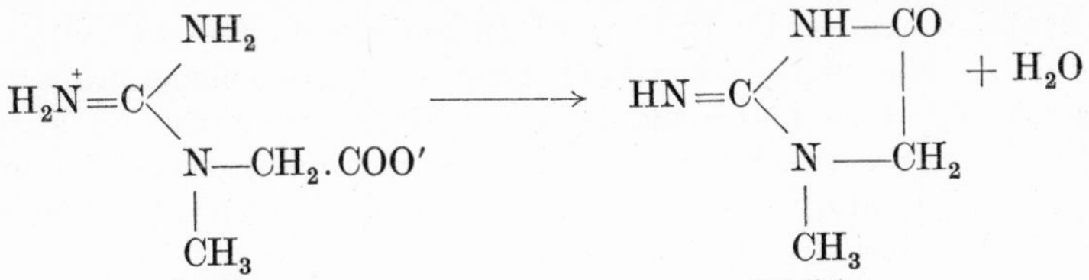

$$\overset{+}{H_2N}=C\diagdown \begin{array}{l} NH_2 \\ \\ N-CH_2.COO' \\ | \\ CH_3 \end{array} \quad \longrightarrow \quad HN=C\diagdown \begin{array}{l} NH-CO \\ \quad\quad | \\ N\ \ -CH_2 \\ | \\ CH_3 \end{array} \ + H_2O$$

Creatine
(Dipolar form).

Creatinine.

Because of its dipolar form, creatine, like a monoamino acid, is a neutral solute. Like urea, its amino groups are in a hybrid state, and do not react readily with nitrous acid or with formaldehyde. Creatinine is a weak base.

Significance. Phosphocreatine, in which the unit —$PO(OH)_2$, has replaced an amino hydrogen, acts as an accumulator of energy in muscle metabolism by supplementing adenosine triphosphate.
It enters into the reversible exchange reaction:

Creatine + ATP $\leftrightharpoons$ Phosphocreatine + ADP; $\varDelta F \pm 1.600$.

Equilibrium is catalysed by creatine phosphokinase, present in muscle and other tissues.

Phosphocreatine is a high-energy phosphate; the free energy of hydrolysis is about —13,000 calories per mole. The free energy of hydrolysis of ATP to ADP is only —6,000 to —8,000 calories per mole. Consequently, the phosphorylation of creatine by ATP is an endergonic reaction, and requires an external source of energy, + 1,600 calories per mole, which is provided by glycolysis. Conversely, the phosphorylation of ADP by phosphocreatine is a spontaneous exergonic reaction, in which 1,600 calories of free energy are released, and escape as heat.

Synthesis. The creatine requirements of the organism can be met entirely by synthesis from the readily available amino acid glycine, which is converted

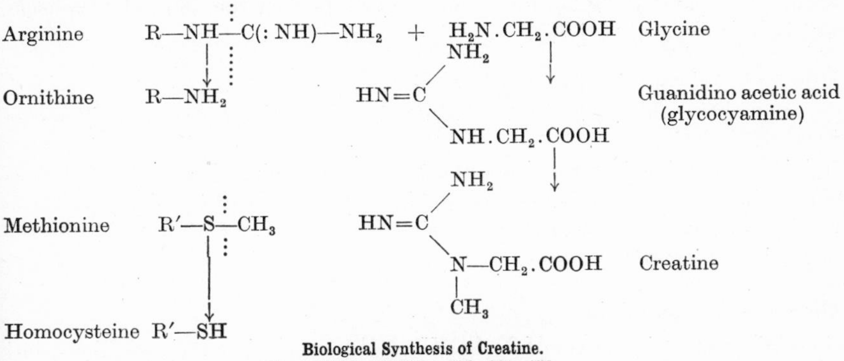

Arginine   R—NH—C(: NH)—NH₂ + H₂N.CH₂.COOH   Glycine

Ornithine   R—NH₂   HN=C
                      \
                      NH.CH₂.COOH

Guanidino acetic acid
(glycocyamine)

          NH₂

Methionine   R'—S—CH₃   HN=C
                        \
                        N—CH₂.COOH   Creatine
                        |
                        CH₃

Homocysteine R'—SH

Biological Synthesis of Creatine.
R = HOOC.CH(NH₂).CH₂.CH₂.CH₂—
R' = HOOC.CH(NH₂).CH₂.CH₂—

337

into guanidino acetate by transfer of an amidine unit, —C(: NH)—NH, from arginine. The transamidination is catalysed by an enzyme, transamidin ase, present in kidney, and in plants, but not in liver. The guanidino acetat is methylated to creatine by transfer of a methyl group from methionine. Th reaction is catalysed by a transmethylase, present in liver but not in kidne working in association with ATP and Mg^{2+}.

Metabolism of Creatine. Surplus creatine is dehydrated to creatinine, an excreted in the urine. During active growth or in metabolic disturbance creatine production may exceed the dehydration capacity of the tissues, an creatinuria occurs. Creatine is a normal solute in the urine of children an other young vertebrates, but disappears after adolescence when the muscula system has fully developed. This creatinuria of growth is attributed to over production beyond the storage capacity of the muscles.

Creatine is a characteristic of the urine of many animals, including cattle sheep, the dog, and the fox. Among birds, it exceeds the creatinine conten

Starvation creatinuria, caused by muscle autolysis, occurs during metaboli disturbances, diabetes, starvation, and febrile conditions. It can be aggravate by lack of vitamin E. Creatinuria occurs towards the end of pregnancy, an may reach 170 mg. per 24 hours at the time of parturition, subsiding withi a month. Creatinuria of low storage capacity is observed in muscular dys trophies and atrophy, where the administration of a small quantity of creatin leads to its rapid excretion. The fact that creatinuria can occur when th diet is free from creatine is evidence of its synthesis.

Creatinine, or N-methylglycocyamidine, the cyclic anhydride of creatine, i a solute in all mammalian urine.

Representative percentage values are: man, 0·06 to 0·22; goat, 0·04; horse ox, sheep, 0·1 to 0·2. Creatinine output varies individually, but is almos constant for each individual. It is expressed as a *creatinine coefficient,* define as the 24-hour output in mg. per kg. body weight. Values range from 18 t 32, for men; and 10 to 25, for women, depending on the amount of muscle but independent of activity.

Human blood contains 1 to 2 mg. creatinine per 100 ml. It is readily excreted as a non-threshold solute, by the kidney, and retention only occurs in sever renal dysfunction.

Origin. Creatinine is formed spontaneously from phosphocreatine by ring closure accompanied by loss of phosphate. It is a waste-product, and by it production serves to keep the creatine content of the tissues within the normal working range.

Miscellaneous Guanidines

Guanidine, or imino urea, $H_2N.C(NH).NH_2$, occurs in vetch seedlings, but has not been found in animal tissues. It is a strong base, and forms stable guanidonium salts, which when injected into the animal evoke spasms resembling those of hypocalcæmic tetany.

Guanidine may be obtained by oxidation of guanine and its nucleosides, and from proteins rich in arginine.

Methyl guanidine, $CH_3.NH.C(NH).NH_2$, is a micro-constituent of muscle and mammalian urine (about 0·1 per cent.). The output is increased by removal of the parathyroid glands.

Arginine, α-amino-δ-guanidino valeric acid, is usually classified as an amino acid among the amino acids.

Canavanine, α-amino-γ-guanidoxy butyric acid,

$$H_2N.C(NH).NH.O.CH_2.CH_2.CH(NH_2).COOH,$$

occurs free in jack bean and some other seeds, but not in soya bean. It is of interest in being a guanidoxy compound, and can act as an arginine antagonist.

Guanidine derivatives other than creatine and the amino acids have a hypo-glycæmic effect, and evoke a fall in blood sugar when injected. Many of them act as pressor bases.

Analytical Reactions of the Guanidines. *Free guanidine*, on treatment with alkaline 1,2-naphthoquinone 4-sulphonate, yields after a few minutes a brown solution that turns bright red on acidification with nitric acid. Substituted guanidines do not give this reaction, but similar colours are obtainable from ammonia, methylamine, and indole (Sullivan, 1935).

Monosubstituted Guanidines. Arginine, glycocyamine, and other compounds of the type H_2N—$C(NH)$—$NH.R$, on treatment with alkaline α-naphthol or thymol, and subsequent oxidation by hypochlorite or hypobromite, yield a colour, which is red, with α-naphthol (Sakaguchi, 1925), and golden yellow, with thymol. Free guanidine, and N-disubstituted guanidines, including creatine do not react chromatically.

Mono- and N-disubstituted guanidines, on treatment with alkaline diacetyl, develop red colours when warmed. The reaction is given by creatine and by arginine, free or protein-bound (Walpole, 1914; O'Meara, 1931).

Creatinine gives none of these tests, but can be detected by reactions that are described in connection with urine analysis in Chapter 22.

UREA

Urea, or carbamide, CON_2H_4, is a characteristic form in which nitrogen leaves the animal, and is the chief organic solute in the urine of vertebrates other than birds and snakes, where it is replaced by urate. It is the simplest and most widely distributed of all the organic compounds of nitrogen found in the biosphere.

History. The ammoniacal fermentation of urine, which occurs on keeping, was familiar in the time of Pliny, and is now known to be caused by the growth of urease-producing organisms. The substrate, urea, was separated by Boerhave in the seventeenth century, and by Rouelle in 1773. Fourcroy and Vauquelin, in 1798, obtained crystalline urea nitrate by addition of excess of HNO₃ to the urine of man and other animals, and concluded that " thi special material of urine, which we now call urea . . . gives rise to the car bonate of ammonia that replaces it when urine ferments." In 1828 Wöhle accidentally synthesised urea when trying to prepare ammonium cyanate by the action of ammonium hydroxide on lead cyanate. Two years later Dumas introduced the carbamide formula, H_2N—CO—NH_2, according to which urea is the diamide of carbonic acid. Although crude preparations of the urea hydrolysing enzyme, urease, had been obtained from bacteria, its unexpected discovery in the long-familiar soya bean agent provided investigators with a specific method for the detection and estimation of urea.

Meanwhile, the general importance of urea as a form of waste-product of protein metabolism was established, and perfusion experiments had shown that it was formed in the liver, but the mechanism remained obscure until in 1932, Krebs and Henseleit showed that urea was synthesised by a cyclic process involving a closed chain of three amino acids. In 1912 E. A. Werner, being unable to reconcile the properties of urea with a simple carbamide structure, proposed a " closed " formula, a prototype of the hybrid, or resonance state, now attributed to urea.

Distribution. Urea is a minor constituent of green plants, but may reach values up to 10 per cent. of the dry weight, in fungi, where it provides a reserve store of nitrogen.

Urea is universal in animals, amongst which two main types can be recognised: (1) ureotelic, or urea synthesising species, which are able to construct urea from CO_2 and NH_3 by a special mechanism; (2) non-ureotelic species, which obtain urea from ureides or arginine supplied by the diet.

Ureotelic animals include most of the invertebrates, amphibia, fishes, and all the vertebrates other than birds, snakes and lizards.

Tissue and tissue fluid values usually are within the range 16 to 70 mg. urea per 100 gm. Elasmobranchs (dog-fish, skate, shark) have an exceptionally high blood urea concentration, which may reach 1·7 gm. per 100 ml., and is employed for maintaining vascular osmotic pressure.

As a solute, urea is uniformly distributed in the organism, with the exception of adipose tissue, which has a low urea content corresponding to its low water content, and renal tissue, in which urea is being concentrated prior to excretion.

Blood Urea. Values for normal human blood are 31 ± 7·5 mg. urea per 100 ml. The level usually is 6 to 8 per cent. higher in males than in females of the same size and age. The level rises with advancing years. Between the ages of 40 and 80, it can be calculated, approximately, from the formula:

$$\text{Urea nitrogen, in mg. per 100 ml.} = 7\cdot55 + 0\cdot122 \, A,$$

where A is age, in years.

340

Blood levels are remarkably uniform throughout the human species, irrespective of race and dietary habits.

Excretion. Urea leaves the animal in the urine, sweat, bile, and intestinal secretions. Of these, the urine is by far the most important, and, in adult man, contains 1·5 to 2·3 gm. per 100 ml., depending on the diet and the concentration of the urine.

Average percentage urea values for mammalian urine: tiger, 6·9; rat, 4·5; cat, 2·2; horse, 1·5 to 2·6; cow, 0·9 to 2·6; rabbit, 0·2 to 0·4.

The urinary output of urea depends on the protein content of the diet, each 100 gm. of which, by contributing 14 to 16 gm. of amino nitrogen, can give rise to about 28 gm. of urea, representing 80 to 89 per cent. of the total urinary nitrogen. According to Van Slyke, when the rate of secretion of urine exceeds an " augmentation limit " of 2 ml. per minute, its urea content is directly proportional to the urea in a given volume of blood passing through the kidney in unit time, the maximal value of which is about 75 ml. blood per minute, which affords the maximum *clearance* of urea from the blood.

Properties. Urea is a colourless, crystalline solid. It is very soluble in water, methanol, and glycerol; moderately soluble in ethanol and acetone; and insoluble in ether, chloroform, and benzene. At human body temperature (36° C.), 1 ml. of water dissolves 1·1 gm. of urea. In concentrated solutions of 40 to 80 per cent., urea is a solvent for starches and for proteins, which it denatures, by loosening hydrogen bonds.

Urea can be separated from urine that has been concentrated to about one-quarter of its original volume on a water-bath by extraction with boiling acetone, or addition of an equal volume of cold nitric acid or saturated oxalic acid, which precipitates it as a crystalline salt. It is obtained industrially in bulk by the dehydration of ammonium carbonate at high temperature, under pressure.

Structure. Urea is an almost neutral solute, displaying none of the basic properties associated with the presence of a free amino group. In presence of strong acids it forms monobasic salts of the type $HO.C(NH).NH_3^+ A'$, derived from the *iso*-carbamide form, $HO.C(NH).NH_2$. This suggests that the neutrality of urea may depend on its existing in the dipolar state, $O^-.C(NH).NH_3^+$, like the monoamino acids. However, unlike the amino acids, urea has no significant buffering power, and cannot be estimated by titration in presence of formaldehyde. Its inertness is attributed to the fact that it exists in a hybrid state of resonance between the three possible forms:

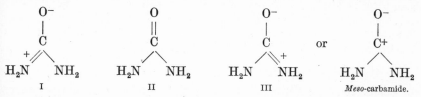

These formulæ do not denote independent individuals, such as would occur

341

in a mixture; the actual urea molecule is intermediate between true carbamide, II, and the dipolar amidines, I and III.

Resonance arises by rearrangement of the valency electrons in the molecule, thereby producing a system of greatest stability. It occurs in aromatic and other compounds, though its biochemical significance is not yet explored fully.

Analytical Reactions of Urea

(1) **Decomposition by Heat.** Heated above its melting point (132·6° C.), urea dissociates into cyanic acid and ammonia:

$$HO.C(NH).NH_2 \rightarrow OC:NH + NH_3$$

Cyanic acid is very reactive, and combines with the residual urea to form biuret, $H_2N.CO.NH.CO.NH_2$, which gives a red-purple colour with Cu^{2+} in alkaline solution, resembling the copper-peptide reaction.

(2) **Hydrolysis.** Urea in *sterile*, aqueous solutions is stable at ordinary temperature, but if boiled, slowly dissociates into ammonia and cyanic acid, which hydrolyses to ammonia and carbon dioxide. Hydrolysis is accelerated by H^+ or OH^-.

(3) **Deamination by Hypobromite.** In strongly alkaline solution, urea is attacked by bromine and by hypobromite and broken down into carbon dioxide which is captured by the alkali, and into nitrogen gas, which can be collected and measured.

$$CON_2H_4 + 3NaOBr + 2NaOH \rightarrow 3H_2O + 3NaBr + Na_2CO_3 + N_2$$

This reaction is the basis of an ancient and popular method for estimating urea. Many other biological compounds, including ammonium ions and amino acids, release nitrogen under similar conditions.

(4) **Precipitation by Xanthydrol.** In presence of an excess of acetic acid, urea is quantitatively precipitated as a dixanthyl ureide on addition of 10 per cent. xanthydrol in methanol (Fosse, 1912). The test, which requires precision technique, will reveal urea in concentrations of 1 in 100,000 to 1 in 800,000, within 10 minutes. Practical details are given in the monographs by Werner and by Fosse.

(5) **Decomposition by Urease.** Urea is quantitatively converted into ammonia and carbon dioxide by the widely distributed enzyme *urease*, found in the seeds of leguminous and other plants, and many micro-organisms. Important sources are: jack bean (*Canavalia ensiformis*), sword bean (*C. gladiata*), soya bean (*Glycine hispida*), and several varieties of melon. The optimal pH is 6·8 to 7. The reaction provides a specific method for the detection of urea, and a micro-method for its estimation. The decomposition involves an intermediate formation of carbamic acid, and its decarboxylation:

$$H_2N.CO.NH_2 + H_2O \rightarrow NH_3 + H_2N.CO.OH \rightarrow NH_3 + CO_2$$

(6) **Colour Tests.** (a) *Ehrlich's aldehyde reagent* (3 per cent. p-dimethylamino benzaldehyde in HCl) forms a bright yellow benzylidine derivative with

compounds containing the carbamide function, —NH.CO.NH₂, including urea and citrulline. Alkalies or excess of strong acids bleach the colour.
(b) *Diacetyl Reaction*. About 2 ml. of the solution is mixed with 3 drops of aqueous 3 per cent. diacetyl monoxime and 2 to 4 ml. of concentrated HCl. On boiling, a bright yellow colour will develop if urea is present. The colour can be intensified by addition of a couple of drops of 1 per cent. potassium persulphate to the mixture after it has been allowed to cool. A slight excess of oxidiser bleaches the colour. Monosubstituted ureas, including citrulline, form red to purple pigments. The test has been adapted for the estimation of blood urea.

Urea Synthesis in the Animal

The necessity for a protein intake imposes on the human body the task of disposing of at least 10 gm. of amino nitrogen every 24 hours. This is done by converting the potentially toxic ammonia into the neutral solute, urea. The mechanism is very efficient, and there appear to be no records of its complete failure in any disease.

In 1927 Mann and his colleagues demonstrated the location of urea synthesis in the liver by showing that total hepatectomy in dogs resulted in complete cessation of urea production. The amino acid nitrogen and the ammonia of the blood, urine, and tissues increased, while, at the same time, the urea of the blood and tissues decreased because of renal excretion. If the kidneys are isolated by ligature, the blood urea will remain constant in the hepatectomised animal.

The Ornithine Cycle. Arginase is the only enzyme known to form urea as one of its reaction products. It is present in the livers of all animals that excrete nitrogen as urea, but is absent from uricotelic animals, such as birds, which excrete protein nitrogen as urate. This indicates that arginase has a metabolic function more important than the removal of surplus dietary arginine.

In 1930 citrulline was isolated from water melon and shown, by Wada, to be the carbamide acid corresponding to arginine. Two years later, Krebs and

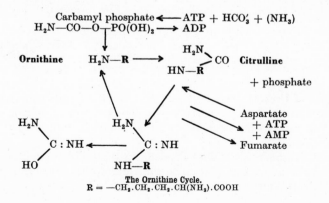

The Ornithine Cycle.
R = —CH₂.CH₂.CH₂.CH(NH₂).COOH

343

Henseleit, by tissue-slice technique, showed that urea synthesis in liver from ammonia and carbon dioxide sources was accelerated by addition of any one of the three amino acids, ornithine, citrulline, or arginine. These, and other observations, were incorporated into a theory of urea synthesis, which has been found to be of wide application, and is of interest in that it represents the first demonstration of the working of a cyclic process in tissue metabolism. The ornithine cycle has been shown to operate in the livers of mammals, amphibia, and chelonian reptiles. It is restricted to hepatic tissue.

In outline, the reaction is $2NH_3 + CO_2 \rightarrow CON_2H_4 + H_2O$. The carbon dioxide comes from tissue bicarbonate; one ammonia unit is provided by glutamine, and incorporated into carbamyl phosphate by means of a phosphate unit transferred from ATP. The second ammonia unit comes from aspartate.

Stage 1. **Ornithine to Citrulline.** This is effected by transfer of a carbamyl unit, —$CO.NH_2$, from carbamyl phosphate, catalysed by *ornithine transcarbamylase* (Cohen *et al.*, 1950–).

Stage 2. **Citrulline to Arginosuccinic Acid.** This condensation with aspartic acid is the rate-limiting factor in the cycle. It is catalysed by a condensing enzyme, and the energy is provided by the break-down of ATP into adenosine monophosphate, AMP, and pyrophosphate.

$$R.NH.CO.NH_2 + H_2N.CH(COOH).CH_2.COOH$$
$$\rightarrow R.NH.C(NH).NH.CH(COOH).CH_2.COOH$$

Stage 3. **Arginosuccinate to Arginine.** By the action of a cleavage enzyme, the succinic radical is released as fumaric acid (Ratner *et al.*, 1951–).

$$\rightarrow R.NH.C(NH).NH_2 + HOOC.CH{=}CH.COOH$$

Stage 4. **Arginine to Ornithine and Urea.** This is catalysed by arginase in presence of Mn^{2+}. The ornithine rejoins the cycle, the urea is excreted.

The dehydration of ammonia and carbon dioxide is an endergonic reaction, $\Delta F +$, and requires an energy input equal to the free energy gain. This is supplied by ATP; and the overall reaction can be formulated:

$$NH_4^+ + HCO_3^- + \text{Aspartate} + 3ATP + H_2O$$
$$\rightarrow \text{Urea} + \text{Fumarate} + 2ADP + AMP + \text{phosphates}$$

Modifications of the cycle are discussed by Fisher (1954).

Significance of Urea. (1) *Detoxication.* Urea provides a stable, inert, and very soluble form in which nitrogen can be eliminated, thus transferring ammonia from its temporary carrier, glutamine, and removing it altogether from the metabolic pool.

The extent to which this is done depends on the acid-base balance requirement. In states of acidosis, glutamine contributes NH_3 to neutralise urinary H^+, thus diverting it from urea synthesis.

(2) *Diuresis.* During renal secretion, urea carries with it sufficient water to keep its concentration below 2·5 per cent., and acts as a natural diuretic. This property is the basis of tests for renal efficiency. The toxicity of very large doses of urea is determined by the inability of animals to excrete it beyond a maximum rate, which is about 1·5 gm. per 1 gm. kidney tissue per 24 hours, in the dog. Conversely, urea added in amounts up to 10 per cent. of the total food intake can serve as a protein sparer in the diet of ruminants. It is hydrolysed by the flora of the alimentary tract and used for synthesis of amino acids capable of being absorbed by the animal.

General References

Baldwin, E. (1947), " Comparative Biochemistry." 3rd Ed. Cambridge.

Barger, G. (1914), " Simpler Natural Bases." *Monographs on Biochemistry.* London.

Barger, G. (1931), " Ergot and Ergotism." London.

Beyer, K. H. (1946), " Sympathomimetic Amines." *Physiol. Rev.,* **26,** 169.

Dale, H. (1953), "Adventures in Physiology." London.

Fearon, W. R. (1939), " Carbamido-diacetyl Reaction." *Biochem. J.,* **33,** 902.

Feldberg, W. (1945), "Acetylcholine in the Central Nervous System." *Physiol. Rev.,* **25,** 598.

Gale, E. F. (1950), " Chemical Activities of Bacteria." 3rd Ed. London.

Guggenheim, M. (1951), " Die Biogenen Amine." 4th Ed. Basle; New York.

Henry, T. A. (1949), " Plant Alkaloids." 4th Ed. London.

" Histamine." (1956). *CIBA Foundation Symposium.*

Hunter, A. (1928), " Creatine and Creatinine." *Monographs on Biochemistry.* London.

Ing, H. R. (1936), "Curariform Action of Onium Salts." *Physiol. Rev.,* **16,** 527.

Ratner, S. (1954), " Urea synthesis." *Advanc. Enzymol.,* **15,** 319.

Welch, A. D. (1945), " Chemical Constitution and Biological Reaction." *Physiol. Rev.,* **25,** 617.

Chapter 22 Excretion

The higher animal returns matter to the environment through four channels:
the lungs, the skin, the intestine and the kidneys. Gaseous waste-products,
notably carbon dioxide and water vapour, escape by the lungs; water and
about 1 per cent. of solutes are lost in the perspiration; insoluble salts, food
residues, mucin, and lipids are excreted by the intestine; and soluble salts
and organic end-products are excreted in the urine.

From the clinical aspect, urine is most significant, since (with the exception
of some ammonia and hippuric acid) every constituent has been derived from
the blood, and has at one time formed part of the internal environment of the
organism.

Average Composition of Normal Human Urine
Solutes excreted in 24 Hours

Total volume . . .	1,250 ml.	pH $6 \cdot 1 \pm 1 \cdot 4$.
Total solids . . .	58 gm.	
Total nitrogen . .	17 gm.	Depends chiefly on protein intake.
Urea . . .	28 gm.	
Creatinine . .	$1 \cdot 5$ gm.	Independent of normal diet.
Uric acid .	$0 \cdot 7$ gm.	Partly independent of diet.
Methyl purines .	$0 \cdot 1$ gm.	Dependent on tea and coffee intake.
Hippuric acid . .	$0 \cdot 65$ gm.	Increased by fruit diet.
Amino acids . .	$+$	Increased in wasting diseases.
Ammonia .	$0 \cdot 7$ gm.	Increased in acidoses.
Indoxyl sulphate .	$0 \cdot 01$ gm.	Depends on intestinal putrefaction.
Chloride, as Cl . .	7 gm.	Depends on salt intake.
Phosphate, as H_3PO_4 .	$2 \cdot 6$ gm.	Depends on phosphoproteins of diet.
Sulphate, as H_2SO_4 .	$2 \cdot 0$ gm.	Depends on proteins of diet.
Sodium	5 gm.	
Potassium . . .	$1 \cdot 6$ gm.	Increased by vegetable diet.
Calcium	$0 \cdot 2$ gm.	
Magnesium . . .	$0 \cdot 2$ gm.	Increased by vegetable diet.
Iron	$0 \cdot 3$ mg.	
Sugar . . .	$0 \cdot 7$ gm.	Mostly pentose.
Oxalate . .	$0 \cdot 03$ gm.	Depends on diet and gastric fermentation of sugar.
Citrate . . .	$0 \cdot 5$ gm.	
Lactate . . .	$+$	Increased by muscular activity.
Thiol compounds .	$0 \cdot 3$ gm.	
Pigments . . .	$+$	
Steroids	$+$	
Enzymes . . .	$+$	

The composition of the urine varies during the day, owing to alterations in
metabolic activity, and for comparative purposes the 24-hour output is taken

as being representative. The extent to which individual variation can occur is shown in the following table compiled from data by Powell White (1925), who has studied the correlations of the various solutes.

Composition of Urine from 50 Normal Subjects
(mg. per 100 ml.)

Solute.	Average.	Maximum.	Minimum.
Urea N . . .	682	1,829	298
Urea . . .	1,459	3,914	638
Creatinine N . .	36	90	17
Creatinine . . .	97·2	243	45·9
Uric acid N . .	12·3	30·7	3·7
Uric acid . . .	36·9	92	11
Amino N . . .	9·7	42·5	0·6
Ammonia N . .	57	189	13
Sodium . . .	212	608	46
Potassium . . .	137	245	56
Calcium . . .	19·5	72·5	0·6
Magnesium . .	11·3	23·9	2·7
Chloride . . .	314	579	99
Total sulphate . .	91	326	34
Inorganic sulphate .	83	304	32
Organic sulphate .	5·3	25·6	0·6
Inorganic phosphate .	179	426	77
pH	6·4	8·2	5·8
Total acidity as ml. N/10 acid . .	27·8	76·8	4·0

Urine essentially is a solution of waste-products removed in order to maintain the proper composition of the cellular, or somatic internal environment of the animal, and its composition fluctuates with the diet and activity of the individual. Analysis of a random sample of urine gives little useful information, other than the presence or absence of abnormal constituents. Routine examination requires samples taken from the collected output over a measured period of at least 24 hours, to allow for changes in the secretion rate.

While it is inaccurate to describe any specimen of urine as being quantitatively normal, urinary solutes can be divided qualitatively into: (1) *normal*, such as occur in healthy subjects irrespective of the type of diet; and (2) abnormal, which only occur in conditions of dysfunction or disease. The term " normal urine " is used conveniently to describe a urine that is free from abnormal

347

solutes, and does not contain abnormally high or low concentrations
normal solutes.

(1) **Total Volume in 24 Hours.** Adult, 950 to 1,500 ml. (33 to 60 oz.); chil
400 to 600 ml. Night urine is about one-quarter to one-half the volume of da
urine.

The total volume varies greatly with diet and season of the year, the averag
secretion rate during the day being 1 ml. per minute.

In polyuria, such as diabetes insipidus due to lack of the anti-diuretic hormor
of the pituitary gland, the daily output of urine may be as great as 10 litre
and is balanced by a corresponding thirst. In oliguria, the output may b
only a few ml., or nil in complete suppression (anuria).

(2) **Specific Gravity.** 1·015 to 1·020 at 15° C. (water = 1·000). This is
measure of the concentration of urinary solutes, and is inversely related t
the total volume. After drinking an excess of water, the specific gravity ma
be as low as 1·002; whereas, after 12 hours' abstention from fluids, it ma
rise to 1·030–1·035.

In finding specific gravity, the urine should be at room temperature (15° C.
and the hydrometer floating freely in the liquid. Froth on the surface can b
removed by a drop of alcohol.

(3) **Appearance.** Fresh urine is usually transparent, but may be opaque afte
meals owing to the " alkaline tide " causing a precipitation of calcium an
magnesium phosphate (p. 363). As urine cools, a cloudy suspension of mucc
protein from the urinary tract may appear in the body of the fluid.

(4) **Colour.** The normal colour of urine is due chiefly to two pigments:

(a) *Urochrome*, a yellow pigment complex invariably present in urine (p. 153
It has no characteristic spectrum, and its excretion has not been correlate
with any particular metabolic condition. Urochrome can be obtained in a
very impure form by extracting acidified urine with amyl or butyl alcohol.

(b) *Urobilins*, brown pigments excreted as colourless precursors, urobilinogen
which gradually oxidise on exposure to light and air. Urines rich in uro
bilinogens darken on standing, because of this spontaneous oxidation.

Urobilinogen is derived from bilirubin that has undergone reduction in th
intestine, and its excretion is an index of the degree of intestinal stasis an
putrefaction. It disappears from the urine in obstructive jaundice, bein
replaced by bilirubin excreted directly from the plasma, but it reappears i
an increased amount during the recovery stage because of liver dysfunction
Urines containing urobilinogen give a red colour on addition of excess of a
acid solution of Ehrlich's aldehyde reagent (p. 447), without application o
heat. Urobilin does not give this reaction, but may be detected by its charac
teristic spectrum (p. 153), and by the green fluorescence developed on additio
of excess of a 2 per cent. solution of zinc acetate in alcohol. Minor pigment
present in urine are *uroerythrin*, which imparts a red colour to uric aci
deposits, and *uroporphyrins*, one of which is greatly increased in the congenita
condition of porphyria.

(5) **H-ion Concentration.** Urine is usually slightly acid in reaction, the averag

value being pH 6·1, but it may vary from pH 4·8 to pH 7·5 during the 24 hours. After rising in the morning, and about half an hour after each meal, the reaction of urine tends to shift towards alkalinity, the so-called " alkaline tide ". This promotes the precipitation of calcium and magnesium phosphates.

The H-ion concentration of urine may be determined electrometrically or colorimetrically by means of selected indicators covering the range pH 4 to pH 8.

(6) **Total or Titration Acidity.** This is found by titrating 10 ml. of urine with N/10 NaOH, using 5 drops of 0·1 per cent. phenol-red or phenolphthalein as indicator. The result is expressed as the quantity of N/10 NaOH required to neutralise (1) 100 ml. urine, or (2) the total volume of urine excreted in 24 hours.

Titration is a measure of the available acidity of urine; this depends chiefly on the concentration of acid phosphate ions, and also on the uric and hippuric acid present. Usually 200 to 500 ml. N/10 NaOH are required to neutralise the acidity of an entire 24-hour sample, using phenol red (end-point, pH 7 to 7·5); and 300 to 800 ml. N/10 NaOH, using phenolphathalein (end-point, pH 8·5 to 9).

To determine the end-point, compare the urine being titrated with an untitrated specimen in a similar test tube. As soon as a colour difference can be detected the titration is complete. Shortly before the end-point is reached, a precipitate of calcium and magnesium phosphate may appear in the solution, caused by the conversion of soluble acid phosphate into insoluble phosphate by action of the alkali.

INORGANIC SOLUTES

Ammonia. The average percentage of ammonia is 0·05, depending on the N in the diet. It is present as NH_4^+, unless the urine has undergone fermentation, when free ammonia may be detected. Urinary ammonia comes from glutamine deamination in the kidney tissue (Van Slyke *et al.*, 1943), in response to acidosis, being part of the neutrality-maintaining mechanism of the organism. *Tests for Ammonia.* (1) *Nessler's Reaction.* To 5 ml. of water add a few drops of Nessler's reagent. There is no colour change if the water is free from ammonia. Add a drop of urine. An intense yellow colour develops owing to the ammonia present in the urine. (2) Heat 5 ml. of urine with a little solid sodium carbonate. Ammonia is set free, and can be detected by the smell and by the bluing of red litmus paper held above the tube. *Estimation of Ammonia.* Neutralise 10 ml. of urine to phenolphthalein, using N/10 NaOH, as in the estimation of the total acidity of urine. Neutralise 2 to 3 ml. of commercial formalin solution (30 to 40 per cent. formaldehyde) in the same manner. Mix the two neutral solutions. The mixture becomes acid, and the pink colour of the indicator is discharged. This is because the H-ions

349

previously combined with the ammonia have been liberated by the formalde
hyde. Titrate this increase in acidity as before with N/10 NaOH. Each ml
of alkali required corresponds to 1·7 mg. of NH$_3$ in the original urine. Th
ammonia value obtained by the formaldehyde method is usually 10 to 25 pe
cent. too high owing to the fact that the —NH$_2$ groups of other urinar
solutes also interact. The discrepancy is usually neglected in clinical estima
tions.

Urinary ammonia may be estimated accurately by (a) aspiration and (b) by
colorimetry, using Nessler's reagent. In 24 hours, the normal adult excrete
the equivalent of 300 to 500 ml. of N/10 NH$_4$+, or 0·5 to 0·9 gm. This represent
about one-tenth of the total ammonium formation capacity of the kidney
when under severe stress from acidosis. Ammonium output is raised in al
conditions of excess acid-formation or retention and by diets rich in protein

Chloride. Next to urea, chloride is the chief solute of urine. Expressed a
NaCl, the average daily excretion is 10 to 15 gm., and the urinary concen
tration is about 0·7 to 1·0 per cent.

Silver Test for Chloride. Add 1 ml. of 1 per cent. AgNO$_3$ to 5 ml. or urine.
whitish precipitate forms, made up of silver chloride, carbonate, and phos
phate. Acidify with about 10 drops of concentrated HNO$_3$. Carbonate an
phosphate dissolve, leaving a white residue of AgCl.

Estimation of Chloride by the Tartrazol Method. Transfer by means of
pipette 10 ml. of N/10 AgNO$_3$ to a 100 ml. measuring cylinder. Acidify wit
5 drops of concentrated HNO$_3$. Add 2 to 4 drops of 0·5 per cent. tartrazin
(tartrazol, or " tartar yellow "). Titrate with the urine, or other chlorid
solution, from a burette, by additions of 0·2 ml. at a time. Shake the yellov
mixture vigorously after each addition of chloride. The first effect of th
chloride is to form a white precipitate of silver chloride, this rapidly adsorb
the indicator, and settles down as a buff-coloured deposit. The surroundin
liquid becomes colourless owing to removal of the tartrazol.

The end-point is reached when all the silver has been precipitated as chloride
At this stage, addition of a slight excess of chloride causes a sudden releas
of the adsorbed indicator. The colourless solution turns bright yellow, an
the silver precipitate changes from buff to pure white. The estimation shoul
be done in duplicate as the end-point is very sharp, and may be overshot th
first time.

Calculation. Since 10 ml. N/10 AgNO$_3$ = 58 mg. NaCl, $x = \dfrac{5·8}{n}$,

where n = number of ml. of chloride solution added,
and x = *percentage* of chloride, expressed as gm. NaCl per 100 ml.
The usual value for n is 5 to 9, corresponding to an NaCl content of 1·16 t
0·63 per cent.
If the chloride content of the urine is less than 0·1 per cent., use 1 ml.
N/10 AgNO$_3$ in a test tube, and add 1 drop of indicator.

350

Proteins in pathological urine interfere with the end-point by inhibiting the aggregation of the AgCl, but do not affect the colour change.

Phosphate. (a) *General Test.* Acidify 5 ml. of urine with about 5 drops of concentrated nitric acid. Add 2 ml. of 2 per cent. ammonium molybdate $((NH_4)_2MoO_4)$, and boil gently. A bright yellow precipitate of phosphomolybdic acid denotes phosphate. Cool, and make just alkaline with NaOH. A deep blue colour forms, owing to reduction of the phosphomolybdate by the uric acid of the urine.

(b) " *Earthy Phosphates.*" Make 5 ml. of urine alkaline with about 10 drops of ammonium hydroxide. A cloudy precipitate of calcium and magnesium phosphates (" earthy phosphates ") forms. Heat the mixture. The precipitate flocculates. Acidify with 20 per cent. acetic acid. The precipitate dissolves. The precipitation of these phosphates when urine is boiled is a common fallacy in the heat-coagulation test for proteins in urine. They can be distinguished from proteins by their solubility in acids. Earthy phosphates tend to precipitate whenever the H-ion value of urine falls below pH 6, and thus they appear during the " alkaline tide " after meals.

(c) *Iron Test.* Add a few drops of 1 per cent. $FeCl_3$ to 5 ml. of urine. A precipitate of ferric phosphate forms. It is insoluble in dilute acetic acid, which distinguishes it from ferric carbonate, but dissolves on addition of a few drops of concentrated HCl.

Estimation of Phosphate. Urinary phosphate may be rapidly and roughly estimated by titration with uranium acetate. Accurate colorimetric methods, suitable for blood filtrates as well as urine, depend on the formation of phosphomolybdate, and its subsequent reduction to " molybdenum blue " by hydroquinone or other appropriate reagent.

The daily phosphate output, expressed as the acid, H_3PO_4, is about 2·6 gm. It is largely derived from the phosphoproteins of the diet.

Sulphate. (a) *Inorganic.* Add a few drops of 2 per cent. $BaCl_2$ to 5 ml. of urine. A white precipitate of $BaSO_4$ forms. This does not dissolve on addition of strong nitric acid, thus being distinguished from $BaCO_3$ and $Ba_3(PO_4)_2$, which are also precipitated on addition of $BaCl_2$.

(b) *Organic.* Add an excess (2 to 3 ml.) of $BaCl_2$ to 5 ml. of urine. Filter off the precipitated sulphate, carbonate, and phosphate, repeating the filtration, if necessary, to obtain a clear filtrate. Acidify the filtrate with a few drops of nitric acid, and boil for a few minutes. Gradually a second precipitate of barium sulphate forms, owing to the hydrolysis of various organic sulphates in the urine. These are compounds of indoxyl and other phenols, and are sometimes termed " ethereal sulphates ".

The total daily sulphate output, expressed as H_2SO_4, is about 2 gm., and is derived from the sulphur-containing amino acids, cystine and methionine, of the protein dietary. About 80 per cent. of total sulphate is SO_4^{2-}, and 20 per cent. is organic, representing the detoxication of phenols produced in the digestive tract.

351

Urinary sulphur also appears in a third form, sometimes termed " neutral sulphur ". This includes thiol compounds, such as $CH_3.SH$, and thiocyanate which do not interact with the barium reagent until they are oxidised t sulphate.

Calcium. Acidify 5 ml. of urine with a few drops of glacial acetic acid, an add about 1 ml. of 5 per cent. potassium oxalate. A white, micro-crystallin precipitate of calcium oxalate gradually appears. When it has subsided examine the sediment microscopically for the characteristic envelope-shape crystals of the salt.

Magnesium. Add 3 to 5 drops of 0·1 per cent. titan yellow to 5 ml. of water Make alkaline with 5 drops of 20 per cent. NaOH. In the absence of Mg^{2+} the mixture turns orange-brown. Repeat the test with 5 ml. of urine. Th orange colour changes to red, and a red precipitate of the Mg-indicator com plex separates.

ORGANIC SOLUTES

Urea, $H_2N.C(NH).OH$, the chief nitrogenous constituent of mammalia urine, is derived from the protein of the diet in the proportions of abou 30 gm. of urea per 100 gm. of protein. The daily output is 25 to 32 gm., an the urinary concentration is usually in the region of 2 per cent.

TESTS: (1) *Zymolysis by Urease.* To 5 ml. urine add a little urease preparatio (soy bean powder or extract) and 5 drops of phenol red or " universal indicator. If the mixture is not acid to the indicator (*i.e.*, yellow to phenc red at the start), carefully acidify with a weak acid (0·2 per cent. acetic Incubate at 40 to 50° C. or keep at room temperature. The presence of urea i shown by the mixture gradually becoming alkaline owing to liberated NH_3 (2) *Decomposition by Hypobromite.* To 5 ml. urine add about 1 ml. fresl HBrO reagent. The urea is decomposed with liberation of free N_2, and th mixture effervesces vigorously. Ammonium salts, amino acids, and othe compounds containing the *amino group* $-NH_2$ are decomposed in the sam way.

(3) *Diacetyl Test.* Apply this test to 2 to 3 drops of urine mixed with 2 t 3 ml. concentrated HCl (p. 343).

Estimation of Urea. *Decomposition by Urease.* This is employed in the standar methods for the accurate estimation of urea in blood, urine and other bio logical liquids. The urea is converted into ammonium carbonate, which i estimated directly by Nessler's reagent, or aspirated into standard aci (Marshall and Van Slyke, 1915), or allowed to diffuse into standard aci (Conway, 1957).

Amino Acids. Microbiological assay shows that the α-amino acids common t the dietary proteins are represented in the 15 $\pm$ 5 mg. of total amino acid I excreted by the human adult in 24 hours. They can be separated and identified chromatographically.

Uric acid, $C_5H_4N_4O_3$, the least soluble organic constituent of urine. Average value, 0·04 per cent., or 0·6 to 0·9 gm. in 24 hours. It is an end-product of nucleoprotein metabolism.

Phosphotungstate Test. Saturate 5 ml. urine with sodium carbonate, or add 10 drops of urine to 10 ml. saturated sodium carbonate solution. Then add about 1 ml. of Folin's uric acid reagent; an intense blue colour develops, approximately proportional to the amount of uric acid present.

In this form, the test is not selective, as other urinary solutes, such as thiols and vitamin C, also reduce the reagent.

Chloroimide Test. Add about 10 drops of urine to 5 ml. of water so as to obtain a nearly colourless solution. Add 2 drops of the reagent (0·4 per cent. alcoholic 2 : 6-dichloro-quinone-chloroimide). Make the mixture slightly alkaline (pH 8 to 10) by addition of about 0·5 gm. solid sodium acetate or 2 to 5 drops of N/10 NaOH. A bright yellow colour develops depending on the concentration of uric acid present.

The test will detect uric acid in calculi and urinary deposits, and in saliva, and can be adapted for colorimetric estimation. None of the other common purine derivatives react, though colours (red to blue) are given by free phenols, and some amino acids, but these do not occur in sufficient quantities in urine to interfere with the test.

Creatinine, $C_4H_7N_3O$, the anhydride of creatine. A constant and characteristic constituent of mammalian urine. The adult daily output is about 1·2 gm., and is independent of the diet.

TESTS: (1) *Picric Acid.* Add 5 drops of saturated picric acid solution to 5 ml. urine. Make alkaline with a few drops of 20 per cent. NaOH. A deep orange colour develops proportional to the amount of creatinine present.

(2) 3,5-*Dinitrobenzoic acid,* similarly applied, gives a purple colour with creatinine in alkaline solution. The reagent is more selective than picric acid.

(3) *Nitroprusside.* Add 5 drops of fresh 5 per cent. sodium nitroprusside solution to 5 ml. urine. Make alkaline with a few drops of 20 per cent. NaOH. A deep ruby colour develops if creatinine be present. Acidify with 20 per cent. acetic acid; the colour is discharged.

Note. Acetoacetic acid and acetone, the pathological solutes found in ketosis, give a similar reaction with alkaline nitroprusside, but the colour is not discharged on acidification with acetic acid.

Hippuric acid, or benzoyl glycine, $C_6H_5.CO.NH.CH_2.COOH$, is synthesised in the kidney and in the liver from benzoic acid and glycine. The adult daily output is about 0·7 gm., being derived mostly from benzoic precursors in the vegetable diet.

Urine is concentrated to one-quarter of its volume, filtered, acidified wit H_2SO_4 and treated with $(NH_4)_2SO_4$ so as to make a 3 per cent. solution. O standing for 24 hours, hippuric acid crystallises out in four-sided prism which may be purified by recrystallisation from hot water. A good yield obtained from the urine of herbivora, such as the horse or the cow.

Phenols. Aromatic hydroxy compounds mostly derived from tyrosine an tryptophan putrefaction occur in the urine in normal health. The adu value on a mixed diet ranges from 20 to 60 mg. *per diem*, but is great increased in intestinal stasis and excessive protein dietaries. *Para*-cresc 1-methyl-4-hydroxybenzene is the commonest urinary phenol.

Urinary phenols are excreted as esters of sulphuric and glycuronic acids, i which form they are non-toxic.

$$R.OH + HO.SO_2.OH \rightarrow R.O.SO_2.OH$$

Phenol.   Phenol sulphate.

General Test for Phenols. To 5 ml. of urine add Millon's tyrosine reage drop by drop as long as a white precipitate forms. The precipitate settles ou and slowly turns red owing to the interaction between the adsorbed pheno and the reagent.

Urinary Chromogens. Tryptophan in the alimentary tract is degraded b bacteria with production of indolyl-3-acetic acid and indole, some of whic enters the blood-stream. Within the body, indole is oxidised to indox (3-hydroxyindole), and is excreted in the urine in the detoxicated form of sulphate ester or a glycuronic ether. Strong acids liberate indoxyl from thes conjugates, and it can be detected by conversion to indigo blue (indigotin) indigo red (indirubin), both of which can be extracted by chloroform or am alcohol.

Indigo Test. Mix 5 ml. of urine, 5 ml. of concentrated HCl, and about 5 droj of 1 per cent. $FeCl_3$. Let the tube stand for 10 to 15 minutes. Indoxyl set fre by the acid is oxidised to indigo blue, and the urine acquires a greenish colou Extract with 2 ml. of chloroform, by transferring several times from one tub to another, so as to avoid emulsification. The chloroform dissolves the pig ment, and separates as a blue layer below.

Indirubin Test. Repeat the test, using 1 per cent. alcoholic isatin instead the $FeCl_3$. Warm gently for a few seconds. The liberated indoxyl combine with the isatin to form indigo red, which can be extracted by chloroform.

Urorosein, a red pigment, is formed when indolyl-3-acetic acid is oxidised i acid solution. It differs from indigo blue and indirubin in being insoluble i chloroform.

Urorosein usually accompanies indigo blue in the indigo test, and can b detected by extracting with amyl alcohol, after the indigo blue has bee

HO
SO₂
CO
CH
NH

Indoxyl sulphate.

⟶

CO   NH
C=C
NH   CO

Indigo blue.

removed by chloroform. The urine of the horse and the cow is relatively rich in urorosein chromogens.

The intensity of the indoxyl and urorosein reactions is an index of the activity of the intestinal micro-flora, as is shown in the indicanuria that accompanies intestinal obstruction, achlorhydria, typhoid fever, and other conditions associated with increased putrefactive fermentations in the intestine.

PATHOLOGICAL CONSTITUENTS OF URINE

While a discussion of the various pathological constituents of urine and their significance is outside the scope of this book, the occurrence and identification of several of them presents features of biochemical interest, and they will be described briefly.

Pathological constituents may be divided as follows:

(a) Tissue components and metabolites that normally do not appear in the urine.

Examples are serum albumin and serum globulin, hæmoglobin, bile pigments, bile salts, blood sugar.

(b) Abnormal or exceptional metabolites that escape by the urine. Examples are β-hydroxy-butyric acid, acetoacetic acid, acetone, homogentisic acid, Bence-Jones' protein, pentoses, lactose, methæmoglobin, uroporphyrin.

(1) **Proteinuria.** Normal urine contains some mucoprotein, probably derived from the urinary tract. Under abnormal renal conditions the serum proteins may appear, giving rise to **albuminuria.** In disease of the kidney and other tissues, protein hydrolytic products may escape and cause **proteosuria.** While in multiple osteo-myelomata, skeletal material may be excreted as " Bence-Jones' protein ".

Usually, however, the term proteinuria denotes albuminuria, the appearance of a heat-coagulable protein in the urine.

TESTS: (1) *Heat Coagulation.* Transfer about 5 ml. of urine to a test tube, and carefully boil the upper layer. If the urine contains albumin a white coagulum may appear in the heated part of the tube. This must not be confused with the white, cloudy precipitate of calcium and magnesium phosphates ("earthy phosphates ") that forms when most specimens of normal urine are boiled. To distinguish, acidify the urine with a few drops of dilute acetic acid. The phosphate precipitate dissolves completely, the protein coagulum remains.

Urine that has become strongly alkaline owing to ammoniacal fermentation must be acidified slightly with acetic acid before the presence of protein can be detected by the heat-coagulation test.

Heat coagulation requires slight acidity and an electrolyte. Normal urine may provide the latter by its 1 per cent. content of NaCl, but urine from subjects of chloride retention may be so deficient in NaCl that any protein present will not coagulate on heating. To avoid this serious fallacy the modified form of the heat coagulation test has been devised, and should be used in all routine urine analysis.

(2) *Modified Test.* To 10 ml. urine add 1 ml. of the protein reagent (12 per cent. sodium acetate in 5 per cent. acetic acid), and boil for thirty seconds. If the urine remains clear, either it contains no coagulable protein or less than 5 mg. per 100 ml.

Bence-Jones' Protein occurs in the urine in conditions of multiple myeloma of bone marrow, in myeloid and lymphatic leucæmia, and, occasionally, after severe fractures. The protein has been obtained from bone marrow by Meyler (1936), who suggests that it is in some way associated with the growth and activities of the leucocytes.

This form of proteinuria was recognised by Bence-Jones by the fact that on heating the urine the protein began to flocculate at the relatively low temperature of 40° and re-dissolved on heating to 100°. On cooling, the precipitate reappears, and persists.

(3) *Nitric Acid Precipitation* (Heller's Test). Place 2 to 3 ml. of concentrated nitric acid in a test tube and carefully add about 5 ml. of urine by means of a pipette so as to form a layer above the denser acid. An opaque white ring or cloud at the junction of the liquids denotes albumin.

(4) *Salicyl Sulphonic Acid Flocculation.* To 3 ml. of urine add about 6 drops of 20 per cent. salicyl sulphonic acid. If the urine contains more than 0·02 per cent. of albumin a white cloud forms almost at once and becomes more dense. Large quantities of protein give an opaque white precipitate.

The modified heat coagulation test and the salicyl sulphonic acid test are each about four times as sensitive as the nitric acid test.

Positive results with these tests do not differentiate between albumin and globulin in the urine. This can be done by fractional precipitation by neutral salts, but the distinction has not yet been shown to have clinical significance. Globulin sometimes accompanies albumin in albuminuria, though the ratio may vary.

Note. All three protein tests should be applied in the routine examination of clinical specimens. To detect a faint precipitate in any one of the tests, hold the tube against a dark background, and compare the contents with some of the untreated specimens.

(2) **Hæmaturia.** Blood may appear in the urine in the form of corpuscles, free hæmoglobin (hæmoglobinuria), and abnormal derivatives (methæmoglobin, and uroporphyrin). In hæmaturia the urine often has a smoky, reddish colour that is very characteristic. Microscopic examination of the sediment may show the presence of blood corpuscles if they have escaped hæmolysis.

TESTS: (1) *Benzidine Test.* Add about 10 drops of a fresh, strong solution of benzidine in glacial acetic acid to 1 ml. of 3 per cent. (10 vol. O_2 per one vol.) hydrogen peroxide. Add 1 ml. of urine, drop by drop. If blood be present the mixture turns blue.

Excess of urine must be avoided, as the sulphate present may precipitate the benzidine before the oxidation pigment has had time to form.

(2) *Guaiacum Test.* Dissolve a small fragment of guaiacum resin in about 3 ml. of alcohol, with the aid of heat. Cool. Add 10 drops of 3 per cent. hydrogen peroxide and 1 ml. of urine. Mix well. If blood be present the mixture turns blue.

(3) *Pyramidon Test.* Mix about 2 ml. of urine with an equal volume of 5 per cent. pyramidon (amidopyrine) in alcohol. Acidify with 2 drops of glacial acetic acid. Add 2 to 4 drops of 3 per cent. hydrogen peroxide. If blood be present, a lilac colour develops.

Notes. These oxidation tests for blood depend on the presence of the heat-stable catalyst hæmatin, which they will reveal in dilutions as low as 1 : 10,000 to 1 : 50,000 in urine, and less than 1 : 200,000 in water.

A heat-labile catalyst, or enzyme, occurs in leucocytes, fresh milk and un-boiled plant extracts, and will give a positive reaction with the reagents used in testing for blood. To distinguish, boil a sample of the urine, and repeat the test after cooling. If the response is still positive, it cannot be attributed to an enzyme.

The presence of leucocytes or pus in urine (pyuria) is most easily confirmed by microscopical examination of the sediment.

Urine, after the administration of iodides, usually gives a positive reaction with the blood reagents, and this may readily be mistaken for hæmoglobin as both reactants survive boiling previous to testing.

To distinguish, apply the spectroscope, and examine for absorption bands of blood pigment; and also centrifuge the specimen, and examine microscopically for unhæmolysed red corpuscles.

(4) *Spectroscopic Test.* This may require special treatment of the urine, as the concentration of pigment is often insufficient to show the characteristic absorption spectra (p. 163).

The urine is acidified with acetic acid and extracted with an equal volume of ether. This dissolves out the hæmatin, which may be extracted with dilute ammonium hydroxide, and identified spectroscopically.

357

Hæmaturia is a serious condition, and the analysis for blood in the urine should be confirmed by more than one test.

(3) **Biliuria.** Bile constituents may appear in the urine in obstructive jaundice (overflow biliuria), toxic jaundice, and various hæmolytic disorders leading to the decomposition of hæmoglobin.

In simple obstructive jaundice bilirubin appears, accompanied later by the bile salts. In the other forms of biliuria, pigments are present unaccompanied by bile salts.

Bile Pigments

Urine containing bile pigment (bilirubin) has a characteristic golden-brown colour and shows a transient yellow froth on being shaken.

(1) *Iodine Test.* To 5 ml. of urine carefully add about 10 drops of 1 per cent. iodine in alcohol (tincture of iodine) so as to form a layer on the surface. A green ring gradually develops between the layers if the urine contains bilirubin. The test may also be carried out by putting a drop of iodine solution on a drop of urine spread on a filter paper.

(2) *Turpentine Test.* Acidify 5 ml. of urine with about 10 drops of glacial acetic acid. Add 2 ml. of turpentine, shake so as to form an emulsion, and warm gently. Do not boil, or the mixture may spurt.

If bile pigment be present, the white turpentine emulsion will turn green. Eventually a layer of turpentine separates out on top; this is colourless in simple obstructive jaundice, but is greenish in the toxic and hæmolytic forms of biliuria.

The reason appears to be that in obstructive jaundice the overflow pigment appears in the urine in an esterified form, insoluble in warm turpentine. In toxic jaundice this esterification has not taken place, and the pigment, free bilirubin, is turpentine-soluble.

Bile Salts

(3) *Sulphur Sedimentation* (Hay's Test). Sprinkle the surface of 10 ml. of urine with some finely powdered sulphur. In normal urine the particles remain on the surface supported by the tension at the urine-air interface. If, however, the urine contains bile salts, the interfacial tension is reduced, and the sulphur particles will sink through the liquid. A control test should be done at the same time, using 10 ml. of water.

This test illustrates an important property of bile salts; reduction of surface tension. It is not as useful clinically as the tests for bile pigment.

(4) **Glycosuria.** Normal urine contains small quantities of reducing sugars, the concentration being between 0·01 and 0·1 per cent., which is insufficient to affect the ordinary Benedict and Fehling tests. These sugars consist largely of pentoses and disaccharides, with a trace of glucose.

(1) *Benedict's Qualitative Test.* Add 0·5 ml. of urine (8 drops, not more) to 5 ml. of Benedict's qualitative reagent. Mix, and heat over a small flame for 1 to 2 minutes, or, much better, immerse the tube in boiling water for 2 to 3 minutes (this avoids spurting of the mixture). Allow to cool for a few minutes, and observe the appearance.

A *positive result* is shown by a greenish turbidity with a yellow or red sediment. A slight yellow precipitate indicates 0·1 to 0·25 per cent. of sugar; a dense orange-red precipitate and a clear supernatant liquid indicates over 1·5 per cent. of sugar.

A *negative result* is shown by the solution remaining a clear blue, with possibly a grey precipitate of urate and phosphate.

If excess of urine be added or if boiling be prolonged, a positive result may be obtained with many specimens of normal urine owing to the traces of sugars they contain. For this reason, the technique of the test must be followed carefully.

A positive result with Benedict's reagent indicates the presence of one or more of the following pathological urinary constituents: glucose, lactose, pentose, fructose, and glycuronic acid.

Glucose is by far the commonest reducing sugar found in urine; it may be identified by the osazone test, and by yeast fermentation, and verified by the observation of an accompanying hyperglycæmia.

Enzyme Test for Glucose. Glucose can be detected specifically in a few drops of urine by means of papers impregnated with the enzymes glucose dehydrogenase and peroxidase, and an indicator that shows the peroxide set free by the reaction (p. 233).

Lactose is a normal constituent of many urines during the lactation period, and has no pathological significance. It can be distinguished from glucose by its non-fermentability by yeast, and by the methylamine test (p. 93). Lactosazone in crystalline form can only be obtained with difficulty from urine containing lactose.

L-xyloketose, the commonest urinary pentose, may be identified by the fact that it can reduce Benedict's reagent at temperatures much below boiling.

Reduction test for pentose and fructose (Lasker and Enklewitz, 1933): mix 1 ml. of urine and 5 ml. of Benedict's qualitative reagent, and incubate at 55° C., for ten minutes. The appearance of a yellow precipitate indicates that the urine contains L-xyloketose or fructose. Fructosuria, which is very rare, may simulate glycosuria in that the urine gives a positive fermentation test and yields glucosazone.

Pentose in urine can also be detected by the aniline test (p. 90).

(2) *Fehling's Test.* Boil equal volumes (3 to 5 ml.) of Fehling's mixed reagent and urine in separate tubes. If spontaneous reduction occur in the reagent, it must be discarded. When boiling, add the reagent in small quantities to

the urine, and look for the colour change to orange that denotes reduction The commoner fallacies of the test are described on p. 451.

(3) *Yeast Fermentation Test*. The method is described on p. 94. Lactose, pen toses and glycuronic acid are the only non-fermentable copper-reducing substances likely to occur in urine, and the fermentation test should be used to check the tests of Benedict and Fehling.

(4) *Osazone Test*. The phenylhydrazine reagent (p. 450) will readily detect glucose in urine down to concentrations of about 0·5 per cent., but is not so satisfactory in the detection of lactose, owing to the interfering effect of other urinary solutes.

Glycuronic acid, $HOOC.(CHOH)_4.CHO$, occurs in urine as a detoxication compound formed after the administration of chloral, camphor, naphthol menthol, phenol, morphine, turpentine, antipyrin, aspirin, and other drugs with which it is conjugated.

The formation of glycuronates is regarded as a test of hepatic efficiency, and may be invoked by administration of 5 grains of aspirin by the mouth. Glycuronic acid reduces Benedict's and Fehling's reagents and is not fermentable by yeast.

Naphthoresorcinol Test (Tollens). Add 5 ml. concentrated HCl and 10 drops of 1 per cent. alcoholic naphthoresorcinol to 5 ml. of urine. Mix, and boil for 1 minute, shaking at intervals. A red colour develops. Let the tube stand for 5 minutes, cool under the tap, and extract with 5 to 10 ml. of ether. If glycuronic acid be present the pigment will dissolve in the ether as a purple solution showing two absorption bands, one on the D-line, and one to the right of it.

Many saccharides give red-violet pigments with the naphthoresorcinol reagent, but these are insoluble in ether (p. 90).

Steroids. Normal urine contains varying amounts of the steroid hormones, usually in the form of soluble glycuronic acid derivatives. The output is greatly increased during pregnancy.

The 17-ketosteroid dehydro-*iso*-androsterone, and related androgens, occur in the urine in conditions of excessive adrenal cortex activity, and are of value in diagnosis. They give a purple colour with *m*-dinitrobenzene in strongly alkaline solution (Zimmermann's Test, 1935).

FATTY ACID METABOLITES IN URINE

(5) **Ketonuria.** This term denotes the presence of one or all of the compounds, β-hydroxy-butyric acid, acetoacetic acid, and acetone. All are derived ultimately from fat metabolism, and appear in the urine when the carbohydrate available is insufficient to effect the complete combustion of the fatty acids (p. 271).

There is no simple direct test for β-hydroxy-butyric acid,

$$CH_3.CH(OH).CH_2.COOH.$$

(1) *Iron Test for Acetoacetic Acid.* Add dilute (1 per cent.) ferric chloride drop by drop to 5 ml. of urine until the buff-coloured precipitate of ferric phosphate, which is given by all specimens of urine, ceases to form. Further addition of the ferric chloride now produces a brown-purple colour if the urine contains more than 0·07 per cent. acetoacetic acid. Urines after administration of salicylates, aspirin, and related drugs, give a violet colour on addition of ferric chloride, which may be mistaken for an acetoacetic acid reaction. To distinguish, boil a sample for five minutes, and repeat the test. Acetoacetic acid is converted into acetone by boiling and no longer gives a colour with ferric chloride; salicylates are unaffected, and still react.

(2) *Sodium Nitroprusside Test for Acetoacetic Acid and Acetone* (Rothera). Fill up about 1 in. of a test tube with solid ammonium sulphate. Add 5 ml. of urine, and shake so as to saturate the mixture. Add 2 to 4 drops of fresh 5 per cent. sodium nitroprusside, and make alkaline with about 10 drops of conc. ammonium hydroxide. A deep violet colour develops in a few seconds if the urine contains more than 0·2 per cent. acetoacetic acid, while 0·005 per cent. will give a pink colour in about 10 minutes.

A similar colour is given by acetone, but the reaction is not so delicate, although it will reveal 0·01 per cent. in urine.

In dilute urines the colour appears first as a ring at the junction of the liquid and the crystals. The reaction should not be regarded as absolutely negative until the mixture has remained colourless for 30 minutes.

Normal urines rich in organic sulphides (thiols) give an immediate but transient red colour with the reagent. This must not be mistaken for a positive ketone reaction, which is stable for several hours, and violet in tint.

In the earlier form of the test, the ammonium sulphate was not used, but its presence greatly increases the sensitivity of the reaction.

Nitroprusside Reactions in Urine

Reagent.	Creatinine.	Acetone.	Acetoacetic Acid.
Na nitroprusside + NH_4OH Na nitroprusside + NaOH .	no change red (soon fades) ↓	purple red (stable) ↓	purple red (stable) ↓
Acidified with acetic acid .	decolourised	purple	purple
Na nitroprusside + NH_4OH + solid $(NH_4)_2SO_4$ . .	no change	violet	violet

Pyruvic acid, which may appear in urines when there is vitamin B_1 deficiency develops a sapphire blue with Rothera's test.

(3) *Diffusion Test for Acetone*. Place about 1 ml. of Nessler's reagent in a Conway unit or in a small watch-glass resting in a petri dish. Acidify abou 2 ml. of urine with a drop of glacial acetic acid or hydrochloric acid. Carefully pour the urine into the dish around the watch-glass, taking care not to mix the liquids. Replace the cover on the petri dish. The presence of acetone in the urine is shown by the rapid appearance of a cream-coloured precipitate in the reagent in the watch-glass owing to the diffusion and fixation of the volatile acetone. This reaction is specific for acetone in urine.

(4) *Iodoform Test*. Addition of 1 to 5 ml. of 1 per cent. aqueous iodine and 1 to 2 ml. 20 per cent. NaOH to 10 ml. of a urine containing acetone produces iodoform, CHI_3, which is recognisable by its smell, and its separation as a pale yellow precipitate with a characteristic microscopic appearance (hexagonal plates and stars). Pyruvic and lactic acid, which are minor constituents of normal urine, give a similar reaction, as also does alcohol, so the test is not reliable for detecting traces of acetone.

Ethyl Alcohol. The detection of ethyl alcohol in urine may be important in the diagnosis of intoxications. Distil carefully 50 to 100 ml. of the urine, and apply the iodoform test and the nitro chromic test (p. 95) to 5 ml. samples of the distillate. Alcohol gives a positive reaction with both tests. Acetone, if present, will also come over in the distillate, and give a positive iodoform reaction, but does not give a blue colour with the nitro chromic reagent.

Only about 10 per cent. of ingested alcohol is excreted by the lungs and the kidneys; the rest is oxidised in the liver (p. 276). The alcohol level in the cerebro-spinal fluid and blood plasma is of chief diagnostic significance, though the resulting degree of intoxication depends on individual tolerance. An alcohol content of 225 to 275 mg. per 100 ml. plasma is toxic for nine-tenths of the community, while over 400 mg. is toxic for all.

ABNORMAL METABOLITES DUE TO INBORN DEFECTS

Alcaptonuria, characterised by the excretion of homogentisic acid. The urine darkens owing to oxidative changes, after addition of alkalis or on under-going spontaneous ammoniacal fermentation. It reduces alkaline copper reagents in an atypical way, and also gives a transient blue colour on addition of ferric chloride. The homogentisic acid arises from the phenylalanine and tyrosine of the diet. Related conditions are **Tyrosinosis** (p. 294) and **Phenyl-ketonuria** (p. 294).

Phenylketonuria. An example of a metabolic disorder associated with mental defect is found in the inherited condition of *imbecellitas phenylpyruvica*, in which phenylpyruvic acid is excreted in the urine. The output is increased by administration of phenylalanine but not by tyrosine.

Tyrosinosis. An inability to metabolise all the phenylalanine and tyrosine of the diet, the surplus being excreted as tyrosine or its deamination product, hydroxyphenyl pyruvic acid.

Cystinuria, characterised by the excretion of cystine, which forms a crystalline deposit of hexagonal plates. The fresh urine has an aromatic smell resembling sweetbriar, and gives a black precipitate of lead sulphide on boiling with lead acetate and sodium hydroxide. The usual output is 1 to 2 gm. in 24 hours. It comes from the cystine and methionine of the dietary protein. The defect in cystinuria is not metabolic, but is the inability of the kidney to reabsorb cysteine and cystine effectively from the glomerular filtrate. The diamines, cadaverine and putrescine often accompany cystine in cystinuria.

Pentosuria, characterised by the excretion of L-xyloketose, or other 5-carbon sugars, which on account of their reducing properties may be mistaken for glucose.

Porphyrinuria, characterised by the increased production and excretion of uroporphyrins, which impart a red or brown colour to the urine. Congenital porphyrinuria occurs in the inborn defect, **porphyria;** it is distinct from the porphyrinuria which may be evoked by lead, sulphonamides, and other agents capable of causing liver injury. The accumulation of porphyrins in the blood may render the subject photo-sensitive to strong light.

Albinism, due to lack of tyrosinase and " dopa " oxidase, which form from tyrosine the natural melanin pigments of skin, hair and retina. The condition is unassociated with any abnormal urinary metabolite. Of these inborn errors, albinism is the most common, cystinuria is moderately rare, and the others are very uncommon. The most dangerous are porphyrinuria, with its hyper-sensitisation to light, and cystinuria, which tends to the formation of renal calculi.

URINARY SEDIMENTS

According to the theory of solutions, dissolved salts are largely ionised, and consequently the electrolytes in urine are present as:

I. *Cations*: Na^+, K^+, Ca^{2+}, Mg^{2+}, NH_4^+.

II. *Anions*: Cl^-, HPO_4^{2-}, CO_3^{2-}, SO_4^{2-}, $C_5H_3N_4O_3^-$ (urate), $(COO)_2^{2-}$ (oxalate).

The appearance of a urinary sediment depends on (i) temperature, (ii) reaction, (iii) relative concentration, and (iv) absence of colloidal anti-precipitants. As secreted, all the urinary constituents are in solution at the temperature of the body, but when urine cools the urates and phosphates tend to separate out if the reaction be favourable. Urine is a better solvent for uric acid than water at the same temperature and pH, a property that appears to be associated with the colloids present in small quantities.

(1) **Carbonates** and **Phosphates.** Those of Na, K and NH_4 are freely soluble, and never form urinary precipitates. Those of Ca and Mg are soluble in acid urine (pH < 6·5) but insoluble in neutral or alkaline urine (pH > 7·0), and tend to precipitate when urine cools or becomes alkaline. Such precipitates

are easily dissolved by acetic and other weak acids. Phosphatic calculi are among the commonest of the renal and bladder concretions.

(2) **Urates.** Dibasic alkaline urates, such as $Na_2C_5H_2N_4O_3$, are soluble, and never occur as sediments, but the conditions for their existence demand a higher degree of alkali than that present in urine. Monobasic urates, especially ammonium dihydrogen urate, $NH_4.C_5H_3N_4O_3$, are sparingly soluble in cold urine, but dissolve on heating or after addition of alkalis. They often appear, along with free uric acid, as an amorphous reddish sediment when urine cools, and are the most common and least important deposit.

(3) **Uric acid** may accompany urates in very acid urine. Acidify 10 ml. urine with a few drops of strong HCl, and set aside for about 24 hours. The uric acid is precipitated as a few dark crystals, heavily pigmented. Remove by pipette and identify microscopically.

(4) **Oxalates** are soluble, with the important exception of calcium oxalate, which separates from acid or alkaline urine in octahedral crystals, and is a common source of calculi.

(5) **Chlorides** and sulphates are sufficiently soluble never to form urinary deposits or concretions.

Urinary Sediments

Acid Urine.	Neutral or Alkaline Urine.
Free uric acid (" cayenne pepper " deposit). Acid urates of NH_4, Na or K (" brick dust " deposit).	Phosphates and carbonates of Ca and Mg (white, amorphous deposit). Ammonium magnesium phosphate (triple phosphate) in ammoniacal urine. (Large, prismatic crystals.) Colourless.
Calcium oxalate, usually in very small amounts. (" Envelope " crystals.)	Ammonium urate. Calcium oxalate.

DETOXICATION

Detoxication is a protective metabolic process whereby the animal modifies dangerous reactants, as when the toxic base, NH_3, a latent end-product in amino acid degradation, is converted into a harmless, neutral solute, *urea*. The term *detoxication*, however, is generally restricted to the transformation of compounds foreign to the working-plan of the organism, such as phenols and cyclic bases, indole and scatole, liberated in the intestine by bacterial attack on amino acids. Other compounds excreted in detoxified form are drugs containing cyclic residues, such as the sulphonamides, and reagents, such as benzoic acid, given experimentally to reveal or test detoxication mechanisms.

Detoxication takes place chiefly in the liver. The process usually involves the masking of physiologically active polar groups, such as —OH, —CHO,

—COOH and —NH$_2$, attached to benzenoid and other cyclic nuclei resistant to tissue oxidation. The operation is effected by conjugation with glycuronic acid, glycine, glutamine, ornithine, acetic or sulphuric acid, or by methylation; according to the type of substrate and the species of animal concerned.

Glycuronic Acid. D-glucuronic acid, $HOOC.(CH.OH)_4.CHO$, the commonest of the glycuronic acids, appears in urine in conjugated form after ingestion of benzoic acid, camphor, and many other drugs. On alkaline hydrolysis, the glycuronate is released and, being a reducing agent, gives all the ordinary copper-reducing reactions, and may be mistaken for sugar in the urine. Unlike the D-series hexoses, however, it is not fermented by yeast, and thus can be recognised. Two types of glycuronic derivatives can arise in detoxications: (1) *glycosides*, or *ethers*, formed by condensation of a phenolic —OH with the carbon 1 hydroxyl of glucuronic acid; and (2) *esters*, by condensation of —COOH with the carbon 1 hydroxyl.

Glucuronic ethers, such as 1-phenyl glucuronide, are alkali-stable, non-reducing, and hydrolysable by strong acids. Glucuronic esters are hydrolysed by alkali, and the released glucuronic acid may be mistaken for a reducing sugar, since it gives the copper tests. The uronic acid used in detoxication is provided by a carrier, *uridine diphosphate gluconate*, assembled in the liver. Quick has shown that a dog on an exclusive carbohydrate diet can produce 5 gm. of glucuronate in 24 hours, without an increase in nitrogen output. Insulin injection increases the capacity for producing glycuronate; if the hormone is absent, as in diabetes, or if the dietary carbohydrates are insufficient, the organism can utilise glucose collected from protein and other sources.

Glycine. Aminoacetic acid is used freely for the detoxication of cyclic carboxyl groups, with which it combines by means of its —NH$_2$ group, forming a peptide-type of linkage. *Hippuric acid*, or benzoyl glycine, derived from benzoic acid, is the best known of these products, being a normal solute in the urine of man and other higher animals. Conjugation is effected by the reversible action of the enzyme, *hippuricase*, which is found in liver and kidney of most animals, except the dog, in which it is restricted to the kidney. Quick (1938) has used the reaction as a test for hepatic function. When 1·77 gm. of sodium benzoate in 20 ml. of water are slowly injected intravenously, the urine excreted during the following hour contains 0·6 to 0·75 gm. of hippuric acid, if the liver be working efficiently. Low values are found in hepatic cirrhosis, carcinoma and cholelithiasis.

The presence of a substituent group in the *ortho* position, adjacent to the carboxyl in benzoic acid, inhibits conjugation with glycine, a fact that may account for the therapeutic potency of ortho-substitution drugs, such as salicylic acid (2-hydroxybenzoic acid).

Glutamine, reacting through its α-amino group, is used similarly by man and apes, in the detoxication of phenylacetic acid, $C_6H_5.CH_2.COOH$, to *phenylacetyl glutamine*. Dogs and other mammals use glycine, forming thereby *phenylaceturic acid* (phenylacetyl glycine). Birds and snakes are exceptional

365

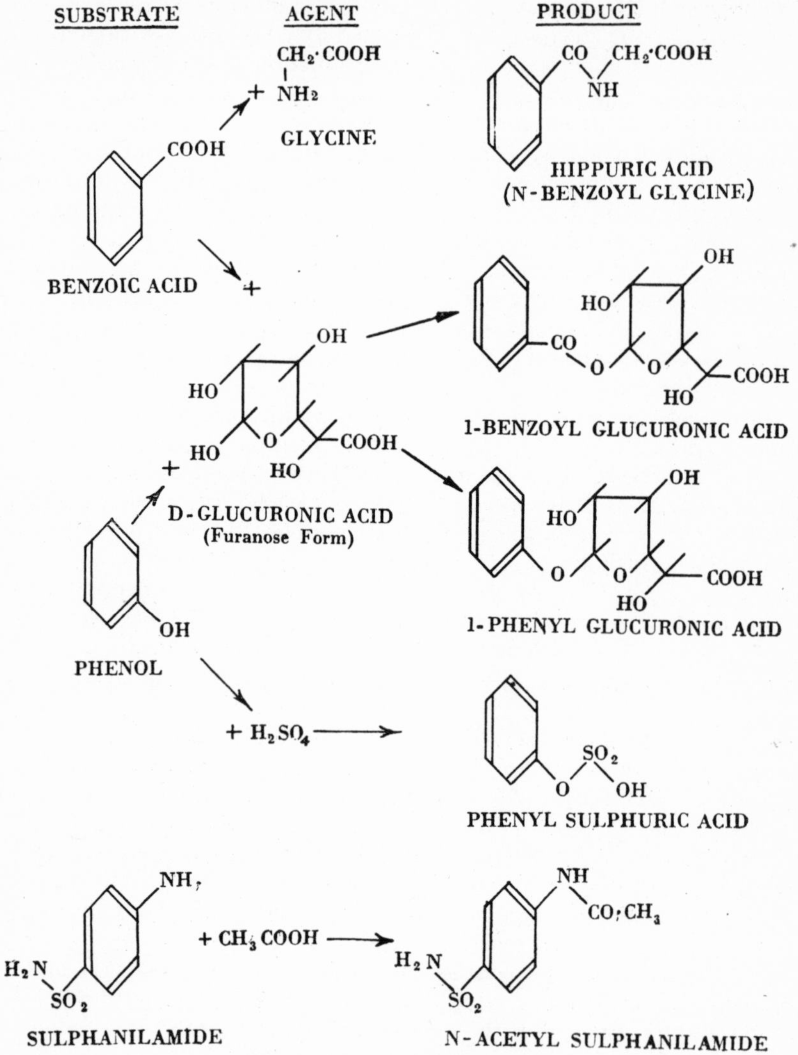

SUBSTRATE　　　　AGENT　　　　　PRODUCT

$CH_2 \cdot COOH$

$+ NH_2$

GLYCINE

$COOH$

BENZOIC ACID　$+$

$CO \quad CH_2 \cdot COOH$

NH

HIPPURIC ACID

(N-BENZOYL GLYCINE)

OH

HO

CO

O

O

$COOH$

HO

1-BENZOYL GLUCURONIC ACID

OH

HO

OH

HO

O

$COOH$

HO

D-GLUCURONIC ACID

(Furanose Form)

$+$

OH

OH

PHENOL

HO

OH

O

O

$COOH$

HO

1-PHENYL GLUCURONIC ACID

$+ H_2SO_4 \longrightarrow$

SO_2

O OH

PHENYL SULPHURIC ACID

NH_2

$+ CH_3 COOH \longrightarrow$

H_2N

SO_2

SULPHANILAMIDE

NH

$CO \cdot CH_3$

H_2N

SO_2

N-ACETYL SULPHANILAMIDE

Detoxication in the Human Body.

in that they employ ornithine instead of glycine for the detoxication of benzoic acid.

Acetic Acid. Acetylation is not of value in detoxication of —OH groups, since acetylated hydroxy compounds, including drugs such as aspirin (acetylsalicylic acid), are readily hydrolysed in the animal. It is, however, the chief way in which cyclic amines are modified, although, as with the sulphonamides, the resulting acetyl-amine may be more toxic than the parent compound, and the process cannot be described accurately as a detoxication. Like glycuronic acid, acetic acid has no detoxicant value when administered, and must arise locally during a coupled metabolism involving sugar or fatty acid.

The urinary excretion of these acetylation products is of interest as providing the first direct proof that acetic acid can be formed in the course of animal metabolism.

Sulphuric Acid. Many phenols, notably indoxyl, are excreted as mono-esters of sulphuric acid, forming the so-called organic sulphates of urine. Inorganic sulphate included in the diet can to some extent provide the acid radicle for the esterification, but the usual sources are the sulphur-containing amino acids.

Methylation. By transfer of CH_3 from methionine and, possibly, choline, both pyridine and its important derived vitamin, nicotinic acid, are excreted as the tetravalent N compounds, methylpyridine hydroxide, and trigonellin, respectively. Since nicotinic acid is necessary for life, its elimination in this inactive form is not, strictly, an example of a protective metabolic operation. Methylation is a common event in plant metabolism.

General References

Cantarow, A., and M. Trumper (1953), " Clinical Biochemistry." 5th Ed. Philadelphia.

Conway, E. J. (1957), " Diffusion Methods in Micro-analysis." 4th Ed. London.

Dukes, C. (1939), " Clinical Pathology of the Urine." London.

Fearon, W. R. (1944), " Estimation of Uric Acid by 2 : 6-dichloro-quinone-chloroimide." *Biochem. J.*, **38**, 399.

Gershenfeld, L. (1943), " Urine and Urinalysis." 2nd Ed., New York.

Harrison, G. A. (1957), " Chemical Methods in Clinical Medicine." 4th Ed. London.

Hawk, P. B., B. L. Oser, and W. H. Summerson (1954), " Practical Physiological Chemistry." 13th Ed. Philadelphia; London.

" The Kidney " (1954). *CIBA Foundation Symposium.*

King, E. J. and I. D. Phemister (1956), " Micro-analysis in Medical Biochemistry." 3rd Ed. London.

Kleiner, I. S., and L. B. Dotti (1951), " Laboratory Instructions in Biochemistry." 3rd Ed. Baltimore; London.

Peters, J. P., and D. D. van Slyke (1947–8), " Quantitative Clinical Chemistry." Vol. II. 2nd Ed. Baltimore; London.

Smith, H. W. (1951), " The Kidney." Oxford; New York.

Varley, H. (1954), " Practical Clinical Biochemistry." London.

Williams, R. T. (1947), " Detoxication Mechanisms." London.

Chapter 23 The Internal Environment:

Blood and Tissue Fluids

The immediate purpose of life is survival. After a period of parasitic growth, the animal reaches a stable form capable of maintaining a biological relationship with its environment. The increasing specialisation of function associated with ascent of the evolutionary scale demands an increasing complexity of organisation and co-ordination which reaches its highest level in the human species, the most elaborate apparatus yet known in cosmic history.

But however multifarious and cryptic the activities of life, one general principle governs all physiological processes; organic existence demands stability in the composition of the internal environment, which in the higher animal is represented by the blood, and the cerebro-spinal and other tissue fluids. This fundamental law has been expressed by Claude Bernard, in a well-known epigram:

La fixité du milieu intérieur est la condition de la vie libre.

Effects of Changes in the Human Internal Environment

Deficiency. ←	Internal Environment.	→ Excess.
Hypopyrexia, Collapse.	Temperature.	Hyperpyrexia, Delirium.
Anoxæmia, Unconsciousness.	Oxygen.	Convulsions, Coma.
Alkalosis.	H-ion concentration.	Acidosis.
Convulsions		Coma.
Dehydration, Thirst.	Water.	Œdema.
Circulatory failure. Collapse	Sodium chloride.	Thirst. Paresis.
Hypoglycæmia, Collapse.	Glucose.	Hyperglycæmia, Glycosuria.
Hypocalcæmia, Convulsions.	Calcium	Hypercalcæmia, Atonia, coma.

As Barcroft has shown, the freedom of human life, as expressed in repose and action, requires constancy in the composition of the blood and the cerebro-spinal fluid, while the stability of the internal environment as a whole requires inter-dependent mechanisms for storage, distribution and removal of solutes. Transitory changes in the blood from metabolic activity are compensated for by specially adapted systems for neutralisation, detoxication, and pulmonary and renal excretion, and form part of the routine physiological activities of life. Excessive changes in the blood composition are the result of pathological processes, resulting in abnormal metabolism or in defective compensation and excretory dysfunction.

WATER BALANCE

The animal body can be regarded as having three water-permeable compartments, containing, respectively, blood plasma, interstitial fluid, and intracellular fluid. An osmotic pressure of approximately 6·9 atm. is maintained throughout, and is regulated by the kidneys, which alter the composition of the urine as required. The volume of the circulating blood is kept within normal limits by the non-diffusible proteins of the plasma, which maintain an independent osmotic effect of 0·03 atm. within the vascular system, in addition to the osmotic effect of the diffusible, non-colloidal solutes of the blood.

Representative Water Distribution 65 kg. Man

Tissue.	Wt. in kg.	Per cent. body weight.	Water content. Per cent	kg.
Muscle . .	27·1	41·7	75·6	20·5
Skin . . .	11·7	18	72	8·4
Blood . . .	5	8·5	80·5	4·1
Skeleton . .	10·3	15·9	22	2·27
Liver . . .	1·5	2·3	68·2	1·0
Brain . . .	1·4	2	74·8	0·97
Lungs . . .	0·4	0·7	78·9	0·35
Heart . . .	0·3	0·5	79·2	0·24
Kidneys . .	0·24	0·37	82·7	0·2

Total water content, or *total fluid volume*, is found in the living animal by injecting a known amount of some freely diffusible substance, such as water labelled with deuterium (heavy hydrogen, ^2H) or tritium (radioactive hydrogen, ^3H), and, after it has had sufficient time to be distributed through the body, estimating its dilution in a known volume of plasma.

Extracellular fluid volume is found by injecting an inert solute, such as sucrose or SO_4^{2-}, that is capable of escaping from the blood stream, or vascular compartment, but is incapable of entering the tissue cells.

Intracellular volume is calculated by subtracting the value for extra-cellular volume from that of the total fluid volume. *Plasma volume* is found by dye-injection methods.

All these procedures are liable to errors due to escape of the indicator through the kidneys during the period of 5 to 30 minutes required before uniform distribution has been attained. The results lead to the general conclusion that plasma volume is about one-third of the interstitial fluid volume, and about one-tenth of the intracellular fluid volume.

Water Depletion. Water is continuously leaving the body in the expired air of the lungs and the " insensible " perspiration of the skin. The output is almost steady and, in adults, is 500 to 1000 ml. *per diem*, depending on the surface area of the body, and the temperature and moisture content of the environment.

In addition, there is the daily output of 800 to 1,500 ml., by the kidneys, and 50 to 200 ml. by the intestine, together with the extra water lost by " sensible ", or visible, perspiration in response to bodily activity.

Whenever water intake is inadequate, or water output is excessive, the water balance of the organism is displaced towards the side of dehydration, the first symptom of which is thirst.

That thirst is from a rise in the osmotic effect of the blood, irrespective of the total amount of water in the body, is shown by the result of injecting 500 ml. of N.NaCl, which in a few minutes reduces the saliva output to one-tenth, or less, of the usual value of 1 ml. per minute, thus causing dryness of the mouth. The thirst sensation may arise from a sensitive zone in the pharynx (Cannon, 1918), or may be one of the responses of the organism to general dehydration (Gilman, 1937). That it is caused by a local stimulus is shown by its temporary abolition, when the back of the mouth is anæsthetised, or when salivary flow is evoked by sialogogues, such as pilocarpine, that do not lower the osmotic effect of the plasma. Pathological thirst, such as follows excessive loss of water by the kidneys, in diabetes insipidus, or by the intestine, in cholera, is not relieved by sialogogues. It accompanies and reveals the serious dehydration of the entire body, in which the muscles and cutaneous tissues may lose 10 to 20 per cent. of their total water. Collapse finally ensues from fall in blood volume by transfer of water from plasma to tissues. Occupational dehydration is experienced by deep-level miners, stokers, and others engaged in hard work in warm surroundings. Large quantities of sweat are secreted to cool the body, and thus both water and sodium chloride are lost. If this type of dehydration be countered by the obvious method of drinking plain water, the osmotic level of the body fluid is lowered abruptly, with nausea and muscular cramp. The proper treatment is the use of normal saline as a beverage to replenish body salt as well as body water.

Vascular Shock. Any rapid reduction in total blood volume predisposes to the syndrome of vascular shock, which includes fall in blood pressure and body temperature, weak and rapid pulse, pallor, apathy and collapse. When the fall in blood pressure is due to hæmorrhage, compensatory transfer of fluid from the interstitial reserves takes place, and may avert death. Vascular shock, however, can come from abnormal loss of fluid by the blood, owing to increase of capillary permeability by release of histamine, adenylic acid, or similar depressor compounds, from injured tissues. The rapid restoration of blood volume is essential in the treatment of any form of vascular shock, and Scudder (1940) emphasises the importance of using the correct saline transfusion fluids in the process.

Water Retention. Rise in osmotic effect of the plasma and tissue fluids is compensated by excretion of more solutes in the urine; fall in osmotic effect, conversely, results in the excretion of a urine sufficiently dilute to remove the surplus water from the organism. If, however, the load of water or of salt ingested exceeds the clearance capacity of the kidneys, fluid accumulates in the body. Partial failure of the kidney to excrete salt or water, even when the diet is normal, is shown by the progressive retention of surplus body fluid. In order to avoid plasmolysis and disintegration of tissue cells, the osmotic pressure of the body fluid must be kept at its normal level, hence any retention of water must be accompanied by a corresponding retention of Na^+ and Cl^-, and any retention of NaCl demands retention of sufficient water to keep it at isotonic concentration, equivalent to 6·9 atm., or 0·9 per cent. NaCl. The renal output of water is controlled by an osmo-receptor in the hypothalamus, implemented by the anti-diuretic factor of the anterior pituitary gland; the Na^+ and Cl^- output is controlled by the hormones of the adrenal cortex. Apart from adrenal dysfunction, with accompanying excessive excretion of NaCl, water depletion is generally from the inability of the organism to retain water; while water retention is generally from inability to excrete sufficient salt.

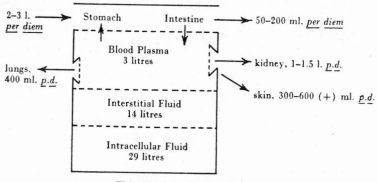

Water Distribution in 70 kg. Man.

Sweat. The *eccrine* sweat glands distributed generally over the body surface, and the *apocrine* glands of the axilla and groin secrete a very dilute fluid of varying composition and reaction, the primary function of which is to facilitate heat-loss by evaporation. The glands are innervated by cholinergic

371

fibres from the sympathetic supply, and the output is evoked by rise in temperature, exercise, the emotional release of hormones, and by drugs such as pilocarpine, and may reach a maximum of 1 to 2 l. per hour, as visible, or " sensible ", perspiration.

The average composition of human sweat, in mg. per 100 ml., is: total solids, 250 to 700; inorganic solutes, 200 to 500; NaCl, 100 to 370 (Kuno), 500 (Dill); lactic acid, 70 to 160; urea, 20 to 46; K, 14 to 39; Ca, 5. Traces of reducing substances and volatile aromatic compounds also occur, especially in apocrine sweat. Sweat as freshly secreted is alkaline (pH 7 to 7·4), but in contact with the skin becomes acid (pH 5·4).
The physiology of human perspiration is reviewed by McSwiney (1935), Kuno (1935) and Dill (1938).

BLOOD

The vascular apparatus in mammals, according to Drinker (1942), has five essential features:
(1) A closed system of blood capillaries with endothelial walls of varied permeability, but capable of retaining almost all of the blood plasma during the usual conditions of rapid transit.
(2) A variable hydrostatic pressure in the capillaries.
(3) The presence of extra-cellular non-respiratory proteins in the plasma.
(4) An extra-vascular tissue fluid lower in protein content than the blood plasma, but otherwise almost identical.
(5) A closed system of lymphatic capillaries with very permeable endothelial walls, which lack an inherent mechanism for moving their contents into the larger, valved lymph vessels, and depend on inconstant external changes, such as muscular contraction, for the uptake of fluid and the eventual flow of the lymph stream back to the general circulating blood.

Blood is a fluid tissue consisting of corpuscles and other particles dispersed in a colloidal medium, the *plasma*. It is opaque, owing to the enormous number of cells in suspension, and red in colour, owing to the pigmented corpuscles, or erythrocytes, which carry the hæmoglobin. Human plasma has no hæmoglobin, and is a clear liquid with a faint yellowish tint, from traces of carotene and xanthophyll, derived from the diet, and bilirubin, from degraded hæmoglobin.

On dilution with water or hypotonic salines, the erythrocytes swell and disintegrate, liberating hæmoglobin, and thus forming a red, transparent solution, " laked blood ". *Hæmolysis*, or dissolution of the red corpuscles, can also be effected by soaps, saponins, fat-solvents, and some snake venoms and bacterial toxins. When hæmolysis occurs in the living animal, the liberated hæmoglobin may be excreted by the kidney, giving rise to hæmoglobinuria.

When blood is centrifuged, or allowed to remain under conditions unfavourable for clotting, the red cells (sp. gr. 1·09) separate from the lighter plasma (sp. gr. 1·03), and are found to have made up 40 to 45 per cent. by volume of the original blood. For accurate measurement of this important ratio, a narrow graduated centrifuge tube, or *hæmatocrit*, is used.

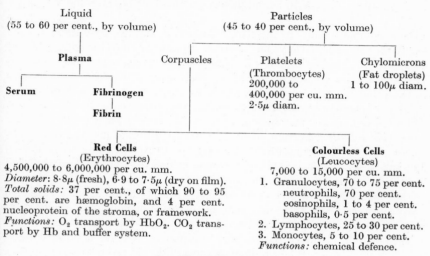

Composition of Human Blood.

Physical Characteristics of Human Blood. Specific gravity, 1·040 to 1·066 (water = 1·000). *Reaction,* slightly alkaline (arterial blood or plasma, pH 7·3 to 7·4; venous blood or plasma, pH 7·3 to 7·5; cell contents, pH 7·1). *Osmotic pressure,* entire blood or plasma, 6·9 to 7·0 atmospheres; plasma colloids, 0·03 atms. (23 to 28 mm. Hg.). *Viscosity,* entire blood, 3·6 to 5·3; plasma, 1·7 to 2 (water = 1·0). Specific gravity of blood or plasma can be found by observing if a drop sinks or floats in an inert liquid of known sp. g., such as can be made by mixing chloroform (sp. g. 1·527) and benzene (sp. g. 0·874). When a mixture has been obtained in which the drop of blood remains poised, its specific gravity is measured by a hydrometer, and is equal to that of the blood. Solutions of copper sulphate of varying concentration have the advantage that the composition is not so readily affected by evaporation. A more convenient method for clinical work in one in which the sp. g. is found from the time of fall of a drop of blood down a column of liquid of known density.

The specific gravity of plasma depends chiefly on its colloid content, and gives an accurate index of protein concentration.

The reaction of blood is found by means of a hydrogen or glass electrode, precaution being taken to avoid escape of CO_2 from the blood during manipulation.

Total Volume. Knowing either the total volume of the plasma or the cells, it is possible to calculate the total volume of the blood in the body from the plasma/cell ratio found by the hæmatocrit. Results by different methods are at variance, but sufficiently consistent to lead to the conclusion that the total blood volume amounts to 7 to 8 per cent. of the entire body weight, or 70 to 80 ml. per kg. A 70 kg. adult has about 5 l. of blood in his body.

Plasma volume is found by injecting a known amount of a harmless dye, such as " vital red " or " Evans blue ", which can neither enter the corpuscles nor escape by the capillaries. After 5 to 30 minutes, to allow for uniform distribution, a known volume of blood is withdrawn, and the dilution of the dye in the plasma is estimated colorimetrically. Error may arise from excretion of some of the dye by the kidneys during the experiment.

Total red cell volume may be found by two independent methods: (a) *Carbon Monoxide Fixation*, introduced by Haldane (1900), and modified by subsequent workers, including Chang and Harrop (1928). Air containing a known but harmless amount of CO is rebreathed until all the CO has been absorbed by the hæmoglobin. After allowing time for dilution, a sample of blood is withdrawn, and its degree of saturation with CO is found by a reversion spectrometer. From this, the total quantity of hæmoglobin required to account for all the CO absorbed is calculated. Then, knowing the percentage of hæmoglobin in the corpuscles, the total red cell volume is obtained.

(b) *Isotope Dilution*. When radioactive iron, ^{59}Fe, is given to anæmic dogs, it is used in formation of new hæmoglobin, and the cells thus labelled do not discharge or exchange the isotope during their lifetime. When such blood, containing a known amount of isotopic hæmoglobin, is injected into another animal of the same species and blood type, uniform distribution of the labelled red cells takes place within 10 minutes of the injection, and remains unchanged after 3 days.

By measuring the concentration of the isotope in a sample of the blood the total red cell volume can be calculated (Hahn *et al.*, 1941). Radioactive phosphate can be used in a similar manner for the measurement of total body fluid.

Sedimentation Rate. From the size and density of the red cells, a sedimentation rate of about 0·2 mm. per hour is required by Stokes's Law (p. 56). Owing to agglutinating factors associated with the plasma proteins, the rate of fall is much greater. Values obtained by Fåhræus (1929), in mm. per hour, are: new-born child, 0·5; normal man, 3·3; woman (non-pregnant), 7·4; woman (pregnant), 44·0.

RESPIRATORY FUNCTIONS OF THE BLOOD

(1) **Oxygen Transport.** The oxygen reserves of man are about 800 ml., as HbO_2, in the blood; 400 ml., in the supplemental and residual air in the lungs; not more than 70 ml., dissolved in tissue and body fluids; and, perhaps

50 ml., in muscle hæmoglobin. Altogether, this represents only about 3 to 4 minutes' supply for the body at rest, and can have no survival value (Barcroft, 1932).

The air in the lung alveoli is, approximately, at atmospheric pressure (760 mm. Hg), and contains about 14 per cent., or one-seventh of its volume of oxygen, which, therefore, has a partial pressure of 1/7 atms., or 108 mm. Hg. This diffusion pressure enables O_2 to enter the pulmonary capillaries and pass into the red cells.

Composition in ml. per 100 ml. of gas or liquid

Gas.	Atmospheric Air.	Alveolar Air.	Arterial Blood.	Venous Blood.	Alveolar Air.	Expired Air.
O_2 .	20·93	14–15 →	19	13	14–15	16·9
CO_2 .	0·03	5·5	45–50	50–60 – →	5·5	3·5
N_2 .	79·04	80	1	1	80	79·5

At 36° C., and a partial-pressure of 1/6 to 1/7 atm., the quantity of O_2 that can dissolve in blood plasma is not more than 0·36 ml. per 100 ml. Arterial blood, however, contains nearly 20 ml. O_2 per 100 ml., which can be released and measured by a vacuum pump, or displaced by ferricyanide. When blood is exposed to an O_2 pressure of 145 mm. Hg, it becomes fully saturated with oxygen, all the available corpuscular hæmoglobin being in the form of HbO_2. Any further increase in O_2 pressure merely increases the small amount of the gas that is dissolved in the plasma. At an O_2 pressure of 105 mm. Hg. (equivalent to alveolar air) blood is 95% saturated with the gas. Consequently, blood leaving the lungs by the pulmonary veins is nearly 100 per cent. saturated, as regards its oxygen capacity. As it circulates through the body, it comes into equilibrium with the tissue fluids, in which the O_2 pressure is very low, because of the demands by tissue respiration systems. With the fall in O_2 pressure, the HbO_2 dissociates, until the blood is about 60 per cent. saturated, which is the ordinary level of venous blood, and represents an O_2 content of 12 ml. per 100 ml. Dissociation of the HbO_2 is also promoted by the decreasing alkalinity of the blood, which changes from pH 7·45 to pH 7·35, owing to entrance of CO_2 from the tissues.

(2) **Carbon Dioxide Transport.** In plasma and other aqueous liquids, carbon dioxide may be present as: (a) dissolved CO_2, (b) hydrated CO_2, or carbonic acid, H_2CO_3, (c) acid carbonate ions, HCO_3^-, and (d) carbonate ions, CO_3^{2-}. All four exist in an equilibrium, the composition of which depends on the pH and the gaseous pressure of CO_2 to which the solution is exposed. Carbonic acid is moderately strong ($K_1 = 2 \times 10^{-4}$), and ionises almost instantaneously, but the hydration of CO_2 to H_2CO_3, or the converse dehydration

375

of H_2CO_3, is slow, unless catalysed by the enzyme *carbonic anhydrase*, which accompanies Hb in the red cells, but does not occur in the plasma.

When plasma is acidified it yields 40 to 60 ml. CO_2 per 100 ml., but when it is exposed to zero CO_2 pressure in a vacuum pump, only about half its total CO_2 is released. In these respects, plasma resembles an aqueous solution of HCO_3^-:

$$\text{(acidification) } 2\ HCO_3^- + 2H^+ - \rightarrow 2H_2O + 2CO_2$$
$$\text{(low pressure) } 2\ HCO_3^- - \rightarrow H_2O + CO_3^- + CO_2.$$

At the pH of blood, 7·4, and at a partial pressure of 40 mm. Hg, which corresponds to the CO_2 content of alveolar air, only 2·7 ml. of CO_2 is present in solution in the plasma, the rest is nearly all in the form of HCO_3^-.

Entire blood resembles plasma in yielding all its free and ionised CO_2 on acidification; but, unlike plasma, it yields its total CO_2 when exposed to low pressures.

This shows that factors within the corpuscles must operate in the retention and release of CO_2. The mechanism has been elucidated, chiefly by the pioneer work of Meldrum and Roughton. Six stages are recognised:

(1) Dissolved CO_2 passes from tissue fluids to plasma, and enters the red cells.

(2) Within the cell, some CO_2 is bound by combining with the free amino groups of the hæmoglobin; the rest is hydrated to H_2CO_3 by means of the enzyme carbonic anhydrase.

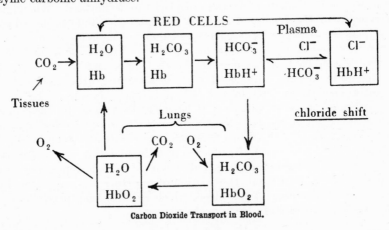

Carbon Dioxide Transport in Blood.

(3) H_2CO_3 ionises to HCO_3^- and H^+, which is buffered by combining with the hæmoglobin.

(4) Some HCO_3^- diffuses out of the cells into the plasma, and is replaced by its equivalent of Cl^-, to maintain the anion-cation balance. This " chloride shift " effect is the means whereby the red cells build up HCO_3^- in the plasma.

(5) When the blood reaches the lungs, O_2 enters the red cells, converts the Hb to HbO_2, and displaces the H^+. This free H^+ combines with HCO_3^- within

the cell, to form H_2CO_3, which is then converted by carbonic anhydrase to H_2O and CO_2.

(6) The free CO_2 escapes from the cells into the plasma, and is excreted by the lungs.

The presence of K^+ in the corpuscles, and Na^+ in the plasma, is not shown, as these ionic species are only concerned in the maintenance of anion-cation balance, and not CO_2 transport. For simplicity, also, the formation of carb-amino derivatives by union between the CO_2 and the cell and plasma proteins is omitted, although they also aid in carrying CO_2.

In the circulating blood, most of the carbon dioxide is carried as the HCO_3^- ions of the plasma, which also function as a buffer system for maintaining blood pH by converting H^+ into H_2CO_3. The red cells operate a mechanism for removing CO_2 from tissue fluids and converting it into plasma HCO_3^-; while in the pulmonary circulation they remove HCO_3^- from the plasma and convert it into CO_2 for excretion by the lungs.

Buffer Capacity of Blood. The pH of the entire organism is kept within proper limits by the buffer action of the blood which, in turn, is maintained by the lungs, which remove CO_2, and the kidneys, which excrete the cations H^+ and NH_4^+ and the anions OH^-, HCO_3^- and HPO_4^{2-}, in accordance with the state of the plasma.

The chief buffers for H^+ in the blood are the proteins of the cells and plasma, the iso-electric points of which are well on the acid side of neutrality (hæmo-globin, pH 6·8; serum albumin, pH 5·5; serum globulin, pH 4·4). At the pH of blood, these proteins have their terminal amino groups free, and are capable of accepting H^+. The carbonate buffer system,

$$HCO_3^- + H^+ \rightleftharpoons H_2CO_3,$$

and the phosphate buffer system,

$$HPO_4^{2-} + H^+ \rightleftharpoons H_2PO_4^-,$$

are not working at their optimum range, but provide emergency systems that protect against sudden or violent strains.

Plasma Alkaline Reserve. According to Van Slyke, this is defined as " the total volume per cent. of CO_2 liberated when an acid acts on plasma previously brought into equilibrium with a gas mixture containing CO_2 at a partial-pressure of that in alveolar air (40 mm. Hg)." It is an index of the reserve buffer capacity and ability of the plasma to protect the organism against *acidæmia*, or fall in pH below 7·3. The normal range for the alkaline reserve is 53 to 75 ml. CO_2 per 100 ml. Values below 50 denote *acidosis*; values above 75 denote *alkalosis*.

The rate of general, or external respiration is governed by the CO_2 output of the tissues, which, by increasing the H^+ and CO_2 concentration in the plasma above the normal level, stimulates the respiratory centre in the pons and

377

upper medulla. For this reason, CO_2 is used to supplement O_2 administration in treatment of carbon monoxide poisoning, and other forms of asphyxia.

THE PLASMA COLLOIDS

Plasma contains 6 to 8 per cent. of colloids out of a total 8·5 to 10 per cent. of solutes.

Human Plasma Proteins
In order of electrophoretic mobility

Protein.	Gm. per 100 ml.	Functions.
Albumin (m.w. 68,000)	4·04 ± 0·27	Osmotic regulation of blood volume. Transport of fatty acids, bile salts and pigments.
a_1-Globulin	0·31 ± 0·05	Metabolic. Transport.
a_2-Globulin	0·48 ± 0·05	Metabolic. Transport.
β-Globulin	0·81 ± 0·13	Immunological.
Fibrinogen	0·34 ± 0·06	Blood coagulation.
γ-Globulin	0·74 ± 0·15	Immunological.

Electrophoretic analysis shows that the globulin fractions are complex mixtures, representing: (1) plasma enzymes (thrombin, proteases, amylase, lipase, alkaline phosphatase, choline esterase); (2) lipoproteins carrying steroids and carotenoids, glycoproteins and mucoids, Fe and Cu carrying crystallisable pseudoglobulins, bilirubin carriers; all these are present as a- and β-globulins; (3) agglutinins, and " antibodies " for the blood type factors A, B, and Rh, and many diseases, including diphtheria, measles, and typhoid, are present as γ-globulins.

Plasma Protein Metabolism. The plasma protein content may be depleted experimentally by *plasmapheresis*, in which a sample of blood is removed, and the washed corpuscles are suspended in isotonic saline and replaced by being reinjected. Œdema develops when the plasma protein level falls below 3 per cent. Injection of isotopically-labelled amino acids results in production of labelled plasma proteins, which can be removed, fractionated, and reinjected. In this way, it can be demonstrated that the plasma proteins, apart from 20 per cent. of the globulins, are synthesised in the liver; that they are in mobile exchange equilibrium with the amino acids in the plasma, and that human plasma albumin has a half-life of 10·5 days.

Osmotic Function of the Proteins. Albumin and, to a lesser extent, the globulins, confer on plasma its colloidal osmotic effect equivalent to 23 to 28 mm. Hg, or about 0·03 atms. Although small compared with the total osmotic pressure of the blood and tissue fluids (6·9 to 7 atms.), it is essential for the retention of water within the vascular system and for the maintenance of blood volume. Results of plasmapheresis show that œdema develops when the plasma protein level falls below 3 per cent.

The capillary walls are permeable to Na^+ and Cl^-, the chief ions of the blood, and when the plasma proteins are depleted by hæmorrhage, renal disease, or starvation, saline fluid escapes into the tissues and accumulates, resulting in local œdema or general dropsy. For this reason, fall in blood volume after severe hæmorrhage cannot be restored for long by injections of isotonic saline. A suitable colloid must be included to enable the transfusate to remain in the vessels. Human plasma is the most effective for this purpose. Blood is collected from healthy donors, treated with an anti-coagulant, and centrifuged free from corpuscles. The resulting plasma is diluted with an equal volume of isotonic saline containing 0·01 per cent. of mercury thiosalicylate as antiseptic, and stored at 5° C., till required. Alternatively, the plasma may be dried to a powder by spraying *in vacuo* at 45° C.

Blood Coagulation. Within 10 minutes of being withdrawn, blood spontaneously thickens and forms a characteristic clot of fibrin strands in which the corpuscles are entangled. Subsequently the clot shrinks and separates from the serum, or defibrinated plasma. Clotting is a very complex process that involves at least four different factors: (1) *fibrinogen*, the soluble precursor of fibrin; (2) *prothrombin*, the precursor of the enzyme *thrombin* that converts fibrinogen into fibrin, and requires (3) *calcium ions*, and (4) *prothrombin activators*.

Prothrombin (prothrombase) can be separated from the globulin fraction of the plasma. It is a protein, and is made in the liver by a process requiring vitamin K. The prothrombin level in plasma, normally about 0·04 per cent., is an index of coagulation efficiency. Hypoprothrombinæmia may come from liver injuries, or lack of vitamin K, owing to faulty diet or defective absorption of fats and fat-soluble vitamins.

Thrombin does not occur to any significant extent in circulating blood, but can be prepared by extracting blood clots with $2M$ NaCl, and precipitating the enzyme by alcohol.

Calcium ions are necessary for the conversion of prothrombin into thrombin, and when removed by precipitation with fluoride or oxalate, or by addition of citrate, which forms a non-ionised Ca complex, the resulting blood or plasma will no longer clot, unless thrombin be added. Removal of Ca^{2+} is the simplest method for preventing the coagulation of blood required for storage, transport or analysis. It can be effected by adding a little powdered potassium fluoride or citrate to the tubes in which the blood will be collected.

Prothrombin Activators. *Thrombokinase* (thromboplastin) occurs in tissues and in the blood platelets, from which it separates out as a granular precipitate that forms when oxalated blood is kept at 0° C. for some days. The thromboplastin from platelets is a lipo-protein, the release of which is controlled by several factors, including an anti-hæmophilic globulin, which is deficient in the congenital disorder, *hæmophilia*. Thromboplastin from tissues is a

379

phospholipid of the cephalin-lecithin type. Its action is slower than ex
platelet thromboplastin, and it is released by tissue damage.

Coagulation Inhibitors. Blood can be defibrinated by being stirred rapidl
by a bundle of fine wires, which collects the fibrin as it forms and leaves a
suspension of corpuscles in plasma. Coagulation of blood in bulk can b
retarded by low temperature, freedom from agitation and absence of rough
surfaces, thus repressing the release of prothrombin activators.

In the circulation clotting is prevented both by the absence of the necessary
factors, thrombokinases and thrombin, and also by the presence of specia
inhibitors that retard the formation of thrombin and fibrin.

Heparin, a coagulation inhibitor discovered by Howell (1918) in liver and
lung extracts and basophil leucocytes. Heparin is an ester of mucoitin sul
phate, and coacts with a factor present in normal plasma to yield a powerfu
anti-coagulant.

Like other complex esters of sulphuric acid, heparin is precipitated and
stained by dyes of the toluidine blue class, staining being accompanied by a
metachromatic change of the dye from blue to red.

The basophil, or " mast " cells that are distributed along the capillary bed
and circulate in the blood, stain metachromatically with toluidine blue. When
ever the heparin content of the blood is increased, as in response to anaphy
lactic shock or peptone injection, these cells lose their stain-fixing granules
which indicates that the basophils are the source of the heparin.

Hirudin, a glycoprotein from the oral secretion of the leech, *Hirudo medi-
cinalis*, is representative of the anti-coagulants secreted by various blood
sucking animals to protect themselves from being choked by blood clots
These factors must have been elaborated at a stage later than the evolution
of the mammalian blood-coagulation mechanism, and they provide an
interesting example of biological adaptation and counter ingenuity.

Dicoumarin. A disease characterised by delayed clotting time and a tendency
to hæmorrhage can arise in cattle that have eaten sweet clover " spoiled "
by infection. The agent has been isolated and identified (Link, *et al.*, 1940).
It is a dicoumarin formed from two molecules of 4-hydroxycoumarin united
by a —CH_2— bridge between the carbons at position 3. The therapeutic
applications of this 3 : 3′-methylene-*bis* (4-hydroxycoumarin) in treatment of
thrombosis have been investigated. The parent compound, coumarin, is
present in many plants, and imparts the characteristic odour to freshly cut
grass. Its ring system is part of the structure of vitamins E.

Coumarin
$C_9H_6O_2$

Dicoumarin
(dicoumarol).

Artificial anti-coagulants of the poly-sulphate ester type have been prepared, including "disodium cellulose disulphate" and "Chicago blue". Chondroitin monosulphate, which occurs free in cartilage, and stains metachromatically with "toluidine blue", only acquires anti-coagulant properties after it has been esterified by an additional $—O.SO_2.OH$ group.

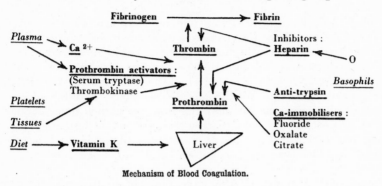

Mechanism of Blood Coagulation.

THE BIOCHEMISTRY OF THE ERYTHROCYTE

The adult human body has 20 to 30 million million red corpuscles in circulation, representing a total of 600 to 700 gm. of hæmoglobin. Tracer studies, using amino acids labelled with ^{15}N, have shown that the four N atoms in the hæm of hæmoglobin, the carbons 2 of the pyrrole rings, and the four bridges joining the rings are all derived from glycine. The remaining carbons come from acetate or formate units. When ^{15}N has become incorporated into the hæm of the hæmoglobin within the erythrocyte, it remains there during the lifetime of the cell; and if the concentration of ^{15}N in the circulating hæm is plotted against time, the duration of life of the red corpuscle can be calculated, which is about 127 days, in the human subject. It is possible also to show by calculation that the erythrocyte population is kept constant by the continuous production and destruction of corpuscles at the rate of $9,000 \times 10^6$ every hour, a rate more than sufficient to provide the 2 gm. of bile pigment secreted daily by the liver.

In addition to glycine and acetate, both of which can be synthesised by the animal, specific nutrients are required for erythrocyte construction. These include iron, some of which may be provided by the reserves of the organism, vitamin B_{12}, and an "intrinsic factor" secreted by the stomach, which enables B_{12} to be absorbed and stored in the liver until required for utilisation in the bone marrow. Associated factors are sulphur-containing amino acids, ascorbic acid, and copper, which is a component of the enzyme ascorbic oxidase.

Hæm, or protoporphyrin assembly from glycine and acetate takes place by way of δ-aminolævulinic acid and porphobilinogen (p. 290). While this is taking place, the primitive corpuscle has been developed from the endothelial

381

cells of the red marrow sinusoids as a *pro-normoblast*, or pseudo-*megaloblast*. Pigmentation of the developing cell now occurs, producing a *normoblast*, in which the hæm has been combined with globin. By loss of the nucleus, an immature erythrocyte, or *reticulocyte*, is formed, and eventually issued into the general circulation as a mature red cell.

Histological evidence from sternal puncture and aspiration of samples of living red marrow shows the changes in depletion by hæmorrhage or starvation, and in stimulation by hæmatinic agents or environments poor in oxygen. In aplastic anæmias, cell-formation is checked at the pre-megaloblastic stage; in pernicious anæmia, from lack of the specific maturation factor, cell development is checked at the megaloblast stage, and the megaloblast population in sternal marrow may rise from the normal range of 25,000 to 35,000 cells per cu. mm., and reach levels of 60,000 to 120,000. When iron, copper or ascorbic acid is deficient, a nutritional hypochromic anæmia may develop, in which the cells have not their full load of hæmoglobin.

Life-span of the Erythrocytes. After having been in circulation for, apparently, about 127 days, the red cells are trapped by the recticulo-endothelial tissue of the spleen, liver and bone marrow, and are disintegrated. The iron is released and most of it is mobilised in the red marrow, and is taken up by the develop-

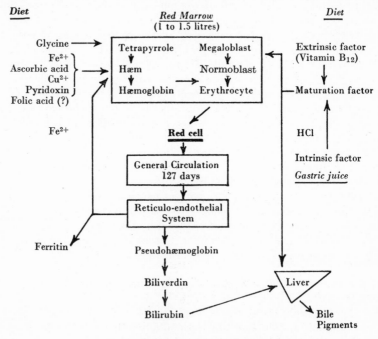

The Biochemistry of the Erythrocyte.

ing erythrocytes and reformed into hæmoglobin. The rest is stored as a protein-ferric complex, *ferritin*, chiefly in liver and kidney tissue. Iron is absorbed from the diet in the form of Fe^{2+}, the process being regulated in accordance with the hæmoglobin need of the organism.

After absorption, iron is not excreted to any significant extent in the urine or secretions of the intestine, apart from a little in the bile, and the store of the metal in the organism increases with the years.

On disintegration of the red cells, hæmoglobin escapes, and is degraded to " pseudohæmoglobin ", or verdohæmoglobin, in which the pyrrole ring is opened up into a linear tetrapyrrole. By loss of globin and Fe, this forms biliverdin.

According to Lemberg, hæmoglobin degradation may begin in the ageing red cell before disintegration, and thus may determine the life-span of the erythrocyte. It is possible, though hard to establish, that some pseudohæmoglobin escapes conversion into bile pigment, and is mobilised in the red marrow for the manufacture of hæmoglobin.

AVERAGE COMPOSITION OF HUMAN BLOOD

	Blood, Entire.	Plasma, or Serum.
Solids, total . . .	18–25	8·5–10
Corpuscles, volume . .	36–51	—
Proteins, total . .	17·8–24·6	5·8–8·6
Hæmoglobin (men) . .	13–17·5	0
(women) .	12–14	0
Total Protein : . .	—	5·8–8·6
Fibrinogen (F) . .	0·1–0·2	0·2–0·4
Albumin (A) . .	—	3·4–6·7 (average, 4)
Globulin (G) . .	—	1·2–2·9 (average, 2)
A : G ratio . .	—	4 : 1–1·2 : 1 (average, 2 : 1)
Lipids, total . . .	0·2–2	0·45–1·2
Fatty acids . .	0·29–0·42	0·19–0·64
Chloride, as NaCl . .	0·45–0·53	0·56–0·62
as Cl⁻ . .	0·28–0·32	0·35–0·38

Major constituents, expressed as gm. per 100 ml.

COMPOSITION OF BLOOD PLASMA AND SERUM

Data for the average or representative composition of human blood plasma and serum have been critically reviewed by Krebs (1950), from whose compilation the accompanying tabulations are taken.

Ranges and values for plasma vitamins, in mg. per 100 ml., are: vitamin A, 0·019 to 0·036 (0·025); carotenoids, total, 0·06 to 0·18 (0·09); tocopherols, 0·9 to 1·59 (1·20); ascorbic acid, 0·1 to 0·7; thiamine, 0·0005; nicotinic acid and amide, 0·02 to 0·05 (0·03); riboflavin, total, 0·0026 to 0·0037; inositol, 0·42 to 0·76; folic acid, 0·00175; biotin, 0·00127; pantothenic acid, 0·006 to 0·022 (0·012).

Hormone values, in mg. per 100 ml., include: adrenaline (entire blood), 0·0041 to 0·0096; corticosteroids, 0·11 to 0·42; œstrogens, as œstriol, 0·0002 to 0·0022; progesterone, 0·5 to 0·8.

Inorganic Solutes
Range and average value, in mg. per 100 ml. plasma.

Bicarbonate, as $NaHCO_3$	205 to 280 (226)
Calcium (serum)	8·2 to 11·6 (10)
Chloride	355 to 380 (365)
Copper	0·086 to 0·16 (0·12)
Fluoride (entire blood)	0·28
Iodine, protein-bound	0·006 to 0·008
Iron	0·028 to 0·21 (0·105)
Lead (entire blood)	0·009 to 0·05 (0·03)
Magnesium (serum)	1·7 to 2·3 (2·0)
Manganese (entire blood)	0·005 to 0·02
Phosphate, as P, total:	10 to 14·1 (12·1)
Inorganic	2·6 to 5·4 (3·2)
Lipoid	6·1 to 9·9 (8·0)
Ester	0·6
Potassium	12·1 to 25·4 (17·2)
Sodium	300 to 330 (316)
Sulphate, as S, non-protein, total: . .	2·95 to 3·75 (3·38)
Inorganic	1·0 to 1·85 (1·57)
Ester	0·25 to 0·65 (0·39)
Neutral	0·9 to 1·95 (1·42)
Zinc	0·12 to 0·48 (0·21)
Water, in gm. per 100 ml.	92·4 to 94·4 (93·6)

Organic Solutes; I, Non-Nitrogenous
Range and average value, in mg. per 100 ml.

Carbohydrates:	
Glucose, fasting, venous blood . . .	80 to 120
Glucose, fasting, capillary blood . .	90 to 130
Glucosamine, total	63 to 88 (77)
Hexuronates, as glucuronic acid . .	0·4 to 1·4
Pentose, total	2 to 3
Polysaccharides, as hexose (serum) . .	73 to 150 (102)
Lipids:	
Fatty acids, total, as stearic . . .	200 to 450
Neutral fat	0 to 150
Cholesterol, total	150 to 260
free	40 to 70
Phospholipids, total:	150 to 250
Lecithin	100 to 200
Cephalin	0 to 30
Sphingomyelin	10 to 30
Bile acids, as cholic	0·2 to 3·0
Miscellaneous:	
Citric acid	1·9 to 2·8 (2·5)
Succinic acid	0·5
Acetoacetic acid, non-fasting . . .	0·8 to 2·8
Lactic acid, resting	8 to 17
Pyruvic acid	0·77 to 1·23 (1·0)

Organic Solutes; II, Nitrogenous
Range and average value in plasma.

Plasma proteins, total (g. per 100 ml.) : ·	6·72
Albumin	4·04 ± 0·27
a_1-Globulin	0·31 ± 0·051
a_2-Globulin	0·48 ± 0·053
β-Globulin	0·81 ± 0·126
γ-Globulin	0·74 ± 0·151
Fibrinogen	0·34 ± 0·059
Non-proteins, as nitrogen, total: (mg. per 100 ml.)	25·7
Amino acid nitrogen, total: . . .	3·7 to 5·9 (4·4)
Choline	0·3 to 1·5
Creatine (serum), male	0·17 to 0·5
Creatine (serum), female	0·35 to 0·93
Creatinine (serum), male	1·05 to 1·65
Creatinine (serum), female . . .	0·9 to 1·5
Urea, male	27·1 ± 4·5
Urea, female	26·4 ± 8·1
Uric acid (serum)	2·9 to 6·9 (4·0)
Bilirubin	1·0

The individual amino acids present in human blood plasma are tabulated on p. 287.

General References

Bland, J. H. (1956), " Body Fluids." Philadelphia; London.
" Blood Cells and Plasma Proteins." Ed. by J. L. Tullis (1953). New York.
Elkington, J. R., and T. S. Danowski (1955), " Body Fluids." London.
Gamble, J. L. (1951), " Extracellular Fluid." 5th Ed. Harvard.
Krebs, H. A. (1950), " Chemical Composition of Blood Plasma and Serum." *Ann. Rev. Biochem.*, **19**, 409.
Marriott, H. L. (1950), " Water and Salt Depletion." Oxford.
Robinson, J. R. (1952), "Active Transport of Water in Living Systems." *Biol. Rev.*, **28**, 158. Cambridge.

Chapter 24 Hormones

" Except during the nine months before he draws his first breath, no man manages his affairs as well as a tree does."

G. B. Shaw.

Hormones are specific autogenous compounds manufactured and employed for the chemical co-ordination of the organism.
They are termed, alternatively, (i) *internal secretions*, or endocrines, because many are sent directly into the blood stream from the tissue that produces them; and (ii) *hormones*, from the fact that those first identified were physiological stimulants (ὁρμάω, I excite).
(1) **Local activators,** affecting the same cell or tissue in which they are produced.
(i) *Intracellular hormones.*
(ii) *Regional hormones,* which are responsible for the predetermination of specific regions in the embryo, such as the limb-disc, the eye-rudiment and the chick pronephros.
(2) **Diffusion activators,** distributed by diffusion through the tissues.
(i) *Growth hormones of plants,* such as the auxins.
(ii) *Evocators* and *organisers* of the vertebrate embryo.
(iii) *Neurocrines,* or chemical transmitters of the nerve impulse. Cholinergic and adrenergic factors.
(3) **Circulating hormones,** which are transported by the blood stream or lymph to all parts of the organism. These are represented by the endocrine secretions of the ductless glands.
Classification. Hormones may be classified according to: (1) tissue of origin; (2) target of action and physiological effect; (3) chemical structure. None of these classifications is precise. Tissues such as pituitary can secrete hormones differing greatly in character; the effects of a single hormone may be multiple, or displayed by other hormones; chemical structure, while it is the intrinsic cause of hormone activity, has not yet been related to functional effect. Many hormones of different sources and actions have chemical features in common.
The most convenient classification of the hormones is by assignment of each to its glandular or cellular source.

Hormones of the Higher Animal
" The fury and the mire of human veins."

W. B. Yeats.

O 2

Source.	Hormone.	Effect.
Adrenal cortex	Deoxycorticosterone	Sodium conserving: promotes retention of Na^+ and Cl^-, and urinary excretion of K^+.
	Corticosterone	Glycogenic, glucotropic, protein catabolic.
	Aldosterone	Sodium conserving.
	Cortisol	Glycogenic, protein catabolic.
	Cortisone	Multi-potent.
	Adrenosterone	Androgenic.
Adrenal Medulla	Noradrenaline	Vaso-constrictor, neuro-humoral.
	Adrenaline	Dilator and constrictor, glycogenolytic.
Thyroid	Thyroglobulin	Promotes tissue aerobic metabolism.
Parathyroid	Parathyrin	Regulates calcium and phosphate metabolism.
Pancreas:		
β-cells	Insulin	Hypoglycæmic, glycogenic, promotes glucose utilisation.
α-cells	Glucagon	Hyperglycæmic, glycogenolytic.
Ovary	Œstradiol	Œstrogenic: maintains sex characteristics, induces œstrus cycle. Protein anabolic, thymolytic.
Corpus luteum	Progesterone	Progestational control of uterus, placental development.
Placenta	Progesterone	
	Gonadotropin	
Testis	Testosterone	Androgenic: maintains male sex characteristics. Protein anabolic.
	Androstanedione	Androgenic.
Anterior Pituitary	Adrenocorticotropin (ACTH)	Evokes secretion of adrenal cortex.
	Follicle stimulant (FSH)	Gonadotropic: promotes growth of ovarian follicle and seminiferous tubules.
	Interstitial-cell stimulant (ICSH), or luteinising hormone (LH)	Promotes growth of corpus luteum. Stimulates secretion of sex hormones in male and female.
	Prolactin (LTH)	Stimulates lactation.
	Thyrotropin (TSH)	Evokes secretion of thyroid gland.
	Growth hormone	Stimulates bone growth, protein anabolic, hyperglycæmic.
Posterior Pituitary	Anti-diuretin, vaso-pressin	Regulates water excretion by kidney, vaso-constrictor.
	Oxytocin	Stimulates uterine contraction.
Intestinal mucosa	Secretin	Stimulates secretion of pancreatic juice and bile.
	Pancreozymin	
	Cholecystokinin	Stimulates gall bladder contraction.
	Enterogastrone	Inhibits gastric motility.
	5-Hydroxytryptamine (enteramine, serotonin)	Stimulates contraction of unstriated muscle.

The existence of a hormone is established in six different ways:

(i) Histological recognition of endocrine tissue. This led Schäfer to conclude that an internal secretion was located in the islet tissue of the pancreas, and he suggested the name *insuline* many years before the actual hormone was discovered.

(ii) Pathological conditions associated with changes in endocrine tissue. Examples are Addison's disease (suprarenals), Graves's disease (thyroid), Fröhlich's syndrome (pituitary).

(iii) Physiological response to administration of endocrine extracts.

(iv) Isolation and identification of the active principle.

(v) Production of characteristic pathological conditions by removal of endocrine tissue.

(vi) Adequate compensation for endocrine deficiency by administration of the hormone, or gland extract, or by gland implantation.

A. Adrenal Cortex

The adrenal gland is composed of two structures, independent in history and physiological function. The cortex is of mesoblastic origin, and arises from the cœlomic epithelium on either side of the root of the mesentery; the medulla arises from the primitive nerve tissue beside the posterior root ganglia, which subsequently differentiates into the sympathetic nervous system. Unlike the medulla, the adrenal cortex is necessary for life, and for this reason removal of the entire gland is fatal in animals not adequately equipped with accessory adrenal tissue.

Corticosterones. By fractional extraction of adrenal cortex with lipid solvents, Hartmann (1928), Swingle, and other workers, obtained an active preparation, *cortin*, later shown to be a mixture of steroids. Corticosterone and deoxycorticosterone are the most active of some thirty steroids separated from the cortex.

Effects of Cortical Deficiency. (1) *Metabolic.* Complete removal of the cortical tissue from an animal results in death within a week. There is rapid loss in weight, general muscular weakness, fall in temperature and reduction in basal metabolism by about 25 per cent. The syndrome is seen in a less acute form in partial removal of the cortex, and in pathological dysfunction, as in Addison's disease and in pituitary deficiency, with absence of ACTH.

By continued injection of cortin extracts, cats have been kept alive for a year after all cortical tissue had been removed.

Cortical deficiency is shown by disturbance of three aspects of metabolism:

(a) *Carbohydrate Utilisation.* Sugar absorption from the intestine is retarded, the glycogen content of liver and muscle decreases, blood lactate increases owing to the inability of the liver to convert it into glycogen. Death is preceded by marked hypoglycæmia.

(b) *Ionic Balance.* Cortical steroids, especially aldosterone and deoxycorticosterone, provide a factor necessary for the reabsorption of Na^+ from the glomerular filtrate, by the renal tubules. When this factor is absent, excess of Na^+ is excreted in the urine, accompanied by an equivalent increase in anions, such as Cl^- and HCO_3^-, to preserve electrolyte balance. Hence, in

389

cortical dysfunction, both Na^+ and Cl^- are lost by the animal. The sodium level in the plasma falls, and migration of K^+ from tissues to plasma occurs. (2) *Androgenic*. Defective androgen production by the adrenal cortex has little significance except as evidence of adrenal cortical insufficiency. Dysfunction of the cortex owing to tumour formation in early childhood is associated with precocious sexual development in boys and virilism in girls. Dysfunction in adult females leads to the appearance of the secondary sexual characters of the male. From this it is inferred that an androgenic or masculine autacoid is being elaborated in the gland. A number of such factors have been isolated from the normal gland, one of which, adrenosterone, $C_{19}H_{24}O_3$, has about one-fifth the potency of androsterone. Adrenosterone can arise by

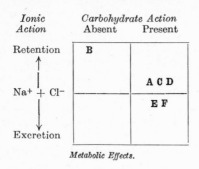

	Carbohydrate Action	
Ionic Action	Absent	Present
Retention	B	
$Na^+ + Cl^-$		**A C D**
		E F
Excretion		

Metabolic Effects.

Cortical Hormone Pattern.

A, Corticosterone.

B, Deoxycorticosterone.

C, 11-Dehydrocorticosterone.

D, 17-Hydroxycorticosterone.

390

E, 17-Hydroxydeoxy-corticosterone.

F, 11-Dehydro-17-hydroxy-corticosterone.

G, Adrenosterone.

H, Dehydro-iso-androsterone.

replacement of the side-chain by $=O$ in 11-dehydro-17-hydroxycortico-sterone. A related androgen, *dehydro-iso-androsterone* occurs in traces in urine of both sexes, and, presumably, is formed in the cortex.

Structure and Function. The corticosteroids require O : at 3 and a double-bond at 4 : 5 in ring I for their hormone activity. Like the androgens, the bile acids, and cholesterol, all the corticosteroids, with the exception of aldosterone, have a methyl group attached to carbon 10, between rings I and II, and a methyl group at carbon 13, between rings III and IV. Aldosterone resembles corticosterone, but for the replacement of —CH_3 at 13 by —CHO. The side-chain, —$CO.CH_2.OH$ at 17 is necessary for metabolic activity.

Hydroxyl. HO— or O= at 11 augments the carbohydrate utilisation effect and decreases the Na^+ conservation effect. When HO— is attached to carbon 17, it is in *trans* position (sometimes denoted by HO..., to indicate that it is in the opposite direction to the side-chain on the same carbon), and it enhances the metabolic effect. In the Reichstein classification, as tabulated, steroids E and F are active in glucose metabolism, but have no sodium-retaining property, while B has little carbohydrate effect, but is a powerful conserver of sodium.

Steroid G, adrenosterone, has neither of these properties. Steroid F (Reich-stein), which is identical with Kendall's " Compound E ", or cortisone, appears to be the most versatile of the corticosteroids.

Nomenclature. Removal of an oxygen atom, usually by replacement of HO— by H—, is indicated by the prefix " deoxy ", or " desoxy ". Attachment of oxygen as O= is indicated by the prefix " oxo ", or, ambiguously, by " keto ", which could also denote OC<.

Important Corticosteroids

Cortisol, 17-hydroxycorticosterone, or " hydrocorticosterone ", is the chief corticosteroid in the blood leaving the adrenal gland, the average value being about 15 μg. per 100 ml. It is a sugar and protein metabolising hormone and has no action on sodium excretion.

Aldosterone, the chief sodium-conserving hormone, occurs as a microconstituent in human urine (0·6 ± 0·5 μg. per 24 hours, rising to 10 μg., in pregnancy).

Deoxycorticosterone, or deoxycortone, is used in the form of its acetate ester, " doca ", in treatment of Addison's disease. The daily dosage by injection is 5 to 10 mg., or the ester may be implanted under the skin, in 100 mg. pellets, which by slow solution release about 0·3 mg. of the hormone, daily.

Cortisone, 11-dehydro-17-hydroxycorticosterone, or Compound E (Kendall), is used free, or as the acetate, in treatment of adrenal cortex deficiency and a variety of other disorders: rheumatoid arthritis, inflammatory eye diseases, asthma, and dermatitis. The hormone appears to act by repressing the inflammatory asthma, and response of cells to irritant stimuli.

Adrenal cortex activity is stimulated by a hormone, *corticotropin*, secreted by the anterior pituitary gland. Preparations of this adrenocorticotropic hormone, ACTH, are used therapeutically to evoke secretion of the adrenal gland of cortisone and other steroids, and in the diagnosis of adrenal insufficiency.

Intramuscular injection of 25 mg. of ACTH results in a rapid fall in the eosinophil level in the blood, and a rise in the excretion of uric acid. This response is absent or weak in conditions of cortical deficiency.

B. Adrenal Medulla

Fresh adrenal medulla contains about 0·1 per cent. of **adrenaline** (epinephrine) and its precursor **noradrenaline** (arterenol). They can be obtained from alcoholic or aqueous extracts of the gland, by precipitation with excess of ammonium hydroxide. Structurally, they are derivatives of 1,2-dihydroxybenzene, or catechol, with a side-chain attached at position 4. This is —$CH(OH).CH_2.NH_2$, in noradrenaline; and —$CH(OH).CH_2.NH.CH_3$, in adrenaline.

Effects of Adrenaline Injection. Adrenaline is a sympathomimetic amine, and produces effects similar to the stimulation of structures innervated by the sympathetic system, the sweat-glands being a notable exception.

(1) *Vaso-motor.* Splanchnic and cutaneous arterioles are constricted, the arterioles of the skeletal muscles are dilated. This leads to a redistribution of blood in the organism.

(2) *Cardiac Stimulation.* The rate and force of the heart-beat are increased, the effect suggesting a heightened sensitivity to the Ca^{2+} ion. The coronary arteries are dilated.

(3) *Glycogenolysis and Increase in Lactic Acid Content of Blood.* This is accompanied by a corresponding breakdown of muscle glycogen. The excess lactic acid is resynthesised to glycogen in the liver, and in turn serves to raise the level of blood sugar. Thus, adrenaline injection causes a mobilisation of carbohydrate, and it may be described as a *glucotropic hormone.*

(4) Stimulation of creatine formation, as shown by rise in the creatine content of muscle.

(5) *Miscellaneous Muscular Responses.* Dilatation of the pupil, retraction of the upper eyelid, and protrusion of the eyeball; relaxation of the bronchioles, relaxation of the detrusor, and contraction of the sphincters in the bladder, inhibition of movement, and contraction of the sphincters of the intestine.

In man, the therapeutic subcutaneous dose is 0·5 ml. of a 0·1 per cent. solution, which represents about 0·007 mg., per kg. body weight.

Effects of Adrenaline Administration. Injected subcutaneously the absorption of adrenaline is retarded owing to the local vasoconstriction it produces, and so it is administered intramuscularly or intravenously. The general cardiovascular response depends on the integrity of the vagal innervation of the heart. If this be abolished, by section or by atropine, the response to adrenaline is a rapid, temporary rise in blood pressure, accompanied by an increase in the frequency and force of the heart beat. The effect subsides in a few minutes owing to destruction of the hormone. Where the vagal innervation is intact, moderate doses of adrenaline (0·1 to 0·5 mg.) cause a rise in blood pressure, accompanied by slowing of the heart, owing to vagal inhibition evoked by an aortic pressor reflex. Large doses of adrenaline (1·0 to 1·5 mg.) cause a 20 per cent. increase in the basal metabolic rate, and a two-fold increase in the cardiac output, the stimulus from the hormone being sufficient to overcome vagal inhibition. The cardiac effect may persist for over an hour, and may be accompanied by disturbances of rhythm, terminating in heart failure.

Significance of Adrenaline. By means of cross-circulation experiments in which the blood of an intact animal was conveyed to the jugular vein of an adrenalectomised animal, Tournade and Heymans obtained evidence to show that adrenaline is continually being secreted in all conditions of bodily activity, reaching maximal values in (i) physical stress, (ii) exposure to cold, (iii) fall in arterial blood pressure, (iv) asphyxia, (v) hypoglycæmia, (vi) central anæsthesia, (vii) sudden or painful stimuli, and (viii) emotional disturbance. Cannon for many years has maintained that adrenaline is the hormone concerned in the expression of terror, rage, panic and pain. By

393

accepting the psychological implication of this theory, adrenaline appears as the chief effector agent employed by the unconscious self for the emergency defence of the organism.

The adrenaline output is controlled by a higher nervous centre, which responds to (i) stimuli from increase in blood pressure, these stimuli being transmitted from the aorta and carotid sinus, and serve in the maintenance of the circulation; (ii) chemical stimuli from the sugar in the blood, which, when it falls below its usual level, evokes a compensatory release of stored carbohydrate; and (iii) thermal stimuli, when the temperature of the external or internal environment falls below a critical value. In response to each of these types of stimuli, the adrenal gland sets in action the mechanism appropriate for meeting each specific demand. Emotional disturbances also may evoke liberation of adrenaline. The efferent impulses to the gland travel in the splanchnic nerves, and when these are cut the emergency secretion of adrenaline ceases.

Noradrenaline, like adrenaline, can function as a sympathomimetic amine, and is liberated in liver and spleen when the sympathetic nerves to the blood vessels are stimulated (Gaddum, 1947). The effects of the two hormones differ in several ways: adrenaline, when injected, has a vaso-dilator action on the arterioles in cardiac and skeletal muscle, and accelerates the heart beat; noradrenaline has a contrary effect. In general, noradrenaline is the chemical transmitter of sympathetic constrictor impulses and is the counterpart of the other neurocrine, acetylcholine, which transmits parasympathetic dilator impulses (p. 418).

History of the Adrenalines. In 1856 Vulpian observed that adrenal medulla and its extracts gave a green colour with $FeCl_3$, and red colours with oxidisers, such as iodine, or chromate. Tissues displaying this property were described as *cromaffin.* During a survey of the effect of injected gland extracts on blood pressure, Oliver and Schäfer (1895) found that both supra-renal and pituitary contain pressor factors. One of these, associated with the chromogenic substance in adrenal extracts, was isolated as a crystalline hormone, in 1901, by Takamine and by Aldrich, and named *adrenaline.* The importance of adrenaline as a sympathomimetic agent was shown by Dale and by Cannon, and for some years it was believed to be the chemical transmitter of the sympathetic nervous system. In 1946 von Euler located noradrenaline in animal tissues, notably in the nerves of the sympathetic chain.

The transmitter obtained from extracts of adrenergic nerves is usually if not invariably noradrenaline; that obtained from frog heart, human coronary nerves, prostate gland, and postganglionic sympathetic nerves, is usually adrenaline.

In the past, confusion arose because of the application of tests that did not differentiate between the two hormones. Noradrenaline can be regarded as adrenaline in which the methyl radical has been removed from the nitrogen atom, hence the prefix " nor " (German: " N ohne radikal ").

Assay of the Adrenalines

Biological Methods. (1) Rise in blood pressure when the hormone is injected into a living animal. Adrenaline is one of the most powerful known vaso-constrictors, and is used in treatment of collapse from shock.

(2) Inhibitory effect on the spontaneous contractions of a strip of intestine or other unstriated muscle, immersed in warm saline.

(3) Pupil-dilating effect on the enucleated eye.

(4) Accelerating effect on the perfused, beating heart.

Some of these methods can be made sufficiently sensitive to detect adrenaline in concentrations of 0.5 μg. per 100 ml.

Colorimetric Methods. Production of red pigments, adrenochrome and nor-adrenochrome, by oxidation with halogens, iodic acid, persulphate or mercuric chloride.

Fluorimetric Methods. Development of a greenish-yellow fluorescence by atmospheric oxidation of the alkaline solutions. These methods will distinguish between adrenaline and noradrenaline, which gives a fluorescence only one-third that the intensity of that obtained from adrenaline.

Biosynthesis of the adrenalines takes place in the adrenal medulla, involves the oxidation of tyrosine to dopa, the decarboxylation of dopa to dopamine, the oxidation of dopamine to noradrenaline, and the methylation of noradrenaline to adrenaline.

The adrenal medulla, unlike the cortex, does not appear to be necessary for life. The requirements of nervous system for transmission can be met by extra-medullary synthesis, in the nerve-endings. Adrenalines injected or liberated locally are rapidly inactivated by adrenaline oxidases, in the nerve tissues and elsewhere, adrenochromes being among the products.

THYROID HORMONE

The thyroid gland arises as an outgrowth of the pharyngeal floor in the embryo. In the human adult it weighs 20 to 25 gm., and is unique among the tissues because of its high content of iodine, the average amount being 15 mg., at least half of which can be extracted in the form of the hormone thyroxine.

L-Thyroxine was isolated by Kendall, in 1914, and identified by Harington and Barger, who subsequently effected its synthesis (1927). The details of this achievement are summarised by Barger (1930).

Thyroxine is derived from two molecules of di-iodo-phenol, and contains an alanine side-chain, thus being related to tyrosine, its precursor in the diet, and iodogorgoic acid. Owing to the asymmetric carbon atom in the side-chain

$$\text{HO}\underset{I}{\overset{I}{\bigcirc}}-O-\underset{I}{\overset{I}{\bigcirc}}CH_2.CH.COOH$$
$$\underset{NH_2}{}$$

Thyroxine.

395

two forms of thyroxine are known, the natural hormone being the L (—)-isomer, derived from L-tyrosine.

3,5,3′,5′-Tetra-iodothyronine

Replacement of I by H produces *thyronine*, the iodine-free hydroxyphenyl ether of tyrosine. *Thyroglobulin*, the form in which the hormone is released by the gland, is a protein containing thyroxine units. In the tissues, thyroxine is released, and de-iodinated into the more active 3,5,3′-tri-iodothyronine.

Effects of Thyroid and Thyroxine Administration

(1) *Stimulation of Metabolism*. One mg. of thyroxine can raise the basal metabolic rate of the adult by 2 to 3 per cent. Larger doses cause a proportionate increase and a prolonged effect. This stimulation is accompanied by a loss in weight, owing to depletion of the fat reserves, and hypertrophy of the active organs, heart, kidney, suprarenal, and liver.

(2) *Mobilisation of glucose*, following increased breakdown of hepatic and cardiac glycogen. The blood sugar level is raised, and hyperglycæmia and glycosuria may result.

(3) *Decalcification of bone*. The effect differs from that of the parathyroid hormone in that the plasma calcium level is not raised and the transferred calcium is excreted by the intestine as well as in the urine.

(4) *Stimulation of metamorphosis* in amphibia, including the tadpole.

(5) *Species desensitisation to methyl cyanide* (aceto-nitrile). A method for assaying thyroid preparations is based on the increased tolerance to methyl cyanide that they confer on mice.

Hypothyroidism. A. *Acute*. Thyroidectomy, uncomplicated by involvement of the parathyroids, in young animals causes cretinoid conditions to develop, including retardation of skeletal growth, hardening of skin and loss of hair, retarded sexual development and absence of secondary sexual characters, and mental dullness and apathy. In man, the condition of *cachexia strumipriva* (κακός, ill; ἕξις, habit; *struma*, goitre; *privus*, deprivation), or operative myxœdema, develops in a week, as shown by: fall in basal metabolic rate, usually by about 25 per cent.; slowing of the heart beat to about 50 per min.; subnormal temperature; cutaneous changes, loss of hair from scalp and outer third of eyebrows, subcutaneous deposition of myxomatous tissue; disturbance of mental activity and sexual functions.

B. *Chronic*. Non-development or atrophy of the gland.

(1) Congenital maldevelopment causes **cretinism,** the signs of which do not appear until about six months after birth, due partly to the autacoids supplied in the mother's milk and partly to the reserve in the child. The signs and symptoms of cretinism are similar to those of hypothyroidism or myxœdema.

(2) Simple goitre accompanied by hypothyroidism may arise when there is a deficiency of iodine in the diet. This is due usually to a faulty environment. A compensational hypertrophy of the gland endeavours unsuccessfully to manufacture sufficient hormone from inadequate material.

(3) Atrophy of the thyroid may occur spontaneously in adults, especially women, after middle age.

All these conditions are specifically relieved by appropriate thyroid administration. One mg. of iodine *per diem*, supplied in any inorganic form, is sufficient to prevent the reappearance of simple goitre.

Hyperthyroidism. Increased secretion of the hormone may occur without obvious signs of gland enlargement, the result being: (i) increased basal metabolism, (ii) mild pyrexia, (iii) pigmentation of the skin, (iv) nervous restlessness, (v) mild exophthalmos, (vi) cardiac and vascular disturbance. Hyperthyroidism is a feature of Graves's disease (Basedow's disease, or exophthalmic goitre), the pathogenesis of which is still obscure. In Graves's disease the basal metabolic rate may be 50 per cent. above normal in an average case, and up to 100 per cent. above normal in a severe case.

Administration of iodine in small but prolonged dosage benefits many types of hyperthyroidism; this is because thyroid hormone synthesis is repressed when the blood iodine exceeds a limiting value.

The most obvious histological effect of the iodine therapy is the restoration of the colloidal appearance to the gland structure.

Regulation of Thyroxine. The thyroid gland is supplied by the middle cervical sympathetic ganglion, but section of the entire nerve supply does not lead to hypothyroid states, from which it is inferred that the gland has a metabolic activity of its own, and continually elaborates, stores and secretes its hormone independently of the autonomic nervous system. Apart from the obvious limiting factors, namely, the supply of iodine and tyrosine or phenylalanine, the gland responds to (i) hormone control by the thyrotropic factor of the anterior pituitary, and (ii) thermal stimuli, which, perhaps, act through the thermotaxic centre in the hypothalamus, and reach the gland by the sympathetic nerves.

Cramer has shown that exposure to cold evokes a protective secretion by the thyroid as well as by the adrenal gland.

Therapeutic Applications of Thyroxine. In addition to their specific use in the hypothyroid states, thyroid preparations are used popularly in the treatment of obesity. Given to a normal subject, small doses lead to a disappearance of storage lipids, provided the diet is kept sufficiently low in fat and carbohydrate to compel the subject to draw on his own reserves. Overdosage leads to alimentary disturbances, tachycardia and loss in weight. Other drugs, notably di-nitrophenol and di-nitro *o*-cresol, have a similar effect in increasing general metabolism, but they are dangerous remedies in comparison with the natural hormone. Unlike thyroxine, they display a catalytic effect in promoting respiration in tissue slices.

Significance of Thyroxine. The iodine content of the thyroid gland varies greatly with the environment and the diet. The dried preparations of ox, sheep or pig gland, used therapeutically, are standardised by admixture with sufficient lactose to give a powder containing 0·1 per cent. iodine in the form of thyroxine. The iodine content of human and other animal thyroids ranges from 0·1 to 0·5 per cent. of the dry weight, but may exceed 1·0 per cent. in animals living on marine foodstuffs rich in the halogen, such as Orkney sheep, which feed on kelp seaweed. When the iodine content falls below 0·1 per cent. of dry weight, the gland enlarges and assumes the goitrous form.

Thyroxine has only about half the activity of a thyroid preparation containing the same amount of iodine, from which it appears that thyroxine is merely a constituent of the actual hormone.

Furthermore, thyroxine differs from adrenaline in that the response to its administration is very slow and sustained. Adrenaline reacts within a minute; thyroxine requires two to four days. This suggests that thyroxine requires biochemical modification before becoming available for metabolic catalysis.

The daily output of thyroxine in the human adult is believed to be of the order of 0·5 to 1·0 mg. *per diem*, which is the amount sufficient to maintain normal health in the thyroidectomised subject.

The iodine thus metabolised is not lost to the organism, but is in part re-synthesised to thyroxine. The urinary output of iodine ranges from about 0·03 to 0·173 mg. *per diem*, depending on the diet, and von Fellenberg has computed that the minimal requirement of the human subject is met by the daily provision of 0·05 mg. I_2 in any soluble inorganic form.

Using radioactive iodine, Chaikoff has found that it reaches the thyroid within a few minutes after alimentary absorption, and in two hours can be detected in the actual hormone.

Thyroxine Metabolism

Tyrosine-containing proteins, such as casein, readily take up iodine in presence of alkali, and on hydrolysis yield 3,5-di-iodotyrosine and thyroxine; a similar process occurs in the thyroid gland, where an accompanying enzyme, *dehalogenase*, prevents the accumulation of mono-iodo- and di-iodo-thyronine, which, like thyroxine, are thyroid inhibitors. Dehalogenase deficiency is responsible for some forms of non-endemic goitre.

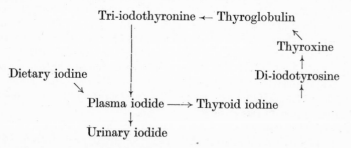

The elaboration of plasma iodide into thyroglobulin is promoted by the thyrotropic hormone of the anterior pituitary, and inhibited by the anti-thyroid agents.

Thyroid Assay. Thyroglobulin, thyroxine, or iodinated proteins, in very low concentration promote the growth and metamorphosis of frog tadpoles; thyroxine in higher concentrations over-accelerates the change and hastens death. By this means, added compounds can be tested for thyroxine-inhibiting properties.

Thyroid Inhibitors. The purine, *paraxanthine*, and some thiols, including *thiourea*, can inhibit the activity of the thyroid. Paraxanthine is a normal microconstituent of urine. Volatile thiols are obtainable from *brassicœ*, including cauliflower and cabbage, and may be responsible for their goitrogenic effect, recorded by McCarrison.

PARATHYROID HORMONE

The parathyroids are the smallest endocrine organs known in the animal body, and are represented by four structures situated at the back of the thyroid gland. Before their existence was recognised, they were removed with the thyroid tissue during experimental thyroidectomy, and the effects of the operation included both hypothyroid and hypoparathyroid phenomena.

Parathyrin, or parathormone (Collip), is obtained by extracting fresh parathyroid tissue with 5 per cent. HCl, and precipitating the higher proteins. Parathyrin is a proteose, and is destroyed by the proteases of the alimentary tract. Subcutaneous or intravenous injection causes:

(1) *Mobilisation of Blood Calcium.* The Ca level is raised from the normal value of about 10 mg. per 100 ml. to a value depending on the number of units given.

The unit is one-hundredth of the amount required to cause a 5 mg. Ca increase per 100 ml. in the blood serum of a 20 kg. dog, 15 hours after injection.

(2) *Abolition of Tetany.* All forms of tetany due to hypocalcæmia are relieved, including those directly due to parathyroid removal. This includes infantile, post-operative, and parathyroid tetany, as well as that due to alkalosis.

(3) *Hypophosphatœmia.* The rise in blood calcium is associated with a fall in blood phosphate, and an increase in urinary phosphate output.

Hyperparathyroidism. A. *Acute.* Collip has shown that over-dosage of parathyrin causes severe hypercalcæmia in which the Ca level may rise above 20 mg. per 100 ml. This is accompanied by (i) depression of motor excitability; (ii) anorexia, drowsiness, and coma; (iii) diarrhœa; (iv) decrease in blood volume and increase in viscosity.

Death is from failure of the heart, and is followed rapidly by intravascular clotting.

B. *Chronic.* Clinical hyperparathyroidism has been recognised by Hunter (1930), Jessop (1935) and other workers. The features are: (i) mobilisation of calcium from the skeleton; (ii) bone rarefaction; (iii) hypercalcæmia; (iv) negative calcium balance with hyperexcretion of calcium in the urine; (v) muscular weakness and hypotonia.

Hypoparathyroidism. A. *Acute.* Complete parathyroidectomy in the dog is followed by: (i) hypocalcæmia, the serum Ca level falling by 50 per cent. to about 6 mg. per 100 ml.; (ii) hyperexcitability of the peripheral nerves to electrical and mechanical stimuli, muscular twitching; (iii) tetanic spasms, due to central stimulation in the brain stem. These increase in violence, with alternate phases of exhaustion, until death results from asphyxia owing to respiratory spasm, or cardiac failure.

Acute hypocalcæmia may be treated by oral administration of large doses of soluble calcium salts, by saline injections, and, specifically, by injections of parathyrin. After about six weeks the organism becomes adapted to life at a lower level of serum calcium.

B. *Chronic.* Idiopathic hypoparathyroidism and some forms of infantilism exemplify the chronic condition. Infantile tetany, which is associated with rickets, cœliac disease and steatorrhœa, is not regarded as being a parathyroid disorder.

Hypoparathyroidism, as far as it can be regarded as a clinical entity, displays: (i) hypocalcæmia; (ii) hyperphosphatæmia; (iii) actual or potential tetany. Probably the age of onset of the disease determines the nature of the symptoms.

Calcium-mobilising steroids, including vitamin D_2 and dihydrotachysterol (AT10), are used therapeutically in treatment of parathyroid deficiency.

Significance of Parathyrin. The hormone regulates the renal excretion of PO_4, and thus controls the PO_4 level, and, indirectly, the Ca level in the plasma. Parathyrin secretion or injection stimulates excretion of urinary PO_4. To compensate for the resulting hypophosphatæmia, PO_4 is withdrawn from the bones, with accompanying release of Ca, which leads to a hypercalcæmia.

The artificially prepared steroid, dihydro-tachysterol (AT10, or anti-tetanic substance 10) has a similar effect, but can be given by mouth.

Tetany. Clinical tetany is characterised by the tendency of muscles to undergo spasmodic contraction, those commonly affected being the muscles of the forearm and hands, the larynx, and, less frequently, the lower limbs. The condition is associated with a fall in the plasma calcium level below 7 mg. per 100 ml., and an accompanying rise in the phosphate level to above 5 mg. per 100 ml.

PANCREATIC HORMONES

History. In 1889, Minkowski showed that complete extirpation of the pancreas in dogs was followed by severe glycosuria and fatal coma, the condition being indistinguishable from diabetes mellitus. Ligature of the gland duct, although causing digestive disturbances from lack of pancreatic juice, did not evoke this artificial diabetes, from which it was concluded that a hormone of internal secretion was still being manufactured.

Attempts to extract this hormone had been inconclusive, until, in 1922,

Banting and Best devised a technique for separating the hormone from the destructive influence of the pancreatic enzymes.

By continuous injection of islet extracts, a depancreatised dog was kept alive for 70 days in 1922. Less than two years later, insulin was in use all over the world in the successful treatment of diabetes.

Preparation of Insulin. (*a*) *Alcohol Fractionation* (Collip, 1923). Fresh minced pancreas is extracted with aqueous alcohol, the extract is concentrated *in vacuo* until most of the fat has separated out, alcohol is added to precipitate the tissue proteins, and then insulin in the filtrate is precipitated by raising the alcohol concentration to 92 per cent., or by addition of ammonium sulphate. It is purified by reprecipitation at the iso-electric point, pH 5·3.

(*b*) *Picric Acid Precipitation* (Dickens and Dodds, 1924). The fresh gland is ground up with solid picric acid, extracted with acetone, and the insulin picrate recovered after distillation of the solvent.

Crystalline insulin has been obtained by various methods, including the addition of pyridine to insulin solutions at pH 5·6. The potency of the crystalline hormone is very little greater than that of some of the amorphous preparations, namely 23 to 26 international units per mg. Chemically, insulin belongs to the peptides, which explains its destruction in the alimentary tract, when given by the mouth.

Effects of Insulin Injection. (1) *Hypoglycæmia.* The level of the blood sugar falls rapidly within 30 minutes of the injection; and, if the dose be sufficiently large, and the carbohydrate reserves depleted by starvation, the condition of hypoglycæmia sets in, the blood sugar level having fallen below 40 mg. per 100 ml. The condition in the rabbit is marked by signs of extreme hunger, violent convulsions, coma, and death from respiratory failure. Rigor mortis follows immediately. In the human subject, hypoglycæmia is accompanied by hunger pangs, exhaustion, tremor, vaso-motor disturbances, sweating, delirium, and coma.

All these hypoglycæmic phenomena may be abolished in a few minutes by intravenous injection of glucose, or less rapidly, by oral administration. Fructose and mannose are not so effective; galactose is almost without action. Injection of the other glucotropic hormones, namely, adrenaline and pituitrin, may cause a rise in blood sugar sufficient to compensate for the effects of the insulin.

Insulin injection is followed by an increased metabolism and a rise in the respiratory quotient, showing that the utilisation of sugar has been stimulated.

The hypoglycæmia, however, is greater than can be accounted for by the immediate combustion of glucose, and two other factors are believed to act in lowering the blood sugar level: (i) increased storage of carbohydrate, and (ii) decreased sugar formation from the glucogenic amino acids. Accompanying the rise in carbohydrate metabolism, is an immediate inhibition of ketone formation from fat metabolism.

(2) *Glycogenesis.* When a diabetic animal is given insulin and more than

401

sufficient sugar to compensate for the insulin hypoglycæmia, it is found that some of the excess of the saccharide has been stored up in the liver and muscles as glycogen. This glycogenic effect is not seen usually after insulin injection because the glycogen stores are rapidly depleted in an endeavour to maintain a normal sugar level in the blood.

Muscle glycogen represents a much more stable location of the polymer than hepatic glycogen. Severe hypoglycæmia ultimately results in an almost complete withdrawal of liver glycogen to meet the aggravated metabolic demands, whereas even a fatal hypoglycæmia may leave an abundant reserve of muscle glycogen.

(3) *Hypophosphatæmia* follows insulin injection, probably owing to a diversion of serum phosphate to form labile hexose phosphate preparatory to sugar utilisation.

(4) *Hypopotassæmia*. Potassium passes from the plasma into the tissue cells. The general effects of insulin are attributable to its ability to protect the sugar-activating enzymes or hexokinases from inhibition by the anti-hexokinase factors released by the anterior pituitary, and, possibly, other tissues. Until glucose has been converted into glucose-6-phosphate it is unable to enter the general metabolic processes of glycogenesis and glycolysis. Other effects attributed to insulin include: promotion of cellular absorption of glucose (Levine, 1950); and stimulation of hepatic glucose-6-phosphatase (Ashmore, 1954).

The Insulin Unit. This was defined originally as the amount required to evoke hypoglycæmic convulsions in a fasting rabbit of 2 kg. weight. Wide variations in animal sensitivity have led to the abandonment of this unit in favour of one based on the use of a standard preparation of crystalline zinc insulin, 1 mg. of which represents 22 units. One insulin unit equals 0·045 mg. of this material.

Insulin forms a salt with protamines and with globin that is more prolonged in action than the free hormone, and this therapeutic effect may be augmented by zinc, which is present in 0·5 per cent. concentration in crystallised insulin.

Regulation of Output. The hormone is continually being secreted to meet demands of carbohydrate metabolism, and is present in the venous blood leaving the pancreas. Secretion is evoked (i) *chemically*, by a rise in the sugar content of the blood, and (ii) *neurally*, by the vagi which innervate the insular tissue, and which on stimulation bring about a fall in blood sugar. The sugar factor in the secretion of insulin has led some workers to attribute diabetes mellitus to failure of the gland owing to prolonged exhaustion by a diet excessively rich in carbohydrate. This notion in a less explicit form inspired the earlier methods of treatment of the disease by complete exclusion of all starches and sugars from the diet, so that the gland might recuperate. The discovery of insulin, however, has made it possible to utilise carbohydrate foodstuffs, and many types of dietary are now available for the diabetic subject. The occasional appearance of an insulin-resistant type of diabetes is attributed to dysfunction involving other gluco-kinetic hormones, notably those of the anterior pituitary.

The Structure of Insulin. Insulin is the first protein to have had its structure pattern completely elucidated, chiefly by the work of Sanger (1944–). The hormone is a polypeptide of m.w. 6,000, and is formed of two chains of amino acid residues, held at two points by disulphide bridges between cysteine units in the opposing chains (p. 119). It contains no unusual amino acids, and there is nothing obvious in its structure that explains its physiological effects. Insulin readily undergoes reversible polymerisation to the dimer, m.w. 12,000, and the tetramer.

Glucagon, the hyperglycæmic factor secreted by the α-cells of the islets, promotes the phosphorylation of glucose, and an accompanying decrease in hepatic glycogen. The factor, first recognised as an " anti-insulin " contaminant of insulin preparations, has been isolated by Staub, *et al.* (1955), and is a macro-peptide of m.w. 4,200.

GYNÆCOGENS: FEMALE SEX HORMONES

In order that the genetically determined vertebrate sex may develop to maturity and function, hormones elaborated by the germinal glands are necessary. These are sometimes termed the secondary sexual hormones to distinguish them from the primary sexual effectors responsible for the sex of the embryo, which at the present time is beyond the scope of experimental control. The various aphrodisiacs employed by the human race have a story that goes back to the fruit tree of Eden, and includes the fantastic pharmacologies of the East as well as the potions of the Middle Ages. It is now established that the sex hormones, both male and female, are lipoid compounds related to the sterols, and are only absorbed with difficulty from the alimentary tract, which may explain the erratic results obtained by empirical therapy.

The experimental foundation of modern knowledge dates from 1912, when Nussbaum showed that the sex characters of the male frog are controlled by a testicular hormone, and that whenever specific structures are associated with animal sex their growth is dependent on chemical factors. Because of the greater complexity of the female organism, two types of hormone are required: (i) an *œstrogen*, controlling the early stage in the uterine cycle, and (ii) a *progesterone*, which prepares the uterus for the implantation of the fertilised ovum.

Progress in the study of the human hormones was delayed, partly through ignorance of the exact nature of the menstrual cycle, and partly because of the lack of a satisfactory test for measuring the activity of the hormone preparations. In 1923, Allen and Doisy obtained a lipoid extract from ovaries which, when injected into castrated rodents, was able to re-establish the reproductive or œstrus cycle, and obviously contained the long-sought œstrogen. The same workers also adapted a " vaginal-smear " test, whereby it was possible histologically to detect the onset of œstrus from changes in the vaginal epithelium.

In 1927, Aschheim and Zondek found that an œstrogen was excreted in large quantities in the urine of pregnant animals, thus providing a source of material for purification and identification. Since then, five closely related œstrogens have been isolated from the ovary, the urine of pregnancy, and from the placenta; a progesterone has been isolated from the corpus luteum, and four *androgens*, or male sex hormones, have been isolated from various sources.

Œstrogens. The ovarian follicular hormone, made in the ripening follicle, is a typical œstrogen, an evoker of sex response in the female. Œstrogens prepare the uterine lining for reception of the fertilised ovum, and stimulate the growth of the mammary glands. At birth time, they activate the uterus. They are used therapeutically to lessen the effects of the sudden onset of the menopause.

Œstrone, or *theelin*, the first œstrogen to be isolated, was obtained in crystalline form from urine by Doisy (1929). It is made in the ovaries and in the placenta. In 1935, Doisy obtained a dihydrotheelin, *œstradiol*, from ovarian tissue, in a yield of 6 mg. per ton of sow ovary, which indicates the low concentration and corresponding high potency of the hormone.

The formulation of the œstrogens is given on p. 412. All are derived from a parent steroid, œstrane, or 13-methyl sterane, in which ring I has been dehydrogenated at 1 : 2, 3 : 5, and 5 : 10, and has a hydroxyl group at carbon 3. This gives the œstrogens phenolic properties which are useful in analytical separation. Œstradiol also has HO— at 17; œstriol has HO— at 16 and 17; œstrone is a 17-oxosteroid, with no hydroxyl groups attached to ring IV.

Sources of the Œstrogens. Ovary, corpus luteum, placenta, adrenal cortex of both sexes, testes of some animals, male and female urine and the urine of pregnancy.

Distribution. Œstradiol and *œstriol*: placenta and urine of pregnancy. *Œstrone*: adrenal cortex, male and female urine, placenta.

Metabolism. Œstradiol, the parent œstrogen, is elaborated in the ovary and adrenal cortex from cholesterol or a pro-cholesterol; transformation into the other œstrogens may take place in the target tissues, or in the liver, where the œstrogens are conjugated for excretion in the urine as glucuronides and sulphuric esters.

Total urinary œstrogen output, in micrograms per 24 hours: children (5 to 10 years), 3 to 6·5; men, 24 $\pm$ 3; women (under 50 years), 30 $\pm$ 20; women (over 50), 0 to 24, pregnancs, later months, 360 to 15,000.

Œstradiol is the actual ovarian follicular hormone. It is a colourless steroid, slightly soluble in water, but freely soluble in organic solvents. *Œstrone* and *œstriol* represent various oxidation forms in which œstradiol is excreted, after esterification, in the urine. The most active of these compounds is œstradiol, and the least active is œstriol, which on account of its three hydroxyl groups is more soluble in water and less soluble in fat-solvents than the other œstrogens. Œstriol is manufactured also in the placenta, during pregnancy, and is excreted partly as a glucuronic acid derivative.

Physiological Effects of Œstrogens. In experimental animals, whose ovaries have been removed, injection of an œstrogen caused rapid growth of the vaginal epithelium, as in normal œstrous states, together with increased growth of the uterine mucosa and the mammary tissue. In the normal animal, œstrogen injection hastens the onset of œstrus. These effects are accompanied by (i) increased metabolism, with loss in weight, especially in obese gonadectomised animals; (ii) glucose mobilisation and increased resistance to insulin. Excessive doses of natural or artificial œstrogens inhibit the gonadotropic activity of the pituitary gland.

Standardisation of the Œstrogens. The original standard was the rat unit (r.u.) or the mouse unit (m.u.), which was defined as the minimal quantity of hormone necessary to evoke œstrus in the gonadectomised animal, the state being recognised histologically by the Allen and Doisy test. These units are apt to vary according to differences in laboratory technique, and a committee established by the League of Nations has recommended an international unit equivalent to $0\cdot1\gamma$ ($0\cdot0001$ mg.) of œstradiol benzoate, which is the average value of the mouse unit. Œstradiol is twice as potent as œstrone, and twenty times as potent as œstriol.

The artificially-prepared ethynylœstradiol, which has the ethynyl group, —C : CH, at 17, is the most effective therapeutically of the œstrogens.

The Luteal Hormone

The corpus luteum, which is formed from the ovarian follicle after escape of the ovum, elaborates a hormone, *progesterone*, or *progestin*, that in the human non-pregnant condition acts by stimulating the growth and secretion of the endometrial mucosa during the 14 days prior to menstruation. During pregnancy, the corpus luteum persists, maintained by a factor secreted by the embryo, and the output of progesterone continues in most animals, except the mare, until parturition. Thus, ovarian activity is associated with the production of two independent hormones, œstradiol and progesterone.

Progesterone, or *luteosterone*, $C_{21}H_{30}O_2$, the luteal hormone, was recognised by Corner, Allen, Gley and other independent workers, and obtained in pure crystalline form by Butenandt. It is a 17-acetyl derivative of a dimethyl sterane nucleus similar to that found in the androgens, and is responsible for the three principal progestational functions of the corpus luteum:

(1) Premenstrual endometrial growth and secretion, in the non-pregnant state.

405

(2) Inhibition of ovulation and menstruation during pregnancy.

(3) Embedding of the fertilised ovum, and placenta formation.

Progesterone is excreted as its inactive reduction derivatives, allo-*pregnanediol* and *pregnanediol*, which occurs as a glucuronidate in human urine during the latter half of the menstrual cycle, the daily yield being 1 to 10 mg., as the Na salt. Progesterone has been obtained, by Marrian, from pregnanediol and from the plant steroid, *stigmasterol*.

The hormone is used therapeutically in treatment of uterine disorders, menorrhagia, threatened abortion and spasmodic dysmenorrhœa. A synthetic steroid, *ethisterone*, has the advantage that, unlike pregnanediol, it is active when given orally.

The international unit (1935) is defined as the potency of 1 mg. of crystalline progesterone.

Significance of the Ovarian Hormones. Extirpation of the ovary before puberty inhibits the development of the secondary sexual characters and the establishment of the menstrual cycle. Extirpation after puberty induces the syndrome characteristic of the menopause, or climacteric, which in the human subject normally occurs between the ages of 45 and 50, and is often associated with a general endocrine disturbance. Ovarian grafts in the ovariectomised subject lead to a temporary restoration of the sexual cycle, but the implanted tissue degenerates usually within a year. Ovarian grafts in the normal male animal are unsuccessful owing to the antagonising effect of a testicular factor. If, however, the animal is previously castrated, ovarian grafts will display a feminising effect, as shown by growth of the mammary glands and partial assumption of the secondary female sex characters. Œstrogens repeatedly injected into normal male animals evoke prostatic hypertrophy and enlargement of the utriculus, which is the homologue of part of the genital tract in the female.

On account of the importance of the ovary, it was formerly assumed that the tissue was more or less autonomous, and produced the hormones automatically; but it is now known that ovarian activity is completely subservient to the control of the anterior pituitary gland, and that many conditions ascribed to ovarian incompetence are caused by pituitary dysfunction.

Pituitary Factors in Ovarian Activity. The anterior lobe of the pituitary gland secretes three factors, which on account of their action on the sex glands are called *gonadotropic* hormones.

(1) *Follicle-stimulating Hormone* (FSH), promotes development of the Graffian follicle in the ovary.

(2) *Interstitial-cell-stimulating Hormone* (ICSH), *Luteinising Hormone* (LH), brings about formation of the corpus luteum.

(3) *Prolactin, lactogenic hormone,* (LTH), stimulates œstrogen and progesterone secretion by the corpus luteum, and also controls lactation.

Rupture of the follicle and liberation of the ovum is caused by pressure within the follicle, following increased secretion of œstradiol.

Thus, it appears that the uterine cycle in non-pregnant and in pregnant conditions is controlled by the operation of two distinct groups of hormones, as shown in the following diagram.

Human Uterine Cycle

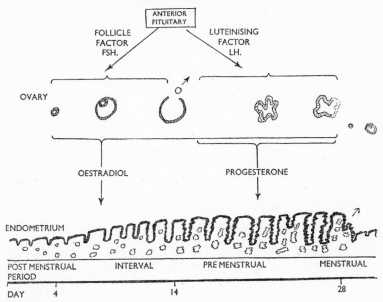

The Menstrual Cycle

Days

1–4   Secretion of FSH induces secretion of œstradiol by granulosa cells of the follicle.

5–11   Rapid growth of follicle. Continued secretion of FSH and œstradiol. Regeneration of the endometrium.

12–14   Rupture of follicle and escape of ovum. Secretion of LH. Formation of the corpus luteum.

15–26   Continued secretion of LH. Persistence of corpus luteum. Secretion of progesterone. Enlargement and secretory activity of endometrial glands.

27   Inhibition of pituitary hormones by the increase in the output of œstradiol. Corpus luteum starts to degenerate.

28   Onset of menstruation. Cessation of secretion of FSH. Rapid degeneration of corpus luteum. Decline in secretion of progesterone and œstradiol.

1–4   Decrease in secretion of ovarian hormones leads to renewal of pituitary activity, and continuation of the cycle.

Hormones in the Urine of Pregnancy. During pregnancy, the persistence of the

407

corpus luteum is assured by the continued secretion of LH, with the result that three types of hormones appear in the urine: (i) œstrogens, which are excreted in the inactive esterified form; (ii) progesterone, excreted in the inactive form of pregnanediol; (iii) gonadotropic hormones.

In human pregnancy urine, œstrone and pregnanediol occur; in urine of the cow or mare, chiefly œstriol. Both œstrogens are excreted as inactive glycuronic derivatives, until the onset of labour, when they appear in the free form.

Œstrogens and Pituitary Gonadotropic Hormones in Urine
(Representative values, expressed in mouse units)

| | Œstrogens. | | | | Gonadotropins, per Litre. | |
| | Non-pregnant. | | Pregnant. | | | |
	Per Litre.	Per Diem.	Per Litre.	Per Diem.	FSH.	LH.
Woman .	425	600	21,000	31,000	20,000	10,000
Man .	160	240	—	—	—	—
Mare .	200	2,000	100,000	1,000,000	300	0
Stallion .	170,000	1,700,000	—	—	—	—
Bull .	330	—	—	—	—	—

In human pregnancy urine, the pregnanediol 24-hour output steadily rises: 2 to 15 mg., during the first 8 weeks; 16 to 80 mg., during the next 20 weeks; and reaching 50 to 120 mg., in the last weeks.

Small quantities of œstrogen appear in human urine about the fifteenth day of the menstrual cycle, and disappear just before the onset of menstruation. During pregnancy, the output rapidly increases to a maximum of 1·5 to 2 mg. per litre, which persists till parturition, and then rapidly falls to the normal minimum.

The œstrogens presumably arise in the developing placenta, as, during pregnancy, the ovarian œstrogens are suppressed, and no follicles are ripening.

Equilin and equilenin occur as reduction derivatives, along with œstrone in the pregnancy urine from the mare, which has a total œstrogen value of about 10 mg. per litre, or five times as great as that of human pregnancy urine. Stallions differ from other male animals in excreting a urine very rich in œstrogens, the hormones having been formed in the testicle, along with the androgens.

The gonadotropin of pregnancy urine also occurs in the blood and the placenta. It is a *chorionic gonadotropin*, made in the chorionic tissue, and somewhat resembles the luteinising hormone of the anterior pituitary.

Non-steroid Œstrogens. Dodds and other workers have prepared a number of cyclic compounds capable of evoking œstrus, the most potent being derivatives of 4 : 4'-dihydroxystilbene, or " stilbœstrol ", $C_{14}H_{12}O_2$.

This discovery shows that the steroid ring is not necessary for œstrogenic function. *Diethyl stilbœstrol* is about two and a half times more potent than estrone, while the more powerful *dihydro-diethyl-stilbœstrol*, or *hexœstrol*, is s active as œstradiol.

Stilbœstrol. Diethyl-Stilbœstrol. Dihydro-Diethyl-Stilbœstrol.

Estrogenic activity requires the presence of the phenolic —OH, when this is esterified as acetate or propionate, the drug is only slowly absorbed and as uch may be implanted in subcutaneous tissue, where it hydrolyses. The stilœstrols have the advantage over the steroid œstrogens in being more oluble and capable of being absorbed when given orally, and also in their ower cost of production. Given in prolonged doses, they, like the natural estrogens, repress the gonadotropic effect of the anterior pituitary, and, thus, ndirectly can cause the regression of prostatic carcinomata by inhibiting the ecretion of androgens.

Sources of the Œstrogens. Œstradiol and œstrone can be obtained from ovarian tissue of domestic animals, and display no species specificity. That these or other œstrogens can arise independently of the follicle is shown by the fact that the œstrus cycle can persist after complete destruction of the ovarian follicles by short-wave irradiation, and also by the persistence of estrogens in urine after ovariectomy. The placenta and the adrenal cortex have been suggested as extra-ovarian sources of the hormones. Commercially, estrogens are now obtained in quantity from the urine of the cow or the horse. The female sex hormones are excreted both in male and in female urine, and, conversely, the male sex hormones have been isolated from female urine. This paradox is explained by the close chemical relationship between both groups of compounds, each member of which is derived from a methylated steroid nucleus. The urine of the stallion is especially rich in œstrogens. Vegetable sources are represented by palm kernels and palm oil.

Biological Tests for Pregnancy. The detection of the chorionic gonadotropic factors in urine constitutes a very delicate and trustworthy test for pregnancy. The test depends on the injection of the urine into young mice (Aschheim-Zondek test), rabbits (Friedman test), or a species of toad, *Xenopus lœvis* (Hogben test), and the observation of subsequent changes.

409

Aschheim-Zondek Test. Five mice, aged 3 to 4 weeks, and weighing 6 to 8 gm. each, are injected individually with 1·2 to 2·4 ml. of urine, divided into six doses given during three days. All are killed on the fifth day. A positive result for the urine is claimed if at least one animal shows ovarian changes, notably the presence of corpora lutea or corpora hæmorrhagica. Positive results have been obtained with urine as early as in the fifth week of pregnancy.

The test will distinguish between true pregnancy and menopausal conditions, including " endocrine repercussions of abnormal emotional states ". It is advisable to extract the urine with three times its volume of ether prior to injection in order to remove a toxic substance present in some urines, and fatal to mice.

The Friedman test only requires 24 to 48 hours, and for this reason is preferable.

ANDROGENS: MALE SEX HORMONES

The existence of chemical factors controlling secondary sexual characters in the male had long been inferred from the more obvious consequences of castration, before or after puberty. Early attempts by Brown-Séquard and others to obtain active extracts from testicular tissue were inconclusive, mainly for two reasons: the preparations were administered by the alimentary tract, from which the hormones are only absorbed with difficulty; and no exact method of chemical assay was available. Since 1930, Moore and others have shown that androgenic activity may be detected by the increased growth of the comb and wattles in castrated birds (capons); and Korenchevsky has based a method of assay on the increased growth of the prostate and seminal vesicles evoked when the hormone is injected into castrated rodents. Aided by these tests, four natural androgens have been isolated, and various artificial androgens have been synthesised, in addition to those from adrenal cortex.

Natural Androgens

Name.	Formula.	Source.	Discoverer.	Potency, in Rat Units.
Androsterone . .	$C_{19}H_{30}O_2$	Male urine.	Butenandt.	1 mg. = 1 r.u.
Dehydroandrosterone	$C_{19}H_{28}O_2$	Male urine.	Butenandt.	1 mg. = 0·3 r.u.
Testosterone . .	$C_{19}H_{28}O_2$	Testicle.	Laqueur.	1 mg. = 0·1 r.u.
Androstanedione .	$C_{19}H_{28}O_2$	Testicle.	—	—

Testosterone, $C_{19}H_{28}O_2$, the testicular hormone, is an unsaturated hydroxy-ketone derived from a parent steroid *androstane*, and appears in the urine as the two derivatives, *androsterone* and *dehydroisoandrosterone*, both of which are much less potent.

A fourth androgen, *androstanedione*, $C_{19}H_{28}O_2$, also prepared by reduction of androsterone, has about one-third the potency of the parent compound.

Testosterone and androsterone can now be manufactured in quantity from cholesterol and other common sterols, which provide a more convenient alternative to the natural sources.

The androgens are all colourless crystalline compounds, sparingly soluble in water but readily soluble in fat solvents, and are usually administered by intramuscular injection of the solution in an oil.

The international unit recommended by the League of Nations (1935) is the hormone activity of 0·1 mg. of crystalline androsterone, as tested by a specific biological reaction. A 15 per cent. increase in the comb area may be expected from administration to a capon of one international unit daily for 5 days.

Effects of Androgen Injection. In the castrated mammal there is a specific growth of accessory genital glands, the prostate, seminal vesicles and glands of Cowper, and a manifestation of the secondary sexual characters. The androgens differ somewhat in their results; testosterone, the most generally active, produces in capons twice as much comb growth as androstandiol and about six times as much as androsterone.

Significance of the Androgens. Castration before puberty induces the eunuchoid state in which the secondary sexual characters fail to develop. Castration after puberty has little obvious effect other than subjective changes following the sterilisation. From this it might appear that the function of the androgens is limited to the maintenance of the reproductive efficiency of the individual; but isolation of androgens from the adrenal cortex, shows that extra-testicular sources are available in the adult.

In man, secretion of testosterone begins between the ages of 10 and 14, reaches a maximum between 22 and 35, and then declines with increasing rapidity, until, by the 60th year, the activity of the interstitial cells is about the pre-puberty level. Normally, the fall in testosterone output is sufficiently slow to allow for adaptation by the organism. Occasionally, secretion rate falls abruptly, evoking the onset of a male climacteric, with asthenia, fatigue, depression, and, sometimes, involutional melancholia. This syndrome, indirectly, can be of pituitary origin, and may be accompanied by adreno-corticoid deficiency. It is treated, therapeutically, by injection or implantation of testosterone propionate. Overdosage can inhibit pituitary activity, and lead to aspermia.

The Pituitary Control of Testicular Activity. Gonadotropic hormones secreted by the anterior pituitary control, (i) the descent of the testicle, (ii) the onset and maintenance of spermatogenesis, and (iii) the output of the androgens, this last effect being homologous with that of FSH and LH in the female. Pituitary gonadotropic activity is slight before puberty, as shown by the low level of androsterone from the urine.

The œstrogenic female hormones (gynæcogens) are all derived from the 13-methyl steroid *œstrane*, $C_{17}H_{27}.CH_3$. Progesterone, pregnandiol and the male

Cyclo-Pentanophenanthrene
(parent steroid).

Œstrane.

Androstane.

Œstradiol.

Œstrone.

Œstriol.

Equilin.

Equilenin.

Progesterone.

Pregnandiol.

Testosterone.

Androsterone.

Dehydroandrosterone.

Androstandiol.

hormones are all derived from the 10 : 13-dimethyl steroid *androstane*, $C_{27}H_{26}(CH_3)_2$.

PITUITARY HORMONES

The pituitary body, or hypophysis, is double in origin and multiple in functions. From the stomodœal pouch of Rathke is developed the anterior lobe and the *pars intermedia*; from the floor of the third ventricle are formed the *pars nervosa* of the posterior lobe, the *infundibulum* and *pars tuberalis*. The pituitary autacoids are of two types: secretions acting directly on other tissues, and *hormotropic* secretions acting indirectly by stimulating other endocrine glands.

A. Anterior Lobe

Six specific proteins with hormone properties have been isolated: the metabolic growth hormone, and the tropic hormones; thyrotropin, adrenocorticotropin, follicle-stimulating hormone, luteinising hormone, and lactogenic hormone.

(1) **Growth Hormone** (Van Dyke, 1930). This hormone has a protein anabolic effect, as shown by nitrogen retention, and increased general growth, particularly that of the osseous, connective, and epithelial tissues. It has no obvious action on the thyroid, the ovaries, or any other endocrine structure.

412

Deficiency results in infantilism; excess causes gigantism and acromegaly, with overgrowth of hands, feet and jaws.

Associated with the hormone are: (a) a diabetogenic or anti-hexokinase factor, which, by retarding the phosphorylation of glucose, evokes hyperglycæmia and glycosuria; (b) a muscle glycogenic, or glycostatic factor; (c) a lipotropic factor that stimulates mobilisation and oxidation of fats, and is ketogenic in effect.

How far these factors exist as hormones or arise as metabolites of a hormone is under discussion; their activities are apt to be obscured by the accompanying effects of other pituitary hormones, notably the tropins.

The Anterior Pituitary Tropins

These hormones do not directly influence metabolism, but regulate the secretion of other ductless glands. They are described variously as exercising a directive (tropic) or nutritional (trophic) effect on the target tissue.

(2) **Thyrotropin** (Crew and Wiesner, 1930) stimulates thyroid development in young animals, and regulates the secretion of the gland. Hyperthyroidism or hypothyroidism may result from excessive or inadequate output of the thyrotropic principle.

(3) **Follicle-Stimulating Hormone,** FSH (Zondek, 1930), evokes the secretion of œstradiol, and thus determines the onset of puberty, the maintenance of the menstrual cycle and the sequence of events in pregnancy. It is present in acid extracts of the anterior gland, and is excreted in the urine of pregnancy, along with the factor from the placenta (chorionic gonadotropin) that is responsible for the Aschheim-Zondek reaction. In males, the follicle-stimulant causes testicle growth and spermatogenesis.

(4) **Luteinising Hormone,** LH, ICSH (Zondek, 1930). This evokes growth of the corpus luteum, secretion of progesterone, and inhibition of œstrogen output, thus inducing the second stage of the ovarian cycle. In males, LH activates the interstitial cells of the testicle, and is alternatively described as the interstitial cell stimulating hormone, ICSH.

(5) **Lactogenic Hormone,** Prolactin (Riddle, 1933). The growth of the mammary glands during pregnancy is ascribed to the action of the œstrogens; the actual onset of lactation is due to a pituitary factor, the effects of which can be demonstrated in the ovariectomised animal, showing that lactation is independent of œstrogen when the mammary gland has developed. Prolactin accompanies LH in alkaline extracts of the anterior pituitary, and potentiates the effect; hence, it is also designated the leutotropic hormone, LTH.

(6) **Corticotropin** (Evans, 1933). Hypophysectomy leads to atrophy of the adrenal cortex as well as atrophy of the thyroid. Pituitary hyperfunction, as seen in gigantism and basophil neoplasmic growths in the gland, is often associated with cortical hypertrophy and with hyperthyroidism. The adrenocorticotropic hormone or ACTH, is the chief regulator of adrenal

cortex activity, and is used therapeutically as an alternative to corticoi« administration.

Significance of the Anterior Pituitary Gland. By means of the gonadotropi« hormones, FSH and LH, the gland regulates ovarian activity. By means o« hormotropic factors, it co-ordinates the activity of the thyroid, adrenal an« pancreas. By means of the growth factor and metabolic principles, it regulate« development and general metabolism.

B. Posterior Lobe (*Pars Nervosa*)

(1) **Anti-diuretic Factor,** anti-diuretin. Selective removal of the posterio« pituitary evokes a polyuria, from inability of the renal tubule to concentrat« the glomerular filtrate. A very dilute urine is excreted, unaccompanied by an« abnormal solutes, although the total sodium chloride output is increased i» the early stages of the diuresis. Pathological pituitary dysfunction is asso« ciated with the disease diabetes insipidus, in which the urinary output ma« exceed 8 to 10 litres *per diem*. This leads to an acute dehydration of th« organism and an attendant abnormal thirst, or *polydypsia*. Some experimenta« and pathological forms of the diuresis are rapidly abolished by injection o« posterior pituitary extract. The recovery is transient, owing to destruction o« excretion of the anti-diuretic factor. The factor has been separated fron« normal urine by Gilman and Goodman (1937). Anti-diuretin is the regulato« of the osmotic pressure in the blood and tissue fluids, and controls th« excretion of water and retention of sodium chloride by the kidney, in respons« to changes in concentrations of Na^+ and Cl^- in the plasma. An " osmo« receptor " centre in the hypothalamus reacts to changes of the order of 1 pe« cent. in the osmotic pressure of the body fluids.

(2) **Oxytocin,** α-hypophamine (Kamm *et al.*, 1928), causes a powerful contrac« tion of the uterine muscle, and also stimulates the musculature of the bladde« the intestine, and the rest of the unstriated muscle of the organism with th« exception of that of the bronchi. A pseudo-galactagogue effect is also seen i» the temporary outpouring of milk that follows injection of oxytocin or o« pituitary extracts. This is ascribed to the expression of preformed milk fron« the gland owing to contraction of the ducts.

(3) **Vaso-pressin,** β-hypophamine, causes contraction of capillaries an« arterioles after injection. The blood pressure slowly rises and remains hig« for several hours. There is little change in the rate and force of the heart bea« other than that due to increased vascular resistance.

Injection of a second dose after the pressor effects of the first have worn o« usually causes little or no response, the vascular system remaining insensitiv« for several« This may be due to the appearance of an anti-vaso-pressi« in the organism, or, more likely, to the exhaustion of a contractile factor i« the vessel walls. Birds for some unexplained reason appear to be immun« from the vaso-pressor action of pituitary extracts. In man, the constrictin« effect on the capillaries is very conspicuous in the blanching of the skin tha« follows subcutaneous injection.

he structure of both oxytocin and vaso-pressin has been elucidated by du
'igneaud (1953–). Both are polypeptides containing nine mono-amino acid
esidues, and exist in cyclic form, closed by a disulphide bridge between two
ysteine residues, as confirmed by synthesis of the hormones. Vaso-pressin is
losely related to anti-diuretin, and they may be identical in some species.
part from its therapeutic value, oxytocin cannot be regarded as a true
ormone, since there is no evidence that it is employed in the regulation of
hysiological activity. Pregnancy and parturition are unaffected by removal
f the posterior pituitary, and the normal uterine contractions during labour
iffer in character from those evoked by oxytocin. No marked circulatory
isturbances follow removal of the posterior pituitary.

Pituitary Hormones

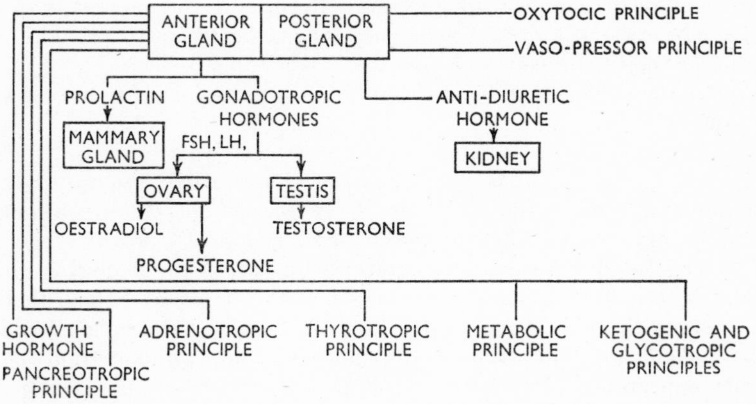

. Pars Intermedia

hromotropic Factor. The pigmentary system of amphibians is controlled by
hormone, *intermedin*, from the *pars intermedia*. Injection of extracts into
dult frogs evokes a rapid darkening of the skin owing to dilatation of the
igment cells, or melanophores. The function of the pars intermedia in the
uman subject is still obscure.

ypopituitarism. This may involve anterior or posterior lobe deficiency, or
he entire gland.
) *Anterior hypopituitarism,* as seen in maldevelopment or atrophy, is
haracterised by (i) dwarfism, (ii) sexual infantilism, (iii) obesity, with lowered
asal metabolic rate. The condition is profoundly modified by the fate of the
hyroid gland.

) Fröhlich's syndrome, dystrophia adiposo-genitalis, occurs in children,
nd is due to infantile hypopituitarism and hypothyroidism. The victims are
tunted, and often distorted by diffuse deposition of fat.

415

(b) Lorain's syndrome. Hypopituitarism unaccompanied by hypothyroidism There is retardation of skeletal growth and absence of secondary sexual characters. Mental ability is unimpaired, and is often much above the normal This type of infantilism is hereditary.

In the adult human female post-partum necrosis of the pituitary, Simmond's Disease or Sheehan's Disease, is associated with asthenia, failure of menstruation and loss of axillary and pubic hair.

Hypopituitarism is frequent in old age, and marks a stage in senility.

(2) *Posterior Hypopituitarism.* There is no convincing evidence that the posterior lobe is essential for life. Complete removal is not followed by specific symptoms of deficiency. This paradoxical result may be due to (i) readjustment of the organism during convalescence to a lower autacoid requirement, or (ii) compensatory secretion by other endocrine organs, or (iii) undetected persistence of sufficient *pars intermedia* tissue to provide antidiuretin for the requirements of life.

Hyperpituitarism. This may be of the anterior or posterior type, according to the tissue involved.

(1) *Anterior hyperpituitarism.* (a) Gigantism, due to early hyperpituitarism before the epiphyses of the long bones have united. The bones continue to grow uniformly, and the skeleton may reach a height of 7 or 8 ft.

(b) Acromegaly, due to late hyperpituitarism after the epiphyses have united. There is little change in the height of the skeleton; instead there is local overgrowth of the bones of the lower half of the face, enlargement of the hands and feet, curvature of the spine, and an approximation to the " gorilla appearance ". There is hyperplasia of the connective tissue and thickening of the skin. The sexual potential is increased, but usually decays prematurely.

Other features of these diseases, such as an erratic glycosuria, may be due to hypersecretion of corresponding anterior lobe hormones.

(2) *Posterior hyperpituitarism* has not yet been recognised as a clinical entity, although it may be involved in miscarriages and premature labour, and, perhaps, in some forms of anuria.

ALIMENTARY HORMONES

The events in the digestive process are controlled partly by the nervous system, and partly by hormones liberated by the action of the digestive products on the gastric and intestinal mucosa.

(1) **Gastrin,** Gastric Secretin. In 1905, Edkins showed that acid extracts of the pyloric mucosa, when neutralised and injected into animals, evoked a secretion of gastric juice, an effect he attributed to the presence of a specific secretagogue, *gastrin.* Subsequently it was found that meat juice, meat extracts, protein digestion products and certain amino acids had a similar

action, indicating that these factors might be of considerable importance in the maintenance of gastric digestion. The most potent secretagogue effect, however, was displayed by histamine and by β-alanine, neither of which is a constituent of the native proteins. β-Alanine is a component of carnosine and of anserine, which occur in muscle tissue (p. 291), and appears to be responsible for the secretagogue property of meat extracts and broths. Histamine is readily formed from the natural amino acid histidine, by decarboxylation, and, according to Ivy (1933), is an actual gastric hormone present in pyloric mucosa, and is liberated during digestion.

Histamine is now employed for the purpose of obtaining human gastric juice for fractional analysis. About 0·1 mg. per 10 kg. of body weight is injected; gastric secretion begins within 5 minutes, and reaches a maximum between 30 to 45 minutes after the injection. The juice evoked by histamine is rich in hydrochloric acid but deficient in enzymes, which indicates that the amine acts preferentially on the parietal cells. Injection of pilocarpine evokes a secretion rich in enzymes and mucin, and when administered along with histamine results in the production of a gastric juice similar to that secreted during normal digestion.

$$CH_2.CH_2.COOH$$
$$|$$
$$NH_2$$

β-Alanine.

$$HC{=\!=}C{-}CH_2.CH_2$$
$$|\quad\ |\qquad NH_2$$
$$HN\quad N$$
$$\diagdown\!\!\diagup$$
$$CH$$

Histamine.

$$HC{=\!=}C{-}CH_2{-}HC{-\!}CH.CH_2.CH_3$$
$$|\qquad|\qquad\quad |\quad\ |$$
$$N\quad N.CH_3\quad H_2C\quad CO$$
$$\diagdown\!\!\diagup\qquad\quad \diagdown\!\!\diagup$$
$$CH\qquad\qquad O$$

Pilocarpine.

(2) **Secretin,** the secretory hormone for the pancreas, is found in the mucosa of the upper two-thirds of the small intestine. It can be extracted by acids, soaps, 70 per cent. alcohol, and 0·6 per cent. NaCl.

The hormone is a peptide of m.w. 5,000. When injected intravenously it causes a rapid secretion of pancreatic juice, and also has a secretagogue effect on the liver and the glands of the small intestine. The action is not species specific, and somewhat resembles that of pilocarpine, but the pancreatic secretion evoked by secretin is richer in alkali and poorer in enzymes than the secretion obtained by vagal stimulation or the use of a vagomimetic drug, such as pilocarpine.

Secretin is of interest historically. The first known example of a chemical messenger, its discovery by Bayliss and Starling (1902) led to the recognition of a new family of biological agents, and the introduction of the term " hormone ".

Secretin is liberated during the course of digestion by the presence of bile salts, fats, or free acid in the upper small intestine. The hormone is inactivated by gastric juice, and is ineffective when given orally.

(3) **Pancreozymin,** obtained from yeast (Harper and Raper, 1943) and duodenal mucosa (Burn and Holton, 1948), on injection stimulates the secretion of pancreatic enzymes without increasing the pancreatic juice outflow, which is regulated by secretin.

The animal used for the purpose of assay is the cat.

(4) **Cholecystokinin,** a hormone evoking contraction of the gall bladder, resembles secretin in its distribution, and is present in extracts of the intestinal mucosa. Separation of the two hormones has been claimed by Ivy and Oldberg (1928).

(5) **Enterogastrone.** A factor inhibiting gastric motility and secretion is, according to Ivy (1937), set free by the presence of fat in the small intestine. *Urogastrone*, obtained from urine, has a similar effect and may be an excretory metabolite of enterogastrone.

(6) *Villikinin*, released by action of acid on duodenal mucosa, and also present in yeast, stimulates contractile pulsations in the intestinal villi.

MISCELLANEOUS HORMONES

Extracts of animal or plant tissues when injected into higher animals often display a vaso-motor effect owing to the presence of *vaso-dilatins* and *vaso-pressins*, acting on arterioles and capillaries. Some of these appear to be artefacts formed during the preparation of the tissue extract, but at least five are known to occur naturally: the vaso-dilators *histamine, acetyl choline,* and *adenylic acid*; and the vaso-constrictors *hypertensin* and *5-hydroxytryptamine*.

(1) **Histamine** has been identified in extracts of intestinal mucosa, liver, lung and posterior pituitary. It displays three characteristic effects:

(i) A secretagogue action on the lachrymal, salivary, gastric and pancreatic glands.

(ii) Contraction of involuntary muscle, notably uterus, intestine and bronchioles.

(iii) Fall in blood pressure owing to generalised capillary dilatation and paralysis, accompanied by increased capillary permeability and transudation of plasma. In the human subject, a subcutaneous injection of 0·3 mg. of histamine evokes a marked fall in diastolic pressure, a rise in pulse rate and temperature, and a flushing of the skin. Arteriolar dilatation accompanies the capillary response in man, dogs and monkeys (p. 334).

(2) **Acetyl choline,** the most powerful reactant known to occur in the animal body, has been identified in fresh spleen by Dale and Dudley, and also occurs as the neurocrine liberated locally when parasympathetic (cholinergic) nerve endings transmit impulses. Characteristic effects following intravenous injection are:

(i) Fall in blood pressure owing to a direct dilator action on peripheral blood vessels. This effect is observed even in doses of 1×10^{-5} mg., and is antagonised by atropine.

The direct vascular effect is accompanied by cardiac inhibition equivalent to vagal stimulation (p. 437).

(ii) *General Cholinergic Phenomena.* These are similar to the effects of parasympathetic stimulation, and include lachrymal, salivary, gastric and pancreatic secretion, increased motility of the alimentary tract, and contraction of the bladder.

Acetyl choline is transient in effect owing to its rapid hydrolysis by the widely distributed enzyme, choline esterase, which resolves it into free choline, with a potency about 100,000 times less than the acetyl ester.

(3) **Adenylic acid,** present in extracts of skeletal and cardiac muscle, and in brain, kidney and spleen, is derived from adenosine triphosphate, the phosphate carrier in glycogenolysis and glycolysis. Adenylic acid, and its nucleoside component adenosine, are active vaso-depressors, evoking general arterial dilatation accompanied by cardiac retardation. The coronary arteries are dilated, and for this reason preparations of the autacoid (" lacarnol ") have been used in the treatment of angina pectoris. Accumulation of adenylic acid in the tissues is prevented by its conversion into the less potent nucleotide inosinic acid.

Adenylic derivatives appear to constitute the " muscle shock factor " released from crushed or ischæmic muscle (Green *et al.*, 1943).

(4) **Hypertensin.** Goldblatt (1942) found that vascular hypertension develops in dogs when the blood supply to the kidney is restricted. A factor, *renin*, has been separated from extracts of ischæmic kidney cortex. It is an enzyme, and acts on a globulin present in normal blood plasma, yielding the pressor agent, *angiotonin*, or *hypertensin*, responsible for the renal effect.

Hypertensin is non-colloidal and thermostable. It is destroyed by an enzyme, *hypertensinase*, present normally in blood plasma. Renin, unlike the other pressors, adrenaline, " pituitrin ", and tyramine, does not decrease peripheral blood flow, and lower skin temperature, on intravenous injection.

(5) **5-Hydroxytryptamine,** 5-HT, Serotonin or Enteramine. It had been known for many years that blood stored under sterile conditions acquired vasoactive properties, and yielded an alcoholic extract that constricted perfused blood vessels, and evoked contractions in unstriated muscle. The agent, termed *serotonin*, is present in the platelets and was isolated and identified as a complex of 5-hydroxytryptamine and creatine sulphate by Rapport *et al.* (1948). Meanwhile, Erspamer (1937) had postulated the existence of a hormone, *enteramine*, in the enterochromaffin cells of the mammalian gastrointestinal tract, which contain granules that reduce ammoniacal silver solutions. Acetone extracts of enterochromaffin tissues provided a source of enteramine, the properties of which closely resembled serotonin, and, in 1952, both were shown by chromatographic analysis to be 5-hydroxytryptamine.

Distribution. 5-HT has been found in the gastro-intestinal tracts and the blood of mammals, birds, reptiles and amphibia.

Ranges in μg. per gm. or ml., fresh tissue are: stomach wall, 0·5 (cat) to 9 (mouse); blood, 0·1 (human) to 4·0 (rabbit); mammalian spleen, 1 to 20; mammalian central nervous system, 0·01 to 0·8. Exceptionally rich sources are: octopod posterior salivary gland, up to 750; amphibian skin, up to 1,000.

Biosynthesis. Tracer experiments, using ^{14}C-labelled tryptophan, show that the amino acid is first hydroxylated in the 5 position, and then deaminated to 5-HT by an enzyme present in stomach wall, liver, kidney, brain, and sympathetic ganglia. The hormone is stored and circulated in the blood platelets, and finally excreted in the urine as a deamination product, 5-hydroxyindolyl acetic acid.

Significance. Psycho-tropic effects. The properties of 5-HT and its association with brain tissue suggest that it may have a specific function in regulating cephalic metabolism at some level. This has received support from two independent lines of investigation. *Reserpine*, the celebrated and popular tranquillising alkaloid of the *Rauwolfia* group, on ingestion liberates 5-HT from the blood platelets, and increases the duration of hypnosis produced by alcohol or barbiturates. 5-HT has similar sedative effects, and the action of reserpine may, in part, be explained in terms of 5-HT mobilisation.

Lysergic acid diethylamide, LSD, an ergot derivative with powerful hallucinogenic properties, is a specific antagonist of 5-HT (Gaddum, 1953); and as LSD in doses as low as 1 μg. per kg. body weight can induce a temporary syndrome of severe psychic disturbances comparable with those in schizophrenia, from a chemical aspect " though this be madness, yet there is method in it."

Cancer Diagnosis. Argentaffinoma, or malignant carcinoid disease of the intestine, involving chromaffin tissue, is characterised by vaso-motor disturbances, and high output of 5-HT and its metabolite, 5-hydroxyindolyl acetate, in the urine. As these substances are easily recognised, their detection can be of diagnostic value.

SIGNIFICANCE OF THE ANIMAL HORMONES

In general, hormones appear to operate in one of two ways: quick-acting hormones, such as the adrenalines, enter into metabolic processes in the target tissue; slow acting hormones, such as the œstrogens and the tropins, appear to work by organising and directing enzyme systems within the cell. By means of a complimentary equipment of hormones, the sympathetic and the parasympathetic systems co-operate in maintaining the equilibrium of the autonomic system nervous system necessary for normal life, and, are in turn controlled by centres in the hypothalamus.

This suggestion does not explain the dominant position of the pituitary gland, and the possibility that its master hormones are, actually, secreted by the hypothalamus. The operation of the hormones is independent of the will, but not entirely independent of the imagination. Working on a sub-conscious

Patterns of Hormone Action

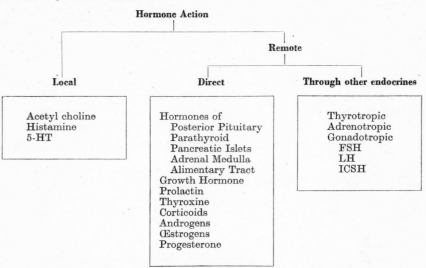

Hormone Action

Remote

Local | Direct | Through other endocrines

| Acetyl choline
Histamine
5-HT | Hormones of
Posterior Pituitary
Parathyroid
Pancreatic Islets
Adrenal Medulla
Alimentary Tract
Growth Hormone
Prolactin
Thyroxine
Corticoids
Androgens
Œstrogens
Progesterone | Thyrotropic
Adrenotropic
Gonadotropic
FSH
LH
ICSH |

plane, they can be aroused by emotional associations and express themselves in emotional responses often far in excess of what the occasion requires, for, in a conflict between reason and emotion, emotion usually wins.

PLANT HORMONES AND GROWTH FACTORS

Higher plants, like higher animals, are subject to chemical control at their organisation level by agents variously described as auxins and phytohormones.

Name.	Source.	Function.
(1) Bios complex . .	Yeast extracts, bran, etc.	Growth factors.
(2) Auxin *a* . . .	Apical tissue of shoots, yeasts, fungi.	Cell elongation, Photo-tropism.
	Pollen.	Geotropism.
(3) Auxin *b* . . .	Plant extracts, malt.	Growth factor.
(4) Indole-3-acetic acid .	Urine, maize.	Root formation.
(5) Traumatic acid . .	Injured tissue.	Wound repair.
(6) Kinetin	Plant extracts.	Cell multiplication.
(7) Gibberellin . . .	The rice fungus, *Gibberella*.	Growth and flowering.

(1) **Bios Complex.** In 1901, Ide and his pupil Wildiers showed that a water-soluble factor, termed *bios*, is necessary for the growth and development of many, but not all, strains of the yeast *Saccharomyces cerevisiœ*. Bios occurs plentifully in yeast extracts, plant leaves, bran and the outer coats of seeds. Various compounds have been isolated from the mixture of substances present in bios extracts, some of which stimulate growth in higher plants.

421

Representative bios substances are: (i) i-inositol, or bios I; (ii) nicotinic acid, which is necessary for the growth of *Staphylococcus* and other bacteria; (iii) uracil; (iv) vitamin B_1; (v) pantothenic acid, a polyhydroxylic acid derived from β-alanine, and necessary for yeast growth, (vi) biotin, and (vii) folic acid, found in green leaves, yeast, and many animal tissues (Mitchell *et al.*, 1941).

(2) **Auxins.** Plant development is attended by elongation of individual cells, as distinct from their multiplication, and by resulting movements of stems towards the light (phototropism) or roots towards the soil (geotropism). All these changes have been shown to be due to hormones, termed auximones or auxins, secreted in the apical regions and spreading by diffusion.

The study of auxins arose, in 1910, with the work of Boysen-Jensen on the coleoptile, or primary leaf sheath, of grasses, and was extended by Went, and other investigators; the isolation and identification of the auxins being due to Kögl and his colleagues (1931-7).

Auxin a and auxin b, the principal phytohormones, are obtained from the ether-soluble fraction of lipoid extracts of rapidly growing apical tissues of roots and tips, and are assayed in terms of their ability to evoke renewed growth in decapitated coleoptiles (auxin a) or in moulds (auxin b). Auxin b is readily destroyed by both acids and alkalis, and thus can be separated from auxin a, which is relatively acid-stable, but decomposed by alkalis. Both the auxins are derivatives of a *cyclo*-pentane ring similar to that forming part of the steroid nucleus.

$$\begin{array}{ccc}
H_2C\text{---}CH_2 & H_2C\text{---}CH\text{---}CHMeEt & R = \text{---}CH.CH_2.CH.CH.COOH \\
| \quad\quad | & \quad\quad Et \quad | \quad\quad | & \quad\quad\quad OH \quad\quad OH\ OH \\
H_2C \quad CH_2 & CH\text{---}HC \quad C.R & \text{Auxin } a. \\
\diagdown\diagup & Me \quad \diagdown\diagup & \\
CH_2 & CH & R = \text{---}CH.CH_2.CO.CH_2.COOH \\
& & \quad\quad\quad OH \\
\textit{Cyclo}\text{-Pentane.} & \text{Auxin nucleus.} & \text{Auxin } b.
\end{array}$$

(3) **Hetero-auxin, Indole-3-acetic Acid.** In the survey of plant and animal extracts for substances having an auxin effect, it was found that urine was very rich in a growth-promoting factor, which on isolation proved to be chemically unrelated to auxin a or b, and was termed hetero-auxin. It was subsequently identified as an indole derivative of acetic acid, and is derived from tryptophan by bacterial decomposition in the intestine.

$$\begin{array}{c}
CH \\
HC\diagup\diagdown C\text{----}C\text{---}CH_2.COOH \\
| \quad\quad || \quad\quad || \\
HC \diagdown\diagup C \diagdown\diagup CH \\
CH \quad NH
\end{array}$$

Hetero-auxin
Indole-3-acetic acid
(indolyl-β-acetic acid).

The effect of the phytohormones is non-specific as regards species; auxin a stimulates growth in a great variety of plants; auxin b has no action on coleoptiles, but promotes growth and mycelium formation in *Aspergillus niger*, and other moulds; hetero-auxin appears to be a general stimulant for root formation.

(4) **Traumatic acid,** the plant wound hormone, is liberated by damaged tissues, and stimulates growth of parenchymatous cells in the repair process. It has been isolated by English (1939) and shown to be

$$\triangle^1 \text{ decene} - 1,10 - \text{dicarboxylic acid,}$$
$$\text{HOOC.CH} = \text{CH.(CH}_2)_7.\text{CH}_2.\text{COOH.}$$

Polyploidogens. The dried ground-stem, or corm, of the autumn crocus, or meadow saffron (*Colchicum autumnale*), used empirically in treatment of gout, contains about 0·2 per cent. of a phenanthrene derivative, *colchicine*,

$$\text{C}_{22}\text{H}_{25}\text{O}_6\text{N.}$$

Colchicine acts as a nuclear poison, or karyotoxin, in plants and animals, and retards cell-division in the later stages of mitosis. The split chromosomes fail to separate, and the resulting daughter-cell shows polyploidy, or abnormal chromosome equipment. By this means it is possible to evoke chemical mutations, and produce new varieties of plants. Acenaphthene, β-naphthol, and some related cyclic hydrocarbons have a similar effect.

A large number of unrelated compounds have been found to be capable of affecting plant growth and metabolism, including *ethylene*, which promotes ripening of fruit; *a-naphthyl acetic acid* and *indolyl-3-butyric acid*, which stimulate flowering, fruiting, and root-growth. These factors, popularly termed plant hormones, irrespective of their origin, are effective when applied in concentrations of 10 to 1,000 parts per million. Indolyl-3-acetic acid, occurs in animal secretions, including perspiration; its presence in excess may confer the gift of " green fingers " on some successful horticulturists.

Anti-auxins. Applied in excess, auxins can harm plants by causing distorted development. Plant-growth also can be inhibited by a variety of organic compounds that are effective in very low concentration, and display preference for certain species of plants. Important anti-auxins derived from phenoxy-acetic acid include: 2,4-*dichlorphenoxy-acetic acid*, or 2,4-*D*, a powerful weed-killer, which is toxic also to fruit trees and broad-leaved vegetables. Applied to soil surfaces, 2,4-*D* kills seedlings, and inhibits seed germination for about two months, thus preventing the production of industrial crops.

2-*Methyl-4-chlorophenoxy-acetic acid*, or " methoxone ", is used to kill weeds in corn crops; it differs in its target from *isopropylphenyl carbamate*, and 2, 2-dichlorpropionic acid, which are specially harmful to all cereals.

In addition to their rational use as weed-killers, anti-auxins are potential agents in chemical warfare directed at destroying food production by poisoning the soil.

AGENTS AFFECTING BACTERIAL GROWTH OF MICRO-ORGANISMS

Biotics and Antibiotics

Microbiological Assay. Heterotrophic micro-organisms, such as moulds, yeasts, and most bacteria, are unable to synthesise all their cell constituents from inorganic substances, and must import organic compounds made by other forms of life. By observing the growth of a given species or strain of organism in a series of culture media enriched with different nutrients, it is possible to ascertain the exact nutritional requirements of that species. When these are known, the organism may be used as an instrument of microbiological assay to detect and estimate the amount of a particular essential nutrient, or growth factor that has been added to a culture medium complete in all necessary ingredients other than the particular nutrient to be assayed. Methods for measuring the response to an added nutrient include:

1. *Rate of growth of bacteria*, as shown by increase in turbidity. The type of organism employed depends on requirements. Thus, the folic acid vitamins are assayed by their effect on the growth of *Lactobacillus casei* R.

2. *Rate of growth of moulds*, as shown by the weight of the mycelium harvested.

3. *Rate of production of acid by bacteria*: riboflavin, biotin, and pantothenic acid can be assayed by measuring their effect on the production of lactic acid by *L. casei*.

4. *Rate of production of carbon dioxide:* (*a*) from decarboxylation of amino acids by selective decarboxylating strains of bacteria; (*b*) from fermentation of sugars by yeasts.

Biotics. The bios complex obtained from yeast contains several factors capable of stimulating growth in higher animals and plants as well as in lower organisms. The term " biotic " is used to describe these specific compounds synthesised by micro-organisms and required by higher organisms. Many of these biotics are typical vitamins.

Antibiotics are specific compounds secreted by lower organisms, and capable of inhibiting the growth of other species (bacterio-static effect), or even poisoning (bactericidal effect) or dissolving (lysis effect) foreign organisms. They are important weapons in the biological warfare that characterises life at the lower levels in the biosphere, and some of them are of great value in animal therapy. Thus, in 1928, Fleming observed that the growth of a staphylococcus colony on a solid medium was checked by lysis in the zone surrounding an accidental infection by a common mould, identified as *Penicillium notatum*. The antibiotic, later named **penicillin,** was extracted, and found to be antagonistic to staphylococci, streptococci, pneumococci and many other gram-positive organisms. Penicillin is active in a dilution of 1 in 50×10^6, and is one of the most powerful antibiotics yet discovered.

The penicillins have a common double-ring nucleus, but differ in the type of side-chain attached at *R*.

424

	Penicillin	Group at R
OC——N——CH.COOH		
HC——CH C(CH₃)₂	I (F)	—CH₂.CH : CH.CH₂.CH₃ pentenyl
HN S	II (G)	—CH₂.C₆H₅ benzyl
OC——R	III (X)	—CH₂.C₆H₄.OH p-hydroxybenzyl
Penicillin Type	IV (K)	—CH₂.(CH₂)₅.CH₃ heptyl

More than fifty different penicillins have been isolated from filtrates of mould cultures enriched with special nutrients. In general, penicillins are characterised by their non-toxicity to man and other higher animals, and by their great toxicity to gram-positive bacteria.

The " Florey ", or " Oxford ", unit is defined as the minimum amount of penicillin in 50 ml. of a standard broth that is able completely to inhibit the growth of a standard inocculum of *Streptococcus aureus*. For example, the sodium salt of *n*-heptylpenicillin has a potency of 2,300 Oxford units per mg. The International unit is equivalent to the potency of 0·6 g. of crystalline sodium benzylpenicillin (G).

Penicillins are rapidly excreted by the kidney, and the therapeutic level in the blood must be maintained by frequent injection, or by intramuscular injection of a large dose of a sparingly-soluble penicillin suspension. Penicillins are destroyed by the enzyme penicillinase in penicillin-resistant bacteria, by a liver enzyme, and by acids or alkalis. On hydrolysis, all give rise to penicillamine, or β-thiovaline, a thiol amino acid that belongs to the uncommon D-series.

From the sporogenic soil organism, *B. brevis*, Dubos (1941) has isolated two crystalline peptides, *gramicidin* and *tyrocidin*, both of which are powerfully bactericidal for gram-positive and other organisms, but too toxic to higher animals to be of therapeutic use. Half the amino acid units in gramicidin occur in the uncommon form of D-isomers.

Streptomycin, $C_{21}H_{39}O_{12}N_7(3HCl)$, isolated by Waksman (1945) from cultures of a soil organism, *Streptomyces griseus*, inhibits both gram-positive and gram-negative organisms, and is effective against some penicillin-resistant species as well as against the tubercle bacillus.

Chloromycetin (J. Ehrlich *et al.*, 1948), originally obtained from *Strep. venezuelæ*, and now prepared synthetically, is a wide-range antibiotic, including in its field Gram-negative bacteria, viruses, and *Rickettsiæ*.

The presence of D-series amino acid residues in many of the antibiotics is suggestive. Proteins of animals and higher plants are assembled exclusively from L-series amino acids, and, presumably, had a common ancestry.

425

Organisms that produce antibiotics may have originated from life-sources other than the main evolutionary stream, and by chance some of their components became fixed in the D-series tradition. The resulting antibiotics, in some instances, appear to act by obstructing the nucleoprotein mechanisms necessary for cell-division and protein-formation in the sensitive types of organism.

General References

Albright, F., and E. C. Reifenstein (1948), " Parathyroid Glands." Baltimore; London.

Burn, J. H. (1950), " Effects of Local Hormones." *Physiol. Rev.*, **30,** 117.

" Chemistry and Mode of Action of Plant Growth Substances." Ed. by R. L. Wain and F. Wrightman (1956). New York.

Dale, H. H. (1954), "An Autumn Gleaning." London.

Dorfman, R. I., and R. A. Shipley (1956), "Androgens: Biochemistry, Physiology, and Clinical Significance." New York; London.

Von Euler, U. S. (1956), " Noradrenaline." Springfield; Oxford.

Farris, E. J. (1956), " Human Ovulation and Fertilization." Philadelphia; Montreal.

Gaunt, R., *et al.* (1949), "Adrenal Cortex and Water Metabolism." *Physiol. Rev.*, **29,** 281.

Pincus, G., and K. V. Thimann (1948, 1955), " The Hormones." New York.

" Recent Progress in Hormone Research," Vol. I. Ed. by G. Pincus (1946–). New York.

Sayers, G. (1950), "Adrenal Cortex and Homeostasis." *Physiol. Rev.*, **30,** 241.

Speert, H. (1948), " Local Action of Sex Hormones." *Physiol. Rev.*, **28,** 23.

" Textbook of Endocrinology." Ed. by R. H. Williams (1955). 2nd Ed. Philadelphia; London.

" The Neurohypophysis." Ed. by H. S. Heller (1957). *Colston Papers*, Vol. VIII. London.

" Thyroid Hormones " (1957). *Ciba Foundation Colloquium on Endocrinology.*

" Vitamins and Hormones," Vol. I. Ed. by R. S. Harris and K. V. Thimann (1943–). New York.

Chapter 25 Tissue Chemistry

Tissues are functional assemblies of cells. They are not structures of fixed composition, but are regions of specialised metabolism and, when integrated into organs and systems, may serve various purposes of secretion, storage and transformation. Hence histochemistry, the chemistry of tissues, is apt to appear as a mere biochemical catalogue of contents, many of which are obscure, unless it is studied along with physiology and microscopic anatomy. Nevertheless, each of the chief tissues has one or more characteristic constituents, which determine its function.

1. **Muscle,** the motor tissue of the animal, makes up about 40 per cent. of human body weight, and dominates metabolism. Voluntary muscle is the instrument of the will, the only physical means whereby man can bring about changes in his environment. Cardiac muscle, by its inherent rhythm, maintains the internal fountain that supports life and, incidentally, provides us with a natural wrist-watch, the pulse, which may be the basis of our sense of time. Involuntary, or unstriated, muscle produces the necessary stresses and automatic movements within the body. All told, muscle activity accounts for about half of the entire metabolism of the body during rest, and upwards of three-fourths during exertion. As a machine, muscle is of interest to the engineer as well as to the biologist. Working at a low temperature (36° C.), and fed by a very dilute solution of glucose (0·1 per cent.), it rapidly converts chemical energy into mechanical energy, with an efficiency of at least 20 per cent. This is done by the alternate contraction and extension of an organised arrangement of protein fibres.

The three varieties of muscle: skeletal (striated), cardiac and visceral (unstriated), differ in composition, even when present in related structures. Representative percentage values for fresh tissue are: water, 75 to 80; proteins, 18 to 20; lipids, 1 to 2; glycogen, 0·5 to 1·5; phosphocreatine, 0·02 (unstriated) to 0·6 (skeletal); adenosine triphosphate (ATP), 0·07 (cardiac) to 0·25 (skeletal); inositol, 0·02; K, 0·2 to 0·33; Na, 0·05 to 0·15; Ca, 0·03 (striated), 0·007 (unstriated); Fe, 0·004; PO_4, 0·2 to 0·6; Cl, 0·28 (striated), 0·1 (unstriated); together with small amounts (0·01 to 0·1) of obscure reactants, such as carnosine, carnitine, anserine, methyl guanidine, hypoxanthine and inosinic acid, some of which may participate in the contraction cycle.

Muscle Proteins. Extraction of minced muscle with isotonic saline removes a mixture of albumins and globulins, representing about 40 per cent. of the total muscle protein. The mixture can be separated by dialysis into a water-soluble albumin fraction, *myogen*, and a residual " globulin X ". Myogen includes the enzymes concerned in the glycolytic process by which glycogen is broken down to lactate. In addition to adenosine triphosphate, phospho-creatine, and inorganic ions, the extract may contain *myoglobin*, or muscle hæmoglobin, which occurs in small amounts (0·1 to 0·2 per cent.) as the pigment in red muscle. After extraction with water or isotonic saline, intact muscle fibres lose their power of contracting. This can be restored briefly by addition of adenosine triphosphate and K+, from which it is inferred that neither myogen nor " globulin X " is immediately concerned in the contraction process.

Further extraction with salines of increasing concentration removes the proteins of the muscle fibrils: *myosin, actin, tropomyosin*, and proteins " X " and " Y ". An insoluble residue of stroma protein remains.

Myosin, or L-myosin, is a fibrous globulin that forms about 55 per cent. of the fibril proteins. It has an affinity for K+, Ca²⁺, and Mg²⁺, and occurs in states of aggregation up to m.w. 850,000. Crude myosin has phosphatase properties, and can catalyse the hydrolysis of ATP to ADP, and other triphosphates to diphosphates. Short-term exposure to trypsin resolves myosin into a globulin, L-meromyosin, and an albumin, H-meromyosin, which is the actual enzyme, muscle adenosine triphosphatase, or ATP-ase. It is activated by K+, Ca²⁺, and some other ions.

Actin, in the absence of electrolytes is a protein of m.w. 57,000 and low viscosity, G-actin. It has a high affinity for Ca²⁺, and is aggregated by electrolytes into a gel, F-actin, which readily combines with myosin to produce filaments of the complex *actomyosin*. The physical properties of myosin, actin, and actomyosin are responsible for the mechanical changes involved in muscle contraction.

Theories of Contraction. Muscle contraction is a complex process accompanied by liberation of heat and performance of work. These changes have been investigated in detail, but their exact relationships await elucidation. In striated muscle, the contraction process is initiated by the release of acetyl choline from the nerve terminals at the myo-neural junction, or end-plate. This causes a local change in membrane permeability, an escape of K+ from the muscle fibre, and the onset of the contraction wave.

Within the resting fibril, the actin and the myosin are segregated into separate sets of adjacent filaments. According to the theory developed by Mommaerts (1950), the actin filament is changed to F-actin by transfer of phosphate from ATP, and each filament draws into close alignment with a neighbouring myosin filament, thus causing the shortening of the muscle fibril by formation of an actomyosin unit. Relaxation is accompanied by regeneration of ATP by phosphate transfer from phosphocreatine. In prolonged contraction the glycolytic process comes into operation to provide energy for maintaining the supply of ATP.

2. **Epithelial tissue,** in which the intercellular material is minimal, forms the epidermis and the skin and epidermal structures (hair, nails and horn) of the body surface and the lining of the respiratory and alimentary tracts.

The percentage composition of fresh skin, as compiled by Williams (1942) is: water, 66; proteins (keratin and collagens), 25; lipids, 7 (phospholipids, 0·6; cholesterol, 1); total ash, 0·65 (Na, 0·16; K, 0·09; Cu, 0·01; Mg, 0·007; Fe, 0·001; PO_4, 0·2; Cl, 0·1, CO_3, 0·005).

Keratins, the characteristic insoluble scleroproteins of skin and hair, have a high percentage (15 to 21) of cystine (p. 107).

3. Connective tissue, in which the intercellular material, or matrix is maximal, forms the tensile and skeletal fabrics of the animal. Five varieties are recognised, depending on the composition of the intercellular substance.

White Fibrous Tissue. Percentage composition: water, 62·9; proteins, 34 (collagen, 31·6; elastin, 1·6); mucoid, 1·2; lipid, 1·0; inorganic residue, 0·5. *Collagen*, the characteristic constituent of white fibres in tendon and elsewhere, is a protein with a high percentage of glycine (25), proline (20) and hydroxyproline (14), but poor in tryptophan (0), valine (0), cystine (0·1) and tyrosine (0·01). It is insoluble in water, but may be hydrolysed by prolonged boiling, when it is converted into *gelatin*, which is soluble.

Yellow Elastic Tissue. Percentage composition: water, 57·6; proteins, 40 (elastin, 31·7; collagen, 7·2), lipids, 1·1; mucoid, 0·5; inorganic residue, 0·5. *Elastin*, the characteristic insoluble protein of yellow elastic tissue, well represented in the *ligamentum nuchæ* of the ox, like collagen has a high percentage of glycine (30), and proline (15), and is poor in tryptophan, cystine and tyrosine.

It differs from collagen in having a high percentage of valine (13·5) and leucines (30). Unlike collagen, elastin is not digested by gastric juice, and does not form gelatin when hydrolysed.

Chondroitin Sulphuric Acid.

A and *B* are galactosamine residues in which the amino group has been acetylated, and the terminal hydroxyl at 6 has been esterified with H_2SO_4.

C and *D* are glucuronic acid residues, united by ether linkage.

Cartilage, the covering material of articular surfaces, and the precursor of bone, has a matrix containing about 30 per cent. of a characteristic glycoprotein, *chondromucoid*, which on hydrolysis liberates *chondroitin sulphate*, a complex mucopolysaccharide assembled from two molecules of a uronic acid and two molecules of N-acetyl galactosamine, each terminal, or 6-hydroxyl group of which is esterified with sulphuric acid.

Small amounts of chondroalbuminoid, a scleroprotein resembling elastin, also occur in cartilage.

Salivary mucin contains *mucoitin sulphate,* the structure plan of which is the same as chondroitin sulphate, but for the hexosamine residues, which are glucosamine instead of galactosamine. These complex mucopolysaccharides are of interest in being components of the heparins that inhibit blood coagulation.

In the connective tissues, chondroitin sulphate exists as a polymer, of m.w. 200,000.

Hyaluronic acid, formed by removal of both sulphate groups from mucoitin sulphate, is the prosthetic group in mucoproteins. It is hydrolysed by the enzyme hyaluronidase, secreted as a diffusing factor by bacteria.

Bone. The skeletal tissue of man and higher animals is a cartilaginous matrix stabilised by deposition of lime salts in a characteristic pattern.

Composition. Intact bone contains 23 to 34 per cent. of water and up to 12 per cent. of marrow fat. Dried, marrow-free bone contains about 60 per cent. of inorganic salts, which may be dissolved by prolonged extraction with HCl; and 40 per cent. of organic material, which may be removed by incineration, leaving bone ash. This organic material is chiefly *ossein*, a bone protein closely resembling collagen, and, like it, yielding gelatin when bones are digested with boiling water. Ossein is accompanied by small amounts of *bone keratin, osseoalbuminoid* and *osseomucoid,* which resembles the chondromucoid of cartilage.

The Bone Salts. The percentage composition of bone ash is: calcium phosphate, $Ca_3(PO_4)_2$, 85; calcium carbonate, $CaCO_3$, 12; magnesium phosphate $Mg_3(PO_4)_2$, 1·4; with a residue of salts of Na(0·4), K(0·13), and traces of Fe, Cl and F. Fresh bone contains 0·2 to 0·7 per cent. of citrate, which reappears as carbonate in bone ash. Bone salt composition varies with region and age, and cannot be referred to any one single mineral type. Chemical analysis and crystalline structure, as shown by X-rays, suggest that bone calcium is present as the double salt, $3Ca_3(PO_4)_2 . CaCO_3$, resembling that found naturally in minerals of the *apatite* series, $[Ca_3(PO_4)_2]_n . CaCO_3$, where n has a value between 2 and 3, and the $CaCO_3$ may be replaced by $Ca(OH)_2$, $CaSO_4$, $CaCl_2$ or CaF_2. In mammalian bone, $n = 3$, and the Ca : P ratio is almost constant between 1·99 and 2·04, which is less than the common apatite ratio of 2·15.

Decrease in the value for n, resulting in " high carbonate " bone, occurs in old age, in rickets due to phosphate insufficiency, and in the pathological condition of " marble bone ".

Calcification. Bone formation is a process in which calcium salts are laid down in a protein matrix. The salts are not precipitated as a more or less homogeneous sediment, but are systematically assembled in a pattern conforming to the physical requirements of growth, stress and repair. Bone salt is derived from ions present in the blood plasma: Ca^{2+}, $H_2PO_4^-$ and HCO_3^-. In accordance with the solubility rule, calcium phosphate and calcium carbonate are precipitated from aqueous solutions whenever the concentrations of the component ions exceed the values for the respective solubility products. The conditions for precipitation at $38°$ C. are:—

$$[Ca^{2+}]^3 \times [PO_4^{3-}]^2 > 10^{-32.5}, \text{ and } [Ca^{2+}] \times [CO_3^{2-}] > 1.7 \times 10^{-8}.$$

Plasma and tissue fluids are in a state of supersaturation with regard to the bone salts. Of the 10 mg. of calcium present in 100 ml. of plasma, only 2 to 3 mg. occur in free, ionic form, the remainder being bound by the proteins, amino acids, citrate and other factors capable of depressing calcium ionisation. From the graph on p. 39, it will be seen that, at the pH of blood most of the phosphate and carbonate are present as $H_2PO_4^-$ and HCO_3^-, the concentration of the ions PO_4^{3-} and CO_3^{2-} being almost zero. Hence, for calcium salts to be deposited in growing bone, some local mechanism must operate to raise the concentration of PO_4^{3-} and CO_3^{2-}. In 1923, Robison found that bone is very rich in a phosphatase of the alkaline type (optimal pH, 8 to 9), and he was able to bring about calcification in strips of rachitic bone by immersing them in solutions of Ca^{2+} and glycerophosphate or hexose monophosphate.

In 1926, Shipley observed that calcification of bone strips can occur when they are immersed in serum or in sterile salines of the same ionic composition, showing that preformed phosphoric esters are not necessary. Under these conditions, however, it was found that cyanide, iodoacetate or fluoride had an inhibitory effect not displayed in Robison's original experiments. As these agents all retard glycolysis, it is now believed that calcification proceeds by a metabolic sequence involving: (a) carbohydrate degradation, with formation of phosphoric esters, and consequent accumulation of phosphate from the plasma, and (b) hydrolysis of the esters by the bone phosphatase. Glycogen, which is present in small amounts in growing bone and teeth, may represent a by-product of this calcification metabolism. The bone salt crystallites are disc-shaped and carry a surface layer of hydrated ions in equilibrium with the surrounding fluid.

Exchange of Ca, PO_4 and OH between bone surface and tissue fluid and blood plasma is in continuous operation, as shown by isotope uptake. The process is regulated by a calcium carrier, citric acid, released locally from bone by the parathyroid hormone. Citrate forms a non-ionised Ca chelate, which diffuses into the tissue fluids and thus enables bone calcium to enter the circulation, in spite of the unfavourable gradient of Ca ions. Thus the surface layers of the bone crystallites are removed by erosion and replaced by fresh crystal formation.

In addition to acting as a reservoir for calcium, bone also can collect and store other metals, such as lead, and products of radioactive fission. The most dangerous of the 200 possible radioactive isotopes released when a nuclear bomb explodes appears to be strontium-90. Although it does not constitute a genetic hazard, as it only emits β-rays, which are unable to penetrate to the germinal tissues, it has a half-life of some 7·5 years, and during its long continuance in skeletal tissues it can induce bone lesions, sarcomata, and leukæmia.

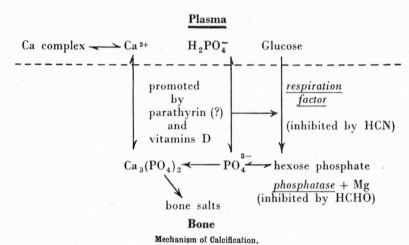

Mechanism of Calcification.

Teeth. A tooth is a highly specialised unit consisting of three calcified parts: (1) an enamel layer of epidermal origin, which is the hardest tissue in the body; (2) the dentin, which is of mesodermal origin, and forms the main substance of the tooth, and encloses the pulp cavity containing the blood vessels and nerves; (3) the cementum, which fixes the root dentin in its socket in the alveolar bone, supported by the gum, or gingival tissue, and the peridontal membrane.

Percentage Composition of Teeth
(Bowes and Murray, 1935)

Enamel: water, 3; calcium, 35·8; magnesium, 0·4; potassium, 0·05 to 0·3; sodium, 0·2 to 0·7; phosphate, 51·6 (as PO_4), 17·4 (as P); H_2O, 1·3 (bound); CO_2, 1·9 (bound); chloride, 0·3; fluoride, 0·01 to 0·02; iron, 0·02; organic substance (keratin), 1; Ca/Mg, 78·9.

Dentin: water, 12; calcium, 26·5; magnesium, 0·8; potassium, 0·07; sodium, 0·2; phosphate, 44·4 (as PO_4), 13·8 (as P); fluoride, 0·02; organic substance (collagen), 18; Ca/Mg, 33·3.

Silicon occurs as a micro-constituent, values for the entire tooth being about 3 mg. Si per 100 gm.

Factors in the Growth and Maintenance of the Teeth. M. Mellanby (1929–34) has shown that dietary factors similar to those concerned in bone calcification operate in the development of the teeth. The erupted tooth, however, differs from bone in that it is continually exposed to abrasion and chemical attack from bacterial products formed in the mouth. Surface abrasion is resisted by the enamel layer, the integrity of which requires the presence of fluoride as a micro-constituent. The halogen is derived principally from the local water supplies, its optimal concentration being 0·5 to 1 part per million. Values below 0·2 p.p.m. predispose to faulty enamel formation, and promote dental caries; values above 5 p.p.m. may lead to chronic *fluorosis*, one of the signs of which is rough, mottled and brittle enamel. Claims have been made of the value of minute doses of fluoride in the prevention of caries, but precautions must be taken to avoid overdosage. In addition to vitamins D and the parathyroid hormone, which regulate the Ca and PO_4 distribution, vitamin A, according to M. Mellanby, is required for the maintenance of the sub-gingival epithelium in contact with the enamel, and vitamin C is necessary for the maintenance of the *odontoblasts*, which cover the pulp, and penetrate into the tubules of the dentin.

The problem of dental decay is complex. In addition to faulty construction, from inadequate maternal or post-natal diet, factors that may be implicated are (1) saliva deficient in buffering action, and (2) local infection of the mouth by acid-forming organisms, such as *L. acidophilus*, fed by excess of sugars in the diet.

4. Brain and Nerve. Two types of material occur in the nervous system: (*a*) *white substance*, forming the sheaths of the medullated nerves; and (*b*) *grey substance*, which is well-represented in the cortical layers of the brain, and consists of nerve cells and their connections. The pioneer work of Thudichum (1884) has shown that both white and grey substance are characterised by a high content of cholesterol and complex lipids, which is not depleted by starvation, and must have functional significance.

Composition. From the data collected by Rossiter (1955) for the white substance (W), grey substance (G), and peripheral nerves (N) of man and higher animals, the percentage values, in gm. per 100 gm. fresh tissue, are: water, 67 to 74 (W), 81 to 87 (G), 56 to 71 (N); proteins, 6 to 12·1 (W), 5·6 to 12·5 (G), 11 to 15 (N); total phospholipids, 6·2 to 9·3 (W), 3·1 to 4·6 (G), 2·2 to 10·6 (N); lecithin, 0·9 to 1·9 (W), 0·6 to 1·5 (G), 0·3 to 1·4 (N); " cephalins ", 2·5 to 5·4 (W), 1·1 to 2·5 (G), 0·4 to 5·2 (N); sphingomyelin, 1·8 to 4·3 (W), 0·3 to 0·9 (G), 1·3 to 4·7 (N); cerebrosides, 4·1 to 7·4 (W), 0·3 to 1·9 (G), 1·1 to 4·7 (N); cholesterol, 3·5 to 5·4 (W), 0·6 to 1·4 (G), 1·1 to 4·5 (N); inorganic residue, 0·7 to 2·7; sodium, 0·1 to 0·2 (W, G), 0·17 to 0·45 (N); potassium, 0·2 to 0·4

433

(W, G); 0·12 to 0·22 (N); calcium, 0·015 (W), 0·011 (G); magnesium, 0·03 (W), 0·02 (G); chloride, 0·11 (W), 0·16 (G), 0·17 to 0·28 (N).

Fresh, entire brain contains about 0·1 per cent. of glycogen. Micro-constituents in mg. per gm. include: deoxypentose nucleic acid, 80; pentose nucleic acid, 100 to 140; acetyl choline, free and bound, 0·018 (cerebellum) to 4 (autonomic nerves and ganglia); iron, 5 to 8; zinc, 0·7; copper, 0·04.

In this tabulation, the " cephalin " fraction includes the phospholipids other than lecithin, namely: phosphatidyl ethanolamine, phosphatidyl serine, and acetal phosphatides. The proteins are chiefly neucloproteins, together with enzymes, and neurokeratin, which occurs as phospholipoprotein in the nerve sheath.

Brain Metabolism. The rate of blood flow through the active human brain is of the order of 700 ml. per minute. Gasometric analysis of samples obtained by internal jugular puncture indicate that although cerebral blood flow may fluctuate with the blood pressure the cerebral oxygen consumption is maintained normally at the high level of 3·3 ml. O_2 per 100 gm. of brain substance per minute. This implies that the adult human brain, of average weight 1·4 kg., is consuming oxygen at the rate of 2 to 3 litres per hour. Cerebral oxygen consumption can be decreased by 40 per cent. in general anæsthesis, and may be increased by 50 per cent. in conditions of excitement or anxiety. It is not significantly decreased during normal sleep.

Brain and nerve, like muscle, operate a glucose to lactate glycolytic process, supplemented by a tricarboxylic cycle. Aerobic glycolysis proceeds to some extent under the normal conditions of cerebral activity, and lactate equivalent to about 16 per cent. of the glucose metabolised is present in the blood leaving the brain area. This may represent, in part, a device for regulating pH, and protecting the brain cells from the effects of alkaline metabolites.

In addition to glucose, its chief and essential nutrient, brain tissue can oxidise fructose, glutamine, and succinate.

Representative respiration rates in terms of micro-litres of oxygen absorbed per mg. dry weight of tissue, per hour, for brain cortex slices suspended in glucose-saline at body-temperature, are: mouse, 14·2; rat, 11·2; guinea pig, 8·7; cat, 8·4; rabbit, 7·4; dog, 7·0; man, 6·1 (Elliott, 1948).

Values in terms of ml. oxygen uptake per gram fresh tissue, per hour, for various parts of dog brain, are: cerebral cortex, 1·16; cerebellum, 1·4; caudate nucleus, 1·36; thalamus, 1·01; mid-brain, 0·92; medulla, 0·69 (Himwich *et al.*, 1941).

Brain tissue glycolysis and respiration are increased by rise in temperature, and by various compounds including phenylhydrazine, phenosafranine, guanidine derivatives, bacterial metabolites, such as pyocyanine, and, indirectly, by anti-depressent drugs. Respiration, but not necessarily glycolysis, is strongly inhibited by cyanide, and by narcotics, including the

434

barbiturates, and some "tranquillisers", and hallucinogens, including mescaline.

Conduction and Transmission in the Nervous System

Functionally, the human brain is a three-dimensional fabric woven from about $10,000 \times 10^6$ nerve cells and their connections. During life, the central nervous system is in a condition of continuous activity, most of which is below the level of consciousness. This activity is maintained by the conduction of impulses within the cells, and the transmission of impulses from cell to cell. Each neuron, or nerve cell, forms a functional unit in the continuum, and by means of a fibre, or axon, which may exceed a metre in length, provides an apparatus for the uni-directional propagation of rapid impulses, at speeds of 20 to 100 metres per second.

Nerve conduction is a complex process; it is too rapid to be explained by ionic diffusion, and too slow to be purely electrical in character, but may be described as an electron effect, propagated by a chain of chemical relays, and involving both surfaces of the fibre membrane. Aided by the fact that some invertebrates, such as the squid, have giant nerve fibres accessible to manipulation, micro-physiological studies have shown that during the resting condition the interior of the fibre is at a negative potential of 80 to 90 millivolts, with respect to the outer surface of the membrane. Furthermore, the axoplasm, or fibre content is relatively rich in K^+ and organic anions, and poor in Na^+ and Cl^-, compared with the environment. This difference in ionic pattern is maintained by an inter-cellular metabolic pump, which expels Na^+ and Cl^- more rapidly than they diffuse in across the membrane. The axoplasm contains about 10 per cent. of proteins, including nucleoprotein, enzymes, and carriers for bound acetyl choline, which may be the relay substance in cellular conduction.

The impulse is conducted as a wave of events, characterised by: rise in negative potential within the fibre; depolarisation of membrane, with local short-circuiting involving the adjacent regions; entrance of sodium ions, favoured by concentration gradient and cell potential; fall in negative potential within the fibre; escape of potassium ions; restoration of membrane polarisation.

In the recovery phase, the metabolic pump expels the sodium ions, and potassium ions re-enter the fibre to balance the inter-cellular organic ions.

The operation of the metabolic pump and the maintenance of the fibre potential require expenditure of energy, as shown by the fact that, even when at rest a nerve absorbs oxygen; the Qo_2 for rabbit nerve at $37°$ C. being about $-1 \cdot 15$, a value increased nearly four times by stimulation. Nerve can go into a state of "oxygen debt", as shown by its ability to continue to conduct for some hours, when in an atmosphere of nitrogen. Under these anaerobic conditions, lactate is formed from carbohydrate. The conduction of the nerve impulse under aerobic conditions is accompanied by oxygen consumption and release of carbon dioxide, showing that nerve operates a respiratory process for maintaining energy supply.

Chemical Mechanisms in Nerve Transmission

Transmission, or passage of nerve impulses from cell to cell, is effected by the local release of agents termed chemical transmitters, or neurocrines, because they resemble the hormones, or endocrines, in some respects. These transmitters are: acetyl choline, noradrenaline, adrenaline, and, possibly, dopamine.

History. Following the isolation of adrenaline from adrenal gland extracts in 1903, and its synthesis, the pharmacological properties of the hormone were investigated, and as many of these resembled the effects obtained by stimulation of sympathetic nerves, adrenaline was described as a *sympathomimetic* agent.

In 1921, Loewi reported that the perfusion fluid from a frog's heart that had been stopped by vagal stimulation was able to induce typical vagal effects when perfused through another heart, from which he concluded that a " vagal substance " was liberated locally. The work was confirmed by other investigators, who showed that similar substances were liberated in various tissues and glands on stimulation of the parasympathetic nerves, and the term *parasympathin* was introduced to denote the reactant. The term *sympathin* was applied to the corresponding substance liberated locally on stimulation of the sympathetic nerves. Parasympathin is dialysable and acid-stable, but rapidly destroyed by alkalis and by esterases present in blood and most tissues.

In all these properties, parasympathin resembles acetyl choline.

In many ways sympathin resembled adrenaline, the secretion of the suprarenal medulla. Following a suggestion of Dale, nerve fibres are now classified as *cholinergic* and *adrenergic*, according to the type of transmitter liberated. Discrepancies between the properties of adrenaline and the postulated sympathin had been noted by many workers, including Barger and Dale (1910), and Cannon (1921). In 1904, Stoltz synthesised an adrenaline substitute, *arterenol*, or *noradrenaline*, which had powerful sympathomimetic properties. In 1946, von Euler produced evidence that noradrenaline occurs in animal tissues, including the nerves of the sympathetic chain, and its significance was confirmed by Peart (1949), who showed that noradrenaline accompanied by small amounts of adrenaline is liberated by stimulation of the sympathetic nerves to the spleen.

Definition and Classification. A neuro-chemical transmitter, neurocrine, or ergone, is a specific agent, liberated at a nerve-ending as the result of the arrival of a nerve impulse, and employed in the transmission of the impulse to a target cell or tissue. The three known transmitters, acetyl choline, noradrenaline, and adrenaline, are all compounds of low molecular weight; they are readily diffusible, and are rapidly inactivated by enzymes operating at the point of release.

Acetyl choline, *ach,* $CH_3.CO.O.CH_2.CH_2.N^+(CH_3)_3$, is liberated at the endings of five types of motor nerves: (1) voluntary, (2) preganglionic parasympathetic, (3) postganglionic parasympathetic, (4) preganglionic sympathetic, and (5) splanchnic sympathetic. It is implicated also in transmission in the brain and spinal cord, even though it may not be the universal synaptic transmitter (Feldberg, 1950).

Acetyl choline is formed from choline in nerve tissue by the aid of an enzyme, *choline acetylase,* which catalyses the transfer of acetyl groups from acetyl-co-enzyme A. The transmitter is stored in a bound form until required.

After release, acetyl choline is very rapidly hydrolysed to choline and acetic acid, by esterases, of which two types can be recognised; specific, or " true " choline esterase, *che* I, which occurs in the nervous system, in red blood corpuscles, and in the placenta; and the much more widely distributed, less selective " pseudo " cholinesterases, *che* II.

Cholinergic Effects. The types of response to stimulation by cholinergic nerves include: *voluntary* and *tonal,* from striated muscle; *visceral* and *glandular,* from unstriated muscle and gland cells; *cardiac,* and ganglionic. The striated muscle response and the ganglion response can be imitated by the tobacco alkaloid *nicotine,* in very low concentration, but is inhibited by high concentration. This double effect of nicotine was applied by Langley in his pioneer work on the organisation of the autonomic nervous system. The action of acetyl choline on striated muscle synapses is abolished by alkaloids from the arrow-poison curare, which render the myo-neural end-plate insensitive to the transmitter, and thus paralyse the muscle, and remove it from voluntary and tonal control. One of the alkaloids, *tubocurarine,* is used therapeutically, to obtain relaxation of striated muscles during operations under light anæsthesia.

The visceral and glandular effects of cholinergic stimulation, but not the striated muscle effects, are imitated by *muscarine,* a toxic alkaloid from the fungus *Amanita muscaria,* and are abolished by the belladonna alkaloid, *atropine,* or d-l-hyoscyamine, which, unlike curarines, has no antagonistic effect on cholinergic stimulation of striated muscle or ganglia.

Anti-cholinesterases. The effects of the release of acetyl choline at synapses can be intensified and prolonged by inhibitors of the enzymes that hydrolyse the transmitter. These inhibitors include substrate competitors, such as tetravalent nitrogen, or *onium* compounds: *decamethonium,*

$$(CH_3)_3N^+.(CH_2)_{10}.N^+(CH_3)_3,$$

which resembles acetyl choline structurally, and competes with it for possession of the enzyme. Another type of inhibitor, represented by the fluorophosphonates, such as the " nerve poison " gases, acts by poisoning the esterases, including *che* II. Prominent among the anti-cholinesterases, because of their therapeutic value, are *eserine,* or *physostigmine,* from Calabar bean, and a synthetic analogue, *neostigmine.*

Effects of Acetyl Choline. Applied locally or injected subcutaneously, acetyl choline salts reproduce the effects of stimulation by cholinergic nerves: vaso-dilation, increased peristalsis, cardiac depression, increased secretion by lachrymal, salivary, gastric and other glands, sweating. The effect is brief, because of the rapid hydrolysis of the ester. Pilocarpine, an alkaloid from jaborandi, resembles acetyl choline in parasympathetic properties.

Noradrenaline, arterenol, or norepinephrine, α-(3,4-dihydroxyphenol)-β-aminoethanol, $(HO)_2C_6H_3 . CH(OH) . CH_2 . NH_2$, is liberated at the post-ganglionic synapses of sympathetic nerves, and constitutes the sympathetic chemical transmitter in all known animal species.

It is accompanied by small amounts of its N-methyl derivative, the hormone adrenaline. In the adrenal medulla, the proportions of noradrenaline and adrenaline vary greatly with species. Noradrenaline is formed in the adrenal medulla and in nerve tissue from tyrosine, probably by way of dopa and dopamine (p. 395). Subsequent transfer of a methyl group from methionine to the N in noradrenaline produces adrenaline.

Effects of the Adrenalines. Adrenaline is a circulatory hormone, and its properties have been discussed in Chapter 24.

Adrenaline raises blood pressure both by constricting skin vessels and by increasing cardiac output. The increase in blood pressure caused by nor-adrenaline is due to its general vaso-constrictor action. It has no direct action on the heart. Adrenaline evokes a secretion of the adrenalcorticotropic hormone by the anterior pituitary; noradrenaline has much less evocative action. The recognition of the individual effects of the two adrenalines is complicated by their closely associated occurrence and properties, and by the fact that noradrenaline can be converted into adrenaline within the organism. However, a general pattern can be traced, in which noradrenaline occupies the position of a transmitter in continuous employment by the sympathetic system, and adrenaline is an overall efficiency hormone, released in response to stress, and representing a reaction of the unconscious self to the challenge of an emergency.

Synthetic compounds with a noradrenaline-like vaso-constrictor effect, which are in therapeutic use include: naphazoline, phenylephrine, and pholedrine; while isoprenaline reproduces some of the effects of adrenaline, notably bronchiodilation. The alkaloids, *ephedrine*, from *Ephedra equisetina*, and *hordenine*, from barley, potentiate the effects of adrenergic nerve stimulation by inhibiting inactivation of the transmitters by amine oxidase.

On liberation at the adrenergic synapses, both noradrenaline and adrenaline are degraded by a local amine oxidase system, with removal of N as NH_3 or $CH_3 . NH_2$, and production of a phenylcarboxylic acid. A less probable mode of disposal is oxidative ring-closure to a melanogen (p. 173). As pseudo-melanoid pigments occur in parts of the brain, and as hallucinogenic proper-ties have been attributed to melanogens, such transformations may represent an exotic or abnormal way of metabolising the adrenalines.

Significance of the Nervous System. Nerve tissue has two dominant functions: (1) as an instrument of purpose, it co-ordinates and centralises the activities of the entire animal; (2) as an instrument of learning, it is the only tissue capable of being trained, and showing the property of recording and remembering past experience. When the brain has reached a certain level of complexity it controls behaviour, and its activity is referable to an entity, the *mind*. In its higher manifestations, mind reveals itself as: (1) an organisation of previous experiences that makes possible the rationalisation of present experiences, and the prediction of future experiences; together with (2) a continual impetus to act, rationalise and predict. The central nervous system provides a well-protected and retentive tissue structure in which the association tracts and patterns that form the memory can be woven by the aid of the intense metabolic activity that characterises the respiration of the brain. Point activity in a single neuron can result in an activity pattern that extends through the brain net-work. In this way, concepts recorded by early experiences enable present experiences to be recognised and used to modify behaviour. During the lifetime of the animal the brain is never at rest; it constitutes both the library and library staff in charge of the " living past ", and its importance has been summarised by Bergson: " We think with only a small part of our past, but it is with our entire past that we desire, will, and act."

AUTOLYSIS

> " There was a purpose in all earthly things;
> And it is gone, and they asunder fall."
>
> *Dunsany.*

Cells have an inherent property of self-construction that enables them to grow and to preserve their character. Under certain conditions the process is reversed, and the cells and tissues undergo *autolysis*, or self-digestion, as is shown by the breakdown of the proteins of the cytoplasm and other cell constituents. Localised autolysis is a normal event during the life-cycle of many animals, and is seen in the atrophy of the uterus and mammary glands, after pregnancy and the lactation period.

A more widespread autolysis occurs during starvation, when there is a selective mobilisation of tissue proteins to provide the amino acids necessary to maintain life. Tissues of less survival value are attacked first, the order being: liver, skeletal muscle and, finally, heart and respiratory muscle. The osseous, cartilaginous, elastic and fibrous tissues which hold the organism together undergo little or no autolysis. The central nervous system appears to be completely resistant.

While the organism is alive, autolysis is a reversible process, and depends on equilibrium maintenance between the products of cell metabolism and the constituents of the internal environment. Thus, muscular atrophy, following immobilisation or nerve injury, may result in loss of half of the total muscle

439

substance, without destruction of the muscle cells. The contraction mechanism persists, and the muscle can regenerate completely as soon as circumstances become favourable.

Immediately after the death of the organism, however, a general post-mortem autolysis sets in, and brings about the softening and liquefaction of the tissues. The process is evoked by lack of available oxygen and by increase in acidity, and depends mostly on the release of protein-splitting enzymes of the cathepsin type, within the cells.

The reaction of the living cell, pH 6·8 to 7·2 (Chambers and Kerr, 1932), is unfavourable for autolysis. The process is detectable about pH 6, reaches a maximum at pH 4, and then falls to zero, when the acidity is raised to pH 2·5 to 2, in which region the enzymes are destroyed.

Post-mortem liberation of acid is independent of protein breakdown, and probably is due to failure of the tissue respiration systems. Autolysis is accelerated by mechanical disintegration of the tissues, and can be brought about in yeasts and bacteria by agents, such as ether or acetone, that damage the cell surface. The progress of the change can be followed by incubating suspensions of finely disintegrated tissue in presence of an antiseptic, such as toluene or salicylic acid, that does not precipitate the proteins or inactivate the enzymes.

Samples are analysed by precipitating the unchanged protein, and estimating the amino acids and peptides in the filtrate.

Autolysis reaches equilibrium within 5 to 10 days, depending on the temperature and the type of tissue. It is inhibited by oxidising agents, such as iodine and iodate, and is promoted by reducing agents, including cysteine and other thiols, which activate enzymes of the cathepsin type. Autolysis is a general process independent of putrefaction or other infective changes. It is initiated by failure of the redox-pump mechanism present in every living cell, and kept constantly at work by being supplied with cellular nutrients. When the pump fails the cell is no longer able to maintain its ionic individuality and is swamped by its environment. As a result, metabolic systems are disorganised, acid accumulates, and the enzymes that have preserved the structure of the cell throughout its lifetime now reverse their catalytic effects and thereby fulfil their last obligation:

" When that which drew from out the boundless deep Turns again home."

General References

Barcroft, J. (1934), " Features in the Architecture of Physiological Function." Cambridge.

Barcroft, J. (1935), " Chemical Conditions of Mental Development." *Irish J. med. Sci.*, **115**, 302.

Bean, J. W. (1945), " Effects of Oxygen at Increased Pressure." *Physiol. Rev.*, **25**, 1.

" Bone Structure and Metabolism." Ciba Foundation Symposium (1956).

" Biochemistry and Physiology of Bone." Ed. by G. H. Bourne (1956). London.

Bradley, H. C. (1938), "Autolysis and Atrophy." *Physiol. Rev.*, **18**, 173.

Dill, D. B. (1938), " Life, Heat and Altitude." Harvard.

Florkin, M. (1948), " Biochemical Evolution." Trans. by S. Morgulis. New York.

Leicester, H. M. (1949), " Biochemistry of the Teeth." London.

" Measurement in medicine." *Brit. med. Bull.*, 1951, **7**, No. 4.

" Neurochemistry." Ed. by K. A. C. Elliot, I. H. Page, and J. H. Quastel (1955). Springfield.

" Neurophysiology." *Brit. med. Bull.*, 1950, **6**, No. 4.

" Physiology of voluntary muscle." *Brit. med. Bull.*, 1956, **12**, No. 3.

Szent-Györgyi, A. (1948), " The Nature of Life." New York.

APPENDIX I

REPRESENTATIVE FOOD MATERIALS

Composition per 100 *gm.*

Foodstuff, 100 gm. (3½ oz.).	Energy, in kilocal.	Water, in gm.	Protein, in gm.	Fat and other lipids, in gm.	Carbohydrate, available, in gm.	Phosphate, as P, in mg.	Calcium, in mg.	Iron, in mg.
Animal products :								
Bacon (raw) . .	500	30	10	40	0	115	13	1·2
Beef, lean (raw) .	117	68	14	10	0	276	5	4·3
Brain, sheep (boiled) .	110	79	12	7	0	339	11	2·2
Chicken (boiled) .	203	61	26	10	0	270	10	2·1
Ham (raw) . .	517	31	15	49	0	104	14	1·2
Kidney, sheep (raw) .	98	77	17	3	0	254	13	11·7
Liver, ox (raw) . .	143	73	16	8	tr.	313	8	14
Mutton (boiled) .	260	45	12	16	0	238	4	5·4
Pork (roast) . .	317	50	24	23	0	363	5	1·7
Rabbit (stewed) .	180	64	26	8	0	119	11	1·9
Tongue, ox (boiled) .	310	49	19	2	0	229	31	3
Veal (raw) . .	108	56	13	5	0	258	7	2·3
Egg, hen (raw or boiled)	163	73	12	12	0	218	56	2·5
Egg, white . .	37	88	9	tr.	0	33	5	0·1
Egg, yolk . .	350	51	16	30	0	495	131	6·1
Milk, cow . .	66	87	3·3	3·6	4·7	100	120	0·03
Milk, powdered . .	485	5	25·6	26·7	35·6	712	900	1·6
Milk, skimmed . .	36	90	3·4	0·2	4·8	98	124	0·08
Butter . . .	745	15	0·5	82	tr.	24	15	0·16
Cream . . .	407	53	1·8	42	2·3	25	59	0·23
Cheese, Cheddar .	423	37	25	34	tr.	545	810	0·57
Fish :								
Cod (steamed) . .	82	79	18	1·9	0	242	15	0·5
Herring (raw) . .	140	50	11	10·5	0	272	70	1·5
Lobster (boiled) .	119	72	21	3·4	0	283	62	0·8
Mackerel (fried) .	187	66	20	11	0	280	28	1·2
Plaice (steamed) .	92	42	18	2·9	0	246	38	0·6
Prawn (cooked) .	104	70	21	2·8	0	349	145	1·1
Salmon (steamed) .	199	65	19	13	0	302	30	0·8
Sardine (canned) .	294	51	20	23	0	683	409	4
Sole (steamed) . .	84	47	18	1·3	0	270	113	0·7
Cereal products :								
Barley, pearl . .	384	10·6	8·4	1·7	81·3	206	8	0·67
Cornflour . . .	387	11·5	0·6	0·7	92	39	15	1·43
Macaroni . . .	383	10·4	11·7	2·0	77	152	26	1·43
Oatmeal . . .	434	3·5	13·3	8·7	73	380	55	4·12
Rice, polished . .	393	11·7	6·8	1·0	87	99	4	4·50

442

Foodstuff, 100 gm. (3¼ oz.).	Energy, in kilocal.	Water, in gm.	Protein, in gm.	Fat and other lipids, in gm.	Carbohydrate, available, in gm.	Phosphate, as P, in mg.	Calcium, in mg.	Iron, in mg.
Wheat, entire (100%).	317	13	8–15	2·4	62	260	30	3·5
Wheat flour (85%) .	346	13	11	1·6	72	213	20	2·5
„ „ (70%) .	351	13	10	1	72·5	73	16	2
Wheaten bread,								
"White" . .	260	32	7 9	0·7	54	73	23	1·0
"Brown" . .	229	37	8·4	1·6	44	213	30	2·7
Biscuits								
"Cream cracker" .	579	3·5	9·3	33	57·5	82	18	0·96
"Rusk" . .	408	6·4	6·6	8	74	81	87	2·66
"Water" . .	462	0·6	12	12·5	73	87	22	0·94
Miscellaneous ·								
Chocolate, plain. .	562	tr.	4·6	32·5	52	139	26	3·28
Cocoa, powder . .	464	2·5	20·4	25·6	35	685	51	14·3
Coffee, ground . .	311	4	12·5	15·4	28·5	161	133	4·1
Tea, Indian . .	58	9·3	14	0	0	628	426	15·2
"Carrageen moss" .	30	14	6·8	tr.	0·4	205	845	8·88
Honey . . .	315	23	0·6	tr.	76·4	17	5	0·39
Marmalade . .	285	28	0·1	0	69·5	12	35	0·58
Sugar, white . .	409	0	0	0	99·9	tr.	1	0·04
Treacle, black . .	281	28·5	1·2	0	67	31	495	9·17
Margarine . .	794	13·7	0·2	85·3	0	12	4	0·3
Olive oil . . .	929	tr.	tr.	99·9	0	tr.	tr.	0·08
Mushroom, raw . .	7	91·5	1·8	tr.	0	136	3	1·0
Bran . . .	169	10	16	6	12	1,215	120	8·52
Fruit, fresh :								
Apple . . .	50	84	0·2	tr.	12	8	3	0·2
Apricot . . .	30	87	0·6	„	6·7	21	17	0·37
Banana . . .	83	71	1·1	„	19	28	6	0·4
Blackberry . .	32	82	1·3	„	6·4	24	63	0·85
Cherry . . .	51	71	0·6	„	12	17	16	0·4
Currant, black . .	31	77	0·9	„	6·6	43	60	1·27
Gooseberry . .	18	90	1·1	„	3·4	34	28	0·32
Grape . . .	66	81	0·6	„	15·5	16	4	0·34
Grapefruit . .	24	91	0·6	„	5·3	16	17	0·26
Lemon . . .	16	85	0·8	„	3·2	21	107	0·35
Melon, yellow . .	23	94	0·6	„	5	8	14	0·24
Orange . . .	38	86	0·8	„	8·5	24	41	0·33
Pear. . . .	46	83	0·2	„	10·8	10	8	0·19
Plum, Victoria . .	42	84	0·6	„	9·6	16	11	0·36
Pineapple . . .	50	84	0·5	„	11·6	8	12	0·42
Raspberry . .	27	83	0·9	„	5·6	29	41	1·21
Strawberry . .	28	89	0·6	„	6·2	23	22	0·71
Tomato (raw) . .	23	93	1	0·3	4	21	9	0·4
Fruit, dried :								
Apricot . . .	198	15	4·8	tr.	43·4	118	92	4·1
Currant . . .	266	22	1·7	„	63	40	95	1·82
Date . . .	270	15	2	„	64	64	70	1·6
Fig	232	17	3·6	„	53	92	28	4·17

Foodstuff, 100 gm. (3½ oz.).	Energy, in kilocal.	Water, in gm.	Protein, in gm.	Fat and other lipids, in gm.	Carbohydrate, available, in gm.	Phosphate, as P, in mg.	Calcium, in mg.	Iron, in mg.
Olive (preserved) .	106	76	0·9	11	0	17	61	1·0
Prune . . .	175	23	2·4	tr.	40	83	38	2·9
Raisin . . .	269	21	1·1	,,	64·4	33	61	1·55
Nuts :								
Almond, sweet . .	600	5	20·5	53·5	4·3	442	247	4·23
Barcelona nut . .	388	7	8	38	3	299	70	1·5
Brazil nut . .	645	9	13·8	61·5	4·1	592	176	2·8
Chestnut . . .	185	52	2·3	2·7	36·6	74	46	0·89
Cob	400	41	9	36	6·8	229	44	1·06
Coconut . . .	366	42	3·8	36	3·7	94	13	2·08
Peanut . . .	606	4	28	49	8·6	365	61	2·04
Walnut . . .	551	23	12·5	51·5	5	510	61	2·35
Green Vegetables :								
Asparagus (boiled) .	18	92	1·1	tr.	3·4	84·5	36	0·9
Brussel sprout (boiled)	17	91	2·4	,,	1·7	45	27	0·6
Cabbage (boiled) .	9	96	0·8	,,	1·3	24	45	0·46
Cauliflower (boiled) .	11	95	1·5	,,	1·2	33	23	0·48
Celery (raw) . .	9	93	0·9	,,	1·3	32	52	0·6
Leek (boiled) . .	26	91	1·8	,,	4·6	27·5	60	2·0
Lettuce (raw) . .	12	95	1·1	,,	1·8	30	26	0·2
Marrow (boiled) .	7	98	0·4	,,	1·4	13	13	0·7
Spinach (boiled) .	27	85	5·1	,,	1·4	93	560	4·0
Watercress (raw) .	14	91	0·7	,,	0·7	52	222	1·6
Roots and tubers (boiled) :								
Artichoke, Jerusalem .	20	36	1·6	tr.	3·2	33	30	0·41
Beetroot . . .	48	83	1·8	,,	9·9	35·6	30	0·7
Carrot . . .	20	87	0·6	,,	4·3	17	37	0·37
Onion . . .	14	97	0·6	,,	2·7	16·4	24	0·25
Parsnip . . .	62	83	1·7	,,	13·5	32	35	0·45
Potato . . .	87	80	1·4	,,	19·7	29	4	0·48
Swede . . .	19	92	0·9	,,	3·8	18	41	0·29
Turnip . . .	12	94	0·7	,,	2·3	19	55	0·35
Pulses (boiled) :								
Bean, broad . .	46	84	4·1	tr.	7·1	99	21	0·98
,, butter . .	283	70	19·2	,,	50	86·5	19	1·67
,, French . .	8	95	0·8	,,	1·1	15	39	0·59
,, haricot . .	95	70	6·6	,,	16·6	122	64	2·5
Lentil . . .	103	72	6·8	,,	18·3	80	10	2·2
Pea, green . .	52	80	5·0	,,	7·7	83	13	1·2
,, dried . .	107	70	6·9	,,	19	113	24	1·4
Soy bean (dry) . .	417	12	36	18	26	580	206	0·78

The tabulated values are selected from data compiled by Mottram and Radloff (1937), McCance and Widdowson (1946), Wokes (1941), and the Council of British Societies for Relief Abroad (1945).

CHARACTERISTICS OF THE CHIEF FOOD TYPES

1. **Animal Products. Meat,** which is chiefly skeletal muscle, is characterised by: (*a*) a high protein value, usually of the order of 20 per cent., which may be concentrated by cooking; (*b*) a variable fat value, up to about 30 per cent.; (*c*) a negligible carbohydrate value; (*d*) an iron value of about 2 mg. per 100 gm., much of which is in the almost unavailable forms of myohæmatin and hæmoglobin; (*e*) a significant amount of the vitamins B_1, B_2, and nicotinic amide; (*f*) inorganic and organic " extractives ", one of which, glutamic acid, is partly responsible for the taste of roast meat. **Myosin,** the principal protein in meat, is the chief protein in the ordinary mixed diet, which includes about 15 to 20 gm., *per diem*. It contains all the known indispensable amino acids. **Glandular organs,** especially liver and kidney, are rich in nucleoprotein, and are valuable sources of the vitamins of the B group and the micro-essential metals Fe and Cu.

Fish resembles mammalian tissue in general composition, but is usually much poorer in fats, with the notable exception of species such as herring, mackerel, salmon and eel, which have a fat value of 10 to 15 per cent.

2. **Milk and Milk Products.** Cow's milk provides high-grade protein (3 per cent.), fat rich in unsaturated fatty acids (3·6 per cent.), phosphate and calcium, and is an important but variable source of vitamins A and B.

Representative values, per 100 gm. fresh English pasture milk, are: A and carotenes, 80 to 250 i. units; B_1, 0·05 mg.; B_2, 0·15 mg.; nicotinic acid, 0·08 to 0·4 mg.; C, 1 to 3 mg.; pantothenic acid, 0·4 mg.; B_6, 0·03 mg.; inositol, 14 mg.; D, 2 i. units.

Good milk has 3·6 per cent. fats, the legal minimum being 3·0 per cent. Condensed milk has a protein value of 7 to 10, and a sugar value that may be raised to 60 per cent. by addition of sucrose. Spray-dried milk powder has a protein value of about 26 per cent., and a water content of 2 to 4 per cent. The *specific gravity* of cow's milk when fresh is 1·029 to 1·033; the *freezing-point*, as estimated by the cryoscope, is almost constant within the limits —0·53° C. and —0·57° C. These properties are important in deciding the quality of a sample of milk.

Butter has 85 to 90 per cent. of fat, which carries the fat-soluble vitamins present in the milk, so that 1 oz. of butter is equivalent to the vitamin A and D values of about 1½ pints of the original milk.

Bacharach (1940) suggests that a reasonable standard for summer butter is not less than 50 i. units of A and provitamin A per gram (1,400 units per oz.), and not less than 0·75 i. units of D per gram (21 units per oz.). The vitamin D value of butter is seldom more than 1 unit per gram, and may be as low as 0·01 unit, in winter butter.

Cheese is a concentrated foodstuff, with a protein value of 20 to 40 per cent., and a fat value of 15 to 40 per cent. It is an important source of phosphate

and calcium (0·3 to 1·2 per cent.), and vitamin A (10 to 50 units per gram).
3. **Vegetables.** With the exception of the tubers and dried pulses, the vegetables are poor sources of energy, but are important protective foodstuffs, capable of supplying all the dietary requirements for vitamin C, most of the requirements for provitamin A, and providing some iron and calcium, as well as magnesium, which is released from the otherwise unassimilated chlorophyll. Much of the carbohydrate present is in the unavailable form of pentosans and cellulose.

Potato is a very important foodstuff on account of its low cost, its availability and popularity. In addition to its high starch content, which is about 20 per cent., potatoes contain 0·7 to 3·6 per cent. of protein, half of which is the globulin *tuberin*, of high nutritional value.

Vitamin values, per 100 gm. fresh tuber, are: B_1, 0·02 to 0·3 mg.; B_2, 0·007 to 0·06 mg.; C, 5 to 40 mg. Although the C value is relatively low and variable, it is significant because of the amount of material eaten, and 1 lb. of potatoes can supply 20 to 150 mg. of ascorbic acid. The fate of the vitamin depends on the method of cooking. The loss on steaming is slight; slicing and long period boiling may reduce the value to zero.

Yeasts. Average values, per 100 gm. dry material brewer's yeast are: protein, 53 gm.; lipids, 1 gm.; Ca, 84 mg.; Fe, 21 mg.; thiamine, 17 mg.; nicotinic acid, 32 to 47 mg.; riboflavin, 4 mg. Baker's yeast is similar in composition, but poorer in Ca (42 mg.) and thiamine (3 mg.), and richer in riboflavin (7·4 mg.).

Reference

" The Nation's Food." Ed. by A. L. Bacharach and T. Rendle (1946). London: Society of Chemical Industry.

APPENDIX II

REAGENTS EMPLOYED IN BIOCHEMISTRY

(*In aqueous solution, unless otherwise stated*)

Ammonium Hydroxide. The concentrated solution (density, 0·88) contains about 35 gm. NH_4^+ and NH_3 per 100 gm., which is equivalent to 17 N $NH_4.OH$.

Antimony trichloride, 30 per cent. in chloroform. Reagent for vitamin A and other carotenoids (p. 171).

Benedict's Qualitative Copper Reagent: 17·3 gm. crystalline $CuSO_4.5H_2O$, with 173 gm. Na citrate and 100 gm. anhydrous Na_2CO_3 in 1,000 ml. water. Used for detecting reducing sugars.

Benedict's Quantitative Copper Reagent: 18·0 gm. crystalline $CuSO_4.5H_2O$, with 200 gm. Na citrate, 125 gm. KSCN, 5 ml. of 5 per cent. K ferrocyanide, and 100 gm. anhydrous Na_2CO_3. Dissolve separately, mix, and make up to 1,000 ml. with water. Before use, add 3 to 5 gm. anhydrous Na_2CO_3 to 25 ml. of reagent. Used for estimating reducing sugars.

Benzidine, fresh saturated solution in glacial acetic acid. Reagent for blood pigment in urine, and for nitrite in saliva.

Diazo-Reagent (Ehrlich, Van den Bergh), freshly prepared mixture of 1 ml. of 0·5 per cent. $NaNO_2$ and 50 ml. of 0·1 per cent. sulphanilic acid in 2 per cent. HCl. Reagent (in acid solution) for free bilirubin; and (in alkaline solution) for histidine, histamine, tyrosine, tyramine, indoxyl, and polyphenols.

2 : 6-Dichloroquinone-chloroimide, 0·4 per cent. in absolute alcohol. Kept in brown glass bottles and in the dark, the reagent is stable for at least three months. In alkaline solution (pH 9 to 10 is best) it gives colours with uric acid (yellow), phenols unsubstituted in the *para*-position (violet-blue), indole, methylamine, glycine, thiourea (violet).

3 : 5-Dinitrobenzoic Acid, 5 per cent. Yields a purple colour with creatinine in alkaline solution. The reagent may be used in alcoholic solution, or dissolved in dilute sodium carbonate.

Ehrlich's Aldehyde Reagent, 2 to 3 per cent. *p*-dimethylamino benzaldehyde in alcohol or in 20 per cent. HCl. Reagent for mucoproteins, indole, indoxyl, urobilinogen, urea, allantoin ; and (in excess of strong acid) tryptophan and scatole. The reagent in 20 per cent. HCl is almost colourless, and is suitable for the urea and allantoin tests.

Fehling's Reagent. See p. 451. Reagent A: Crystalline $CuSO_4.5H_2O$, 34·65 gm.; water, 500ml. Reagent B: Sodium hydroxide, 60 gm.; sodium potassium tartrate (Rochelle salt), 173 gm.; water, 500 ml. The reagents are kept separate because the tartrate tends to undergo degradation when exposed to light in presence of Cu^{2+} and can bring about reduction on boiling in the absence of reducing sugar. When testing for traces of sugar, the mixed Fehling reagent should be diluted 1 in 5, otherwise the deep blue may conceal a faint precipitate of cuprous oxide.

Fallacies of Fehling's test are noted on page 451.

Guaiacum, 2 per cent. in alcohol. With H_2O_2, it is a reagent for peroxidases, and hæmoglobin in urine.

Gunzberg's Reagent, phloroglucinol, 2 gm., vanillin, 1 gm., in 100 ml. ethanol.

H-ion Indicators. These reagents change colour sharply at a particular concentration of H-ions. A large number are in practical use, covering the acid-alkali scale from pH 0·1 to about pH 13.

H-ion Indicators

Indicator.	pH Range ←Acidity—Alkalinity→		
Crystal violet . . .	yellow	0·1—1·5	green
Thymol blue	red	1·4—2·8	yellow
Crystal violet . . .	green	1·5—3·2	violet
Tropæolin OO . . .	pink	1·5—3·0	yellow
Methyl yellow . . .	red	2·9—4·0	yellow
Methyl orange . . .	orange	3·0—4·4	yellow
Tetrabromphenol blue . .	yellow	3·0—4·6	blue
Bromcresol green . . .	yellow	3·8—5·4	blue
Methyl red	red	4·3—6·2	yellow
Litmus	red	5·0—8·0	blue
Tashiro's indicator . .	pink	5·45—5·50	green
Bromthymol blue . . .	yellow	6·0—7·6	blue
Phenol red	yellow	6·7—8·3	red
Thymol blue	yellow	8·0—9·6	blue
Phenolphthalein . . .	colourless	8·2—10·0	red

These indicators are generally used in 0·04 per cent. aqueous solution, with the exception of phenolphthalein, which is dissolved in alcohol.

For gastric analysis and titration stronger solutions (1 per cent.) of crystal violet, thymol blue, and methyl yellow are used.

Methyl yellow is also known as Töpfer's indicator or dimethyl-amino-azo-benzene. It will be seen that some of the indicators have an extended pH range in that they show more than two colours as the reaction changes from acidity to alkalinity. Examples of these indicators are crystal violet, which changes from yellow, green, blue, to violet, and thymol blue, which changes from red, yellow, green, to blue.

This property is developed in the use of mixed reagents, such as the B.D.H. " universal indicator ", which has the following colour range:

pH up to 3·0	Red	pH 8·0	Green
,, 4·0	Deeper Red	,, 8·5	Bluish Green
,, 5·0	Orange Red	,, 9·0	Greenish Blue
,, 5·5	Orange	,, 9·5	Blue
,, 6·0	Orange Yellow	,, 10·0	Violet
,, 6·5	Yellow	,, 10·5	Reddish Violet
,, 7·0 to 7·5	Greenish Yellow	,, 11·0	Deeper Reddish Violet

Litmus is included in the list to show how insensitive it is, relatively, when compared with the newer reagents. A change of three pH degrees is required to alter it from red to blue. Phenol red is a much sharper indicator for titrations to the end-point of absolute neutrality, pH 7·0.

For general use, one drop of indicator is added to each millimetre of solution examined. In exact work, the resulting colour is matched with a standard in a comparator.

Tashiro's Indicator. The stock solution is made by mixing 200 ml. of 1 per cent. alcoholic methyl red with 50 ml. of 0·1 per cent. alcoholic methylene blue. Both dyes must be dissolved in pure alcohol. For use, 1 part of stock solution is mixed with 1 part of alcohol and 2 parts of distilled water. This is an example of a *screened* indicator, or one in which the colour change is made more distinct by addition of a second pigment (methylene blue) to cut out part of the spectrum. The indicator is used in the Conway methods for the micro-analysis of ammonia and urea.

Fluorescent Indicators. These reagents respond to a change in pH by changing in colour or in intensity of fluorescence when exposed to ultra-violet light, and are very useful for analysis involving darkly-coloured liquids. The solution to be titrated is placed in a thin-walled flask or beaker on a black surface

Fluorescent Indicators

Indicator.		pH Range ←—Acidity—Alkalinity—→
3 : 6-Dihydroxy-phthalimide	colourless	0·0—2·5 yellow-green
	yellow-green	7·5—8·5 green
3 : 6-Dihydroxy-phthalonitrile	colourless	0·2—1·5 blue
	blue	6·0—8·0 green
Fluorescein . . .	green	0·1—0·5 yellow
Eosin	red	2·0—3·5 yellow
Erythrosin B . . .	red	3·0—5·0 yellow
Acridine	green	4·5—5·5 blue
Quinine sulphate . .	blue	4·5—8·5 violet
	violet	8·5—9·5 colourless
β-Naphthol . . .	colourless	6·0—6·5 blue

screened from sunlight. During the titration the mixture is illuminated obliquely by a beam of ultra-violet light to show the change in fluorescence.

Methylene Blue, 1 per cent. Redox indicator used in determining the end-point in Fehling's sugar estimation.

Millon's Mercury Reagent. 3 gm. Hg dissolved in 4 ml. concentrated HNO_3, diluted to 10 ml. with water, and filtered. Used for detecting tyrosine in proteins and phenols in urine.

a-**Naphthol,** 2 per cent. in alcohol. General reagent for carbohydrates, also used to detect arginine in proteins and indoxyl in urine.

β-**Naphthoquinone-4-Sulphonate,** 5 per cent. General reagent for proteins and amino acids.

Naphtho-resorcinol, 1 per cent. in alcohol. Special reagent for glycuronic acid in urine.

Ninhydrin, 0·2 per cent. General reagent for proteins and amino acids.

Phenylhydrazine Hydrochloride: Osazone reagent for sugars. Because of the instability of the free base, the hydrochloride is used in presence of sodium acetate to reduce the acidity. Phenylhydrazine hydrochloride, 10 gm.; crystalline sodium acetate, 15 gm.; water, 100 ml. Warm the mixture to 60° C., and filter to remove impurities, such as aniline, in the phenylhydrazine. Osazone formation requires an excess of the reagent.

Phosphomolybdate and Phosphotungstate Reagents. Both of these complex salts on reduction form deep blue solutions suitable for colorimetry.

1. *Phosphomolybdate Reagent* (Folin). Dissolve 50 gm. of pure sodium molybdate in 130 ml. distilled water. Add, while stirring, 50 ml. of 85 per cent. H_3PO_4, 10 ml. of pure H_2SO_4, and 20 ml. of glacial acetic acid. Filter through sintered glass, if necessary.

In alkaline solution, the reagent gives a blue colour with cysteine, tyrosine and other phenols, uric acid, and cuprous ions formed in reducing sugar reactions.

The reagent is unstable, and slowly acquires a blue tint, owing to impurities in the constituents.

2. *Phosphotungstate Reagent* (Folin, Marenzi, Koch). Dissolve 100 gm. "analytical" sodium tungstate in 700 ml. distilled water. Add 75 ml. of 85 per cent. H_3PO_4. Reflux the mixture gently in a round flask for 24 hours. Decolorise, if necessary, with a few drops of bromine, and boil-off the excess. Dilute to 1 litre, and store in absence of light.

This solution of phospho-18-tungstic acid is used for the estimation of uric acid. It is relatively insensitive to phenols, but is reduced by cysteine and other thiols.

Potassium Chromate, 5 per cent. With concentrated HNO_3, reagent for all primary and secondary alcohols, including sugars, glycerol, lactic acid, β-hydroxy-butyric acid, and tartaric acid.

Resorcinol, 5 per cent. in alcohol. Reagent for ketoses and indoxyl.

Schiff's Rosaniline Reagent, 1 per cent. rosaniline decolorised by SO_2. General reagent for free aldehyde groups.

Salicylsulphonic Acid, 20 per cent. General precipitant for higher proteins.

Sodium Nitroprusside (Nitrosoferricyanide), 5 per cent. Fresh aqueous nitro-prusside gives red or purple colours with thiol compounds (cysteine, gluta-thione), creatinine, ketones, and acetaldehyde, at pH 9. If the pH is set between 8 and 9, the reaction will be restricted to thiols. This can be done by using a saturated solution of $NaHCO_3$ as buffer.

The reagent is unstable if exposed to light.

Standard Sugar Solution (Lane and Eynon). Dissolve exactly 9·5 gm. of pure sucrose in 100 ml. of approximately 2 per cent. (or 0·6 Normal) HCl. The mixture is kept for a week, during which time it undergoes hydrolysis to " invert " sugar, an equimolecular mixture of glucose and fructose. It is then diluted to 1 litre and stored. For standardisation, 50 ml. is neutralised and made up to 100 ml. with water to yield a 0·5 per cent. solution of " invert " sugar.

Thymol 3 per cent. in alcohol. General reagent for carbohydrates. Also reacts with indoxyl.

Xanthydrol, 10 per cent. in methyl alcohol. Reagent for urea and indole.

Note :   Fallacies of Fehling's Test for Sugar in Urine

1. Albumin interferes with the test and if present in more than a small concentration should be removed by acidifying with acetic acid, boiling and filtering.

2. Very concentrated urines may reduce Fehling's solution owing to the action of uric acid. If doubtful dilute the urine and repeat the test.

3. Lactose, pentose and glycuronic acid.

4. Homogentisic acid. The reduction accompanied by a darkening of the urine and this should indicate the nature of the reducing substance.

5. Formalin is a strong reducing agent and contamination of a specimen with it may lead to error.

ABBREVIATIONS AND EQUIVALENTS

Weight

1 kilogram, kg. = 2·2046 lb. = 35·274 oz. avoirdupois.
1 gram, gm., or g. = 0·001 kg. = 15·432 gr. = 0·03527 oz. avoirdupois.
1 milligram, mg. = 0·001 gm. = 10^{-6} kg.
1 microgram, μg., or γ = 0·001 mg. = 10^{-6} gm.
1 pound avoirdupois, lb. = 7,000 grains = 16 oz. avoirdupois = 453·59 gm.
1 ounce avoirdupois, oz. = 16 drams = 437·5 gr. = 28·35 gm.
1 grain, gr. = 64·8 mg.
1 ton = 2,240 lb. = 1,006 kg.
1 metric ton, or tonne = 1,000 kg. = 2,204 lb. = 0·9842 tons.

Length

1 metre, m. = 1·0936 yards = 3·281 ft. = 39·37 in.
1 centimetre, cm. = 0·01 m. = 0·394 in.
1 millimetre, mm. = 0·001 m. = 0·0394 in.
1 micrometer, or micron, μ = 0·001 mm. = 10^{-6} m.
1 millimicron, or micromillimetre, mμ = 0·001 μ = 10^{-6} mm.
1 Ångström unit, Å. = 0·1 mμ.
1 kilometer, km. = 1,000 m. = 0·6214 miles = 3,280·83 ft.
1 yard, yd. = 3 ft. = 0·9144 m.
1 foot, ft. = 12 in. = 30·48 cm.
1 inch, in. = 2·54 cm.
1 mile = 5,280 ft. = 1·6093 km.

Volume

1 litre, l. = volume at 4° C. of 1,000 gm. of water.
    = 1,000·027 cubic cm. (c.c.).
    = 0·22 gallons (British) = 0·2642 gallons (U.S.A.).
    = 1·76 pints (British) = 2·11 pints (U.S.A.).
    = 35·196 fluid oz. (British) = 33·8 fluid oz. (U.S.A.).
1 millilitre, ml. = 0·001 l., or, approximately, 1 c.c.
        = 0·0352 fluid oz. (British) = 16·9 minims.
1 microlitre, μl. = 0·001 ml. = 1 cubic mm. = 10^{-6} l.
1 cubic metre, cu.m. = 1,000 l.
1 gallon (British), gal. = volume at 62° F. of 10 lb. of water.
        = 70,000 gr. = 4·54 l.
        = 1,201 gal. (U.S.A.) = 8 pints (British).

1 gallon (U.S.A.) = 8·313 lb. of water = 8 pints (U.S.A.) = 3·785 l.
1 pint (British) = 20 fluid oz. = 0·568 l.
1 fluid oz. (British) = 28·41 ml. = 8 fluid drachms = 480 minims.
1 minim = 59μ l. = 0·0592 ml. = 0·96 minims (U.S.A.).

Miscellaneous

mol, or mole, M = formula-weight of a substance (ions or molecules) expressed in gm.; the weight in gm. numerically equal to the ionic or molecular weight.
millimol, mM. = 0·001 mol.
molar solution = 1 mol per l. of solution.
molar concentration, [ ] = the number of mols. present per l. of solution.
gram-equivalent, gm.-eq. = mol value divided by valency value; the ionic weight in gm. divided by the valency.
normal solution, N. = 1 gm. eq. per l. of solution.
normal acid = 1 mol available H^+ per l. = 1 gm. available H^+ per l.
normal alkali = 1 mol available OH^- per l. = 17 gm. available OH^- per l.
$[H^+]$, C_H = hydrogen ion concentration, in mol H^+ per l.
$[OH^-]$, C_{OH} = hydroxyl ion concentration, in mol OH^- per l.
pH = hydrogen ion exponent = $-\log_{10}[H^+]$; $[H^+] = 10^{-pH}$.
pK_a = acid-dissociation exponent = $-\log_{10}Ka$.
1 atmosphere, atm. = 14·7 lb. per sq. in. = 1,033 gm. per sq. cm. = 33·9 ft. of water at 4° C. = 760 mm. Hg at 0° C.
1 calorie, gram-calorie, or small calorie, gm. cal. = quantity of heat required to raise the temperature of 1 gm. of water through 1° C. (from 14·5° to 15·5° C., for *normal* gm. cal.).
1 kilogram-calorie, kilocalorie, or large calorie, kilocal., or kg. cal. = 1,000 gm. cal., = 41·8 × 10^{10} ergs.
Freezing-point of pure water at 1 atm. = 0·0° C. = 32° F.
Temperature of maximum density of water = 4·0° C. = 39·2° F.
Boiling-point of pure water at 1 atm. = 100° C. = 212° F.
Temperature scale conversion: Centigrade to Fahrenheit; multiply °C. by 9, divide by 5, and add 32.
Fahrenheit to Centigrade; subtract 32 from °F., multiply by 5, and divide by 9.
Human body temperature, normal level, approx., 36·9° C., or 98·4° F.
Respiratory quotient, *R.Q.* = CO_2/O_2 = ratio of the volume of liberated CO_2 to volume of O_2 absorbed during a given period.
Respiratory coefficient, tissue respiration quotient, Q_o- or Q_{co2} = volume in microlitres of gas absorbed or liberated per hour by an amount of tissue representing 1 mg. dry weight.
parts per million, p.p.m. = mg. per kg. = gm. per cubic m.
grains per gallon = 1 part per 70,000, for aqueous solutions.
Wavelength, λ = distance in mμ or in Å between corresponding phases of two consecutive waves = speed divided by frequency (number of vibrations per second).

Electromagnetic radiation, vibration-effect transmitted at the speed of 3×10^{10} cm. per sec., the quality of which depends on the wavelength.

1. electrical waves, $\lambda = 30$ km. to 1 mm.
2. infra-red $\qquad \lambda = 1$ mm. to 760 mμ.
3. visible $\qquad \lambda = 760$ mμ (red) to 400 mμ (violet).
4. ultra-violet $\qquad \lambda = 4,000$ Å to 5Å.
5. X-rays $\qquad \lambda = 5$Å to 0·1Å.
6. a-rays $\qquad \lambda = 0·1$Å to 0·01Å.
7. cosmic rays $\qquad \lambda = 0·01$Å to 0·000,01Å.

Extinction coefficient, $E = \log_{10} \dfrac{I_0}{I}$, where I_0 is the intensity of the incident light, and I is the intensity of the emergent light. Suffixes are added to denote: the thickness of the absorbing layer, the concentration of the solute, and the wavelength of the absorbed light.

INDEX

How index-learning turns no student pale,
Yet holds the eel of science by the tail.

ALEXANDER POPE.

Page numbers in bold type indicate principal or substantial references

Ehrlich's reagent for biladienes, 154
Elaidic acid, 65
Elastic fibres, 101
Elastic tissue, chemistry, 429
Elastin, 101
  amino acids in, 429
  in elastic tissue, 429
  in fibrous tissue, 429
Electric organ, 47
Electrode, glass, 37
  hydrogen, 37
  quinhydrone, 37
Electrolyte, 34, 51
Electrometric titration, 68
Electron, 9
Electrophoresis, 55
Elements, invariable primary, 8
  invariable secondary, 8
  periodic classification, 9
  variable secondary, 8
EMP process, 274
Emulsin, 77, 78
Emulsion, 54
Enamel, chemistry of, 432
Enediol bond, transfer, 91
Enediol reactions, 91
Enediol rearrangement of sugars, 90
Enediol structure, 204
Energy accumulators, 318
Energy exchange in biological systems, **317, 318**
  requirements of the organisms, **209**, 319
  storage in the organism, **318**
Enolase, 15, 236, 276
Enteramine, 388, 419
Enterochromaffin cells and 5HT, 419
Enterogastrone, 388, 418
Enterokinase, 221, 223
Environment, internal, **368**
Enzootic marasmus, 31
Enzyme, activators, 215
  adsorption, 242
  characteristics, 213
  classification, 216
  copper-containing, 230, 232
  distribution within cell, 242
  extraction, 241, 242
  flocculation, 242
  fractionation, 242
  Haldane's Strain theory, 244
  induction, 243
  inhibitors, 215, 241, 244
  Lineweaver Burk equation, 240
  Michaelis constant, 240
  optimum pH, 240
  pH effect, 214
  purification, 241
  salting out, 242
  selectivity, 213, 244
  temperature effect, 214
  test for sugars, 94
  turn-over number, 241
P-enzyme. See Glucosan phosphorylase.
Q-enzyme. See Glucosan transglycolase.
Enzyme action, mechanism, 243
Enzyme substrate, activation, 244
Ephedrine, 438
Epidermal tissue, keratin in, 101
Epimer, 71
Epinephrine, 392
Epithelial tissue, chemistry, 432
Equilenin, 408
  structure, 146, 412
Equilibrium, 408, 412
Equilin, 408
  structure, 146, 412

Equivalent measures and weights, 452, 453
Equivalent weight, 48
Ergocalciferol, 140, 142, 182, 187
Ergosterol, 139, 140, 187
  occurrence, 140
  structure, 140, 142
Ergot, 76, 107
Erucic acid, 128
Erythrocruorin, 104, 157
Erythrocyte, 373, 381
Erythro-dextrin, 81
Erythrol, 85
Erythrose 4-phosphate, 279
Eserine, 437
Essential oil, 130
Ester linkage, 63
Esterase, 28, 217
Ethane, 19, 62
Ethanolamine, 127, 235, 290
Ether linkage, 63
Ethisterone, 406
Ethyl alcohol, 276
  detection in urine, 362
Ethylene, 19
  in plant growth, 423
Ethynyloestradiol, 405
Evans' blue in blood volume estimation, 374
Evocator, 387
Excelsin, 102
  molecular weight, 116
Excretion, 5, **346** *et seq.*
Exophthalmic goitre, 397
Expired air, composition, 375
Extrinsic factor, 202

FÆCES, composition, 262
Fat, **130**, 207
  concentration in plasma, 298
  human, 131
  lipid content, 180
  metabolism, 180
  significance of, 130
  solvents, 126
  synthesis in organism, 301
  true, 126
  vegetable, 131
Fatty acids, total concentration in plasma, 298
Fehling's reagent, 447
  test, 92, 98, 359
Female sex hormones, 403
Fermentable sugars, 96
Fermetation by yeast, 94
  acid formation, 94
  alcohol production, 94
Fermentation test, 98
Ferric sulphate, 30
Ferri-globulin, 262
Ferritin, 30, 104, 262, 383
Ferrous carbonate, 30
  protoporphyrin, 103
  silicate, 30
  sulphate, 30
Feulgen reaction, 134
Fibrin, 223, 373, 379, 381
Fibrinogen, 373
  in blood coagulation, 379, 381
Fibrolysin, 223
Fibrous tissue, chemistry, 429
  collagen in, 101
Fibrous proteins, 117
Ficin, 223
Fish liver oil, 131
Fistula bile. See Hepatic bile.
Flavin, 20, 61, 104, **172**, 229, 309
  310, 318
Flavin, concentration in,
  liver, 172
  kidney, 172
  whey, 172

Flavin, definition, **172**
  distribution, 172
  history, 172
  properties, 172
  structure, 172, 173
Flavin adenine dinucleotide (FAD), 104, 196, 214, 229, 310 327
  mononucleotide (FM), 196, 229 310
  phosphate, 104
Flavo-enzymes, 228, **230**
Flavone, 61, 175
Flavoproteins, 104, 196, 308, 309
  dehydrogenase, 308
  oxidase, 30
Flavoxanthin, 168
Fluid volume, extracellular, 369 371
  intracellular, 369, 371
  total, 369, 371
Fluorapetite, 27
Fluorescence indicators, **449**
Fluoridation, 27
Fluorine, 8, 26, **27**, 178, 208
Fluorine, concentration in
  blood, 27
  bone, 27
  earth's crust, 27
  sea water, 27
Fluorine in,
  baking powder, 28
  fish, 28
  higher animals, 27
  tea, 28,
  teeth, 27
  water, 28
Fluorine, inhibition of enzymes, 28
Fluorine, significance, 27, 28
  skeletal, 27
  metabolic, 28
Fluorine, sources, 28
Fluorophosphonates, as anticholinesterases, 437
Fluorosis, 27, 28, 433
Foam, 54
Fog, 54
Folacin, 182
Folic acid, 174, 182, 201
  biological assay, 202
  microbiological assay, 424
  significance, 201
  sources, 202
  synthesis in alimentary tract, 265
iso-folinic acid, 201
N⁵-folinic acid, 202
N¹⁰-folinic acid, 201
Follicle stimulant, 388
Follicle-stimulating hormone, 406, 407, 413
Food, characteristics of chief types, 445, 446
Food, composition tables, 442, 443, 444
Foods, recommendad daily allowances, 209
Formaldehyde condensation with amino acids, 111, 231
Formic acid, 127, 290
Formino units, 201
N-formyl glycinamide ribosyl phosphate, 330
N-formyl pteroic acid, 201
Formyl units, 201
Free energy in reactions, 317
Friedman test, 409, 410
Fröhlich's syndrome, 389, 415
Froth, 54
Fructofuranosidase, 219
Fructokinase, 267
Fructopyranose, 79